JOHN KIERAN'S TREASURY OF GREAT NATURE WRITING

BY JOHN KIERAN

Footnotes on Nature

Poems I Remember

John Kieran's Nature Notes

An Introduction to Birds

An Introduction to Wild Flowers

An Introduction to Trees

An Introduction to Nature
(Birds, Wild Flowers and Trees combined in one volume)

JOHN KIERAN'S
Treasury of
Great Nature Writing

Edited with comments and
biographical notes by
John Kieran

HANOVER HOUSE

Garden City, N. Y., 1957

CONTENTS

ACKNOWLEDGMENTS

Grateful acknowledgment is made by the editor and the publisher to the following publishers, authors, and others for permission to use the material contained in this book.

Appleton-Century-Crofts, Inc., for "An Ornithologist in Cuba" from *Autobiography of a Bird-Lover* by Frank M. Chapman, copyright, 1933, by D. Appleton-Century Company, Inc.; and "The Water Ouzel" from *The Mountains of California* by John Muir.

J. Brooks Atkinson for "Smoke from a Valley Cabin" from his book *East of the Hudson*, copyright, 1928, 1929, 1931, by J. Brooks Atkinson.

Audubon Magazine and the author for "Enigma of the Pacific" by C. J. Guiguet, copyright, 1956, by National Audubon Society.

Dodd, Mead & Company for "In Defense of Octopuses" from *The Ocean Island* (originally published as *Inagua*) by Gilbert C. Klingel, copyright © 1940, by Dodd, Mead & Company, Inc.; "World's Greatest Waterworks" and "The Dynamic Spiral of Plants" from *This Green World* by Rutherford Platt, copyright © 1942, by Dodd, Mead & Company, Inc.; "Winged Bullets" from *Grassroot Jungles* by Edwin Way Teale, copyright © 1937, by Dodd, Mead & Company, Inc., and copyright © 1944, by Edwin Way Teale.

Dodd, Mead & Company, Inc.

Dodd, Mead & Company, and Wm. Heinemann, Ltd. (London), for Swinburne's "Title Chorus" from *Atalanta in Calydon*.

Doubleday & Company, Inc., and J. M. Dent & Sons, Ltd. (London), for "My Friend the Pig" from *The Book of a Naturalist* by W. H. Hudson.

Duell, Sloan & Pearce, Inc., for "Too Deep to Be Seen" from *Unseen Life of New York* by William Beebe, copyright, 1953, by William Beebe.

E. P. Dutton & Company, Inc., and J. M. Dent & Sons, Ltd. (London), for "Seen and Lost" by W. H. Hudson from *The Naturalist in La Plata*.

Harcourt, Brace and Company, Inc., for "The Air Bladder in Fishes" from *The Life Story of the Fish* by Brian Curtis, copyright, 1949, by Brian Curtis.

Harper & Brothers for "Above Politics" from *Spring in Washington* by Louis J. Halle, Jr., copyright, 1947, by Louis J. Halle, Jr.; parts of "Macharia the Mamba-Catcher" from *Many Happy Days I've Squandered* by Arthur Loveridge, copyright, 1944, by Arthur Loveridge; and "Jungles under Moonlight" from *The World of Night* by Lorus J. Milne and Margery J. Milne, copyright, 1956, by Lorus J. Milne and Margery J. Milne.

Houghton Mifflin Company, and Secker & Warburg, Ltd. (London), for a selection from *Song of the Sky* by Guy Murchie, copyright, 1954, by Guy Murchie; "Turtle Eggs for Agassiz" from *The Face of the Fields* by Dallas Lore Sharp, copyright, 1911, by Houghton Mifflin Company.

Alfred A. Knopf, Inc., for "The Riddle of the Ridley" from *Windward Road* by Archie Carr, copyright, 1955, by Archie Carr.

Wolfgang Langewiesche for "What Makes the Weather," copyright, 1942, 1950, by Wolfgang Langewiesche.

Little, Brown & Company for "The Glory Hole" by Thomas Barbour from *A Naturalist at Large*, copyright, 1942, by Thomas Barbour; "Armies of Ants" from *Ant Hill Odyssey* by William M. Mann, copyright, 1948, by William M. Mann; and "The Love Song of the Wolf" (Wolves and the Aurora) from *Driftwood Valley* by Theodora C. Stanwell-Fletcher, copyright, 1946, by Theodora C. Stanwell-Fletcher.

Donald MacCampbell, Inc., for "Is There Life on Other Worlds?" by Gary Webster from *Natural History Magazine*, copyright, 1956, by American Museum of Natural History.

The Macmillan Company for "The Serpent's World" from *Snakes of the World* by Raymond L. Ditmars, copyright, 1931, by The Macmillan Company; and "A Sparrow's Nest" from *Birds in the Wilderness* by George Miksch Sutton, copyright, 1936, by The Macmillan Company.

The Macmillan Company, and Pearn, Pollinger & Higham, Ltd. (London), for "The snakes are about . . ." from *England Have My Bones* by T. H. White.

McGraw-Hill Book Company for "Antarctica" from *Quest for a Continent* by Walter Sullivan, copyright, 1957, by Walter Sullivan.

Robert Cushman Murphy for "The Guanay" from his book entitled *The Bird Islands of Peru*, copyright, 1925, by Robert Cushman Murphy.

Natural History Magazine for "The Adventures of Georg Wilhelm Steller" by Ann and Myron Sutton, copyright, 1956, by American Museum of Natural History.

Oxford University Press, Inc., for "The Long Snowfall" from *The Sea Around Us* by Rachel Carson, copyright, 1951, by Rachel Carson; and "Good Oak" from *A Sand County Almanac* by Aldo Leopold, copyright, 1949, by Oxford University Press, Inc.

Peoples First National Bank & Trust Co. of Pittsburgh, Pa. (Trust under Will of Moorehead B. Holland for Muriel McKaig Miller) for "Sugaring for Moths" from *The Moth Book*, published by Doubleday & Company, Inc., copyright, 1903, by W. J. Holland.

Rinehart & Company, Inc., for "The Headlong Wave" from *The Outermost House* by Henry Beston, copyright, 1928, 1949, by Henry Beston.

Howard J. Shannon for "The Ghost Crab" from his book entitled *The Book of the Seashore*, copyright, 1935, by Howard J. Shannon.

Sheridan House for "The Well-traveled Eel" by Paul Bulla from *Strangest Creatures on Earth*, copyright, 1953, by The American Museum of Natural History; and "The Lassoing Spider" by Willis J. Gertsch from *Strangest Creatures on Earth*, copyright, 1953, by The American Museum of Natural History.

Lewis Ketcham Sillcox for "Fortune of Forests," an address presented at the Student Branch ASME, Massachusetts Institute of Technology, February 7, 1956.

Simon & Schuster, Inc., for "The Linnaean Age" from *Green Laurels* by Donald Culross Peattie, copyright, 1936, by Donald Culross Peattie.

William Sloane Associates, Inc., for "The Contemplative Toad" from *The Desert Year* by Joseph Wood Krutch, copyright, 1951, 1952, by Joseph Wood Krutch.

The Society of Authors (London) as Literary Representative of the Trustees of the Estate of the late A. E. Housman, and Messrs. Jonathan Cape, Ltd., publishers of A. E. Housman's *Collected Poems*; and Henry Holt & Company, Inc. (New York), for "Loveliest of Trees," a selection from *The Shropshire Lad*, copyright, 1940, by Henry Holt & Company, Inc.

Staten Island Historical Society for "South Beach" from *Days Afield on Staten Island*, copyright, 1937, by William T. Davis.

The Viking Press, Inc., for "A Century of Platypus" from *The Lungfish, the Dodo, and the Unicorn* by Willy Ley, copyright, 1941, 1945, 1948, by Willy Ley.

A. J. R. Wallace and The Macmillan Co., Ltd. (England), and Harper & Brothers for "The Great Bird of Paradise" from *The Malay Archipelago* by Alfred Russel Wallace.

The editor especially wishes to thank Lillian F. Robins (Robbie) for her genuine interest in the book and her indispensable assistance in seeing it through to completion.

FOREWORD

IN MAKING the selections offered herein I deliberately tried to provide reading matter that touched many aspects of Nature and varied departments of Natural History. I might as well confess that I never have been able to discern any clear line dividing the love of Nature from the study of Natural History. It seems to me that one overlaps the other or merges into it. It was with the idea of demonstrating the width and breadth and depth of the subject, the many facets for examination, the many beauties for appreciation, and the ever-accumulating fund of fascinating facts for pure intellectual enjoyment that this collection was put together. This book is designed to be entertaining but not authoritative; informative but not instructive. In making the selections, their value as literature was considered as well as their worth in the way of science. Where there was any doubt, I leaned to the side of literature. Pure science sometimes can be baffling to good citizens.

It will be noted immediately that many honored and oft-quoted ancient authorities in the field of Natural History are missing from this collection. By this I mean such notables as Plato, Aristotle, Pliny the Elder, and so on down the centuries. In the first place, in this book we could have them only in translation, which by no means would have the flavor of the original. In the second place, I always found most of these translations rather dull reading, and this despite the fact that those ancient worthies of matchless minds accomplished wonders of observation and conclusion with the materials and equipment available to them. But the modern author has one overwhelming advantage. He has all the knowledge gleaned from the writings of these early explorers in the field and a vast supply of added knowledge that has accumulated through the invention of the microscope, the telescope, the printing press, the camera, the internal combustion engine, the airplane, and a hundred other aids to the gaining of knowledge by exploration, collection, identification, classification, dissection, and general comprehension of life processes in all their forms. For these reasons, and believing that most readers would agree with me, I did my picking and choosing from the works of modern authors. If I have made a mistake, there is no retreat now.

Most of the selections are from books in my own library. I lovingly recommend these books to your attention. May the excerpts offered herein serve as *hors-d'oeuvres* to a great feast of reading to come. With many of the authors I have had some personal acquaintance and with some of them I have enjoyed not only years of friendship but great days afield. To each and every one—both the quick and the dead—I owe a lasting debt of gratitude for the knowledge I gained and the enjoyment I found in the reading of their books.

John Kieran

N.B. The insertion of verse in this volume is all my fault. I am incorrigibly fond of poetry. I managed to get it in over the dead bodies of several publishing executives who threw themselves out of various windows when I insisted.

ON THE GENTLE ART OF FISHING

by Izaak Walton

Just recently a literary archeologist dug up evidence indicating that the famous author of The Compleat Angler or The Contemplative Man's Recreation *might have filched some of his material from an earlier book on the same subject. However, the charm of the classic on fishing remains unaffected by any dispute as to the authorship of various paragraphs or pages. Izaak Walton, born in Staffordshire, England, August 9, 1593, spent most of his life in London as a shopkeeper. He was successful enough in business to allow himself to indulge in two hobbies: fishing and writing. He achieved fame through his fondness for fishing and writing when* The Compleat Angler *was published in 1653, at which time Walton was sixty years old. He committed some other matters to print, including biographies of John Donne and Henry Wotton, but the book on fishing was his magnum opus. In it he described not only the lure of the sport in general but also the ways and means of catching fish and the haunts and habits of the different species. There is offered here a part of the introductory chapter of* The Compleat Angler *and—to show the manner in which he treated different denizens of the watery depths or shallows—his account of that formidable creature known as the pike. It must be kept in mind that Izaak Walton was writing out of the limited knowledge of natural history of his day, which was mostly lore and legend. Furthermore, the genial London shopkeeper was not under oath when he took up his pen to describe the pleasures of his favorite pastime. He lived long and happily, enjoying the esteem and affection of his countrymen to the end, and died at Winchester, on December 15, 1683, in his ninety-first year.*

GENTLEMEN, let not prejudice prepossess you. I confess my discourse is like to prove suitable to my recreation, calm and quiet; we seldom take the name of God into our mouths, but it is either to praise him, or pray to him: if others use it vainly in the midst of their recreations, so vainly as if they meant to conjure, I must tell you, it is neither our fault nor our custom; we protest against it. But pray remember, I accuse nobody; for as I would not make a "watery discourse," so I would not put too much vinegar into it; nor would I raise the reputation of my own art, by the diminution or ruin of another's. And so much for the prologue to what I mean to say.

And now for the Water, the element that I trade in. The water is the eldest daughter of the creation, the element upon which the Spirit of God did first move, the element which God commanded to bring forth living creatures abundantly; and without which, those that inhabit the land, even all creatures that have breath in their nostrils, must suddenly return to putrefaction. Moses, the great lawgiver and chief philosopher, skilled in all the learning of the Egyptians, who was called the friend of God, and knew the mind of the Almighty, names this element the first in the creation: this is the element upon which the Spirit of God did first move, and is the chief ingredient in the creation: many philosophers have made it to comprehend all the other elements, and most allow it the chiefest in the mixtion of all living creatures.

There be that profess to believe that all bodies are made of water, and may be reduced back again to water only; they endeavour to demonstrate it thus:

Take a willow, or any like speedy growing plant, newly rooted in a box or barrel full of earth, weigh them all together exactly when the tree begins to grow, and then weigh all together after the tree is increased from its first rooting, to weigh a hundred pound weight more than when it was first rooted and weighed; and you shall find this augment of the tree to be without the diminution of one drachm weight of the earth. Hence they infer this increase of wood to be from water of rain, or from dew, and not to be from any other element; and they affirm, they can reduce this wood back again to water; and they affirm also, the same may be done in any animal or vegetable. And this I take to be a fair testimony of the excellency of my element of water.

The water is more productive than the earth. Nay, the earth hath no fruitfulness without showers or dews; for all the herbs, and flowers, and fruit, are produced and thrive by the water; and the very minerals are fed by streams that run under ground, whose natural course carries them to the tops of many high mountains, as we see by several springs breaking forth on the tops of the highest hills; and this is also witnessed by the daily trial and testimony of several miners.

Nay, the increase of those creatures that are bred and fed in the water are not only more and more miraculous, but more advantageous to man, not only for the lengthening of his life, but for the preventing of sickness; for it is observed by the most learned physicians, that the casting off of Lent, and other fish days, which hath not only given the lie to so many learned, pious, wise founders of colleges, for which we should be ashamed, hath doubtless been the chief cause of those many putrid, shaking intermitting agues, unto which this nation of ours is now more subject, than those wiser countries that feed on herbs, salads, and plenty of fish; of which it is observed in story, that the greatest part of the world now do. And it may be fit to remember that Moses appointed fish to be the chief diet for the best commonwealth that ever yet was.

And it is observable, not only that there are fish, as namely the Whale, three times as big as the mighty Elephant, that is so fierce in battle, but that the mightiest feasts have been of fish. The Romans, in the height of their glory, have made fish the mistress of all their entertainments; they have had musick to usher in their Sturgeons, Lampreys, and Mullets, which they would purchase at rates rather to be wondered at than believed. He that shall view the writings of Macrobius, or Varro, may be confirmed and informed of this, and of the incredible value of their fish and fish-ponds.

*   *   *   *

The mighty Luce or Pike is taken to be the tyrant, as the Salmon is the king, of the fresh water. 'Tis not to be doubted, but that they are bred, some by generation, and some not; as namely, of a weed called pickerel-weed, unless learned Gesner be much mistaken, for he says, this weed and other glutinous matter, with the help of the sun's heat, in some particular months, and some ponds, apted for it by nature, do become Pikes. But, doubtless, divers Pikes are bred after this manner, or are brought into some ponds some such other ways as is past man's finding out, of which we have daily testimonies.

Sir Francis Bacon, in his *History of Life and Death*, observes the

Pike to be the longest lived of any fresh-water fish; and yet he com-
putes it to be not usually above forty years; and others think it to be
not above ten years: and yet Gesner mentions a Pike taken in Swede-
land, in the year 1449, with a ring about his neck, declaring he was
put into that pond by Frederick the Second, more than two hundred
years before he was last taken, as by the inscription in that ring, being
Greek, was interpreted by the then Bishop of Worms. But of this no
more; but that it is observed, that the old or very great Pikes have in
them more of state than goodness; the smaller or middle-sized Pikes
being, by the most and choicest palates, observed to be the best meat:
and, contrary, the Eel is observed to be the better for age and bigness.

All Pikes that live long prove chargeable to their keepers, because
their life is maintained by the death of so many other fish, even those
of their own kind; which has made him by some writers to be called
the tyrant of the rivers, or the fresh-water wolf, by reason of his bold,
greedy, devouring, disposition; which is so keen, as Gesner relates. A
man going to a pond, where it seems a Pike had devoured all the fish,
to water his mule, had a Pike bite his mule by the lips; to which the
Pike hung so fast, that the mule drew him out of the water; and by
that accident, the owner of the mule angled out the Pike. And the
same Gesner observes, that a maid in Poland had a Pike bite her by
the foot, as she was washing clothes in a pond. And I have heard the
like of a woman in Killingworth pond, not far from Coventry. But I
have been assured by my friend Mr. Segrave, of whom I spake to you
formerly, that keeps tame Otters, that he hath known a Pike, in extreme hunger, fight with one of his Otters for a Carp that the Otter
had caught, and was then bringing out of the water. I have told you
who relate these things; and tell you they are persons of credit; and
shall conclude this observation by telling you, what a wise man has
observed, "It is a hard thing to persuade the belly, because it has no
ears."

But if these relations be disbelieved, it is too evident to be doubted,
that a Pike will devour a fish of his own kind that shall be bigger than
his belly or throat will receive, and swallow a part of him, and let the
other part remain in his mouth till the swallowed part be digested,
and then swallow that other part that was in his mouth, and so put
it over by degrees; which is not unlike the Ox, and some other beasts
taking their meat, not out of their mouth immediately into their belly,
but first into some place betwixt, and then chew it, or digest it by
degrees after, which is called chewing the cud. And, doubtless, Pikes

will bite when they are not hungry; but, as some think, even for very anger, when a tempting bait comes near to them.

And it is observed, that the Pike will eat venomous things, as some kind of frogs are, and yet live without being harmed by them; for, as some say, he has in him a natural balsam, or antidote against all poison. And he has a strange heat, that though it appear to us to be cold, can yet digest or put over any fish-flesh, by degrees, without being sick. And others observe, that he never eats the venomous frog till he have first killed her, and then as ducks are observed to do to frogs in spawning-time, at which time some frogs are observed to be venomous, so thoroughly washed her, by tumbling her up and down in the water, that he may devour her without danger. And Gesner affirms, that a Polonian gentleman did faithfully assure him, he had seen two young geese at one time in the belly of a Pike. And doubtless a Pike in his height of hunger will bite at and devour a dog that swims in a pond; and there have been examples of it, or the like; for as I told you, "The belly has no ears when hunger comes upon it."

The Pike is also observed to be a solitary, melancholy, and a bold fish; melancholy, because he always swims or rests himself alone, and never swims in shoals or with company, as Roach and Dace, and most other fish do: and bold, because he fears not a shadow, or to see or be seen of anybody, as the Trout and Chub, and all other fish do.

And it is observed by Gesner, that the jaw-bones, and hearts, and galls of Pikes, are very medicinable for several diseases, or to stop blood, to abate fevers, to cure agues, to oppose or expel the infection of the plague, and to be many ways medicinable and useful for the good of mankind: but he observes, that the biting of a Pike is venomous, and hard to be cured.

And it is observed, that the Pike is a fish that breeds but once a year; and that other fish, as namely Loaches, do breed oftener: as we are certain tame Pigeons do almost every month; and yet the Hawk, a bird of prey, as the Pike is a fish, breeds but once in twelve months. And you are to note, that his time of breeding, or spawning, is usually about the end of February, or, somewhat later, in March, as the weather proves colder or warmer: and to note, that his manner of breeding is thus: a he and a she Pike will usually go together out of a river into some ditch or creek; and that there the spawner casts her eggs, and the melter hovers over her all that time that she is casting her spawn, but touches her not.

I might say more of this, but it might be thought curiosity or worse, and shall therefore forbear it; and take up so much of your attention as to tell you that the best Pikes are noted to be in rivers; next, those in great ponds or meres; and the worst, in small ponds.

SONG
(from *The Princess*)

"Come down, O maid, from yonder mountain height:
What pleasure lives in height (the shepherd sang)
In height and cold, the splendour of the hills?
But cease to move so near the Heavens, and cease
To glide a sunbeam by the blasted Pine,
To sit a star upon the sparkling spire;
And come, for Love is of the valley, come,
For Love is of the valley, come thou down
And find him; by the happy threshold, he,
Or hand in hand with Plenty in the maize,
Or red with spirted purple of the vats,
Or foxlike in the vine; nor cares to walk
With Death and Morning on the Silver Horns,
Nor wilt thou snare him in the white ravine,
Nor find him dropt upon the firths of ice,
That huddling slant in furrow-cloven falls
To roll the torrent out of dusky doors:
But follow; let the torrent dance thee down
To find him in the valley; let the wild
Lean-headed Eagles yelp alone, and leave
The monstrous ledges there to slope, and spill
Their thousand wreaths of dangling water-smoke,
That like a broken purpose waste in air:
So waste not thou; but come; for all the vales
Await thee; azure pillars of the hearth
Arise to thee; the children call, and I
Thy shepherd pipe, and sweet is every sound,
Sweeter thy voice, but every sound is sweet;
Myriads of rivulets hurrying thro' the lawn,
The moan of doves in immemorial elms,
And murmuring of innumerable bees."

ALFRED TENNYSON

THE ADVENTURES OF
GEORG WILHELM STELLER

by Ann and Myron Sutton

Anyone who reads much of the literature of natural history is bound to run into frequent references to early explorers and collectors, many of whom suffered horrible hardships and almost all of whom led adventurous lives. This is the story of one such sturdy and energetic character whose name is memorialized in various check lists in the field of natural history and whose short but stirring life and untimely death are briefly chronicled here by the husband-and-wife team of Ann and Myron Sutton, both naturalists but not always working in the same particular field. Ann Sutton hammers away at geology as a profession and has a position with the United States Geological Survey. Myron Sutton is with the National Park Service. But they make many exploring and collecting trips together, and they share the trials and tribulations of authorship in the general field of natural history.

WHEN the great Swedish botanist Linnaeus chose the name *Stelleria* for a new plant genus, he asked: "Who has earned a greater or more precious glory for his name than he who undertakes journeys among the barbarians? Everybody in the botanical world who knows plants loves Mr. Steller. If my appeal has any influence with you, I beg you to adopt the name."

Were Linnaeus alive today he would find, happily, that Steller's name now applies to an Alaskan heather, a blue jay, a duck, a mollusk, three fishes, a sea cow, a sea lion, a sea cliff and two mountains!

This is the avalanche of honors that history has heaped upon Georg Wilhelm Steller, the plucky Bavarian who sledged through Russian

snows, crossed Siberian prairies, and sailed through raging Pacific seas
to become the first naturalist of Alaska and probably the first white
man to set foot on Alaskan soil.

In his pitching cabin aboard Vitus Bering's flagship, Steller wrote
some of the world's finest descriptions of North Pacific sea animals.
He gave astonishingly complete and detailed accounts of the fur seal,
sea cow, sea lion, and sea otter at a time when the world scarcely knew
such animals existed. Most of these works were published in his immortal *De bestiis marinis*, an ambitious scientific project if there ever
was one. But writing alone did not make Steller famous. Curiosity
and adventure did.

Steller's abiding passion for natural history kindled his destiny early.
He was born in the Bavarian town of Windsheim in 1709, fourth
among eleven children in the family of Cantor and Frau Jacob Stöller.
It was a good life. Cantors—whose eighteenth-century contemporaries
included such noteworthy figures as Bach and Handel—had no trouble
becoming respected members of the community, and young Georg
Wilhelm grew in prosperous musical tradition.

Persistent though he may have been as a scholar, poet, and musician, the irresistible appeal of Windsheim's Schossback Forest lured
him deeper and deeper into the magic of the outdoors. Fox and deer
bounded among the trees. Blackcock and capercaillie mated noisily
in spring. Hazel grouse whistled deep in the woods. Soon partridges
and river otters began to impress Steller more than rondos and
minuets. The inspiration of Windsheim's forests filled him with a desire to learn more about the natural sciences.

In 1730, Steller transferred from the University of Wittenberg where
he had been a theology student to the University of Halle to study
and teach natural history. But even as he explored the forests and
gardens of Halle, even as he toured the tunnels and galleries of Stol-
berg or hiked the beautiful valley of Tyra, his imagination flamed with
an unquenchable curiosity about the great wide world beyond.

He vowed to see it. He read the voyages of Dampier and other sea-
farers, pored over *Robinson Crusoe*, and dreamed of sailing to remote
and uninhabited islands where untapped natural history lay waiting
for discovery.

After his botany lectures mushroomed into wide popularity at Halle,
Steller went to Berlin for an official certificate of professorship. He had
no difficulty with the examination, but the king—who dispensed such

appointments personally—fell ill at the wrong time, and Steller failed his professorship by royal default.

Unsubdued, Steller turned his clear, piercing eyes toward new horizons. Now more than ever the lure of the unknown gripped him. He needed a job. University life seemed dull and listless. The pages of *Robinson Crusoe* swam again before his vision.

At this psychological moment news arrived from Russia that Fleet Commander Vitus Bering had begun outfitting prodigiously in St. Petersburg for an expedition to the vast, unknown Kamchatka region north of Japan. Steller needed no second cue. He hired on as a doctor with the Russian Army in Danzig and sailed to St. Petersburg in hopes of attaching himself to Bering's expedition.

But the fact remained that Steller knew neither Russian nor Russia itself. A bewildering hodgepodge of strange customs, languages, and nationalities confronted this young, impetuous German. Though Peter the Great had taken Russia out of medieval mothballs, there still remained a wild barbarism: the public torture of witches, and robbers hung in muddy streets. Even that august body and patron of learning, the Academy of Sciences, adjourned so its members could witness humanity's sidewalk spectacles.

Nevertheless, as Bering's expedition departed for Siberia, Steller settled patiently at the newly organized Academy of Sciences to study languages, geography, and science. He didn't wait long. News soon came from the east that Bering had decided to add two new scientists to his command. Within a year Steller's dream came true. He had been selected as one of them. Thus it was that a Russian expedition under a Danish leader came to have a German as its outstanding narrator.

Nothing before or since has benefited Russia quite so much as the wave of scientific and cultural enlightenment that swept her during Peter the Great's reign. Frontiers of knowledge expanded in all directions, and the physical frontiers of Russia's vast borders were being explored and mapped. Although Bering's first voyage had been a part of that nationwide reawakening, it had stirred up such wondrous tales that the authorities could not quite credit all the results. Thus his second voyage, which Steller joined, was intended not only to expand but to corroborate the first.

The Admiralty's instructions were to survey and map northern Asia and parts of America, to chart the Arctic coast, to establish astronomical positions throughout Siberia, and to find out, once and for all, if Russia touched America. To do so, Bering organized several expeditions and hauled his supplies and equipment 4,000 miles across Asia.

Steller was jubilant. He finished his projects at the Academy of Sciences and eagerly made preparations for traveling cross-country to join the expeditions then in or en route to the Pacific.

With the lighthearted temperament that flooded him, Steller fell in love with the widow of the nation's leading authority on Siberia. Presently they were married. But he was so happily in love and so intent on taking his bride along (he would be many years in the wilderness and at sea) that he was unprepared for the shock that followed. When they had traveled as far as Moscow, she refused to accompany him farther. She may have been right: still ringing in her ears were bitter descriptions of Siberian winters detailed by her first husband. No amount of persuasion could change her mind; she preferred the gaiety and comforts of St. Petersburg—and she went back.

After that, Steller continued alone—and lonely—across the brooding steppes, by boat up Siberian rivers, by troika over snow-covered plains, grieving for his shattered happiness. But before he reached the other end of the white continent, the gripping fascination of Siberia's wilderness had captured his innermost being and wrung from his heart the last bit of remorse for his wife. Soulfully he wrote: "I have entirely forgotten her and fallen in love with Nature."

He had indeed. East of the Urals, Steller found barbarism and ruthlessness but paid scant attention to it. So that he could collect and observe more intently, he reduced his personal gear to a minimum. He cooked and ate in a single dish. He wore what clothes he could find or make. When he came down with fever, he pushed on through sub-zero temperatures. In fact, contemporaries described him as impulsive, full of life, tough and indefatigable, unassuming, good-natured, and above all passionately devoted to science.

No branch of natural history escaped him. He encompassed everything from the coloration of redstarts to crustaceans in the Angara River. To secure badly needed paper for pressing plant specimens, he once sledged 333 miles in the middle of winter to a trading center on the Mongolian border.

For three years Steller trekked across the immensity of Russia—through Tobolsk, Tomsk, Irkutsk, Yakutsk, and finally to the Pacific seaport of Okhotsk.

There Vitus Bering's ships—two identical packet boats named *St. Paul* and *St. Peter*—lay at anchor, being outfitted for the trip to

America. For this Steller had waited, worked, and planned; for this he had studied at Halle and St. Petersburg. Here lay the goal of his dreams.

With Steller sharing the Commander's cabin on the *St. Peter* and listed officially as ship's surgeon and mineralogist, the expedition departed from Avatcha Bay—on Kamchatka's eastern shore—on June 4, 1741. Of the 78 aboard, almost half were never to return.

Carrying "all sails except the sprit-sail," they headed east-southeast into the unknown Pacific. Five hundred miles eastward lay Attu and the Aleutian chain, which no white man had ever seen. No one knew where America lay. No chart gave a direction, no log a distance.

On June 20, storm and wind forced the companion ship *St. Paul* to heave to under the mizzensail, and the expedition's two ships lost sight of each other. The *St. Paul* arrived back at Kamchatka the following autumn. For six weeks the *St. Peter* sailed across the Pacific, occasionally sighting driftwood and seaweed which suggested the nearness of land. Had Bering turned north, he might have found land within 100 nautical miles. But fate guided his course parallel to the Aleutians until at last, on July 16, the clouds unrolled above a majestic panorama of snow-covered mountains and towering peaks. They had reached the Alaska mainland.

Imagine Steller's elation at this epic moment! An entire country lay unexplored at his feet. He noted "with the greatest of pleasure the beautiful forests close down to the sea, as well as the great level ground in from shore at the foot of the mountains." The exultant crew named the highest peak after the Saint of the day: Mount St. Elias.

On Bering, however, the burden of 60 years of toil and hardship lay heavily. He had labored incessantly preparing for this expedition —building ironworks, ships, towns, and forts in the face of innumerable delays, vexations, and setbacks. Little wonder that, having discovered the "big country," he turned his attention not to wild exploration but to the safe and immediate return of ship and crew.

Not so Steller. To him this was the culmination of years of planning and preparation. When Bering tacked the *St. Peter* in close to Kayak Island and ordered a boat ashore for fresh water, Steller, beside himself with anticipation, refused to be left behind and peremptorily lowered himself into the boat.

Steller's biographer, Leonhard Stejneger, presumes that Steller's eagerness—borne on a decade of dreams and plans—prompted him to leap out of the boat as soon as it nudged the gravelly beach. Thus, though no one knows for sure, it is possible that Alaska's first naturalist was also the first European to set foot on its soil.

At any rate, honors had not beckoned him. Nature had. Leaving the crew to fill the water casks, Steller set out to explore Kayak Island as comprehensively as possible in the scant time available. Abruptly he came upon an Indian cache and fireplace from which the natives had just departed, and he sat down at once to itemize every facet of the scene.

Alone and unarmed, he continued through the thick forest, observing, digging, collecting, always hoping to find his first "Alaskans." From a hilltop he spied the smoke of a distant campfire and rejoiced at the prospect of meeting the natives, learning their customs and language, and securing complete data for a scientific description.

Hurrying back to the beach, he dispatched his plant collections on the boat and asked Bering to send gifts for the Indians. That was at 4 P.M.

Waiting for Bering's reply, Steller sat on the beach and in approximately an hour penned a summary of the scientific accomplishments of his first day in America. He listed and described the flora, including upland cranberry, black crowberry, and an exotic new species called raspberry. He recorded the wildlife in detail, describing a magnificent blue bird which was later to be named *Cyanocitta stelleri*, Steller's Jay—familiar to pine-country bird watchers from the Yukon to Mexico. This meticulous set of observations, consisting of more than 144 entries laboriously jotted down in Latin, became the first scientific paper of any kind dealing with Alaskan natural history.

And the Indians? Bering sent word that if Steller didn't hie himself back to the ship at once, he could remain on Alaskan soil forever. Steller complied.

Summer goes quickly from the Alaskan scene, once August has arrived. As the *St. Peter* zigzagged through the Aleutians, Steller, ever persistent with pen and journal and keen eye, critically analyzed the behavior of fur seals, sea lions, porpoises, sea otters, and other animals along the way.

The weather worsened steadily. When Kamchatka still lay many leagues away, the bane of explorers struck Bering and his crew. Scurvy! Long weeks without fruit, fresh meat, or vegetables had brought the men to a disastrous state of debilitation. One by one they lost strength and fell to bed.

With disease mounting and autumn arriving, the expedition leaders bent the *St. Peter's* prow steadily for Kamchatka. Steller must have stood at the bow for many a cold and bleak Aleutian hour, peering longingly into the mists, remembering the rising snow tower of Mount St. Elias and fancying himself deep in the interior, discovering its many strange, fantastic natural wonders.

Relentless gales and persistent running seas drove the ship off course. Again fresh water ran low, and the ship's kegs turned foul and brackish. Bering veered north, anchored in the Shumagin Islands, and sent ashore for water. Steller went along to bring out antiscorbutic plants and to scout for new wildlife. Here the expedition sighted its first "Alaskans," several Aleuts who approached the ship with great curiosity. Although this brief encounter lasted no more than fifteen minutes (at close range), Steller's subsequent account of it is spirited and remarkably detailed. It constitutes history's first technical knowledge of the Alaskan natives.

Delay in the Shumagin Islands proved almost fatal, and for two weeks the *St. Peter* traveled without sighting land, rolling, pitching, and tossing under powerful storms. "Every moment we expected the destruction of our vessel," said Steller, "and no one could lie down, or sit up, or stand. We were drifting . . . whither the angry heavens willed to send us. Half our crew lay sick and weak; the other half . . . crazed and maddened from the terrifying motion of the ship."

By the end of October, they had passed Kiska and swung north of Attu out into the raging Pacific. Fog and cloud obscured the sun, making navigational observations impossible. On November 6, with the crew exhausted, the ship damaged, and hope flagging, all who could walk or crawl held ship's council.

That dramatic council may well have been history's most fateful hour in the North Pacific. At dawn on the day before, an island had been sighted, and the joyous crew, thinking it to be the Kamchatka mainland, had rejoiced. Now dilemma lay before them: should they land or go on? Aboard ship, conditions had vastly deteriorated. Sailmasts had weakened. Scurvy lay like a pall over the vessel. Winter had arrived.

Bering, himself bedridden, counseled his crew to make a few more leagues to Avatcha Bay—or some outpost of civilization. But their ebbing strength finally turned the decision toward immediate self-preservation, and they turned toward shore. Then they collapsed in utter exhaustion, and Steller alone remained alert as the vessel lurched toward the breakers of this barren island.

The ship was virtually out of control. As she drew closer to the jagged rocks that fringed the bay, the officers rounded up as many crewmen as were able and pulled them on deck to manage the violent landing. Seeing the danger, the crewmen fought desperately with fading strength to keep away from the reef. They pitched an anchor over the side, and the cable snapped. Panic-stricken, they flung out another, and again the cable snapped. Wind-whipped waves plunged in the darkness toward the ship and broke in thunderous breakers against the rocks. When it seemed that the vessel would be smashed to pieces, a giant wave lifted it miraculously over the reef and into the quiet waters of an inland channel.

Thus did the *St. Peter*, broken and battered by heavy seas, deliver its crew to Bering Island, on which no man had ever set foot. Sea otters and blue foxes yipped and barked on the beach, and ptarmigan fed on snow-capped ridges inland.

The only available wood was driftwood, and in the days that followed, the crew gathered it and built pit huts along the beach. Owing to the storms that lashed the coast with increasing intensity, it took two weeks to transfer the sick from ship to shore. On November 28, a gale blew the vessel squarely up on the beach.

Soon Vitus Bering succumbed to scurvy and was buried a short distance from camp. But by January, the disease had been arrested, and the survivors, under Steller's care, began their long road to recovery.

At length Steller was free to pursue his explorations in natural history, and on Bering Island he made his most sensational observations. He was the only naturalist ever to see the spectacled cormorant alive, and his eye-witness scientific description remains the only one in existence. Within a hundred years, the bird was completely exterminated by uncontrolled hunting.

He was the only naturalist ever to see, dissect, and describe the sea cow, or northern manatee. This monstrous animal, which has no close relationship to either seal or whale, reached 30 feet in length and weighed 6,000 pounds. Dissecting it was an almost superhuman achievement. With disgruntled assistants, inefficient tools, and the constant depredations of blue foxes slashing at the carcass and destroying what Steller was trying to describe, it's a wonder he succeeded at all. But he did, and this, more than any other accomplishment, places Steller in the naturalist's Hall of Fame. Not long afterward, the sea cow was slaughtered to extinction.

Steller also pioneered the technique of observing wildlife from a "blind." He built a temporary hut in the midst of the seal grounds and sat in it for days, penning one of the finest interpretations of a fur-seal colony that has ever been written.

As summer came to the island, he described the equally unknown sea lion. Flowers sprang up profusely in the sphagnum marshes and on the tundra, and Steller collected specimens such as violets, anemones, buttercups, cloudberries, and Sarana lilies.

Meanwhile the *St. Peter's* crew had disassembled the broken ship and built it anew. By the middle of August, after nine months on Bering Island, the craft, laden with diminished supplies and increased scientific specimens, sailed from the bay and headed homeward.

Great rejoicing filled Avatcha Bay when the battered remnants of Bering's shipwrecked crew returned. Shortly afterward, Steller left the expedition and plunged into collecting and describing the natural history of the Kamchatka Peninsula.

Within a year, he received instructions from the Academy of Sciences to conclude the Kamchatka project and return to St. Petersburg, collecting along the way.

He never made it.

While botanizing in the interior, he was arrested and hauled to Irkutsk to answer for an argument he had had with the vice-governor. Higher authorities fortunately rescinded the arrest, and Steller was quickly released. But while celebrating with friends in Tobolsk, he came down with a violent fever and as usual paid no attention to it.

Anxious to be under way, he climbed into a sledge for the 170-mile trip in sub-zero temperatures to Tyumen, much against the advice of his friends. He arrived in Tyumen on November 12, 1746, and fell lifeless before the day was out, at the age of only thirty-seven.

Steller was buried in a shallow grave in hard-frozen ground on the right bank of the river Tura. Eventually the river undercut its banks, carrying his bones away to mingle with the creatures he loved so well and described so faithfully.

No photograph or drawing exists anywhere in the world to show us what Steller looked like. But the legacy he left in his brief eventful 37 years will remain a long, long time.

Linnaeus was right. Who indeed earns more precious glory than he who journeys among barbarians? Today, in American's tall pine country, a breed of happy-go-lucky, black-crested jays bears living tribute to Georg Wilhelm Steller—an eighteenth-century Robinson Crusoe whose dreams of adventure came true.

DAFFODILS

I wandered lonely as a cloud
That floats on high o'er vales and hills,
When all at once I saw a crowd,
A host, of golden daffodils;
Beside the lake, beneath the trees,
Fluttering and dancing in the breeze.

Continuous as the stars that shine
And twinkle on the Milky Way,
They stretched in never-ending line
Along the margin of a bay:
Ten thousand saw I at a glance,
Tossing their heads in sprightly dance.

The waves beside them danced; but they
Out-did the sparkling waves in glee:
A poet could not but be gay
In such a jocund company:
I gazed—and gazed—but little thought
What wealth to me the show had brought:

For oft, when on my couch I lie
In vacant or in pensive mood,
They flash upon that inward eye
Which is the bliss of solitude;
And then my heart with pleasure fills,
And dances with the daffodils.

WILLIAM WORDSWORTH

SELBORNE

by Gilbert White

Gilbert White was born in the vicarage in the village of Selborne in Hampshire, England, July 18, 1720. He was graduated
from Oriel College, Oxford, and subsequently took holy orders,
which accounts for occasional references to him as "the Reverend Gilbert White." He did indeed serve a few short terms as
curate here and there, but in 1755 he returned to his native village to live the life of a layman for the remainder of his days.
He had inherited a house and a modest competence that allowed
him the leisure to pursue a study of all the natural phenomena
of the region throughout a long and placid span of years. He
never married. He took no part in politics. He kept track of the
weather. He studied the geology of the area. He looked into the
matter of resident mammals and migrant birds. He had ideas on
the growth and cutting of local timber. He made notes on the
haunts and habits of mice, snakes, spiders, bats, and other creatures that he encountered on his daily walks around the countryside. He corresponded with other and more famous naturalists of
his time. He himself lived in obscurity in this little village of Selborne, which indeed was obscure in its own right. And Gilbert
White, still osbcure, died there June 26, 1793.

But the kindly old bachelor left behind him a little volume
—published in 1789, about four years before his death—in the
form of a collection of his notes and letters under the title: The
Natural History and Antiquities of Selborne. The book created
no stir on its appearance, but behold the verdict of Time! Selborne is known the world over, and "Gilbert White" is a famous
name in the literature of natural history. The little classic that is
called "White's Selborne" for short is a leisurely book about the
Hampshire countryside and its occupants, animal, vegetable, and
mineral. The excerpts offered here will give the reader a fair idea

of the tone and contents of The Natural History and Antiquities
of Selborne *and the solid virtues of Gilbert White, early field
naturalist and late village historian.*

ADVERTISEMENT

THE Author of the following Letters takes the liberty, with
all proper deference, of laying before the public his idea of
parochial history, which, he thinks, ought to consist of natural productions and occurrences as well as antiquities. He
is also of opinion that if stationary men would pay some attention to
the districts on which they reside, and would publish their thoughts
respecting the objects that surround them, from such materials might
be drawn the most complete county-histories, which are still wanting
in several parts of this kingdom, and in particular in the county of
Southampton.

And here he seizes the first opportunity, though a late one, of returning his most grateful acknowledgments to the reverend the President and the reverend and worthy the Fellows of Magdalen College
in the University of Oxford, for their liberal behaviour in permitting
their archives to be searched by a member of their own society, so far
as the evidences therein contained might respect the parish and priory
of Selborne. To that gentleman also, and his assistant, whose labours
and attention could only be equalled by the very kind manner in which
they were bestowed, many and great obligations are also due.

Of the authenticity of the documents above-mentioned there can
be no doubt, since they consist of the identical deeds and records that
were removed to the College from the Priory at the time of its dissolution; and, being carefully copied on the spot, may be depended
on as genuine; and, never having been made public before, may gratify the curiosity of the antiquary, as well as establish the credit of the
history.

If the writer should at all appear to have induced any of his readers
to pay a more ready attention to the wonders of the Creation, too
frequently overlooked as common occurrences; or if he should by any
means, through his researches, have lent an helping hand towards the
enlargement of the boundaries of historical and topographical knowledge; or if he should have thrown some small light upon ancient customs and manners, and especially on those that were monastic, his

purpose will be fully answered. But if he should not have been successful in any of these his intentions, yet there remains this consolation behind—that these his pursuits, by keeping the body and mind employed, have, under Providence, contributed to much health and cheerfulness of spirits, even to old age:—and, what still adds to his happiness, have led him to the knowledge of a circle of gentlemen whose intelligent communications, as they have afforded him much pleasing information, so, could he flatter himself with a continuation of them, would they ever be deemed a matter of singular satisfaction and improvement.

GIL: WHITE.

Selborne, January 1st, 1788

LETTER VI

(*To Thomas Pennant, Esquire*)

Should I omit to describe with some exactness the forest of Wolmer, of which three-fifths perhaps lie in this parish, my account of Selborne would be very imperfect, as it is a district abounding with many curious productions, both animal and vegetable; and has often afforded me much entertainment both as a sportsman and as a naturalist.

The royal forest of Wolmer is a tract of land of about seven miles in length, by two and a half in breadth, running nearly from north to south, and is abutted on, to begin to the south, and so to proceed eastward, by the parishes of Greatham, Lysse, Rogate, and Trotton, in the county of Sussex; by Bramshot, Hedleigh, and Kingsley. This royalty consists entirely of sand covered with heath and fern; but is somewhat diversified with hills and dales, without having one standing tree in the whole extent. In the bottoms, where the waters stagnate, are many bogs, which formerly abounded with subterraneous trees; though Dr. Plot says positively, that "there never were any fallen trees hidden in the mosses of the southern counties." But he was mistaken: for I myself have seen cottages on the verge of this wild district, whose timbers consisted of a black hard wood, looking like oak, which the owners assured me they procured from the bogs by probing the soil with spits, or some such instruments: but the peat is so much cut out, and the moors have been so well examined, that none has been found of late. Besides the oak, I have also been shown pieces of fossil-wood of a paler colour, and softer nature, which the inhabitants called fir: but, upon a nice examination, and trial by fire, I could discover nothing resinous in them; and therefore rather suppose that they were parts of a willow or alder, or some such aquatic tree.

This lonely domain is a very agreeable haunt for many sorts of wild fowls, which not only frequent it in the winter, but breed there in the summer; such as lapwings, snipes, wild-ducks, and, as I have discovered within these few years, teals. Partridges in vast plenty are bred in good seasons on the verge of this forest, into which they love to make excursions: and in particular, in the dry summer of 1740 and 1741, and some years after, they swarmed to such a degree, that parties of unreasonable sportsmen killed twenty and sometimes thirty brace in a day.

But there was a nobler species of game in this forest, now extinct, which I have heard old people say abounded much before shooting flying became so common, and that was the heath-cock, black-game, or grouse. When I was a little boy I recollect one coming now and then to my father's table. The last pack remembered was killed about thirty-five years ago; and within these ten years one solitary greyhen was sprung by some beagles in beating for a hare. The sportsmen cried out, "A hen pheasant"; but a gentleman present, who had often seen grouse in the north of England, assured me that it was a greyhen.

Nor does the loss of our black-game prove the only gap in the *Fauna Selborniensis*; for another beautiful link in the chain of beings is wanting, I mean the red deer, which toward the beginning of this century amounted to about five hundred head, and made a stately appearance. There is an old keeper, now alive, named Adams, whose great-grandfather (mentioned in a perambulation taken in 1635), grandfather, father and self, enjoyed the head keepership of Wolmer-forest in succession for more than an hundred years. This person assures me, that his father has often told him, that Queen Anne, as she was journeying on the Portsmouth road, did not think the forest of Wolmer beneath her royal regard. For she came out of the great road at Lippock, which is just by, and reposing herself on a bank smoothed for that purpose, lying about half a mile to the east of Wolmer-pond, and still called Queen's-bank, saw with great complacency and satisfaction the whole herd of red deer brought by the keepers along the vale before her, consisting then of about five hundred head. A sight, this, worthy the attention of the greatest sovereign! But he further adds that, by means of the Waltham blacks, or, to use his own expression, as soon as they began *blacking*, they were reduced to about fifty head, and so continued decreasing till the time of the late Duke of Cumberland. It is now more than thirty years ago that his highness sent down an huntsman, and six yeomen-prickers, in scarlet jackets laced with gold, attended by the stag-hounds; ordering them to take every deer in this forest alive, and convey them in carts to Windsor. In the course of the summer they caught every stag, some of which showed extraordinary diversion; but, in the following winter, when the hinds were also carried off, such fine chases were exhibited as served the country people for matter of talk and wonder for years afterwards. I saw myself one of the yeomen-prickers single out a stag from the herd, and must confess that it was the most curious feat of activity I ever beheld, superior to anything in Mr. Astley's riding-school. The exertions made by the horse and deer much exceeded all my expectations; though the former greatly excelled the latter in speed. When the devoted deer was separated from his companions, they gave him, by their watches, law, as they called it, for twenty minutes; when, sounding their horns, the stop-dogs were permitted to pursue, and a most gallant scene ensued.

LETTER X

(To Thomas Pennant, Esquire)

August 4, 1767.

It has been my misfortune never to have had any neighbours whose studies have led them towards the pursuit of natural knowledge; so that, for want of a companion to quicken my industry and sharpen my attention, I have made but slender progress in a kind of information to which I have been attached from my childhood.

As to swallows (hirundines rusticae) being found in a torpid state during the winter in the Isle of Wight, or any part of this country, I never heard any such account worth attending to. But a clergyman, of an inquisitive turn, assures me that, when he was a great boy, some workmen, in pulling down the battlements of a church tower early in the spring, found two or three swifts (hirundines apodes) among the rubbish, which were, at first appearance, dead, but, on being carried toward the fire, revived. He told me that, out of his great care to preserve them, he put them in a paper bag, and hung them by the kitchen fire, where they were suffocated.

Another intelligent person has informed me that, while he was a

schoolboy at Brighthelmstone, in Sussex, a great fragment of the chalk
cliff fell down one stormy winter on the beach; and that many people found swallows among the rubbish; but, on my questioning him
whether he saw any of those birds himself, to my no small disappointment, he answered me in the negative; but that others assured him
they did.

Young broods of swallows began to appear this year on July the
eleventh, and young martins (*hirundines urbicae*) were then fledged
in their nests. Both species will breed again once. For I see by my
Fauna of last year, that young broods come forth so late as September
the eighteenth. Are not these late hatchings more in favour of hiding
than migration? Nay, some young martins remained in their nests last
year so late as September the twenty-ninth; and yet they totally disappeared with us by the fifth of October.

How strange is it that the swift, which seems to live exactly the
same life with the swallow and house-martin, should leave us before
the middle of August invariably! while the latter stay often till the
middle of October; and once I saw numbers of house-martins on the
seventh of November. The martins and red-wing fieldfares were flying
in sight together; an uncommon assemblage of summer and winter
birds.

A little yellow bird (it is either a species of the *alauda trivialis*, or
rather perhaps of the *motacilla trochilus*) still continues to make a
sibilous shivering noise in the tops of tall woods. The *stoparola* of Ray
(for which we have as yet no name in these parts) is called, in your
Zoology, the fly-catcher. There is one circumstance characteristic of
this bird, which seems to have escaped observation, and that is, that it
takes its stand on the top of some stake or post, from whence it springs
forth on its prey, catching a fly in the air, and hardly ever touching
the ground, but returning still to the same stand for many times together.

I perceive there are more than one species of the *motacilla trochilus*: Mr. Derham supposes, in Ray's *Philos. Letters*, that he has discovered three. In these there is again an instance of some very common
birds that have as yet no English name.

Mr. Stillingfleet makes a question whether the blackcap (*motacilla
atricapilla*) be a bird of passage or not: I think there is no doubt of it:
for, in April, in the very first fine weather, they come trooping, all at
once, into these parts, but are never seen in the winter. They are delicate songsters.

Numbers of snipes breed every summer in some moory ground on the verge of this parish. It is very amusing to see the cock bird on wing at that time, and to hear his piping and humming notes.

I have had no opportunity yet of procuring any of those mice which I mentioned to you in town. The person that brought me the last says they are plenty in harvest, at which time I will take care to get more; and will endeavour to put the matter out of doubt, whether it be a nondescript species or not.

I suspect much there may be two species of water-rats. Ray says, and Linnaeus after him, that the water-rat is web-footed behind. Now I have discovered a rat on the banks of our little stream that is not web-footed, and yet is an excellent swimmer and diver: it answers exactly to the *mus amphibius* of Linnaeus (See *Syst. Nat.*) which he says "*natat in fossis et urinatur.*" I should be glad to procure one "*plantis palmatis.*" Linnaeus seems to be in a puzzle about his *mus amphibius*, and to doubt whether it differs from his *mus terrestris*; which if it be, as he allows, the "*mus agrestis capite grandi brachyuros*" of Ray, is widely different from the water-rat, both in size, make, and manner of life.

As to the *falco*, which I mentioned in town, I shall take the liberty to send it down to you into Wales; presuming on your candour, that you will excuse me if it should appear as familiar to you as it is strange to me. Though mutilated "*qualem dices . . . antehac fuisse, tales cum sint reliquiae!*"

It haunted a marshy piece of ground in quest of wild-ducks and snipes: but, when it was shot, had just knocked down a rook, which it was tearing in pieces. I cannot make it answer to any of our English hawks; neither could I find any like it at the curious exhibition of stuffed birds in Spring-gardens. I found it nailed up at the end of a barn, which is the countryman's museum.

The parish I live in is a very abrupt, uneven country, full of hills and woods, and therefore full of birds.

LETTER XI

(*To Thomas Pennant, Esquire*)

Selborne, September 9, 1767.

It will not be without impatience that I shall wait for your thoughts with regard to the *falco*; as to its weight, breadth, etc., I wish I had set

them down at the time; but, to the best of my remembrance, it
weighed two pounds and eight ounces, and measured, from wing to
wing, thirty-eight inches. Its cere and feet were yellow, and the circle
of its eyelids bright yellow. As it had been killed some days, and the
eyes were sunk, I could make no good observation on the colour of
the pupils and the irides.

The most unusual birds I ever observed in these parts were a pair
of hoopoes (*upupa*) which came several years ago in the summer, and
frequented an ornamented piece of ground, which joins to my garden,
for some weeks. They used to march about in a stately manner, feeding
in the walks, many times in the day; and seemed disposed to breed
in my outlet; but were frightened and persecuted by idle boys, who
would never let them be at rest.

Three gross-beaks (*loxia coccothraustes*) appeared some years ago
in my fields, in the winter; one of which I shot: since that, now and
then one is occasionally seen in the same dead season.

A cross-bill (*loxia curvirostra*) was killed last year in this neighbourhood.

Our streams, which are small, and rise only at the end of the village,
yield nothing but the bull's head or miller's thumb (*gobius fluviatilis
capitatus*), the trout (*trutta fluviatilis*), the eel (*anguilla*), the lam-
pern (*lampaetra parva et fluviatilis*), and the stickle-back (*pisciculus
aculeatus*).

We are twenty miles from the sea, and almost as many from a great
river, and therefore see but little of sea-birds. As to wild fowls, we
have a few teams of ducks bred in the moors where the snipes breed;
and multitudes of widgeons and teals in hard weather frequent our
lakes in the forest.

Having some acquaintance with a tame brown owl, I find that it
casts up the fur of mice, and the feathers of birds in pellets, after the
manner of hawks: when full, like a dog, it hides what it cannot eat.

The young of the barn-owl are not easily raised, as they want a
constant supply of fresh mice: whereas the young of the brown owl
will eat indiscriminately all that is brought; snails, rats, kittens, puppies, magpies, and any kind of carrion or offal.

The house-martins have eggs still, and squab-young. The last swift
I observed was about the twenty-first of August; it was a straggler.

Red-starts, fly-catchers, white-throats, and *reguli non cristati*, still
appear; but I have seen no black-caps lately.

I forgot to mention that I once saw, in Christ Church College quadrangle in Oxford, on a very sunny warm morning, a house-martin flying about, and settling on the parapet, so late as the twentieth of November.

At present I know only two species of bats, the common *vespertilio murinus* and the *vespertilio auritus*.

I was much entertained last summer with a tame bat, which would take flies out of a person's hand. If you gave it anything to eat, it brought its wings round before the mouth, hovering and hiding its head in the manner of birds of prey when they feed. The adroitness it showed in shearing off the wings of the flies, which were always rejected, was worthy of observation, and pleased me much. Insects seem to be most acceptable, though it did not refuse raw flesh when offered: so that the notion that bats go down chimnies and gnaw men's bacon, seems no improbable story. While I amused myself with this wonderful quadruped, I saw it several times confute the vulgar opinion, that bats when down on a flat surface cannot get on the wing again, by rising with great ease from the floor. It ran, I observed, with more dispatch than I was aware of; but in a most ridiculous and grotesque manner.

Bats drink on the wing, like swallows, by sipping the surface, as they play over pools and streams. They love to frequent waters, not only for the sake of drinking, but on account of insects, which are found over them in the greatest plenty. As I was going, some years ago, pretty late, in a boat from Richmond to Sunbury, on a warm summer's evening, I think I saw myriads of bats between the two places: the air swarmed with them all along the Thames, so that hundreds were in sight at a time.

LETTER XX

(*To Thomas Pennant, Esquire*)

Selborne, October 8, 1768.

It is, I find, in zoology as it is in botany: all nature is so full, that that district produces the greatest variety which is the most examined. Several birds, which are said to belong to the north only, are, it seems, often in the south. I have discovered this summer three species of birds with us, which writers mention as only to be seen in the northern countries. The first that was brought me (on the 14th of May) was the sandpiper, *tringa hypoleucus*: it was a cock bird, and haunted the banks of some ponds near the village; and, as it had a companion, doubtless intended to have bred near that water. Besides, the owner has told me since, that, on recollection, he has seen some of the same birds round his ponds in former summers.

The next bird that I procured (on the 21st of May) was a male red-backed butcher bird, *lanius collurio*. My neighbour, who shot it, says that it might easily have escaped his notice, had not the outcries and chattering of the white-throats and other small birds drawn his attention to the bush where it was: its craw was filled with the legs and wings of beetles.

The next rare birds (which were procured for me last week) were some ring-ousels, *turdi torquati*.

This week twelve months a gentleman from London, being with us, was amusing himself with a gun, and found, he told us, on an old yew hedge where there were berries, some birds like blackbirds, with rings of white round their necks: a neighbouring farmer also at the same time observed the same; but, as no specimens were procured little notice was taken. I mentioned this circumstance to you in my letter of November the 4th, 1767: (you, however, paid but small regard to what I said, as I had not seen these birds myself:) but last week, the aforesaid farmer, seeing a large flock, twenty or thirty of these birds, shot two cocks and two hens: and says, on recollection, that he remembers to have observed these birds again last spring, about Lady-day, as it were, on their return to the north. Now perhaps these ousels are not the ousels of the north of England, but belong to the more northern parts of Europe; and may retire before the excessive rigor of the frosts in those parts; and return to breed in the spring, when the cold abates. If this be the case, here is discovered a new bird of winter passage, concerning whose migrations the writers are silent: but if these birds should prove the ousels of the north of England, then here is a migration disclosed within our own kingdom never before remarked. It does not yet appear whether they retire beyond the bounds of our island to the south; but it is most probable that they usually do, or else one cannot suppose that they would have continued so long unnoticed in the southern counties. The ousel is larger than a blackbird, and feeds on haws; but last autumn (when there were no haws) it fed on yew-berries: in the spring it feeds on ivy-berries, which ripen only at that season, in March and April.

I must not omit to tell you (as you have been so lately on the study of reptiles) that my people, every now and then of late, draw up with a bucket of water from my well, which is 63 feet deep, a large black warty lizard with a fin-tail and yellow belly. How they first came down at that depth, and how they were ever to have got out thence without help, is more than I am able to say.

My thanks are due to you for your trouble and care in the examination of a buck's head. As far as your discoveries reach at present, they seem much to corroborate my suspicions; and I hope Mr. —— may find reason to give his decision in my favour; and then, I think, we may advance this extraordinary provision of nature as a new instance of the wisdom of God in the creation.

As yet I have not quite done with my history of the *oedicnemus*, or stone curlew; for I shall desire a gentleman in Sussex (near whose house these birds congregate in vast flocks in the autumn) to observe nicely when they leave him (if they do leave him), and when they return again in the spring; I was with this gentleman lately, and saw several single birds.

LETTER XXIII

(To The Honourable Daines Barrington)

Selborne, June 8, 1775.

On September the 21st, 1741, being then on a visit, and intent on field-diversions, I rose before daybreak: when I came into the enclosures, I found the stubbles and clover-grounds matted all over with a thick coat of cobweb, in the meshes of which a copious and heavy dew hung so plentifully that the whole face of the country seemed, as it were, covered with two or three setting-nets drawn one over another. When the dogs attempted to hunt, their eyes were so blinded and hoodwinked that they could not proceed, but were obliged to lie down and scrape the incumbrances from their faces with their forefeet, so that, finding my sport interrupted, I returned home musing in my mind on the oddness of the occurrence.

As the morning advanced the sun became bright and warm, and the day turned out one of those most lovely ones which no season but the autumn produces; cloudless, calm, serene, and worthy of the South of France itself.

About nine an appearance very unusual began to demand our attention, a shower of cobwebs falling from very elevated regions, and continuing, without any interruption, till the close of the day. These webs were not single filmy threads, floating in the air in all directions, but perfect flakes or rags; some near an inch broad, and five or six long, which fell with a degree of velocity which showed they were considerably heavier than the atmosphere.

On every side as the observer turned his eyes might he behold a continual succession of fresh flakes falling into his sight, and twinkling like stars as they turned their sides towards the sun.

How far this wonderful shower extended would be difficult to say; but we know that it reached Bradley, Selborne, and Alresford, three places which lie in a sort of a triangle, the shortest of whose sides is about eight miles in extent.

At the second of those places there was a gentleman (for whose veracity and intelligent turn we have the greatest veneration) who observed it the moment he got abroad; but concluded that, as soon as he came upon the hill above his house, where he took his morning rides, he should be higher than this meteor, which he imagined might have been blown, like thistle-down, from the common above: but, to his great astonishment, when he rode to the most elevated part of the down, 300 feet above his fields, he found the webs in appearance still as much above him as before; still descending into sight in a constant succession, and twinkling in the sun, so as to draw the attention of the most incurious.

Neither before nor after was any such fall observed; but on this day the flakes hung in the trees and hedges so thick, that a diligent person sent out might have gathered baskets full.

The remark that I shall make on these cobweb-like appearances, called gossamer, is, that, strange and superstitious as the notions about them were formerly, nobody in these days doubts but that they are the real production of small spiders, which swarm in the fields in fine weather in autumn, and have a power of shooting out webs from their tails so as to render themselves buoyant, and lighter than air. But why these apterous insects should that day take such a wonderful aërial excursion, and why their webs should at once become so gross and material as to be considerably more weighty than air, and to descend with precipitation, is a matter beyond my skill. If I might be allowed to hazard a supposition, I should imagine that those filmy threads, when first shot, might be entangled in the rising dew, and so drawn up, spiders and all, by a brisk evaporation into the region where clouds are formed: and if the spiders have a power of coiling and thickening their webs in the air, as Dr. Lister says they have [see his Letters to Mr. Ray] then, when they were become heavier than the air, they must fall.

Every day in fine weather, in autumn chiefly, do I see those spiders shooting out their webs and mounting aloft: they will go off from your finger if you will take them into your hand. Last summer one alighted on my book as I was reading in the parlour; and, running to the top of the page, and shooting out a web, took its departure from thence. But what I most wondered at, was that it went off with considerable velocity in a place where no air was stirring; and I am sure that I did not assist it with my breath. So that these little crawlers seem to have, while mounting, some loco-motive power without the use of wings, and to move in the air, faster than the air itself.

LETTER XXVII

(To The Honourable Daines Barrington)

Selborne, December 12, 1775.

We had in this village more than twenty years ago an idiot-boy, whom I well remember, who, from a child, showed a strong propensity to bees; they were his food, his amusement, his sole object. And as people of this cast have seldom more than one point in view, so this lad exerted all his few faculties on this one pursuit. In the winter he dozed away his time, within his father's house, by the fire-side, in a kind of torpid state, seldom departing from the chimney-corner; but in the summer he was all alert, and in quest of his game in the fields, and on sunny banks. Honey-bees, humble-bees, and wasps, were his prey wherever he found them: he had no apprehensions from their stings, but would seize them *nudis manibus*, and at once disarm them of their weapons, and suck their bodies for the sake of their honey-bags. Sometimes he would fill his bosom between his shirt and his skin with a number of these captives; and sometimes would confine them in bottles. He was a very *merops apiaster*, or bee-bird; and very injurious to men that kept bees; for he would slide into their bee-gardens, and, sitting down before the stools, would rap with his finger on the hives, and so take the bees as they came out. He has been known to overturn hives for the sake of honey, of which he was passionately fond. Where metheglin was making he would linger round the tubs and vessels, begging a draught of what he called bee-wine. As he ran about he used to make a humming noise with his lips, resembling the buzzing of bees. This lad was lean and sallow, and of a cadaverous complexion; and, except in his favourite pursuit, in which he was wonderfully adroit, discovered no manner of understanding. Had his capacity been better, and directed to the same object, he had perhaps abated much of our wonder at the feats of a more modern exhibitor of bees; and we may justly say of him now,

> . . . "Thou,
> Had thy presiding star propitious shone,
> Should'st Wildman be." . . .

When a tall youth he was removed from hence to a distant village, where he died, as I understand, before he arrived at manhood.

ODE TO A NIGHTINGALE

I

My heart aches, and a drowsy numbness pains
  My sense, as though of hemlock I had drunk,
Or emptied some dull opiate to the drains
  One minute past, and Lethe-wards had sunk:
'Tis not through envy of thy happy lot,
  But being too happy in thine happiness,—
    That thou, light-winged Dryad of the trees,
      In some melodious plot
Of beechen green, and shadows numberless,
  Singest of summer in full-throated ease.

II

O, for a draught of vintage! that hath been
  Cool'd a long age in the deep-delved earth,
Tasting of Flora and the country green,
  Dance, and Provençal song, and sunburnt mirth!
O for a beaker full of the warm South,
  Full of the true, the blushful Hippocrene,
    With beaded bubbles winking at the brim,
      And purple-stained mouth;
That I might drink, and leave the world unseen,
  And with thee fade away into the forest dim:

III

Fade far away, dissolve, and quite forget
    What thou among the leaves hast never known,
The weariness, the fever, and the fret
    Here, where men sit and hear each other groan;
Where palsy shakes a few, sad, last gray hairs,
    Where youth grows pale, and spectre-thin, and dies;
        Where but to think is to be full of sorrow
        And leaden-eyed despairs,
    Where Beauty cannot keep her lustrous eyes,
        Or new Love pine at them beyond to-morrow.

IV

Away! away! for I will fly to thee,
    Not charioted by Bacchus and his pards,
But on the viewless wings of Poesy,
    Though the dull brain perplexes and retards:
Already with thee! tender is the night,
    And haply the Queen-Moon is on her throne,
        Cluster'd around by all her starry Fays;
        But here there is no light,
Save what from heaven is with the breezes blown
    Through verdurous glooms and winding mossy ways.

V

I cannot see what flowers are at my feet,
    Nor what soft incense hangs upon the boughs,
But, in embalmed darkness, guess each sweet
    Wherewith the seasonable month endows
The grass, the thicket, and the fruit-tree wild;
    White hawthorn, and the pastoral eglantine;
        Fast fading violets cover'd up in leaves;
        And mid-May's eldest child,
The coming musk-rose, full of dewy wine,
    The murmurous haunt of flies on summer eves.

VI

Darkling I listen; and, for many a time
    I have been half in love with easeful Death,
Call'd him soft names in many a musèd rhyme,
    To take into the air my quiet breath;

Now more than ever seems it rich to die,
To cease upon the midnight with no pain,
While thou art pouring forth thy soul abroad
In such an ecstasy!
Still wouldst thou sing, and I have ears in vain—
To thy high requiem become a sod.

VII

Thou wast not born for death, immortal Bird!
No hungry generations tread thee down;
The voice I hear this passing night was heard
In ancient days by emperor and clown:
Perhaps the self-same song that found a path
Through the sad heart of Ruth, when, sick for home,
She stood in tears amid the alien corn;
The same that oft-times hath
Charm'd magic casements, opening on the foam
Of perilous seas, in faery lands forlorn.

VIII

Forlorn! the very word is like a bell
To toll me back from thee to my sole self!
Adieu! the fancy cannot cheat so well
As she is fam'd to do, deceiving elf.
Adieu! adieu! thy plaintive anthem fades
Past the near meadows, over the still stream,
Up the hill-side; and now 'tis buried deep
In the next valley-glades:
Was it a vision, or a waking dream?
Fled is that music:—Do I wake or sleep?

JOHN KEATS

THE LINNAEAN AGE

by Donald Culross Peattie

This is a brief account of the life and work of Linnaeus by Donald Culross Peattie, which means that nothing further need be set down here except a few vital statistics. Author Peattie was born in Chicago, June 21, 1898, and was graduated, cum laude, from Harvard in 1922. He settled down to science as a career and, luckily for so many of us, took to writing down his observations and reflections on the subject. He practically leaped to literary fame with the publication of Almanac For Moderns in 1935. His two volumes on the trees of North America have become standard works of reference. These and other books have put him in the front rank of modern writers of natural history. The selection offered here—from Green Laurels, published in 1936—is meant to serve a double purpose. One is to give the reader a glimpse of Donald Culross Peattie at his scintillating best in a field that he knows and loves. The other is to offer the reader a description of one of the greatest figures ever to emerge in the field of natural history, Linnaeus, and how he tried to reduce the riot of animate things on earth to some semblance of scientific order.

IN 1707, when Carl Linnaeus was born in a little red farm cottage near Rashult, no one, surely, expected that the greatest naturalist of the age would come out of Sweden. When continental Europe thought of that peninsular country at all, it was as a big icicle hanging from the eaves of the North Pole.

At the moment, Sweden was enjoying a meteoric military ascendancy, but it had neither the men nor the resources to keep its Baltic empire. In a few years the fireworks were to come down as a dead stick, so that the whole land, during Linnaeus's youth, was anemic with debt and shaken in its self-confidence. The sense of decline was felt throughout the country, from its timid king, down through its contracting, listless universities, to the impoverished rural population out of which Linnaeus sprang.

Yet from this rocky, snow-bound kingdom was to come the man who would really create in science all that order that Buffon supposed you could make by being *raisonnable*. The babe in the red cottage was to become the thinker who brought the scholastic ideal of abstract concepts to some useful culmination. Now was born Nature's tender lover who would awaken all the world to intense enthusiasm for his beloved. To the astonishment of all the wise men, he was not a product of Wittenberg, or the parks of Versailles or even of English country life, that nurse of so much delicate feeling for natural beauty. But genius so seldom grows where the highly born and the members of the eugenical societies tell us to expect it! Possibly there is a misconception about genius. If Buffon was right in supposing that it is an infinite capacity for taking pains, then bank clerks would be geniuses. But Sir Isaac Newton could never add up the household accounts either as correctly or as swiftly as his cook.

Nor will the advantages of good teachers or a well-equipped library or laboratory suffice in themselves to make a naturalist. Linnaeus, born out of peasant stock, never had more than a few hours' formal instruction in the very subjects where his name was to be graved with the immortals. The scientific equipment of his university was inferior to that of a rural public high school in our age. And as for books, he had frequently to write the ones that he needed most. A stultifying environment—for mediocrity.

But the making of a naturalist may well begin before all formal tutelage. The gift, like a grass-flower, will spring up almost unmarked in a country childhood, and to the countryside that nurtured the childhood of this man we must look back.

In after-life Linnaeus remembered it with tender sentiment.

"Lake Möckeln," he says, "here extends in a quarter of a mile long bay" (one of those appalling Swedish miles, seven of ours) "and almost reached the foundations of the church. The level farmlands surround the church on all sides except the west, where Möckeln displays its limpid waters. A little way off, the fine beech woods show themselves toward the south. . . . The fields are sheltered from the north by coniferous woods, and east and south are pleasant fields and leafy trees. . . . The meadows resemble more the most splendid groves and richest flower gardens, than their actual selves, so that one may sit in summer and hear the cuckoo with other different bird songs, insects piping and humming, and at the same time view the glowing and splendidly colored flowers. One cannot but turn giddy at the Creator's magnificent arrangement. . . . Stenbrohult parish is like a queen among sisters, she has predominancy of rare and scarce plants, which in other localities in the country seldom or never show themselves. Yes, the surroundings seemed as if they had been adorned by Flora herself. . . . I doubt if there is a spot in the whole world set out in more pleasant fashion."

So he speaks of his *ljuve natale*, his dear birthplace, as he calls it in a characteristic blend of Swedish and Latin. And we might take it that an old man is merely remembering a childhood through sentimental eyes.

Mayhap, and yet is he not trying to tell us that, as a naturalist, he was born with a silver spoon in his mouth? That marching spruces, and not topiary, were the first impressions to print themselves upon the retina of memory?

Through the woods that swept down to the edge of the cultivated fields of Stenbrohult, the wild stepped lightly, and gazed with its bright, curious eyes at the garnered fields, the red farmhouses and the white church. Elemental forces were close at hand, and the child who walked only a little way into those woods stepped straight into the most primeval part of Europe still remaining. Bear there were, and wolves, and tiny elvish forests of black moss, deep hangings of lichens, delicate ferns sprung high and green in the unexpected lushness of northern vegetation, and mushroom villages with their red-warted gables. Many children, of course, came there, to count the cuckoo's notes. And they were all a little awed, I suppose, with the solemnity of the forest, conscious that it stretched away without bound, to unknown Lapland, to give place at last to the tundras, where under the blazing midnight sun the reindeer sped and the boggy sward was enameled with the intense colors of the wide-eyed arctic flowers. But one child who wandered there, made preternaturally old, perhaps, by his father, took fire from the thought of the width of the green world. He had no need to think his home surrounded by a rose hedge, as some domestic souls would like to have it. It stretched away, on the north at least, toward a bit of infinity, where winter and summer, day and night, beauty and terror, life and death, were abrupt and imminent and absolute. One whole side of this boy's nature seems from the first to have tingled with the consciousness of such elementals.

And so, while all of central and southern Europe was being ransacked in the unreal search for some lost wisdom of the ancients, in the north a glistening, a stirring, a clear-eyed reality awaited the coming of an appointed seer.

The first clear picture that Linnaeus had of himself was of a child who ran about the rectory garden at Stenbrohult, telling off the names of the flowers. When he forgot the name of one, his father gently reproved him for shortness of memory or want of attention, and sometimes tears of mortification came to the little boy's eyes.

According to tradition the pastor used to put the year-old Carl on the grass with a flower in his hand, and on this the child bent such rapt attention that he would be good for hours. It is not necessary to believe the legends of a great man's babyhood, but in this case I am inclined to listen to the tale. Pastor Nils Linnaeus was himself a passionate lover of flowers. When a father sets out, pridefully, to teach his eldest little son that thing which he holds dear, that favorite hobby, that vocation which he gave up for a more practical calling, he may succeed in communicating all his suppressed excitement. And Pastor Linnaeus was more than an ordinary gardener; he collected what he believed to be rarities, and though his taste in horticultural design might now be thought atrocious, it was the pride of the parish of Stenbrohult.

In the long summer evenings that lasted until eleven o'clock, the pastor would take the listening child to walk over the flowering meadows by the lake, while he discoursed upon the plants, telling how each one had a name, a name in goodly Latin that had been bestowed upon it by the ancients, or by the wise herbalists—how this was an *Orchis*, that a *Rosa*, and this other a *Lilium*. So the father taught the son to see all things, the lake and the sky, the birds and the blossoms. He laid for him that indispensable foundation for a naturalist, the long view and the quick sight. By showing the child, repeatedly, that which is usual instead of trying to amaze him with the marvelous and exceptional, he taught him what is natural in the woods and fields, and that which was strange could be left thereafter to proclaim itself.

The name Linnaeus was a prophecy. For in old Sweden only the nobility had family names. The pastor's original cognomen had been Nils Ingemarsson, that is to say, Nils the son of Ingemar, whose name in turn had not been Ingemarsson, but Ingemar Bengtsson, Ingemar the son of Bengt. Such names are not familial but patronymic, and correspond to a Russian name like Ivan Stepanovitch, John the son of

Stephen. But when peninsular Sweden became Continentalized, many persons elected a family name, and Nils chose Linnaeus, a Latinized form of *Linn*, the word for the linden or lime tree. There are few "flowering" trees in Sweden, but the linden is one of them. With its deep green shade, its gracious, heart-shaped, talkative leaves, and its honey-sweet flowers that bloom at the joyful northern festival of Midsummer, it was held by the peasantry to be sacred, and one majestic lime in particular was venerated by Nils Ingemarsson. From it he took his name, though you may know it in some other language; thus the great naturalist is sometimes put down as Karl or Carl or Charles Linnaeus, Carl von Linné, or Carolus Linnaeus. In after-life, he said it mattered little to him what he was called. Probably he was glad to escape the ubiquitous name of Nilsson which would logically have been his if his pastor father had not had a bit of pagan tree-worship in his soul.

His good mother wanted to make a priest of the boy. Carl had no way of explaining that what he wanted to be was a naturalist. There were as yet no scientists such as he wanted to become, and perhaps not even any word for them. The only road to his half-realized career lay through medicine, at that time the least reputable and certainly the most poorly paid profession in the country. But Nils Linnaeus, after a proper show of reluctance, consented at last to let the boy go as far as the university at Lund, where he had a rich relative on the faculty.

Lund at that time was as little likely a place for studying medicine and natural science as any small country academy of today, whose curriculum is ridden by trustees drawn from the body of Fundamentalist divines. At last the disgusted boy left it abruptly for Upsala, a rich man's college located near the wicked great city of Stockholm.

And there we find him, putting paper in the soles of his worn-out shoes, wandering the neglected, dusty, autumnal botanical garden, and nervously awaiting, as so many boys have had to wait, the arrival of his academic credits. He scuffed the dead leaves and wondered what he would do when his money was gone. He had made the usual miscalculation of country boys who go far from home to a big university, and was beginning to see that by spring he would inevitably find lodgings in the graveyard. His father had many other children to support; his mother was out of sympathy with the whole undertaking, and the rich relative at Lund was in a huff with him.

And even Upsala held disillusion. It had recently been razed by fire and though rebuilt it was still intellectually in ashes. The botanical garden, laid out in his youth by the famous Olaf Rudbeck, had suffered equally. It was shrunk to two hundred sorts of flowers, half of them commonplace. But Rudbeck, who had seen a lifetime of manuscript researches go up in flames, had no heart left to restore an herb garden.

Rudbeck it was, indeed, under whom Linnaeus had supposed he had come to study, and under Roberg. But both were aged, weary of teaching, weary of students, lost in abstruse research.

There was a surgical theater for giving anatomical demonstrations, but no one to perform them, and the religious temper of the regents was probably opposed to human dissection. So that both the faculty and the students were glad, on one occasion, to go to Stockholm to hold a public dissection on a woman who had been hanged. Linnaeus for this privilege spent the last of his money on the trip.

But if Upsala was not fitted to make a physician of Linnaeus, there were still crumbs of natural history to be picked up. The library at least was fair, and there Linnaeus forgot his hunger and wet feet as he read for hours, unconscious of the gathering dusk outside—one of those earnest boys with wrists grown out of their frayed cuffs, whom librarians still have to put out at closing hour.

And a bursar of the university had once pasted up a "plant book" —probably an album of pressed specimens—which Linnaeus used to ask to see till doubtless the custodians were weary of lifting the massive volume down for him. Some lectures on birds were given by Rudbeck, though they never went farther than the domestic fowl. But they were at least an introduction to anatomy. Roberg occasionally expounded Aristotle and Descartes, and gave five medical lectures during the entire year, but Linnaeus was not even successful in getting into the hall to hear these.

Bitterly lonely, Linnaeus in the first autumn quarter inquired everywhere for some one of similar tastes. The answer was always the same —Pehr Artedius, Artedi, as they called him and as he has since become known—a lad who had arrived from the borders of Lapland a *summa cum laude* divinity student who yet insisted on practising the hellborn science of alchemy and entertained a mad passion for icthyology. *Fishes*, forsooth! Even the medical students gave him up, yet by all accounts he and Linnaeus should get on together. But Artedi was at home, taking leave of his dying father.

In the winter quarter he returned, and Linnaeus found him, "pale, cast-down and tearful." But the friendship was like a chemical attraction; the two young exiles met together with a shock of surprise and happiness.

Is there any one who has so far forgotten his young self that he cannot remember that friend, discovered out of all the meaningless faces at school, that one right and consanguineous soul? Perhaps you can recall your excitement at the thought of meeting him again, the anxiety lest you fall short in his estimation, the honor you felt when you could loan him a farthing, or when he casually tossed you the necessary clothes when you were asked to dinner at the dean's house, and the dean's wife and daughter snubbed you. But where is he now? Have your wives separated you? Has he gone on in the impossible dream, the impractical calling that you so prudently gave up? Can you even recall what it was that you talked of so passionately?

"The ideas which Artedi propounded were new to me," Linnaeus records, "and the knowledge which he disclosed astonished me."

Ah, yes, those ideas, those preposterous cosmogonies, those unearthly systems of thought, those wild young ideas you had! Yet in this case they were nothing less than the very grammar of the natural sciences as we know them today. They were not more Artedi's than Linnaeus's, for in a measure they had been Aristotle's, they were Bauhin's, they were Ray's, Camerarius's and Grew's. I have written thus far in vain if I have not made it plain that science grows layer by layer, like a snail shell, and that in natural history, at least, no discovery and no hypothesis come suddenly, or may be born at all without a long chain of parents and grandparents. Its beliefs must be perfected, polished, and pruned by many loving hands. They only become celebrated and accepted several hundred years after they are first conceived, or even several thousand.

Only the desperately young and brilliantly ignorant would have attempted what now Artedi and Linnaeus did attempt. Aristotle and Augustine and the great Ray had already failed gloriously at it, and in a measure Bruno and Spinoza too. But between them these two lads began to map out nothing less modest than all God's good creations upon earth. They sought to make a great schema or system of all the three kingdoms, animal and mineral and vegetable.

And they labored to invent a new language for it. Their *lingua* merely availed itself of the still universal language of Latin; it was not Latin in any literary sense. This language was to enable men to speak in universals of Nature; it was to make an orderly community out of the staggering, slippery profusion of the tangible world. And withal, this categorical science must be provided with some finding-key, some intelligible syllabus, some Blue Guide that would make straight a path in the wilderness.

For every day that wilderness seemed to grow up with higher thorns and weeds. To all that natural science already knew of temperate Europe, Asia, and America, there was abruptly added the overwhelming influx of tropical proliferation. Knowledge of the floras of Malay and Brazil, the two largest in the world, had come almost simultaneously to swamp reason, and mounting upon this green tidal wave came a second wave, ten times as high—the tropical insect world, unknown, unnamed, unmanageable.

How this superabundant life was dealt with and made science, what was the language and what the great system of Nature conceived by Linnaeus and Artedi, and who the many were who labored before and after them at the great task, there will be time enough, I take it, to tell in the unwritten chapters before me. For the moment it was all only a shared secret, a dream conceived perhaps with the same abstract purity, the same scorn of its practicability, as Plato's rule by philosophers.

The two lads, like conquerors, divided up the kingdoms between them. Artedi took chemistry, fishes, amphibians and insects; Linnaeus elected the birds, flowers and minerals. The contrast in their temperaments he has recorded for us: the lad from the north tall, silent, deliberate and earnest, and a little melancholy, while Linnaeus himself was small and quick-witted, hasty and vivacious. He could not then foresee the deeper contrast that is apparent to us, for he was, all unconscious, destiny's favorite child, who was to grow rich in years, to be heaped with honors, to live a man's full-rounded life; he stood in sunshine, while close at his side Artedi was shadowed by his own young death. As brilliant as his friend, perhaps, Artedi was to leave behind him this epitaph—that, had he lived, he might have been the Linnaeus of zoölogy.

But the prospect that Artedi would die in less than ten years seemed less likely than that Linnaeus would starve before spring. It was late in April, on one of the first days of early spring as it comes to bleak Uppland province, that the old Dean Olaf Celsius, a flower lover and a friend to science, came for a stroll in the dilapidated botanical garden. He was presently aware of a young, unknown student sitting on a bench, with flowers in his hand, writing notes upon them in a book.

So strange a sight had not been witnessed for many a year. Celsius drew near, and fell into talk with the student.

The answers came back so charged with significant enthusiasm, so knowledgeable of the neglected subject, that the oldster could scarce credit his ears. He supposed, no doubt, that Linnaeus must know with whom he talked. But in truth the young man had no idea that he was addressing the august Celsius, who had been long absent in Stockholm and was known to him only as a mighty name. It was not until, talking as they walked, and warming to each other, they entered the imposing door of the dean's house, that Linnaeus comprehended in whose presence he stood.

The upshot of it all was that Linnaeus was comfortably lodged in Dean Celsius's house, gratis, and by grace of his benefactor was made recipient of a royal scholarship. Later his patron secured for him a small position as a demonstrator in the botanical gardens. He had the run, too, of the dean's library, better suited, it may be, to his need than the university's. And there it was, no doubt, that he first encountered what other men had accomplished toward that great chart of creation at which he worked, and that grammar of science. His discoveries, he must have learned then, were not half so original as they seemed. And he must have perceived those holes and lacunae and blind-spots that are inevitable in every young man's early science. After all, it appeared, Bauhin had already devised a binomial nomenclature for plants and animals; Ray had already attempted a classification of plants by their flowers and fruits; Camerarius had done marvels in demonstrating the still half-unaccepted sexuality of the vegetable kingdom, and Belon, with his anatomy of birds, had long ago laid down the fundamentals of a schema for the animal world. Toward the delineation of natural families the patient Tournefort, the boy must have found, had mightily wrought.

But you are nowhere in science until you are humbled; the art of practising a science consists in a perfect willingness to learn, coupled with an assertive tendency to doubt, to check, to re-verify even highest authority. And these two temperamental tendencies are so difficult to wed and bed in the same human intellect that many promising careers, many geniuses, indeed, have broken up in wreckage because these two faculties warred rather than worked together, as they worked for Linnaeus.

In particular the work of Vaillant on the sexuality of plants allured and charmed the young man. I would almost venture to say that his

predilection for this subject—which was to waft his celebrity to the
ends of the earth—was at the start connected with the emotions, with
something consanguineous with art and with love. It is not possible to
analyze the psyche of the long dead, but we know today how far the
choice of career is determined by some personal and chancy mental
association. The wording of Linnaeus's youthful manuscripts on the
ultimately renowned "sexual system" reveals traces, mere traces, of an
artist's love of symmetry and perfection, bound up with an intellectual
sublimation of the young man's very normal preoccupation with sex.
Scientists who have forgotten where they first found their present im-
personal vocations may frown or look away in embarrassment at this
suggestion. Or they may snort that it is imaginative nonsense. And we
shall have to endure their wrath as best we may.

In all events, history was made when on New Year's Day, 1730,
Dean Celsius discovered on his desk a manuscript that bore the title
(which I translate out of the Latin), *Preliminaries on the marriage of
plants, in which the physiology of them is explained, sex shown,
method of generation disclosed, and the true analogy of plants with
animals concluded*, by Carolus Linnaeus. The introduction read:

"It is an old custom to awaken one's eminent patrons on New Year's
Day with verses and good wishes, and I also find myself obliged to do
so. I would gladly write in verse, but . . . was not born a poet, but a
botanist instead, so I offer the fruit of the little harvest which God has
vouchsafed me. In these few pages is handled the great analogy which
is found between plants and animals, in their increase in like measure
according to their kind, and what I have here simply written I pray
may be favorably received."

The errors in this tract, ineluctable in the state of knowledge then,
stand out pathetically to us in our boundless wisdom. But the text
shows at least that Linnaeus was striding down the right road. In that
hour of fuddled theorizing and windy classicism, it was something so
direct and convincing that the delighted Celsius went about waving
the pages at every one he encountered. As there was only the one
manuscript copy, students gladly toiled to handwrite copies of their
own, or quietly lifted them from one another's desks—always a healthy
sign for a book! And finally one of these transcriptions came to the
aged eyes of the titan Rudbeck. He carried it close to his short vision,
and having read, put it down with one of those half-sentences of mild
commendation that from the old and wise means more than the rapture of court ladies. Presently, sighing and groaning with his senile

aches and hypochondria, he pottered around to Celsius's door. Who
was this Linnaeus, and what did Celsius mean by keeping him dark?
And what was anyone doing about him?

What Rudbeck did about him was to take him into his house and
lodge him at a good stipend as a tutor; intellectually he adopted the
youth. It was a mighty friend to whose home the lucky Linnaeus now
removed—a man for whom the double doors at court swung open, a
man who could grumble a word or two to a bigwig of either political
party—Count Tessin or Count Horn—and secure reserved appointments, or set the dilatory presses to flashing, or pry money loose from
miserly state coffers for traveling scholarships and exploration.

Not that Rudbeck exerted himself at once. He was too battered a
veteran of life to trust any one very far. He bided his time, and while
he seemed to doze at the fire, watched around the wings of his easy
chair, as it were, with a sly old eye.

But bit by bit he relaxed, and, in the comfort of house slippers, he
opened out the mighty storehouse of his memory. He too had been
young once—a botanist, like his father before him, a zoölogist, an
ethnographer and philologist. Forty years ago he had made a journey
to Lapland—did Linnaeus know the north? Linnaeus did not; perhaps
he spoke some prideful words of Småland. But we can hear Rudbeck
snort. A tepid province, a place for invalids and women. He began to
tell of the mighty miles of travel, over bog, over boiling rivers, past
cataracts whose spume and thunder rose up to heaven like a forest
fire. He remembered for the young ears the dark fierce men, the pagan
girls, fair only for an earliest month of maturity, like the arctic wildflowers. And it all came back to him—the high geese crying, the loons
diving, the wild swans drifting upon lakes so far from human ken that
even the Devil had never found it worth his while to visit them.

Of that land-faring nought but a truncated fragment had ever been
told in print, a fragment that carried the reader only along the first
leg of the journey, and was disfigured (for all but the author) by
windy philological digressions. The rest of the pages had risen to the
sky as flames in the Upsala fire. But the diary—the battered old log of
his travels—was still by him. And in this primitive Odyssey we know
now that the young Linnaeus read, for, though its existence was unsuspected for a century or more, it was discovered some forty years
gone by among Linnaeus's papers in the British Museum.

It was in 1731 that Rudbeck and Linnaeus began agitating for a
scientific expedition to Lapland, petitioning the Crown and the Royal

Scientific Society of Upsala. It is necessary to realize, in this day when
you can pass the hat and somehow find the tens of thousands necessary to finance a useless submarine dash under the North Pole, that
such a journey as the old and the young man then proposed had no
precedent in history. Every previous scientific reconnaissance had been
made in connection with a boundary survey, a diplomatic or commercial mission, a search for precious metals conceived in an alchemical or a purely gainful spirit. Or at best there had been a research
after the legendary wisdom of the ancients, one more ransacking of
exhausted Greece and the Holy Land. In the explorative field of natural science, Europe continued to be literally *oriented,* as late as the
days of George III when John Sibthorp traveled and suffered in Greece
and Turkey like a good medieval, a Don Quixote of botany, in quest
of the ambiguous herbs of Dioscorides.

But this project on the Royal Society's table in 1731 was startling
because it was twentieth century in spirit. No wonder if the good
gentlemen scratched their blond Swedish heads under their white wigs.
But, tell it to their credit, they voted Linnaeus at last something nearly
half as much as he would need in the way of money, and that delighted
young fellow shortly after New Year dashed home to see his parents.

His father resigned all into God's hands. But his mother was too
human a woman for that. Like every good Scandinavian, she quoted
at him one of those sayings intended to prevent the young from doing
youthful things:

> "In thy country
> Born and bred,
> By God's bounty
> Duly fed,
> Be not lightly
> From it led!"

Linnaeus might well have protested that he was not leaving his
country. But Lapland was only politically Sweden. For Frü Linnaeus
it was—rather accurately—a heathen land. In point of peril and obstacle, the land of the midnight sun in that age presented mountain
barriers of difficulty such as today are buried in Tibet or in Antarctica.

So having kissed him an unforgiving farewell, this sensible lady
marched into the gloom of the rectory parlor and began to mourn
her son for dead.

At last, on the twelfth of May, Swedish Old Style (the twenty-sec ond of May by our calendar), in the year of grace 1732, Linnaeus, then twenty-five years old, lacking but a single day, rode out alone through the old north customs gate of walled Upsala town, his blood singing with adventure—rode past the three high mounds of the cemetery, symbol of the dead past and of all the wise and cautious of earth who are under the sod. He rode out of winter, out of all pedantry and musty book learning, into the springtide of science.

"My clothes consisted of a light coat of Westgothland linsey [woolsey]," he records, "lined with red shalloon, having cuffs and collar of shag; leather breeches; a round wig; a green leather cap, and a pair of half-boots. I carried a small leather bag, half an ell in length, but somewhat less in breadth, furnished on one side with hooks and eyes, so that it could be opened at pleasure. This bag contained one shirt, two pairs of false sleeves and two half shirts; an inkstand, pencase, microscope and spying glass, a gauze cap to protect me occasionally from the gnats, a comb, my journal, and a parcel of paper stitched together for drying plants, both in folio, and my manuscripts on Ornithology, *Flora Uplandica* and *Characteres Generici*. I wore a hanger [knife] at my side, and carried a small fowling-piece as well as an octangular stick, graduated for the purpose of measuring. My pocket-book contained a passport from the Governor of Upsala, and a recommendation from the Academy. . . .

"It was a splendid spring day; the sky was clear and warm, while the west wind refreshed one with a delicious breath. The winter rye stood six inches high and the barley had newly come into leaf. The birch was beginning to shoot, and all trees were leafing, except the elm and aspen."

There were dandelions, rye-flower, forget-me-not and pansy and sweet violet, primrose and water cowslip in bloom—pale, simple little flowers of early spring, common in many lands. But this time there was coming forth one whose eyes were clear, on whose fresh vision the commonest phenomenon would fall as marvelous.

The lark was his companion all the way, he said, quivering upon the air as it trilled its *tirra-lirra*. In the distance the dark coniferous forests rose up ahead of him in the north, and far away, in the changeable spring sky, a blue-black rain cloud unfolded its soft cumuli, while all about him the fields were spangled with dew and sunlight.

When the dark woods closed around his way, he left the lark behind, and heard instead "the amorous warblings" of the redwing. Almost at once he found himself in one of those gnomish forests of

northern Europe where ancient spruces, centuries old, with thick and
knotted trunks like twisted muscles, are still dwarfed as if under some
curse of eld. Deep lichens hung upon their boughs, like sorrow upon
an ill-fated castle. Black moss, ankle-deep, closed about his horse's
hoofs, and out of it peeped frail windflowers, shivering in the chill
young day.

So it began, that great Lapland journey, the first of all its kind in the
world. Like the south wind Linnaeus came to it; he came like an army
of youth; he came with the spring, that surged, wave upon wave of
greenness, flash upon flash of flowers; he came like the wild geese
and the swans winging arrowy straight and sure, over the lakes and the
tundra, for their secret rites in the North. He led the way for us all.

For have we not, all of us, had our young particular Lapland? For
some of us it lay in the south, or the west, or east. Perhaps it was
Colorado, and you knee-deep in lupine and columbine, with a breath
of the glaciers cold upon you and the tingling western air in your lungs.
Perhaps it was Florida, with the wealth of the King of the Sea washed
up as iridescent shells on the strand at your feet. Perhaps it was the
Blue Ridge, when the rhododendron petals snowed on the pool at
the foot of the waterfall, and a redbird swept with a burst of song from
a flowering dogwood to a flowering tulip tree. Wherever it lay, it is the
living world as you came to it with the ardor of first love.

You know now that you wouldn't go, at your age, to see fabled
Roraima, not if they came and besought you. You know too well when
you are best off, nor would you endure again your young discomforts,
for a princely purse.

But sometimes you will remember how you set out once to see your
first snow-capped peak. You will recall how you struggled up the
slopes, through briar, through mire, the pack straining at your shoulders, and the adventurous wind freezing the sweat beneath your shirt.
Until you stood at last upon a knoll and waved your hat, and shouted
up the wind to see the clouds draw back, unveiling the longed-for,
ice-cased virginity, glittering and cruel. Just so Linnaeus saw, across
the desolate bogs, the first spearhead gleam of the Norway fells, flashing a pale enticement to death, swimming like a moon through the
banks of drifting fog. Remember it all, back to the high-hearted faring
forth, and you may catch your old self gazing after your young self, as
Olaf Rudbeck once watched a young man ride away, into the morning,
into the lark song, into the springtide.

*   *   *   *

It was long the custom that on Linnaeus's birthday botanists in all countries should take down from the shelf their vascula or plant boxes, and set forth for a ramble in the great old style of the Linnaean field trips. These commemorative excursions seem to have been held at first upon the twenty-first day of May, owing to a misconception about the date of the anniversary. And it is said that even when the error was pointed out, many of the older men refused to change their *mumpsimus* for the new-fangled *sumpsimus*; they held, and probably rightly, that the traditional day of the celebration was more important than a barren truth.

So they set forth, in little companies, to re-discover the modest floral treasures of the countryside, as if they returned to their origins; as if they would recapture a lost delight in the age of innocence of their science. Men who knew things that Linnaeus could never have known returned to the fresh surface of experience; they cut through the bark, as it were, down to the green cambium layer that is found in every living branch. It was as if they needed to reassure themselves that still, under the arc of the sky and in their niches in the rocks or their stations on the moor, good green things grew and kept their faith with spring.

And what more natural, you ask, than that botanists should collect plants? The public conception of a botanist is little other than a man with a vasculum, who can name on sight any and all plants. Alas, what antiquated notions one may retain! Modern botany has almost ceased to concern itself with living plants. In many places, particularly in Germany and in the Germanized American universities, the "amiable science," as Goethe called it, is become an affair of titration tubes, spectroscopes, microtomes, chromosomes, and the mathematics of genetics. The botanical faculty are practically vassals of the physics and chemistry departments. Through their mills, vegetable tissue passes as the raw materials of the laboratory. It is in many cases of so little apparent moment to know the names or the life habits of the living plant which furnishes forth the experimental material, that it is possible now to be a bespectacled young doctor of botany without having a speaking acquaintance with half a dozen living plants where they grow.

In fact, it is a matter of some pride, especially to the young instructors, to profess a joking ignorance of Linnaean science. "Linnaeus could not now be considered a botanist at all," is a statement that I have recently read. Its author doubtless conceives of Linnaeus as the one who invented Latin names, a man who betrayed the essential frivolity of his character by devising the floral clock—a plot where diurnal and nocturnal flowers, opening at their different and appointed times, told off the hours in the garden of his country estate at Hammerby. And there was an emotional strain in Linnaeus's character, a candid love of beauty, an impetuous enthusiasm for Nature (whose very name is now in poor repute), and a partisan insistence upon his great artifact of a schema, that intensely embarrass the thin-lipped and the ardorless.

Who that has passed through college has not had the pleasure of one or two field trips with a grey-cheeked biologist of today? You must surely remember it—how the class straggled behind, harkening listlessly, feeling as ill at ease out in the open, in all that sweet natural chaos, as the instructor looked in his business suit with his Phi Beta Kappa key sparkling unnaturally on his vest, while he pointed out a few organisms that it is not feasible to bring into the laboratory.

And all the while a beseeching wind was passing through the grasses whispering an eery *see, see!* Somewhere a meadowlark flashed his song about in the sunlight; and you stooped to pick a flower that leaped up from the earth on a tense slim stem and fell in a burst of blossoms. Perhaps you admired it openly, and others were embarrassed for you.

I tell this much of our modern wisdom, our fortunate freedom of all that might be construed as eighteenth century, because we need to orient ourselves when we relate the history of a movement. We have, after all, no triangulation point from which to survey save our own age and our own methods, and so perforce I must set down the contrast with others, not in malice, but in the offices of clarity. I must point out that we have returned natural science to the indoors, out of which Linnaeus led it joyfully forth upon those high-hearted farings of which I purpose now to tell.

Let me not say that what we have done is not all for the best, or more precisely that it is not the best we can do. But I wonder if our age will not be known as the renaissance of Scholasticism. In our age of doubt we are tending to reintroduce philosophy, to question how we know what we know, to analyze the nature of matter down to something that is no longer material but energic only, and to realize the poignant limitations of human comprehension. Perhaps opposing philosophical attitudes revolve in cycles. Perhaps we best approach absolute truth by alternating between schools that believe only what they see, and those that believe less than they see.

But the age of Linnaeus was one of simple-hearted discovery. In its naïve, poetic empiricism, it was, with what it could see, content. And it saw with the marvelous fresh vision of childhood.

I always think of Linnaeus as a student has described him in the years of his greatness, waiting under a tree outside the walls of Upsala, joking with his students as they came up, speaking Latin with the foreigners, while he smoked and attended on the late ones. Two hundred followers were sometimes gathered at the rendezvous.

Never were there field trips in the world like those, so ceremonious and so high-spirited. A whole convention of procedure was laid down. Every student was to carry a lens, a botanical penknife and dissecting needles, a lead pencil, a notebook, a Dillenian vasculum of sheet copper for plant collections, and an insect box. He must be provided with Linnaeus's *Systema Naturae* and other useful books, and even the dress was prescribed; pupils in the field must go clad in thin linen trousers, with a broad-brimmed hat upon the head.

Once all were assembled, an *Annotator* was appointed to take dictation, a *Fiscal* or monitor to keep order. And then with a shout and a fanfare, the horde was loosed upon a world still largely unexplored.

How we should like to go off with them, we as moderns, conscious of the coming greatness of those students then mere boys, or distinguished foreigners come from Russia and France, England and Germany, Switzerland and Holland! We might have wandered the Baltic strand with Peter Thunberg, aware that beside us strode the man who would penetrate forbidden Japan, the first naturalist ever to see the flowers upon Fujiyama's slopes. We might have started a lark from the low meadows beside the Fyris River, and listened to its song along with Johan Falck, foreseeing for him how he would capture the hunting eagles of the ranges. Have you found a fossil, and do you pass it over into the curious palm of a field companion? He is Forskål, who will penetrate Arabia Felix disguised as a Bedouin, and die for science, under a vulture-filled sky.

A young man has plucked a sprig of rare white heather, amidst the intense abundant purple. His name is Solander, and he is a Thursday's child. Far to go, he has, far to go—in good Captain Cook's voyage round the world; he shall discover breadfruit of Tahiti, tree ferns of New Zealand; eucalyptus of Australia. At Botany Bay there will fall to his hands the first specimens of the flora of an old continent newly found, when in a single day's haul hundreds of new species, scores of new genera and whole families will be brought to light. He will tumble out of his vasculum forms of flowers so bizarre, so unpredicted in the modest little *Systema Naturae*, that to accommodate them within the Linnaean system, great breaches will have to be made in its quaint walls. And here we see him, happy because he has found a sprig of white heather.

The tall positive fellow who climbs up the steep sides of Jumkil hill beside you is Dr. Adam Kuhn of Philadelphia, the only American student at Linnaeus's court, who has journeyed all this way to bring a living specimen of a little flower of the New World, which he could not identify in Linnaeus's system. Today, in his honor, it bears the name of *Kuhnia*.

Then, when at last you stand on Jumkil's summit, where blue distance aches away into infinitely ulterior horizons, while the sweet cool wind of the long summer day whistles in your ears, the master comes. On his right is Löfling—he who will make of all Spain his Lapland, and die in the Spanish New World—and on his left tramps tall Peter Kalm, the Finn, envoy extraordinary from Linnaeus to America, for whom our mountain laurel bears the name his master gave it, *Kalmia*.

Linnaeus, the accounts all tell us, walked with a quick, almost a shuffling gait; his brilliant brown eyes, says his student Acrel, blinked perpetually; his head was large, his stature medium; his nose, like that of many a great man, was big, and (Linnaeus sets it down himself) he bore a small wart on his right nostril, a large one on his left cheek. So we see him, coming up into the midst of his students, the wind of health and confidence about him, as he marches to the spot that is the trove of the innocent foray. A tall plant, laden with a spire of brilliant golden two-lipped flowers, rises, startling and almost tropic-seeming in the northern air. It is *Sceptrum Carolinum* of the students' books, a *Pedicularis*, we should call it now, wood betony of the foxglove family. Here, long ago, when he was a boy, Linnaeus had been brought by Celsius, to gaze on the mysterious, stately inflorescence. And both of them, in their pre-Linnaean science, puzzled then what plant it was that could be named in no herbal and no classic.

Now, on the wild turf, boxes are emptied, and every find of the day displayed, discussed, discoursed upon—fossils and mosses, fungi and birds, newts and insects. Where it is a matter of insects, Linnaeus politely takes off his cap and bows to Fabricius the Dane. "You are the master, I the pupil," he says. With mosses he turns deferentially to the pale Zoega, who stands beside him breathing delicately in the fashion of a dying man; Zoega must name them.

Would we smile now at Linnaeus's lectures? But certainly. Who has not heard of his childlike piety, referring all causes to the great First Cause? What student does not know that in zoölogy he was inferior to Ray? That his classification of minerals is untenable, his conception of the lower plants quite slipshod? The whole of his System of Nature, unillumined by any notion of evolution, was capable of expressing none of Nature's true relationships. But it is not the little that Linneaus knew that captivates us. It is the wisdom in his ignorance, the wisdom to aim so purely, to learn so joyfully, to care so deeply.

When the sun was turned toward afternoon, the whole company would march back again; Sparmann, who shall see Cathay and the incredible flora of the Cape, linking arms with Rolander, who was to return from tropic heat a madman, clutching grey seeds that he fancied precious pearls. Rotheram the Englishman, whose father wrote Linnaeus complaining that he had bewitched his son, on the way back talks fluent Swedish with Hasselquist, who shall die leaving the curses of his widow upon Linnaeus for having lured her husband to his death in Syria.

Back to the old botanic garden of Upsala, where once Linnaeus had wandered forlorn amid neglected plots, his pupils would march, to the sound of French horns and kettledrums, with banners fluttering. And there they all disbanded, giving the rousing cheer of *Vivat scientia! Vivat Linnaeus!*

Great days. Wonderful golden years, when all of natural science was polarized toward the most northerly university in the world, when to the little farm at Hammerby trooped the wise of earth, and the worldly great no less. Lord Baltimore rolled up in a coach and four of such sweeping proportions that all the gate posts on the way had to be taken down to let him pass. Some one whispered to Linnaeus that the English lord had come straight to Hammerby without waiting to see the king. "Why should I go to see the King of Sweden," asked Baltimore, "when I have never even cared to look at my own monarch?"

Fabricius the Dane (Linnaeus of insects, he was called) has left delightful recollections of his student days at Upsala. In the winter the foreign students were lodged close to the master, Fabricius, Zoega, and Dr. Kuhn bunking together. Of an evening Linnaeus would present himself at their door in a short red dressing-gown and green furred cap, his pipe in his hand, and promising to stay but half an hour, would grant his audience two, while he chatted of his travels and his correspondence—that great correspondence with all the learned of earth. Or he would answer his pupils' questions and doubts. His laugh rang up to the rafters; his face, between pipe whiffs, beamed with enjoyment.

In summer the foreign students adjourned to Hammerby, Linnaeus's country estate. In that season it was Linnaeus's habit to rise at four in the morning, when the blue convolvulus was just opening; he usually breakfasted with his pupils at six, and lectured informally until ten. In the evening they strolled in the prim of his garden; perhaps they even told time by his floral clock; I cannot say; great men are boundlessly frivolous at times. But when a shiver ran through the great horse-chestnut, and the night-blooming cereus opened its petals, they would all go inside and please Sara Lisa by playing at *trisett*, her favorite card game.

The Lutheran Sundays at Hammerby were not too blue. The students were permitted to send for a hurdy-gurdy, of the old-fashioned sort such as one still sees in old corners of Europe, a kind of lute most hideously vibrated by a wheel turned with a crank. The music for the polkas and minuets was bad, the old barn floor was worse, but how distinguished the company! Immortals, with no laurels yet but the crown of youth on their heads, capered with Linnaeus's three daughters and squeezed the waists of the country girls. Linnaeus himself sat apart, contentedly pulling on his pipe, talking with the frail Zoega who dared not dance. But at rare intervals he would arise and step a polonaise that no youngster there had breath for. Unless he saw that every one was cheerful, and even uproarious, he feared they were not enjoying themselves. "*Interpone tuis interdum gaudia curis,*" he laughed to them—Mingle sometimes your joys with your earnest occupations.

Ennobled, Linnaeus went to court. At blindman's buff it was not etiquette to catch the queen, the majestic Louisa, sister of Frederick the Great. Yet Linnaeus clapped a big hand on her shoulder. "Clap, woman!" he chuckled. "Who plays at this game may expect to be caught."

Old age advanced. His teeth fell out; he could not hear so well the skirl of the hurdy-gurdy; he must hold the specimens from world's end come to his door far from his blinking old eyes. Even in summer he hugged the comfort of the fire. He slept the sleep of the old—cat-naps in which he snored, from which he awoke with a start and fell at once to work.

Senility. The tender indulgence of his pupils. A scene at court where he upbraided the king, magnificent Gustavus III, and wept. Others saw—he could not—that Sara Lisa was grown a shrew, a clutch-penny, that his son on whom he had lavished such doting love was pettish, a frenetic spender and boundless egotist.

And finally, in the dark of a December night in 1777, he did not return from the sleigh drive on which he had stolen away like a bad child. The search was scattered far and wide, until he was found, on his sleigh where it had been drawn right into a peasant's hearth room. He lay there with his pipe at his mouth, half conscious. Upon the tenth of the following month, with Rotheram, the English student, at his side, the end fell.

Upsala, under young Linnaeus and Sara Lisa, became intolerable. But the flight of the students was like the dispersal of winged seeds out of a ripe pod. Not only his own pupils (of whom I have mentioned only a handful) but learned men the world over set out upon the great search. There had been scientific exploration before, and collecting before. Sir Hans Sloane, called the greatest collector of all time, had by his own labors and what his fortune could procure, laid the foundations of the British Museum's collections. But the Linnaean system revolutionized the way of looking at categories of things, and things themselves. It not only permitted a systematic method of naming that which was collected; the names themselves implied relationships; they automatically distributed Nature into a pattern that, if the times were not ripe for reading its full meaning, was nevertheless the most significant pattern yet devised. Aristotle, with all his cosmology, had been able to think of nothing better than alphabetical order for the enumeration of particulars.

In still another way the Linnaean system stimulated research; collecting came to subserve the end of enhancing the system, of filling up the gaps and lacunae, of presenting what (it was mistakenly hoped) would soon be a complete series illustrative of a definitive exhibit of the whole of Nature.

So the land masses of the world were crisscrossed in every direction by Linnaean exploration. The oceans were coursed for the tiniest of unmapped coral atolls or the last, ice-swept islets of the Antarctic. At last scientific exploration had turned its face away from Greece and Palestine (actually two of the most sterile and uninteresting fields for biological field work of which I can conceive), and even from a preoccupation with the directly useful.

Men were converted now to a new point of view, antithetical to that of the herbalists. They were content no longer to devote attention only to that which happens (most fortuitously) to be good for the human digestive tract, or to serve human comfort. Such lines of inquiry are almost as sterile as alchemy. Nature is a whole; she must be approached along every line of investigation at once; she must be viewed as the mother, not the drudge, of man. She is greater than we, and the purely human point of view will not comprehend her.

Knowing for the sake of knowledge is the true Philosopher's Stone. In the times immediately post-Linnaean this credo was fresh and new. Its converts, in the way of converts, went to excess. Collecting reached fantastic lengths, collecting for collecting's sake—an end which Linnaeus, we can be sure, would have deplored, could he have foreseen it.

The joys of collecting, some wise and some foolish, are many, and the adventure tales of the great collectors are more. But the telling of them would lead me far afield, so I pass swiftly over that princely gentleman, Sir Joseph Banks, famous now as the instigator of the search for breadfruit that culminated in the mutiny on the ship *Bounty.* Around the world with Solander and Sparmann, Linnaeus's pupils, went Banks, under the sails of Captain Cook, skimming the cream of collecting on new-found continents and isles, from New Zealand to Iceland. At home in his beautiful mansion in Soho, he kept open house each Sunday night for the naturalists of the world. His purse, his friendship, his boundless enthusiasm carried on the great tradition.

And I can but notice the voyage of Sonnerat to the East Indies after its gorgeous-plumaged, screaming birds. Or the marches and countermarches of the mighty Pallas through the new Asiatic dominions of the Tsar, from the crumbling cities of Turkestan to the frozen tundras of the Samoyed. Or the penetration of Andrew Smith, the ornithologist, beyond the Orange River, into the heart of central South Africa, or the wanderings of Robert Brown in Australia, continent of missing links. Into Abyssinia, that last Eden where great beasts walk in the gentleness of innocence, journeyed Rueppel. The Portuguese friar, Louriero, single-handed gathered out of the jungles of Cambodia the material for his great *Flora.* And for every illustrious name that I have mentioned, ten must pass without notice. The world is so wide.

And so richly stored with wonders! A great light began to break upon men's minds; it was, after all, not the age of man, they saw, but the age of birds, of fishes, of orchids, of composites—to judge by abundance of species, by endless adaptation of form to environment.

There was, of course, a belief that the number of species in the world must be finite, just as the land areas of the world are finite. True, Linnaeus's *Systema Naturae* looked, soon after his death, naïve in its ignorance. But even so, it seemed, it should be possible to chart the whole of Nature.

Yet collectors and systematists were astonished to find that a definitive knowledge even of mere species receded like the horizon. For they had no conception of evolution, no idea that new species are in the making. Nor were they conscious that their own ideas of species were undergoing constant refinement and fractionation. Almost every old Linnaean species was turning out to be in fact two, three, fifty or a hundred species. Indeed, any artificial concept of Nature's slippery prolificity, of its thoughtless melting of form into form, can lead to no other result.

But of this men had no notion. They were haunted by the illusion that, with just a little more discovery, all gaps in knowledge would close up. So the collecting went on and on, and so, back in the museums and universities of Europe, did the systematizing.

In all this amassing of specimens, until they filled miles and miles of groaning, sagging, dusty, cluttered shelves and drawers in the museums of all Europe, there lurked a danger—that the collections should fail, at the last, to *think*. That, after all, they would represent nothing. And that scientists would begin to conceive of Nature as existing in order to give grey old gentlemen of a philosophic turn something to identify and classify. What useful end classification served was not questioned—except by the sound good sense of the public.

For what, of course, these mighty collections cried aloud (or so it seems to our ears) was the concept of evolution, to give them meaning. Connected series of specimens would then take on significance, prove or disprove something. But though the idea of evolution was already nearly two thousand years old, though some one propounded it upon the average, at least once every two hundred years, it was not heeded. Even in times immediately post-Linnaean it was put forward once again, more appealingly than ever, and was greeted with ridicule by the very men who needed it to justify the refined futility of their life work. But the time to tell of Lamarck, Cuvier and their contemporaries will come later.

All the while the collecting went on, ever mounting up; the describing fed upon itself and could lead only to more describing. Here was the same dilemma in which Buffon found himself, but Buffon at least makes better reading; he actually has more to tell than those tedious Germans and Englishmen who practised their Linnaeanism like the grammar of a dead language.

Or they drew up schemes for "Natural Systems" of their own. (The Linnaean system had not pretended to be more than a finding syllabus; Linnaeus knew that he had not established natural families, and beyond a few very obvious ones he did not know what such families were or how related.) But lacking any idea of evolution, the architects of these systems could only pattern them on royalist lines. The noblest beasts were put first. Thus our old manuals of ornithology all open with the eagle (our ancestors admired its rapacity as the highest virtue, it seems), and they ended with the booby, stupidest of birds.

In the passion for collection lay another evil, one that was realized to the full and reached ultimate follies. This was the danger that commercial exploitation should set in, to purvey specimens to people not remotely interested in science, but avid only of prideful and personal arrays, with emphasis, of course, upon the rare. It seems impossible to make people realize that the rare is of trivial biological interest compared with the common. The very commonness of any living thing is the most miraculous and meaningful fact about it. But now the rare was searched out, and the pretty or the bizarre. Shells, butterflies, beetles, hummingbirds, ferns and orchids have for their loveliness suffered from the attentions of persons who happen to collect them instead of postage stamps or autographs.

Some commercial firms maintained their own collectors of orchids and butterflies. The brothers Verraux of Paris were famous for their clearing house of rare bird specimens, which they bought up all over the world, received from sea captains and globe-trotters, or had collected for them by men as athletic, intrepid and slaughterous as they were ignorant. Books, too, responded to the collecting mania and frivolous curiosity. The stuffed-bird fancier's delight was John Gould, who in endless folio volumes illustrated the birds of India, the birds of Australasia, the birds of everywhere, in the most insipid attitudes and the most exaggerated coloration.

The research after the rare, a quasi-commercial, quasi-scientific research, is typified, glorified and carried to the point of exhausting the fun of the game, in the career of the excellent Englishman Hugh Cuming, a wealthy amateur, who set out in a private yacht to cruise the world for new shells, something to tickle the jaded fancy of the European collector in his castle or parsonage or shell-shop. In the Philippines Cuming sent native collectors into the jungles after tropical tree snails, and saw one fellow returning with a sack full from which specimens (every one possibly a genus new to science) were dribbling carelessly along the jungle floor. On a reef in the South Seas (which has since been destroyed by a hurricane) he came on eight living shells of the "Glory-of-the-Sea." Almost fainting with delight he took all eight away, and it seems unlikely that the world will ever see any others. Anyone who understands the commercial value of such singularities will not need to be told what a bull market in conchology set in when Cuming's molluscs reached the auction rooms. Shells the size of the finger nail went for five hundred dollars a piece; others could be purchased only by Rothschilds. In such romances—and orchids and butterflies have had similar ones—the part played by science is naturally limited.

But the *scientia amabilis* was not the property of the pedant and the collector only. Linnaean clarity had popularized all the natural sciences. They were available now to every good intellect. Rousseau gave lectures on botany to classes of ladies; Jane, the daughter of the urbane Cadwallader Colden of New York, was taught the Linnaean system by her father, and by it described the "parts" of four hundred flowers of the New World. Country doctors, driving or riding on their rounds, became ornithologists; priests on their solitary walks stopped to notice the ways of the insect people; ladies pressed ferns; small boys spitted *Lepidoptera*.

A patronizing manner toward these amateur efforts is usually assumed by the professional naturalists. What museum has not had to turn away Great-aunt Lucinda's parlor album of orchids, the abalone shells that Uncle Abner gathered when he went out to California, and Willy's taxidermic efforts?

But at its worst, amateur science could never have sunk to such abysmal depths as professional Linnaeanism. It was stigmatized—it still is—by endless guesswork as to what Linnaeus meant, tedious squabbles over priority of publication, ungenerous and quibbling little reviews, parochial lists of Latin names. Such, and not the well-meant and sometimes very important work of the devoted amateur, have made modern science ashamed of Linnaeanism.

Linnaeus himself has not escaped the blame for the sterility of his followers. It has been said, and truly said, that he was too often content with naming and classifying. That he took no interest in the physiology of plants and animals; that he neglected the microscope; that he never experimented; that he was in effect the most scholastic of all the Schoolmen, entirely preoccupied with abstract categories. He was, in short, no modern.

But is this really a reproach to Linnaeus? Is it not enough that he accomplished what he did? That, however superficially, with however many slips and errors as to detail, he conquered those provinces that he set out to conquer? His was a triumph, a first necessity. It held the ground for science until the modern artillery of attack could be brought up.

The life work of Charles Darwin has had to endure quite as much destructive criticism as Linnaeus's. So have the cosmology of Aristotle, Newtonian physics, and the anatomy of Cuvier. Their claims to finality have had to be retracted and retracted; their reputations have receded from point to point. Until it seems as though nothing is left them—except their greatness.

And I am not alluding to the obvious fact that such men were great in their age, which is all we may ask of mortal flesh and blood. They were great in an absolute sense, great for all time. That we have, to-day, new methods of apprehending scientific truth does not necessarily mean that we have better methods. The years three thousand and four thousand will judge better of that. Whatever truth is, whatever life is, or matter, we shall never know more of them than some purely human concepts, and by a concept we mean a reduction into artificial terms such as we can talk of, such as we may shift about conveniently. Ideas are like money—small, round or symmetrical symbols (some dross, some gold) that stand for large, irregular, unmanageable values. In the natural sciences no one has yet minted any coinage more practicable than the Linnaean, and still, all over the world, it passes on its face value.

There is another way in which a scientist may be great, and that is in his personality, his magnetic power to sway his followers. Some great scientists have lacked this quality entirely. A general may also lack it, and still win battles. But Linnaeus was dowered with a temperament so glowing that across the years we may warm the heart at its geniality. Most of the historians of science have been at pains to efface personality from the individual humans whom we call scientists. They regard this peculiar expunging as part of their duty, a sort of rule of public decency. They are applauded in this by the modern scientists, themselves a prudish lot, constantly afraid that you will discover that they are human. The eulogies that scientists write of each other in the black-leaded obituary pages of their tedious little journals are like country photography, where every wrinkle is touched out. To judge only from these accounts the same scientist keeps dying all the time; I defy you to tell the difference between his incarnations.

The city of Chicago—rather surprisingly—boasts a statue to Linnaeus, in Lincoln Park. Under its stone gaze pass nurses and men out of work, little girls on roller skates, a lethargic white-wing, a tall, ragged boy earnestly studying *The Elements of Chemistry*. Such, at least, was the public I beheld there when yesterday, on a delicate, high-arched day of spring (that languid, awkward spring in the city that puts such torment into the bones of adolescence), I hunted out the memorial to the sage of Hammerby. I found him at last as a rotund gentleman in stone cape and stone wig, standing on a pedestal where, rather trustingly, I thought, no inscription but his name proclaimed him. Two girl children, that grown boy knitting his brows over the periodic table of the elements, and a nursemaid sat at his feet quite unconcerned with him. The whole city, no doubt, is equally oblivious. But in the statue's out-held hand, confidingly, a sparrow had built its nest.

Long ago it happened, long ago when the world was younger—the Lapland faring, the boy scuffing the leaves in the sleeping botanical garden, the child in the sunlight naming the flowers in the garden of Stenbrohult parsonage. But still out in the woods, beyond the city, the trillium and adder's-tongue carpet the woods; the birds still build, under the eaves, in the marsh, in the hollow of a stone hand. And there are many of us left to cry, with Thunberg and Kalm and Kuhn, *Vivat scientia! Vivat Linnaeus!*

Why do our joys depart
For cares to seize the heart?
I know not. Nature says,
Obey; and man obeys.
I see, and know not why
Thorns live and roses die.

WALTER SAVAGE LANDOR

THE START OF A FAMOUS JOURNEY

by William Bartram

This might be a chapter out of the colonial history of North America. As a matter of fact, it is the second chapter of a book that was published in 1791 under the title The Travels of William Bartram. *The author was a botanist and the son of a botanist. John Bartram, the father, was born in Chester County, Pennsylvania, March 23, 1699, turned his attention to plant life for study and profit, and founded the first botanical garden and plant nursery in North America in a spot that was then outside the city of Philadelphia but is now part of the public park system of that city. The elder Bartram, self-educated, corresponded with noted botanists in Europe, including Linnaeus, and attained such distinction in his field that he was appointed—being a loyal subject at that time—Honorary Botanist to His Majesty, King George II of Great Britain and Ireland and sundry possessions overseas.*

William Bartram, born February 9, 1739, literally was raised in the family botanical garden, lived there—except for his travels— all his life, and died there in his eighty-fifth year, July 22, 1823. The travels described in the book began in 1773 and continued over a period of years in the form of various expeditions to the Carolinas, Georgia, and Florida. Collections were made for planting in the family nursery, and one such collected species has an odd history. On his first trip to Georgia, William found a shrub in beautiful cream-white bloom on the banks of the Altamaha River. He collected a few specimens and later planted them in his nursery at home, where they lived and flourished for years under the name he had given them in honor of Philadelphia's great citizen and the Georgia river along which he had found the plants in bloom, Franklinia alatamaha. Cuttings from the shrubs produced other shrubs for public sale, and today there are thousands of Franklinias in public and private gardens over all but the

northern tier of the United States, all descended from the original
plants collected along the Altamaha and grown in the Bartram
nursery. There are two curious things to note. One is that, to the
best of deponent's knowledge and belief, all the surviving Frank-
linias in the world are in cultivation. At least, nobody has been
able to find a wild Franklinia along the Altamaha or anywhere
else in the last 150 years, though the search has been diligent.
Another odd point is that William Bartram found the Franklinia
in bloom in the wild in the spring, whereas in his northern nursery
the plants—and all their descendants—start to bloom after mid-
summer and continue into autumn, often until the first frost.

Incidentally, there are literary indications that Wordsworth and
Shelley delved into William Bartram's Travels *and made poetical*
use of many of his floral findings. It should be added that there
is a great deal more than botany in the book. Bartram also had
an eye for other forms of wild and cultivated life along the many
colonial roads he traveled. Keep in mind that the date mentioned
in the first sentence refers to the year 1773.

ARRIVING in Carolina very early in the spring, vegetation
was not sufficiently advanced to invite me into the western
parts of this state; from which circumstance, I concluded
to make an excursion into Georgia; accordingly, I embarked on board a coasting vessel and in twenty-four hours arrived in
Savanna, the capital, where, acquainting the governor, Sir J. Wright,
with my business, his excellency received me with great politeness,
shewed me every mark of esteem and regard, and furnished me with
letters to the principal inhabitants of the state, which were of great
service to me. Another circumstance very opportunely occurred on my
arrival: the assembly was then sitting in Savanna, and several members
lodging in the same house where I took up my quarters, I became
acquainted with several worthy characters, who invited me to call at
their seats occasionally, as I passed through the country; particularly
the hon. B. Andrews, esq., a distinguished, patriotic, and liberal character. This gentleman's seat, and well-cultivated plantations, are
situated near the south high road, which I often travelled; and I seldom passed his house without calling to see him, for it was the seat of
virtue, where hospitality, piety, and philosophy, formed the happy

family; where the weary traveller and stranger found a hearty welcome, and from whence it must be his own fault if he departed without being greatly benefited.

After resting, and a little recreation for a few days in Savanna, and having in the mean time purchased a good horse, and equipped myself for a journey southward, I sat off early in the morning for Sunbury, a sea-port town, beautifully situated on the main, between Medway and Newport rivers, about fifteen miles south of great Ogeeche river. The town and harbour are defended from the fury of the seas by the north and south points of St. Helena and South Catharine's islands; between which is the bar and entrance into the sound; the harbour is capacious and safe, and has water enough for ships of great burthen. I arrived here in the evening, in company with a gentleman, one of the inhabitants, who politely introduced me to one of the principal families, where I supped and spent the evening in a circle of genteel and polite ladies and gentlemen. Next day, being desirous of visiting the islands, I forded a narrow shoal, part of the sound, and landed on one of them, which employed me the whole day to explore. The surface and vegetable mould here is generally a loose sand, not very fertile, except some spots bordering on the sound and inlets, where are found heaps or mounds of sea-shell, either formerly brought there by the Indians, who inhabited the island, or which were perhaps thrown up in ridges, by the beating surface of the sea: possibly both these circumstances may have contributed to their formation. These sea-shells, through length of time, and the subtle penetrating effects of the air, which dissolve them to earth, render these ridges very fertile; and, when clear of their trees, and cultivated, they become profusely productive of almost every kind of vegetable. Here are also large plantations of indigo, corn, and potatoes*, with many other sorts of esculent plants. I observed, amongst the shells of the conical mounds, fragments of earthen vessels, and of other utensils, the manufacture of the ancients: about the centre of one of them, the rim of an earthen pot appeared amongst the shells and earth, which I carefully removed, and drew it out, almost whole: this pot was curiously wrought all over the outside, representing basket work, and was undoubtedly esteemed a very ingenious performance, by the people, at the age of its construction. The natural produce of these testaceous ridges, besides many of less note, are, the great Laurel Tree (Magnolia grandiflora), Pinus taeda, Laurus Borbonia, Quercus sempervirens, or Live Oak,

* Convolvulus batata.

Prunus Lauro-cerasus, Ilex aquifolium, Corypha palma, Juniperus Americana. The general surface of the island being low, and generally level, produces a very great variety of trees, shrubs and herbaceous plants; particularly the great long-leaved Pitch-Pine, or Broom-Pine, Pinus palustris, Pinus squamosa, Pinus lutea, Gordonia Lisianthus, Liquid ambar (Styraciflua), Acer rubrum, Fraxinus excelcior; Fraxinus aquatica, Quercus aquatica, Quercus phillos, Quercus dentata, Quercus humila varietas, Vaccinium varietas, Andromeda varietas, Prinos varietas, Ilex varietas, Viburnum prunifolium, V. dentatum, Cornus florida, C. alba, C. sanguinea, Carpinus betula, C. Ostrya, Itea, Clethra alnifolia, Halesia tetraptera, H. diptera, Iva, Rhamnus frangula, Callicarpa, Morus rubra, Sapindus, Cassine, and of such as grow near water-courses, round about ponds and savannas, Fothergilla gardini, Myrica cerifera, Olea Americana, Cyrilla racemiflora, Magnolia glauca, Magnolia pyramidata, Cercis, Kalmia angustifolia, Kalmia ciliata, Chionanthus, Cephalanthos, Aesculus parva; and the intermediate spaces, surrounding and lying between the ridges and savannas, are intersected with plains of the dwarf prickly fan-leaved Palmetto, and lawns of grass variegated with stately trees of the great Broom-Pine, and the spreading evergreen Water-Oak, either disposed in clumps, or scatteringly planted by nature. The upper surface, or vegetative soil of the island, lies on a foundation, or stratum, of tenacious cinereous-coloured clay, which perhaps is the principal support of the vast growth of timber that arises from the surface, which is little more than a mixture of fine white sand and dissolved vegetables, serving as a nursery bed to hatch or bring into existence the infant plant, and to supply it with aliment and food, suitable to its delicacy and tender frame, until the roots, acquiring sufficient extent and solidity to lay hold of the clay, soon attain a magnitude and stability sufficient to maintain its station. Probably if this clay were dug out, and cast upon the surface, after being meliorated by the saline or nitrous qualities of the air, it would kindly incorporate with the loose sand, and become a productive and lasting manure.

The roebuck, or deer, are numerous on this island; the tyger, wolf, and bear, hold yet some possession; as also raccoons, foxes, hares, squirrels, rats, and mice, but I think no moles. There is a large ground rat, more than twice the size of the common Norway rat. In the night time it throws out the earth, forming little mounds, or hillocks. Opossums are here in abundance, as also pole-cats, wild-cats, rattle-snakes, glass-snake, coach-whip-snake, and a variety of other serpents.

Here are also a great variety of birds, throughout the seasons, inhabiting both sea and land. First I shall name the eagle, of which there are three species. The great grey eagle is the largest, of great strength and high flight; he chiefly preys on fawns and other young quadrupeds.

The bald eagle is likewise a large, strong, and very active bird, but an execrable tyrant: he supports his assumed dignity and grandeur by rapine and violence, extorting unreasonable tribute and subsidy from all the feathered nations.

The last of this race I shall mention is the falco-piscatorious, or fishing-hawk: this is a large bird, of high and rapid flight; his wings are very long and pointed, and he spreads a vast sail, in proportion to the volume of his body. This princely bird subsists entirely on fish which he takes himself, scorning to live and grow fat on the dear-earned labours of another; he also contributes liberally to the support of the bald eagle.

Water-fowl, and the various species of land-birds, also abound, most of which are mentioned by Catesby, in his Hist. of Carolina, particularly his painted finch (Emberiza Ceris Linn.) exceeded by none of the feathered tribes, either in variety and splendour of dress, or melody of song.

Catesby's ground doves are also here in abundance: they are remarkably beautiful, about the size of a sparrow, and their soft and plaintive cooing perfectly enchanting.

> How chaste the dove! "never known to violate the
>   conjugal contract."
> She flees the seats of envy and strife, and seeks the
>   retired paths of peace.

The sight of this delightful and productive island, placed in front of the rising city of Sunbury, quickly induced me to explore it; which I apprehended, from former visits to this coast, would exhibit a comprehensive epitome of the history of all the sea-coast Islands of Carolina and Georgia, as likewise in general of the coast of the main. And though I considered this excursion along the coast of Georgia and northern border of Florida, a deviation from the high road of my intended travels, yet I performed it in order to employ to the most advantage the time on my hands, before the treaty of Augusta came on, where I was to attend, about May or June, by desire of the Superintendent, J. Stewart, esq. who, when I was in Charleston, proposed, in order to facilitate my travels in the Indian territories, that, if I would be present at the Congress, he would introduce my business to the chiefs of the Cherokees, Creeks, and other nations, and recommend me to their friendship and protection; which promise he fully performed, and it proved of great service to me.

Obedient to the admonitions of my attendant spirit, curiosity, as well as to gratify the expectations of my worthy patron, I again sat off on my southern excursion, and left Sunbury, in company with several of its polite inhabitants, who were going to Medway meeting, a very large and well-constructed place of worship, in St. John's parish, where I associated with them in religious exercise, and heard a very excellent sermon, delivered by their pious and truly venerable pastor, the Rev. —— Osgood. This respectable congregation is independent, and consists chiefly of families, and proselytes of a flock, which this pious man led about forty years ago, from South Carolina, and settled in this fruitful district. It is about nine miles from Sunbury to Medway meeting-house, which stands on the high road opposite the Sunbury road. As soon as the congregation broke up, I re-assumed my travels, proceeding down the high road towards Fort Barrington, on the Alatamaha, passing through a level country, well watered by large streams, branches of Medway and Newport rivers, coursing from extensive swamps and marshes, their sources: these swamps are daily clearing and improving into large fruitful rice plantations, aggrandizing the well inhabited and rich district of St. John's parish. The road is straight, spacious, and kept in excellent repair by the industrious inhabitants; and is generally bordered on each side with a light grove, consisting of the following trees and shrubs: Myrica, Cerifera, Calycanthus, Halesia tetraptera, Itea stewartia, Andromeda nitida, Cyrella racemiflora, entwined with bands and garlands of Bignonia sempervirens, B. crucigera, Lonicera sempervirens and Glycene frutescens; these were overshadowed by tall and spreading trees, as the Magnolia grandiflora, Liquid ambar, Liriodendron, Catalpa, Quercus sempervirens, Quercus dentata, Q. Phillos; and on the verges of the canals, where the road was causwayed, stood the Cupressus disticha, Gordonia Lacianthus, and Magnolia glauca, all planted by nature, and left standing by the virtuous inhabitants, to shade the road, and perfume the sultry air. The extensive plantations of rice and corn, now in early verdure, decorated here and there with groves of floriferous and fragrant trees and shrubs, under the cover and protection of pyramidal laurels and plumed palms, which now and then break through upon the sight from both sides of the way as we pass along;

the eye at intervals stealing a view at the humble, but elegant and neat habitation, of the happy proprietor, amidst harbours and groves, all day, and moon-light nights, filled with the melody of the cheerful mockbird, warbling nonpareil, and plaintive turtle-dove, altogether present a view of magnificence and joy, inexpressibly charming and animating.

In the evening I arrived at the seat of the Hon. B. Andrews, esq. who received and entertained me in every respect, as a worthy gentleman could a stranger, that is, with hearty welcome, plain but plentiful board, free conversation and liberality of sentiment. I spent the evening very agreeably, and the day following (for I was not permitted to depart sooner): I viewed with pleasure this gentleman's exemplary improvements in agriculture; particularly in the growth of rice, and in his machines for shelling that valuable grain, which stands in the water almost from the time it is sown, until within a few days before it is reaped, when they draw off the water by sluices, which ripens it all at once, and when the heads or panicles are dry ripe, it is reaped and left standing in the field, in small ricks, until all the straw is quite dry, when it is hauled, and stacked in the barn yard. The machines for cleaning the rice are worked by the force of water. They stand on the great reservoir which contains the waters that flood the rice-fields below.

Towards the evening we made a little party at fishing. We chose a shaded retreat, in a beautiful grove of magnolias, myrtles, and sweet bay-trees, which were left standing on the bank of a fine creek, that, from this place, took a slow serpentine course through the plantation. We presently took some fish, one kind of which is very beautiful; they call it the red-belly. It is as large as a man's hand, nearly oval and thin, being compressed on each side; the tail is beautifully formed; the top of the head and back of an olive-green, be-sprinkled with russet specks; the sides of a sea-green, inclining to azure, insensibly blended with the olive above, and beneath lightens to a silvery white, or pearl colour, elegantly powdered with specks of the finest green, russet and gold; the belly is of a bright scarlet-red, or vermilion, darting up rays or fiery streaks into the pearl on each side; the ultimate angle of the branchiostega extends backwards with a long spatula, ending with a round or oval particoloured spot, representing the eye in the long feathers of a peacock's train, verged round with a thin flame-coloured membrane, and appears like a brilliant ruby fixed on the side of the fish; the eyes are large, encircled with a fiery iris; they are a voracious fish, and are easily caught with a suitable bait.

The next morning I took leave of this worthy family, and sat off for the settlements on the Alatamaha, still pursuing the high road for Fort Barrington, till towards noon, when I turned off to the left, following the road to Darian, a settlement on the river, twenty miles lower down, and near the coast. The fore part of this day's journey was pleasant, the plantations frequent, and the roads in tolerable good repair; but the country being now less cultivated, the roads became bad. I pursued my journey almost continually through swamps and creeks, waters of Newport and Sapello, till night, when I lost my way: but coming up to a fence, I saw a glimmering light, which conducted me to a house, where I stayed all night, and met with very civil entertainment. Early next morning I sat off again, in company with the overseer of the farm, who piloted me through a large and difficult swamp, when we parted; he in chase of deer, and I towards Darian. I rode several miles through a high forest of pines, thinly growing on a level plain, which admitted an ample view, and a free circulation of air, to another swamp: and crossing a considerable branch of Sapello river, I then came to a small plantation by the side of another swamp: the people were remarkably civil and hospitable. The man's name was M'Intosh, a family of the first colony established in Georgia, under the conduct of general Oglethorpe. Was there ever such a scene of primitive simplicity, as was here exhibited, since the days of the good king Tammany! The venerable grey-headed Caledonian smilingly meets me coming up to his house. "Welcome, stranger; come in, and rest; the air is now very sultry; it is a very hot day." I was there treated with some excellent venison, and here found friendly and secure shelter from a tremendous thunder storm, which came up from the N. W. and soon after my arrival began to discharge its fury all around. Stepping to the door to observe the progress and direction of the tempest, the fulgour and rapidity of the streams of lightning, passing from cloud to cloud, and from the clouds to the earth, exhibited a very awful scene; when instantly the lightning, as it were, opening a fiery chasm in the black cloud, darted with inconceivable rapidity on the trunk of a large pine-tree, that stood thirty or forty yards from me, and set it in a blaze. The flame instantly ascended upwards of ten or twelve feet, and continued flaming about fifteen minutes, when it was gradually extinguished by the deluges of rain that fell upon it.

I saw here a remarkably large turkey of the native wild breed; his head was above three feet from the ground when he stood erect; he was a stately beautiful bird, of a very dark dusky brown colour, the tips of the feathers of his neck, breast, back, and shoulders, edged with a copper colour, which in a certain exposure looked like burnished gold, and he seemed not insensible of the splendid appearance he made. He was reared from an egg, found in the forest, and hatched by a hen of the common domestic fowl.

Our turkey of America is a very different species from the meleagris of Asia and Europe; they are nearly thrice their size and weight. I have seen several that have weighed between twenty and thirty pounds, and some have been killed that weighed near forty. They are taller, and have a much longer neck proportionally, and likewise longer legs, and stand more erect; they are also very different in colour. Ours are all, male and female, of a dark brown colour, not having a black feather on them; but the male exceedingly splendid, with changeable colours. In other particulars they differ not.

The tempest being over, I waited till the floods of rain had run off the ground, then took leave of my friends, and departed. The air was now cool and salubrious, and riding seven or eight miles, through a pine forest, I came to Sapello bridge, to which the salt tide flows. I here stopped, at Mr. Bailey's, to deliver a letter from the governor. This gentleman received me very civilly, inviting me to stay with him; but upon my urging the necessity of my accelerating my journey, he permitted me to proceed to Mr. L. M'Intosh's, near the river, to whose friendship I was recommended by Mr. B. Andrews.

Perhaps, to a grateful mind, there is no intellectual enjoyment, which regards human concerns, of a more excellent nature, than the remembrance of real acts of friendship. The heart expands at the pleasing recollection. When I came up to his door, the friendly man, smiling, and with a grace and dignity peculiar to himself, took me by the hand, and accosted me thus: "Friend Bartram, come under my roof, and I desire you to make my house your home, as long as convenient to yourself; remember, from this moment, that you are a part of my family, and, on my part, I shall endeavour to make it agreeable," which was verified during my continuance in, and about, the southern territories of Georgia and Florida; for I found here sincerity in union with all the virtues, under the influence of religion. I shall yet mention a remarkable instance of Mr. M'Intosh's friendship and respect for me; which was, recommending his eldest son, Mr. John M'Intosh, as a companion in my travels. He was a sensible virtuous youth, and a very agreeable companion through a long and toilsome journey of near a thousand miles.

Having been greatly refreshed, by continuing a few days with this kind and agreeable family, I prepared to prosecute my journey southerly.

CHORUS
(from *Atalanta in Calydon*)

When the hounds of spring are on winter's traces,
 The mother of months in meadow or plain
Fills the shadows and windy places
 With lisp of leaves and ripple of rain;
And the brown bright nightingale amorous
Is half assuaged for Itylus,
For the Thracian ships and the foreign faces,
 The tongueless vigil, and all the pain.

Come with bows bent and with emptying of quivers,
 Maiden most perfect, lady of light,
With a noise of winds and many rivers,
 With a clamor of waters, and with might;
Bind on thy sandals, O thou most fleet,
Over the splendor and speed of thy feet;
For the faint east quickens, the wan west shivers,
 Round the feet of the day and the feet of the night.

Where shall we find her, how shall we sing to her,
 Fold our hands round her knees, and cling?
O that man's heart were as fire and could spring to her,
 Fire, or the strength of the streams that spring!
For the stars and the winds are unto her
As raiment, as songs of the harp-player;
For the risen stars and the fallen cling to her,
 And the southwest-wind and the west-wind sing.

For winter's rains and ruins are over,
 And all the season of snows and sins;
The days dividing lover and lover,
 The light that loses, the night that wins;
And time remembered is grief forgotten,

And frosts are slain and flowers begotten,
And in green underwood and cover
　Blossom by blossom the spring begins.

The full streams feed on flower of rushes,
　Ripe grasses trammel a travelling foot,
The faint fresh flame of the young year flushes
　From leaf to flower and flower to fruit;
And fruit and leaf are as gold and fire,
And the oat is heard above the lyre,
And the hoofèd heel of a satyr crushes
　The chestnut-husk at the chestnut-root.

And Pan by noon and Bacchus by night,
　Fleeter of foot than the fleet-foot kid,
Follows with dancing and fills with delight
　The Maenad and the Bassarid;
And soft as lips that laugh and hide
The laughing leaves of the trees divide,
And screen from seeing and leave in sight
　The god pursuing, the maiden hid.

The ivy falls with the Bacchanal's hair
　Over her eyebrows hiding her eyes;
The wild vine slipping down leaves bare
　Her bright breast shortening into sighs;
The wild vine slips with the weight of its leaves,
But the berried ivy catches and cleaves
To the limbs that glitter, the feet that scare
　The wolf that follows, the fawn that flies.

ALGERNON CHARLES SWINBURNE

INTRODUCERS OF EXOTIC
FLOWERS, FRUITS, ETC.

by Isaac D'Israeli

Despite the difference in the way the name is written, the author of this essay was the father of Benjamin Disraeli, famous Prime Minister of the Victorian era, "Dizzy" to his friends and enemies, and Lord Beaconsfield by way of royal reward in his later days. Though "Dizzy" also won plaudits as a popular novelist, the father was a better writer than his famous son. Isaac D'Israeli was born at Enfield, Middlesex, England, in May, 1766. His father was a wealthy merchant, and Isaac received a fine education, most of it in school on the Continent, where he later traveled for several years in pursuit of culture. When he returned to England he turned his back on commerce, joined the literary set, and settled down to a life of study and writing. He wrote and published two series of scholarly essays under the title: Curiosities of Literature. The contents of the little volumes had a far wider range than the title would indicate. The author dealt with all sorts of topics such as laws and customs, famous crimes, economics, politics, history, art, medicine, and, to be sure, language and literature. The essays were published in book form— five little volumes—over the years 1832 to 1834. This selection is typical of the series in that it deals with an interesting topic and reveals the author as a real scholar and a most pleasant writer. He did not live to see his son Benjamin rise to Cabinet height. He died at his country estate, Bradenham House in Buckinghamshire, January 19, 1848, in his eighty-second year.

THERE has been a class of men whose patriotic affection, or whose general benevolence, have been usually defrauded of the gratitude their country owes them: these have been the introducers of new flowers, new plants, and new roots into Europe; the greater part which we now enjoy was drawn from the luxuriant climates of Asia, and the profusion which now covers our land originated in the most anxious nursing, and were the gifts of individuals. Monuments are reared, and medals struck, to commemorate events and names, which are less deserving our regard than those who have transplanted into the colder gardens of the North the rich fruits, the beautiful flowers, and the succulent pulse and roots of more favoured spots; and carrying into their own country, as it were, another Nature, they have, as old Gerard well expresses it, 'laboured with the soil to make it fit for the plants, and with the plants to make them delight in the soil.'

There is no part of the characters of PEIRESC and EVELYN, accomplished as they are in so many, which seems more delightful to me, than their enthusiasm for the garden, the orchard, and the forest.

PEIRESC, whose literary occupations admitted of no interruption, and whose universal correspondence throughout the habitable globe was more than sufficient to absorb his studious life, yet was he the first man, as Gassendus relates in his interesting manner, whose incessant inquiries procured the great variety of jessamines; those from China whose leaves, always green, bear a clay-coloured flower, and a delicate perfume; the American, with a crimson-coloured, and the Persian, with a violet-coloured flower; and the Arabian, whose tendrils he delighted to train over 'the banqueting-house in his garden;' and of fruits, the orange-trees with a red and parti-coloured flower; the medlar; the rough cherry without stone; the rare and luxurious vines of Smyrna and Damascus; and the fig-tree called Adam's, whose fruit by its size was supposed to be that with which the spies returned from the land of Canaan. Gassendus describes his transports when Peiresc beheld the Indian ginger growing green in his garden, and his delight in grafting the myrtle on the musk vine, that the experiment might show us the myrtle wine of the ancients. But transplanters, like other inventors, are sometimes baffled in their delightful enterprises; and we are told of Peiresc's deep regret when he found that the Indian cocoa nut would only bud, and then perish in the cold air of France, while the leaves of the Egyptian papyrus refused to yield him their vegetable paper. But it was his garden which propagated the exotic fruits and flowers, which he transplanted into the French king's, and into Cardinal Barberini's, and the curious in Europe; and these occasioned a work on the manuring of flowers by Ferrarius, a botanical Jesuit, who there described these novelties to Europe.

Had EVELYN only composed the great work of his 'Sylva, or a discourse of Forest Trees,' &c, his name would have excited the gratitude of posterity. The voice of the patriot exults in the dedication to Charles II, prefixed to one of the later editions. 'I need not acquaint your majesty, how many millions of timber-trees, besides infinite others, have been propagated and planted throughout your vast dominions, at the instigation and by the sole direction of this work, because your majesty has been pleased to own it publickly for my encouragement.' And surely while Britain retains her awful situation among the nations of Europe, the 'Sylva' of Evelyn will endure with her triumphant oaks. It was a retired philosopher who aroused the genius of the nation, and who, casting a prophetic eye towards the age in which we live, has contributed to secure our sovereignty of the seas. The present navy of Great Britain has been constructed with the oaks which the genius of Evelyn planted!

Animated by a zeal truly patriotic, De Serres in France, 1599, composed a work on the art of raising silk-worms, and dedicated it to the municipal body of Paris, to excite the inhabitants to cultivate mulberry-trees. The work at first produced a strong sensation, and many planted mulberry-trees in the vicinity of Paris; but as they were not yet used to raise and manage the silk-worm, they reaped nothing but their trouble for their pains. They tore up the mulberry-trees they had planted, and, in spite of De Serres, asserted that the northern climate was not adapted for the rearing of that tender insect. The great Sully, from his hatred of all objects of luxury, countenanced the popular clamour, and crushed the rising enterprise of De Serres. The monarch was wiser than the minister. The book had made sufficient noise to reach the ear of Henry IV; who desired the author to draw up a memoir on the subject, from which the king was induced to plant mulberry-trees in all the royal gardens; and having imported the eggs of silk-worms from Spain, this patriotic monarch gave up his orangeries, which were but his private gratifications, for that leaf which, converted into silk, became a part of the national wealth. It is to De Serres, who introduced the plantations of mulberry-trees, that the commerce of France owes one of her staple commodities; and although the patriot

encountered the hostility of the prime minister, and the hasty prej-
udices of the populace in his own day, yet his name at this moment
is fresh in the hearts of his fellow-citizens; for I have just received a
medal, the gift of a literary friend from Paris, which bears his portrait,
with the reverse, 'Societé d'Agriculture du Department de la Seine.'
It was struck in 1807. The same honour is the right of Evelyn from
the British nation.

There was a period when the spirit of plantation was prevalent in
this kingdom; it probably originated from the ravages of the soldiery
during the civil wars. A man, whose retired modesty has perhaps obscured his claims on our regard, the intimate friend of the great spirits
of that age, by birth a Pole, but whose mother had probably been an
English woman, SAMUEL HARTLIB, to whom Milton addressed his
tract on education, published every manuscript he collected on the
subjects of horticulture and agriculture. The public good he effected
attracted the notice of Cromwell, who rewarded him with a pension,
which after the restoration of Charles II was suffered to lapse, and
Hartlib died in utter neglect and poverty. One of his tracts is, 'A design
for plenty by an universal planting of fruit-trees.' The project consisted in enclosing the waste lands and commons, and appointing officers, whom he calls fruiterers, or wood-wards, to see the plantations
were duly attended to. The writer of this project observes on fruits,
that it is a sort of provisions so natural to the taste, that the poor
man and even the child will prefer it before better food, 'as the story
goeth,' which he has preserved in these ancient and simple lines.

> 'The poor man's child invited was to dine,
> With flesh of oxen, sheep, and fatted swine,
> (Far better cheer than he at home could find,)
> And yet this child to stay had little minde.
> You have, quoth he, no apple, froise, nor pie,
> Stew'd pairs, with bread and milk, and walnuts by.'

The enthusiasm of these transplanters inspired their labours. They
have watched the tender infant of their planting, till the leaf and the
flowers and the fruit expanded under their hand; often indeed they
have even ameliorated the quality, increased the size, and even created
a new species. The apricot, drawn from America, was first known in
Europe in the sixteenth century: an old French writer has remarked,
that it was originally not larger than a damson; our gardeners, he says,
have improved it to the perfection of its present size and richness. One

of these enthusiasts is noticed by Evelyn, who for forty years had in vain tried by a graft to bequeath his name to a new fruit; but persisting on wrong principles, this votary of Pomona has died without a name. We sympathise with Sir William Temple when he exultingly acquaints us with the size of his orange-trees, and with the flavour of his peaches and grapes, confessed by Frenchmen to have equalled those of Fontainebleau and Gascony, while the Italians agreed that his white figs were as good as any of that sort in Italy: and of his 'having had the honour' to naturalize in this country four kinds of grapes, with his liberal distributions of cuttings from them, because 'he ever thought all things of this kind the commoner they are the better.'

The greater number of our exotic flowers and fruits were carefully transported into this country by many of our travelled nobility and gentry; some names have been casually preserved. The learned Linacre first brought, on his return from Italy, the damask-rose; and Thomas Lord Cromwell, in the reign of Henry VIII, enriched our fruit-gardens with three different plums. In the reign of Elizabeth, Edward Grindal, afterwards Archbishop of Canterbury, returning from exile, transported here the medicinal plant of the tamerisk: the first oranges appear to have been brought into England by one of the Carew family; for a century after, they still flourished at the family seat at Beddington, in Surrey. The cherry orchards of Kent were first planted about Sittingbourne, by a gardener of Henry VIII; and the currant-bush was transplanted when our commerce with the island of Zante was first opened in the same reign. The elder Tradescant in 1620 entered himself on board of a privateer, armed against Morocco, solely with a view of finding an opportunity of stealing apricots into Britain: and it appears that he succeeded in his design. To Sir Walter Rawleigh we have not been indebted solely for the luxury of the tobacco-plant, but for that infinitely useful root, which forms a part of our daily meal, and often the entire meal of the poor man—the potatoe, which deserved to have been called a *Rawleigh*. Sir Anthony Ashley first planted cabbages in this country, and a cabbage at his feet appears on his monument. Sir Richard Weston first brought clover grass into England from Flanders, in 1645; and the figs planted by Cardinal Pole at Lambeth, so far back as the reign of Henry VIII, are said to be still remaining there: nor is this surprising, for Spilman, who set up the first paper-mill in England, at Dartford, in 1590, is said to have brought over in his portmanteau the two first lime-trees, which he planted here, and which are still growing. The Lombardy poplar was introduced

into England by the Earl of Rochford in 1758. The first mulberry-
trees in this country are now standing at Sion-house.* By an Harleian
MS. it is mentioned that the first general planting of mulberries and
making of silk in England was by William Stallenge, comptroller of
the custom-house, and Monsieur Verton, in 1608. It is probable that
Monsieur Verton transplanted this novelty from his own country,
where we have seen De Serres's great attempt. Here the mulberries
have succeeded better than the silk-worms.

The very names of many of our vegetable kingdom indicate their
locality: from the majestic cedar of Lebanon, to the small Cos-lettuce,
which came from the isle of Cos; the cherries from Cerasuntis, a city
of Pontus; the peach, or *persicum*, or *mala Persica*, Persican apples,
from Persia; the pistachio, or *psittacia*, is the Syrian word for that nut.
The chestnut, or *chataigne*, in French, and *castagna* in Italian, from
Castagna, a town of Magnesia. Our plums coming chiefly from Syria
and Damascus, the damson, or damascene plum, gives us a recollection of its distant origin.

It is somewhat curious to observe on this subject that there exists
an unsuspected intercourse between nations, in the propagation of
exotic plants, &c. Lucullus, after the war with Mithridates, introduced
cherries from Pontus into Italy; and the newly-imported fruit was
found so pleasing that it was rapidly propagated, and six and twenty
years afterwards, as Pliny testifies, the cherry-tree passed over into
Britain.† Thus a victory obtained by a Roman consul over a king of
Pontus, with which it would seem that Britain could have no concern,
was the real occasion of our countrymen possessing cherry-orchards.
Yet to our shame must it be told, that these cherries from the king
of Pontus's city of Cerasuntis are not the cherries we are now eating;
for the whole race of cherry-trees was lost in the Saxon period, and
was only restored by the gardener of Henry VIII, who brought them
from Flanders—without a word to enhance his own merits, concerning
the *bellum Mithridaticum!*

A calculating political economist will little sympathize with the
peaceful triumphs of those active and generous spirits, who have thus
propagated the truest wealth, and the most innocent luxuries of the
people. The project of a new tax, or an additional consumption of
ardent spirits, or an act of parliament to put a convenient stop to

---

* The reader may find more dates amassed respecting the introduction of fruits,
&c, in Gough's British Topography, vol. 1, p. 133, Harl. MS 6884.
† Pliny, Nat. Hist. Lib. XV, c 25.

population by forbidding the banns of some happy couple, would be more congenial to their researches; and they would leave without regret the names of those, whom we have held out to the grateful recollections of their country. The Romans, who with all their errors were at least patriots, entertained very different notions of these introducers into their country of exotic fruits and flowers. Sir William Temple has elegantly noticed the fact. 'The great captains, and even consular men, who first brought them over, took pride in giving them their own names, by which they ran a great while in Rome, as in memory of some great service or pleasure they had done their country; so that not only laws and battles, but several sorts of apples and pears were called Manlian and Claudian, Pompeyan and Tiberian, and by several other such noble names.' Pliny has paid his tribute of applause to Lucullus, for bringing cherry and nut-trees from Pontus into Italy. And we have several modern instances, where the name of the transplanter, or rearer, has been preserved in this sort of creation. Peter Collinson, the botanist, to 'whom the English gardens are indebted for many new and curious species which he acquired by means of an extensive correspondence in America,' was highly gratified when Linnaeus baptised a plant with his name; and with great spirit asserts his honourable claim: 'Something, I think, was due to me for the great number of plants and seeds I have annually procured from abroad, and you have been so good as to pay it, by giving me a species of eternity, botanically speaking; that is, a name as long as men and books endure.' Such is the true animating language of these patriotic enthusiasts!

Some lines at the close of Peacham's Emblems give an idea of an English fruit-garden in 1612. He mentions that cherries were not long known, and gives an origin to the name of filbert.

> 'The Persian Peach, and fruitful Quince;*
> And there the forward Almond grew,
> With cherries knowne no long time since;
> The Winter Warden, orchard's pride;
> The *Philibert*† that loves the vale,

* The quince comes from Sydon, a town of Crete, we are told by Le Grand, in his Vie privée des François, vol. 1, p. 143; where may be found a list of the origin of most of our fruits.

† Peacham has here given a note. 'The filbert, so named of *Philbert*, a king of France, who caused by arte sundry kinds to be brought forth: as did a gardener of Otranto in Italie by cloue-gilliflowers, and carnations of such colours as we now see them.'

And red queen-apple,* so envide
Of school-boies, passing by the pale.'

THE RHODORA

In May, when sea-winds pierced our solitudes,
I found the fresh rhodora in the woods
Spreading its leafless blooms in a damp nook,
To please the desert and the sluggish brook:
The purple petals fallen in the pool
   Made the black waters with their beauty gay,—
Here might the red-bird come his plumes to cool,
   And court the flower that cheapens his array.
Rhodora! if the sages ask thee why
This charm is wasted on the marsh and sky,
Dear, tell them, that if eyes were made for seeing,
Then beauty is its own excuse for being.
   Why thou wert there, O rival of the rose,
I never thought to ask; I never knew,
   But in my simple ignorance suppose
The selfsame Power that brought me there brought you.

RALPH WALDO EMERSON

*The queen-apple was probably thus distinguished in compliment to Elizabeth.
In Moffet's 'Healths Improvement,' I find an account of apples which are said
to have been 'graffed upon a mulberry-stock, and then was thorough red as our
queen apples, called by Ruellius, *Rubelliana*, and *Claudiana* by Pliny.' I am told
the race is not extinct; an apple of this description is yet to be found.

THE CAROLINA PAROQUET

by Alexander Wilson

Poor Alexander Wilson. He was talented, industrious, and unfortunate. He was born in Paisley, Scotland, July 6, 1766. His father was a weaver and tried to train his son to the trade, but the boy had other ideas. He became an itinerant pedlar and, on the side, a composer of dialect ballads and lampoons aimed at the rich and powerful overlords of the weaving industry. One of these satirical productions brought him into court on the charge of libel. He was convicted and fined, and when he couldn't pay the fine, he was imprisoned for debt.

When he emerged from prison he left for America with a young nephew, a gun, and little more than the clothes on his back. Somehow he obtained a position as a schoolmaster near Philadelphia. He loved Nature. He wanted to become a naturalist but was faced with the problem of how to make a living at such a profession. Being particularly fond of birds, he decided that he would publish a work containing colored plates and accurate descriptions of every species of bird to be found in North America. He would paint all the pictures and write all the text himself. He met William Bartram, the famous botanist, who encouraged him in his plan. Wilson had no money and certainly no great knowledge of many of the birds of North America. He aimed to obtain both. He began to travel the country, collecting, painting, and writing down details of bird life and his adopted country. He also solicited subscriptions at a price of $120 a set for the completed work that eventually ran to nine volumes. His wanderings in search of birds—and subscribers—led him to Louisville, Kentucky, in March, 1810, and there he encountered a storekeeper by the name of John James Audubon who, he had been told, was much interested in birds and had done wonderful sketches of many kinds.

Wilson's story of his stay in Louisville and Audubon's account of their meeting are by no means in agreement. Audubon stated that he was sympathetic and helpful to Wilson in obtaining some local species but that he didn't subscribe to his work for two reasons. One, and a rather important one, was that he couldn't spare the money. A second one was that he thought his own drawings were superior to those of Wilson, which they were. Wilson's melancholy tale was that he obtained neither help nor sympathy from a single soul in Louisville, and he condemned it as a benighted community. Yet the meeting of the two men was significant in that it gave Audubon, who up to that time hadn't thought of it, the idea of producing a work of the kind Wilson was doing, but on a bigger and finer scale. He, Audubon, would paint all the birds of North America better than Wilson could, and life-size! And publish them that way! Which he did many years later in the famous folio edition at a cost of $1000 a set.

But it was Wilson who struck the spark in passing through Louisville in 1810. Poor Wilson didn't live to complete his own work. Seven of the projected nine volumes had appeared when the author died of dysentery August 23, 1813. George Ord of Philadelphia, enemy of Audubon and friend of Wilson, brought out the last two volumes of the set. The offering here is an example of the bird biographies in Wilson's work.

OF one hundred and sixty-eight kinds of parrots, enumerated by European writers as inhabiting the various regions of the globe, this is the only species found native within the territory of the United States. The vast and luxuriant tracts lying within the torrid zone seem to be the favourite residence of those noisy, numerous, and richly plumaged tribes. The Count de Buffon has, indeed, circumscribed the whole genus of parrots to a space not extending more than twenty-three degrees on each side of the equator: but later discoveries have shewn this statement to be incorrect, as these birds have been found on our continent as far south as the Straits of Magellan, and even on the remote shores of Van Diemen's Land, in Terra Australasia. The species now under consideration is also known to inhabit the interior of Louisiana, and the shores of Mississippi and Ohio, and their tributary waters, even beyond the Illinois River, to the neighbourhood of Lake Michigan, in lat. 42 deg. north; and, contrary to the generally received opinion, is chiefly *resident* in all these places. Eastward, however, of the great range of the Allegheny, it is seldom seen farther north than the state of Maryland; though straggling parties have been occasionally observed among the valleys of the Juniata; and, according to some, even twenty-five miles to the northwest of Albany, in the state of New York. But such accidental visits furnish no certain criteria by which to judge of their usual extent of range; those aërial voyagers, as well as others who navigate the deep, being subject to be cast away, by the violence of the elements, on distant shores and unknown countries.

From these circumstances of the northern residence of this species, we might be justified in concluding it to be a very hardy bird, more capable of sustaining cold than nine-tenths of its tribe; and so I believe it is; having myself seen them, in the month of February, along the banks of the Ohio, in a snow-storm, flying about like pigeons, and in full cry.

The preference, however, which this bird gives to the western countries, lying in the same parallel of latitude with those eastward of the Allegheny Mountains, which it rarely or never visits, is worthy of remark; and has been adduced, by different writers, as a proof of the superior mildness of climate in the former to that of the latter. But there are other reasons for this partiality equally powerful, though hitherto overlooked; namely, certain peculiar features of country to which these birds are particularly and strongly attached: these are, low rich alluvial bottoms, along the borders of creeks, covered with a gigantic growth of sycamore trees, or button-wood; deep, and almost impenetrable swamps, where the vast and towering cypress lift their still more majestic heads; and those singular salines, or, as they are usually called, licks, so generally interspersed over that country, and which are regularly and eagerly visited by the paroquets. A still greater inducement is the superior abundance of their favourite fruits. That food which the paroquet prefers to all others is the seeds of the cockle bur, a plant rarely found in the lower parts of Pennsylvania or New York; but which unfortunately grows in too great abundance along the shores of the Ohio and Mississippi, so much so as to render the wool of those sheep that pasture where it most abounds, scarcely worth the cleaning, covering them with one solid mass of burs, wrought up and imbedded into the fleece, to the great annoyance of this valuable animal. The seeds of the cypress tree and hackberry, as well as beech nuts,

are also great favourites with these birds; the two former of which are
not commonly found in Pennsylvania, and the latter by no means so
general or so productive. Here, then, are several powerful reasons, more
dependent on soil than climate, for the preference given by these birds
to the luxuriant regions of the west. Pennsylvania, indeed, and also
Maryland, abound with excellent apple orchards, on the ripe fruit of
which the paroquets occasionally feed. But I have my doubts whether
their depredations in the orchard be not as much the result of wanton
play and mischief, as regard for the seeds of the fruit, which they are
supposed to be in pursuit of. I have known a flock of these birds
alight on an apple tree, and have myself seen them twist off the fruit,
one by one, strewing it in every direction around the tree, without
observing that any of the depredators descended to pick them up. To
a paroquet, which I wounded and kept for some considerable time,
I very often offered apples, which it uniformly rejected; but burs, or
beech nuts, never. To another very beautiful one, which I brought
from New Orleans, and which is now sitting in the room beside me,
I have frequently offered this fruit, and also the seeds separately, which
I never knew it to taste. Their local attachments, also, prove that food,
more than climate, determines their choice of country. For even in
the states of Ohio, Kentucky, and the Mississippi territory, unless in
the neighbourhood of such places as have been described, it is rare
to see them. The inhabitants of Lexington, as many of them assured
me, scarcely ever observe them in that quarter. In passing from that
place to Nashville, a distance of two hundred miles, I neither heard
nor saw any, but at a place called Madison's lick. In passing on, I next
met with them on the banks and rich flats of the Tennessee river:
after this, I saw no more till I reached Bayo St. Pierre, a distance of
several hundred miles: from all which circumstances, I think we cannot, from the residence of these birds, establish with propriety any
correct standard by which to judge of the comparative temperatures
of different climates.

In descending the river Ohio, by myself, in the month of February,
I met with the first flock of paroquets, at the mouth of the Little
Sioto. I have been informed, by an old and respectable inhabitant of
Marietta, that they were sometimes, though rarely, seen there. I ob-
served flocks of them, afterwards, at the mouth of the Great and Little
Miami, and in the neighbourhood of numerous creeks that discharge
themselves into the Ohio. At Big Bone lick, thirty miles above the
mouth of Kentucky River, I saw them in great numbers. They came

screaming through the woods in the morning about an hour after sunrise, to drink the salt water, of which they, as well as the pigeons, are remarkably fond. When they alighted on the ground, it appeared at a distance as if covered with a carpet of the richest green, orange, and yellow: they afterwards settled, in one body, on a neighbouring tree, which stood detached from any other, covering almost every twig of it, and the sun, shining strongly on their gay and glossy plumage, produced a very beautiful and splendid appearance. Here I had an opportunity of observing some very particular traits of their character: having shot down a number, some of which were only wounded, the whole flock swept repeatedly around their prostrate companions, and again settled on a low tree, within twenty yards of the spot where I stood. At each successive discharge, though showers of them fell, yet the affection of the survivors seemed rather to increase; for, after a few circuits around the place, they again alighted near me, looking down on their slaughtered companions with such manifest symptoms of sympathy and concern, as entirely disarmed me. I could not but take notice of the remarkable contrast between their elegant manner of flight, and their lame crawling gait among the branches. They fly very much like the wild pigeon, in close compact bodies, and with great rapidity, making a loud and outrageous screaming, not unlike that of the red-headed woodpecker. Their flight is sometimes in a direct line; but most usually circuitous, making a great variety of elegant and easy serpentine meanders, as if for pleasure. They are particularly attached to the large sycamores, in the hollow of the trunks and branches of which they generally roost, thirty or forty, and sometimes more, entering at the same hole. Here they cling close to the sides of the tree, holding fast by the claws and also by the bills. They appear to be fond of sleep, and often retire to their holes during the day, probably to take their regular *siesta*. They are extremely sociable with, and fond of each other, often scratching each other's heads and necks, and always, at night, nestling as close as possible to each other, preferring, at that time, a perpendicular position, supported by their bill and claws. In the fall, when their favourite cockle burs are ripe, they swarm along the coast, or high grounds of the Mississippi, above New Orleans, for a great extent. At such times, they are killed and eaten by many of the inhabitants; though, I confess, I think their flesh very indifferent. I have several times dined on it from necessity, in the woods: but found it merely passable, with all the sauce of a keen appetite to recommend it.

A very general opinion prevails, that the brains and intestines of the Carolina paroquet are a sure and fatal poison to cats. I had determined, when at Big Bone, to put this to the test of experiment; and for that purpose collected the brains and bowels of more than a dozen of them. But after close search, Mistress Puss was not to be found, being engaged perhaps on more agreeable business. I left the medicine with Mr. Colquhoun's agent, to administer it by the first opportunity, and write me the result; but I have never yet heard from him. A respectable lady near the town of Natchez, and on whose word I can rely, assured me, that she herself had made the experiment, and that, whatever might be the cause, the cat had actually died either on that or the succeeding day. A French planter near Bayo Fourche pretended to account to me for this effect by positively asserting, that the seeds of the cockle burs on which the paroquets so eagerly feed, were deleterious to cats; and thus their death was produced by eating the intestines of the bird. These matters might easily have been ascertained on the spot, which, however, a combination of trifling circumstances prevented me from doing. I several times carried a dose of the first description in my pocket till it became insufferable, without meeting with a suitable *patient*, on whom, like other professional gentlemen, I might conveniently make a fair experiment.

I was equally unsuccessful in my endeavours to discover the time of incubation or manner of building among these birds. All agreed that they breed in hollow trees; and several affirmed to me that they had seen their nests. Some said they carried in no materials; others that they did. Some made the eggs white; others speckled. One man assured me that he cut down a large beech tree, which was hollow, and in which he found the broken fragments of upwards of twenty paroquet eggs, which were of a greenish yellow colour. The nests, though destroyed in their texture by the falling of the tree, appeared, he said, to be formed of small twigs glued to each other, and to the side of the tree, in the manner of the chimney swallow. He added, that if it were the proper season, he could point out to me the weed from which they procured the gluey matter. From all these contradictory accounts nothing certain can be deduced, except that they build in companies, in hollow trees. That they commence incubation late in summer, or very early in spring, I think highly probable, from the numerous dissections I made in the months of March, April, May, and June; and the great variety which I found in the colour of the plumage of the head and neck of both sexes, during the two former of these months, convinces me, that the young birds do not receive their full colours until the early part of the succeeding summer.

While parrots and paroquets, from foreign countries, abound in almost every street of our large cities, and become such great favourites, no attention seems to have been paid to our own, which in elegance of figure and beauty of plumage is certainly superior to many of them. It wants indeed that disposition for perpetual screaming and chattering that renders some of the former pests, not only to their keepers, but to the whole neighbourhood in which they reside. It is alike docile and sociable; soon becomes perfectly familiar; and, until equal pains be taken in its instruction, it is unfair to conclude it incapable of equal improvement in the language of man.

As so little has hitherto been known of the disposition and manners of this species, the reader will not, I hope, be displeased at my detailing some of these, in the history of a particular favourite, my sole companion in many a lonesome day's march.

Anxious to try the effects of education on one of those which I procured at Big Bone lick, and which was but slightly wounded in the wing, I fixed up a place for it in the stern of my boat, and presented it with some cockle burs, which it freely fed on in less than an hour after being on board. The intermediate time between eating and sleeping was occupied in gnawing the sticks that formed its place of confinement, in order to make a practicable breach; which it repeatedly effected. When I abandoned the river, and travelled by land, I wrapt it up closely in a silk handkerchief, tying it tightly around, and carried it in my pocket. When I stopped for refreshment, I unbound my prisoner, and gave it its allowance, which it generally despatched with great dexterity, unhusking the seeds from the bur in a twinkling; in doing which it always employed its left foot to hold the bur, as did several others that I kept for some time. I began to think that this might be peculiar to the whole tribe, and that they all were, if I may use the expression, left-footed; but by shooting a number afterwards while engaged in eating mulberries, I found sometimes the left, sometimes the right foot stained with the fruit; the other always clean; from which, and the constant practice of those I kept, it appears, that like the human species in the use of their hands, they do not prefer one or the other indiscriminately, but are either left or right footed. But to return to my prisoner: In recommitting it to "durance vile" we generally had a quarrel; during which it frequently paid me in kind for the wound I had inflicted, and for depriving it of liberty, by cutting and almost disabling several of my fingers with its sharp and powerful bill. The path through the wilderness between Nashville and Natchez is in some places bad beyond description. There are dangerous creeks to swim, miles of morass to struggle through, rendered almost as gloomy as night by a prodigious growth of timber, and an underwood of canes and other evergreens; while the descent into these sluggish streams is often ten or fifteen feet perpendicular into a bed of deep clay. In some of the worst of these places, where I had, as it were, to fight my way through, the paroquet frequently escaped from my pocket, obliging me to dismount and pursue it through the worst of the morass before I could regain it. On these occasions I was several times tempted to abandon it; but I persisted in bringing it along. When at night I encamped in the woods, I placed it on the baggage beside me, where it usually sat, with great composure, dozing and gazing at the fire till morning. In this manner I carried it upwards of a thousand miles in my pocket, where it was exposed all day to the jolting of the horse, but regularly liberated at meal times and in the evening, at which it always expressed great satisfaction. In passing through the Chickasaw and Choctaw nations, the Indians, wherever I stopped to feed, collected around me, men, women, and children, laughing and seeming wonderfully amused with the novelty of my companion. The Chickasaws called it in their language "*Kelinky*"; but when they heard me call it Poll, they soon repeated the name; and wherever I chanced to stop among these people, we soon became familiar with each other through the medium of Poll. On arriving at Mr. Dunbar's, below Natchez, I procured a cage, and placed it under the piazza, where by its call it soon attracted the passing flocks; such is the attachment they have for each other. Numerous parties frequently alighted on the trees immediately above, keeping up a constant conversation with the prisoner. One of these I wounded slightly in the wing, and the pleasure Poll expressed on meeting with this new companion was really amusing. She crept close up to it as it hung on the side of the cage, chattering to it in a low tone of voice, as if sympathizing in its misfortune, scratched about its head and neck with her bill; and both at night nestled as close as possible to each other, sometimes Poll's head being thrust among the plumage of the other. On the death of this companion, she appeared restless and inconsolable for several days. On reaching New Orleans, I placed a looking glass beside the place where she usually sat, and the instant she perceived her image, all her former fondness seemed to return, so that she could scarcely absent herself from it a moment. It was evident that she was completely deceived. Always when evening drew on, and often during the day, she laid her head close to that of the image in the glass, and began to doze with great composure and satisfaction. In this short space she had learnt to know her name; to answer and come when called on; to climb up my clothes, sit on my shoulder, and eat from my mouth. I took her with me to sea, determined to persevere in her education; but, destined to another fate, poor Poll, having one morning, about daybreak wrought her way through the cage, while I was asleep, instantly flew overboard, and perished in the Gulf of Mexico.

The Carolina, or Illinois parrot, (for it has been described under both these appellations,) is thirteen inches long, and twenty-one in extent; forehead and cheeks, orange red; beyond this, for an inch and a half, down and round the neck, a rich and pure yellow; shoulder and bend of the wing, also edged with rich orange red. The general colour of the rest of the plumage is a bright yellowish silky green, with light blue reflections, lightest and most diluted with yellow below; greater wing-coverts and roots of the primaries, yellow, slightly tinged with green; interior webs of the primaries, deep dusky purple, almost black, exterior ones, bluish green; tail, long, cuneiform, consisting of twelve feathers, the exterior one only half the length, the others increasing to the middle ones, which are streaked along the middle with light blue; shafts of all the larger feathers, and of most part of the green plumage, black; knees and vent, orange yellow; feet, a pale whitish flesh colour; claws, black; bill, white, or slightly tinged with pale cream; iris of the eye, hazel; round the eye is a small space without feathers, covered with a whitish skin; nostrils placed in an elevated membrane at the base of the bill, and covered with feathers; chin, wholly bare of feathers, but concealed by those descending on each side; from each side of the palate hangs a lobe or skin of a blackish colour; tongue, thick and fleshy; inside of the upper mandible near the point, grooved exactly like a file, that it may hold with more security.

The female differs very little in her colours and markings from the male. After examining numerous specimens, the following appear to be the principal differences. The yellow on the neck of the female does not descend quite so far; the interior vanes of the primaries are brownish, instead of black, and the orange red on the bend and edges of the wings is considerably narrower; in other respects, the colours and markings are nearly the same.

The young birds of the preceding year, of both sexes, are generally destitute of the yellow on the head and neck, until about the beginning or middle of March, having those parts wholly green, except the front and cheeks, which are orange red in them as in the full grown birds. Towards the middle of March the yellow begins to appear, in detached feathers, interspersed among the green, varying in different individuals. In some which I killed about the last of that month, only a few green feathers remained among the yellow; and these were fast assuming the yellow tint: for the colour changes without change of plumage. A number of these birds, in all their grades of progressive change from green to yellow, have been deposited in Mr. Peale's museum.

What is called by Europeans the Illinois parrot (*Psittacus pertinax*) is evidently the young bird in its imperfect colours. Whether the present species be found as far south as Brazil, as these writers pretend, I am unable to say; but, from the great extent of country in which I have myself killed and examined these birds, I am satisfied that the present species, now described, is the only one inhabiting the United States.

Since the foregoing was written, I have had an opportunity, by the death of a tame Carolina paroquet, to ascertain the fact of the poisonous effects of their head and intestines to cats. Having shut up a cat and her two kittens, (the latter only a few days old,) in a room with the head, neck, and whole intestines of the paroquet, I found, on the next morning, the whole eaten except a small part of the bill. The cat exhibited no symptom of sickness; and, at this moment, three days after the experiment has been made, she and her kittens are in their usual health. Still, however, the effect might have been different, had the daily food of the bird been cockle burs, instead of Indian corn.

When icicles hang by the wall,
  And Dick, the shepherd, blows his nail,
And Tom bears logs into the hall,
  And milk comes frozen home in pail,
When blood is nipp'd and ways be foul,
Then nightly sings the staring owl,
              Tu-who;
Tu-whit, tu-who—a merry note,
While greasy Joan doth keel the pot.

SHAKESPEARE, *Love's Labour's Lost*

THE PASSENGER PIGEON

by John James Audubon

The story of John James Audubon is a real-life romance. Born in San Domingo (April 26, 1785), raised in France, and sent to this country as a young man of eighteen to look after some family property near Philadelphia, he survived an appalling series of financial misadventures—largely his own fault, it must be admitted —to achieve not only success but world fame through his artistic talent and his love of birds. Think of the United States as it was between 1800 and 1850. During such an era this man who couldn't run a grocery store, couldn't make a sawmill pay, couldn't support his family, and once actually was jailed for debt, proposed to paint in full color all the birds of North America life-size and publish reproductions and text to match in a work to sell at a price of $1000 a set!

He not only proposed to do it; he did it. He painted the birds. He hired the printers and engravers—in England, to make sure the work would be of the highest quality. He solicited subscriptions himself in the United States, in Great Britain, and on the Continent. It took him eleven years to produce Birds of America in the elephant folio edition, but he sold almost two hundred sets and enough separate colored plates to make the venture a financial success as well as an artistic triumph. These were not stiff portraits of stuffed birds in glass cases. These were beautiful live creatures seemingly caught in action on the ground, on the water, or in the air.

His name now is almost a household word through the work of the National Audubon Society and all the regional Audubon societies, but this tends to obscure the real character of the man. He survives as "the great bird man" and the inspiration for Audubon societies that are devoted to bird protection and wildlife conservation in general. It's true that Audubon's love of birds was *the lodestar of his life, but it was as an artist that he excelled, not as a "bird man" or ornithologist. There were better ornithologists in his day, and indeed he had to call in one of them, William Mac-Gillivray, to aid him with the text of his Ornithological Biographies. As an artist he was—and to many persons he still is—unrivaled in his field. He was also a somewhat flamboyant figure, a fine dancer, a musician, an accomplished rider, a good shot, and a very welcome addition at any social gathering. He died at his home on the bank of the Hudson River in New York City on January 27, 1851, in his sixty-seventh year. His story of the passenger pigeon and its abundance in his day must be read in the light of the fact that, of the countless flocks that were seen in Audubon's time, not a single descendant is alive today. The passenger pigeon is extinct.*

THE Passenger Pigeon, or, as it is usually named in America, the Wild Pigeon, moves with extreme rapidity, propelling itself by quickly repeated flaps of the wings, which it brings more or less near to the body, according to the degree of velocity which is required. Like the Domestic Pigeon, it often flies, during the love season, in a circling manner, supporting itself with both wings angularly elevated, in which position it keeps them until it is about to alight. Now and then, during these circular flights, the tips of the primary quills of each wing are made to strike against each other, producing a smart rap, which may be heard at a distance of thirty or forty yards. Before alighting, the Wild Pigeon, like the Carolina Parrot and a few other species of birds, breaks the force of its flight by repeated flappings, as if apprehensive of receiving injury from coming too suddenly into contact with the branch or the spot of ground on which it intends to settle.

I have commenced my description of this species with the above account of its flight, because the most important facts connected with its habits relate to its migrations. These are entirely owing to the necessity of procuring food, and are not performed with the view of escaping the severity of a northern latitude, or of seeking a southern one for the purpose of breeding. They consequently do not take place at any fixed period or season of the year. Indeed, it sometimes happens that a continuance of a sufficient supply of food in one district will keep these birds absent from another for years. I know, at least, to a certainty, that in Kentucky they remained for several years constantly, and were nowhere else to be found. They all suddenly disappeared one season when the mast was exhausted, and did not return for a long period. Similar facts have been observed in other States.

Their great power of flight enables them to survey and pass over an astonishing extent of country in a very short time. This is proved by facts well known. Thus, Pigeons have been killed in the neighbourhood of New York, with their crops full of rice, which they must have collected in the fields of Georgia and Carolina, these districts being the nearest in which they could possibly have procured a supply of that kind of food. As their power of digestion is so great that they will decompose food entirely in twelve hours, they must in this case have travelled between three and four hundred miles in six hours, which shews their speed to be at an average of about one mile in a minute. A velocity such as this would enable one of these birds, were it so inclined, to visit the European continent in less than three days.

This great power of flight is seconded by as great a power of vision, which enables them, as they travel at that swift rate, to inspect the country below, discover their food with facility, and thus attain the object for which their journey has been undertaken. This I have also proved to be the case, by having observed them, when passing over a sterile part of the country, or one scantily furnished with food suited to them, keep high in the air, flying with an extended front, so as to enable them to survey hundreds of acres at once. On the contrary, when the land is richly covered with food, or the trees abundantly hung with mast, they fly low, in order to discover the part most plentifully supplied.

Their body is of an elongated oval form, steered by a long well-plumed tail, and propelled by well-set wings, the muscles of which are very large and powerful for the size of the bird. When an individual is seen gliding through the woods and close to the observer, it passes like a thought, and on trying to see it again, the eye searches in vain; the bird is gone.

The multitudes of Wild Pigeons in our woods are astonishing. Indeed, after having viewed them so often, and under so many circumstances, I even now feel inclined to pause, and assure myself that what I am going to relate is fact. Yet I have seen it all, and that, too, in the company of persons who, like myself, were struck with amazement.

In the autumn of 1813, I left my house at Henderson, on the banks of the Ohio, on my way to Louisville. In passing over the Barrens a few miles beyond Hardensburgh, I observed the Pigeons flying from north-east to south-west, in greater numbers than I thought I had ever seen them before, and feeling an inclination to count the flocks that might pass within the reach of my eye in one hour, I dismounted, seated myself on an eminence, and began to mark with my pencil, making a dot for every flock that passed. In a short time finding the task which I had undertaken impracticable, as the birds poured in in countless multitudes, I rose, and counting the dots then put down, found that 163 had been made in twenty-one minutes. I travelled on, and still met more the farther I proceeded. The air was literally filled with Pigeons; the light of noon-day was obscured as by an eclipse; the dung fell in spots, not unlike melting flakes of snow; and the continued buzz of wings had a tendency to lull my senses to repose.

Whilst waiting for dinner at YOUNG's inn at the confluence of Salt river with the Ohio, I saw, at my leisure, immense legions still going by, with a front reaching far beyond the Ohio on the west, and the beech-wood forests directly on the east of me. Not a single bird alighted; for not a nut or acorn was that year to be seen in the neighbourhood. They consequently flew so high, that different trials to reach them with a capital rifle proved ineffectual; nor did the reports disturb them in the least. I cannot describe to you the extreme beauty of their aerial evolutions, when a Hawk chanced to press upon the rear of a flock. At once, like a torrent, and with a noise like thunder, they rushed into a compact mass, pressing upon each other towards the centre. In these almost solid masses, they darted forward in undulating and angular lines, descended and swept close over the earth with inconceivable velocity, mounted perpendicularly so as to resemble a vast column, and, when high, were seen wheeling and twisting within their continued lines, which then resembled the coils of a gigantic serpent.

Before sunset I reached Louisville, distant from Hardensburgh fifty-five miles. The Pigeons were still passing in undiminished numbers, and continued to do so for three days in succession. The people were all in arms. The banks of the Ohio were crowded with men and boys, incessantly shooting at the pilgrims, which there flew lower as they passed the river. Multitudes were thus destroyed. For a week or more, the population fed on no other flesh than that of Pigeons, and talked of nothing but Pigeons.

It is extremely interesting to see flock after flock performing exactly the same evolutions which had been traced as it were in the air by a preceding flock. Thus, should a Hawk have charged on a group at a certain spot, the angles, curves, and undulations that have been described by the birds, in their efforts to escape from the dreaded talons of the plunderer, are undeviatingly followed by the next group that comes up. Should the bystander happen to witness one of these affrays, and, struck with the rapidity and elegance of the motions exhibited, feel desirous of seeing them repeated, his wishes will be gratified if he only remain in the place until the next group comes up.

As soon as the Pigeons discover a sufficiency of food to entice them to alight, they fly around in circles, reviewing the country below. During their evolutions, on such occasions, the dense mass which they form exhibits a beautiful appearance, as it changes its direction, now displaying a glistening sheet of azure, when the backs of the birds come simultaneously into view, and anon, suddenly presenting a mass of rich deep purple. They then pass lower, over the woods, and for a moment are lost among the foliage, but again emerge, and are seen gliding aloft. They now alight, but the next moment, as if suddenly alarmed, they take to wing, producing by the flappings of their wings a noise like the roar of distant thunder, and sweep through the forests to see if danger is near. Hunger, however, soon brings them to the ground. When alighted, they are seen industriously throwing up the withered leaves in quest of the fallen mast. The rear ranks are continually rising, passing over the main-body, and alighting in front, in such rapid succession, that the whole flock seems still on wing. The quantity of ground thus swept is astonishing, and so completely has it been cleared, that the gleaner who might follow in their rear would find his labour completely lost. Whilst feeding, their avidity is at times so great that in attempting to swallow a large acorn or nut, they are seen gasping for a long while, as if in the agonies of suffocation.

On such occasions, when the woods are filled with these Pigeons, they are killed in immense numbers, although no apparent diminution ensues. About the middle of the day, after their repast is finished, they settle on the trees, to enjoy rest, and digest their food. On the ground they walk with ease, as well as on the branches, frequently jerking their beautiful tail, and moving the neck backwards and forwards in the most graceful manner. As the sun begins to sink beneath the horizon, they depart en masse for the roosting-place, which not unfrequently is hundreds of miles distant, as has been ascertained by persons who have kept an account of their arrivals and departures.

Let us now, kind reader, inspect their place of nightly rendezvous. One of these curious roosting-places, on the banks of the Green river in Kentucky, I repeatedly visited. It was, as is always the case, in a portion of the forest where the trees were of great magnitude, and where there was little underwood. I rode through it upwards of forty miles, and, crossing it in different parts, found its average breadth to be rather more than three miles. My first view of it was about a fortnight subsequent to the period when they had made choice of it, and I arrived there nearly two hours before sunset. Few Pigeons were then to be seen, but a great number of persons, with horses and wagons, guns and ammunition, had already established encampments on the borders. Two farmers from the vicinity of Russelsville, distant more than a hundred miles, had driven upwards of three hundred hogs to be fattened on the Pigeons which were to be slaughtered. Here and there, the people employed in plucking and salting what had already been procured, were seen sitting in the midst of large piles of these birds. The dung lay several inches deep, covering the whole extent of the roosting-place. Many trees two feet in diameter, I observed, were broken off at no great distance from the ground; and the branches of many of the largest and tallest had given way, as if the forest had been swept by a tornado. Every thing proved to me that the number of birds resorting to this part of the forest must be immense beyond conception. As the period of their arrival approached, their foes anxiously prepared to receive them. Some were furnished with iron-pots containing sulphur, others with torches of pine-knots, many with poles, and the rest with guns. The sun was lost to our view, yet not a Pigeon had arrived. Every thing was ready, and all eyes were gazing on the clear sky, which appeared in glimpses amidst the tall trees. Suddenly there burst forth a general cry of "Here they come!" The noise which they made, though yet distant, reminded me of a hard gale at sea, passing through the rigging of a close-reefed vessel. As the birds arrived and passed over me, I felt a current of air that surprised me. Thousands were soon knocked down by the pole-men. The birds continued to pour in. The fires were lighted, and a magnificent, as well as wonderful and almost terrifying, sight presented itself. The Pigeons, arriving by thousands, alighted everywhere, one above another, until solid masses were formed on the branches all round. Here and there the perches gave way under the weight with a crash, and, falling to the ground, destroyed hundreds of the birds beneath, forcing down the dense groups with which every stick was loaded. It was a scene of uproar and confusion. I found it quite useless to speak, or even to shout to those persons who were nearest to me. Even the reports of the guns were seldom heard, and I was made aware of the firing only by seeing the shooters reloading.

No one dared venture within the line of devastation. The hogs had been penned up in due time, the picking up of the dead and wounded being left for the next morning's employment. The Pigeons were constantly coming, and it was past midnight before I perceived a decrease in the number of those that arrived. The uproar continued the whole night; and as I was anxious to know to what distance the sound reached, I sent off a man, accustomed to perambulate the forest, who, returning two hours afterwards, informed me he had heard it distinctly when three miles distant from the spot. Towards the approach of day, the noise in some measure subsided: long before objects were distinguishable, the Pigeons began to move off in a direction quite different from that in which they had arrived the evening before, and at sunrise all that were able to fly had disappeared. The howlings of the wolves now reached our ears, and the foxes, lynxes, cougars, bears, racoons, opossums and pole-cats were seen sneaking off, whilst eagles and hawks of different species, accompanied by a crowd of vultures, came to supplant them, and enjoy their share of the spoil.

It was then that the authors of all this devastation began their entry amongst the dead, and dying, and the mangled. The Pigeons were picked up and piled in heaps, until each had as many as he could possibly dispose of, when the hogs were let loose to feed on the remainder.

Persons unacquainted with these birds might naturally conclude that such dreadful havoc would soon put an end to the species. But I have satisfied myself, by long observation, that nothing but the gradual diminution of our forests can accomplish their decrease, as they not unfrequently guadruple their numbers yearly, and always at least double it. In 1805 I saw schooners loaded in bulk with Pigeons caught up the Hudson River, coming in to the wharf at New York, when the birds sold for a cent a piece. I knew a man in Pennsylvania, who caught and killed upwards of 500 dozens in a clap-net in one day, sweeping sometimes twenty dozens or more at a single haul. In the month of March 1830, they were so abundant in the markets of New York, that piles of them met the eye in every direction. I have seen the Negroes at the United States Salines or Saltworks of Shawanee Town, wearied with killing Pigeons, as they alighted to drink the water issuing from the leading pipes, for weeks at a time; and yet in 1826, in Louisiana, I saw congregated flocks of these birds as numerous as ever I had seen them before, during a residence of nearly thirty years in the United States.

The breeding of the Wild Pigeons, and the places chosen for that purpose, are points of great interest. The time is not much influenced by season, and the place selected is where food is most plentiful and most attainable, and always at a convenient distance from water. Forest-trees of great height are those in which the Pigeons form their nests. Thither the countless myriads resort, and prepare to fulfill one of the great laws of nature. At this period the note of the Pigeon is a soft coo-coo-coo-coo, much shorter than that of the domestic species. The common notes resemble the monosyllables kee-kee-kee-kee, the first being the loudest, the others gradually diminishing in power. The male assumes a pompous demeanour, and follows the female, whether on the ground or on the branches, with spread tail and drooping wings, which it rubs against the part over which it is moving. The body is elevated, the throat swells, the eyes sparkle. He continues his notes, and now and then rises on the wing, and flies a few yards to approach the fugitive and timorous female. Like the Domestic Pigeon and other species, they caress each other by billing, in which action, the bill of the one is introduced transversely into that of the other, and both parties alternately disgorge the contents of their crop by repeated efforts. These preliminary affairs are soon settled, and the Pigeons commence their nests in general peace and harmony. They are composed of a few dry twigs, crossing each other, and are supported by forks of the branches. On the same tree from fifty to a hundred nests may frequently be seen:—I might say a much greater number, were I not anxious, kind reader, that however wonderful my account of the Wild Pigeon is, you may not feel disposed to refer it to the marvellous. The eggs are two in number, of a broadly elliptical form, and pure white. During incubation, the male supplies the female with food. Indeed, the tenderness and affection displayed by these birds towards their mates, are in the highest degree striking. It is a remarkable fact, that each brood generally consists of a male and a female.

Here again, the tyrant of the creation, man, interferes, disturbing the harmony of this peaceful scene. As the young birds grow up, their enemies, armed with axes, reach the spot, to seize and destroy all they can. The trees are felled, and made to fall in such a way that the cutting of one causes the overthrow of another, or shakes the neighbouring trees so much, that the young Pigeons, or squabs, as they are named, are violently hurried to the ground. In this manner also, immense quantities are destroyed.

The young are fed by the parents in the manner described above; in other words, the old bird introduces its bill into the mouth of the young one in a transverse manner, or with the back of each mandible opposite the separations of the mandibles of the young bird, and disgorges the contents of its crop. As soon as the young birds are able to shift for themselves, they leave their parents, and continue separate until they attain maturity. By the end of six months they are capable of reproducing their species.

The flesh of the Wild Pigeon is of a dark colour, but affords tolerable eating. That of young birds from the nest is much esteemed. The skin is covered with small white filmy scales. The feathers fall off at the least touch, as has been remarked to be the case in the Carolina Turtle-dove. I have only to add, that this species, like others of the same genus, immerses its head up to the eyes while drinking.

In March 1830, I bought about 350 of these birds in the market of New York, at four cents a piece. Most of these I carried alive to England, and distributed them amongst several noblemen, presenting some at the same time to the Zoölogical Society.

> So, naturalists observe, a flea
> Hath smaller fleas that on him prey;
> And these have smaller still to bite 'em;
> And so proceed *ad infinitum*.
>
> JONATHAN SWIFT

> Delightful task! to rear the tender thought,
> To teach the young idea how to shoot.
>
> JAMES THOMSON, *The Seasons*

A RURAL RIDE

by William Cobbett

In the famous Greville Diary there is a passing reference to "fierce old Cobbett." The description was well merited. For many years he was fulminating against many things in voice and print. He was an editor and a political economist after his own fashion. He denounced "radicals" in early life, and later was denounced and sent to jail as a "radical" himself. On three different occasions sentence was passed upon him in court, and he lived to become a Member of Parliament. During a stay in the United States—to avoid serving a jail term in England for libel—he accused the esteemed Dr. Benjamin Rush of Philadelphia of killing George Washington with repeated "bleedings." There was never a dull moment when Cobbett was about.

He was the son of an English farmer, a native of Surrey, where William was born in the village of Farnham, March 9, 1763. As a young man he joined the British army, was sent to Nova Scotia, rose to be sergeant-major, and, when he was returned home and honorably discharged, accused his superior officers of having stolen regimental funds. When the case came to trial he was denied access to army evidence that he needed to substantiate his charges, and, feeling that the tables would be turned on him, he fled to France. But this was 1792. France was seething. Cobbett didn't favor the French Revolution. He sailed for America, where his talent for oratory and violent writing brought him notoriety as a pamphleteer and lampooner. Among those he denounced was Dr. Joseph Priestley, the English scientist who had settled in Pennsylvania after his English home had been burned down over his head by a mob because he favored the French Revolution. Having polished off Priestley, Cobbett turned his attack on the eminent Dr. Rush, who fired back through a lawyer and had Cobbett haled into court on a libel charge. The judge found Cobbett *guilty and assessed a fine, whereupon Cobbett wrote a pamphlet attacking the judge. Such actions made it unprofitable for him to remain long in one region. He had gone first to Wilmington, Delaware. Then he moved on to Philadelphia. In turn he made each place too hot to hold him, and he returned to England in 1800, by which time his early brush with the law over military matters had been either forgiven or forgotten.*

He launched himself as a political pamphleteer and agricultural reformer. He founded a weekly paper called The Political Register *in 1802, and in its columns he attacked the Government, Prime Minister Pitt (the Younger), the Napoleonic Wars, the tax system, paper money, bankers, the established clergy, and particularly the city of London, which he designated "the Wen." In 1810 he was fined 1000 pounds for denouncing in his* Political Register *the flogging of some soldiers, and in addition he was sentenced to two years in jail. He served his term and edited his paper from his jail cell. In 1817 he was threatened with arrest for his attacks on the Government, and he fled a second time to the United States. He spent two years on Long Island, once again editing his paper under difficulties, and returned to England late in 1819 when the hue and cry against him had died down. Between 1820 and 1830 he rode horseback over most of the farm districts of England, observing and reporting the condition of farmers and crops wherever he went. These reports, published regularly in his* Political Register, *were gathered and published under the title of* Rural Rides, *in which guise the collection remains a treasury of detailed information on the rural England of Cobbett's time. With the passage of the Reform Bill in 1832, the old warrior was elected to Parliament from Oldham. Still in harness and firing away at his political opponents, he died of hard work and influenza June 18, 1835, in his seventy-third year.*

The curious thing is that Cobbett is best known today not for the vigor and even violence with which he attacked what he believed to be the political and economic evils of his time, but for his evident love of the soil and all growing things that he saw about him in his rural rides of old. There is a touch of irony in the fact that what he meant to be flaming political diatribes survive as pastoral literature. Note the reference to Gilbert White and Selborne, which Cobbett later visited on one of his rides.

November 24, 1822.
(Sunday.) From Hambledon to Thursley (*continued.*)

FROM East-Meon, I did not go on to Froxfield church, but
turned off to the left to a place (a couple of houses) called
Bower. Near this I stopped at a friend's house, which is in
about as lonely a situation as I ever saw. A very pleasant place
however. The lands dry, a nice mixture of woods and fields, and a
great variety of hill and dell.

Before I came to East-Meon, the soil of the hills was a shallow loam
with flints, on a bottom of chalk; but, on this side of the valley of
East-Meon that is to say, on the north side, the soil on the hills is a
deep, stiff loam, on a bed of a sort of gravel mixed with chalk; and
the stones, instead of being grey on the outside and blue on the inside, are yellow on the outside and whitish on the inside. In coming
on further to the North, I found that the bottom was sometimes gravel
and sometimes chalk. Here, at the time when *whatever it was* that
formed these hills and valleys, the stuff, of which Hindhead is composed, seems to have run down and mixed itself with the stuff of which
Old Winchester Hill is composed. Free chalk (which is the sort found
here) is excellent manure for stiff land, and it produces a complete
change in the nature of *clays*. It is therefore dug here, on the north
of East-Meon, about in the fields, where it happens to be found, and
is laid out upon the surface, where it is crumbled to powder by the
frost, and thus gets incorporated with the loam.

At Bower I got instructions to go to Hawkley, but accompanied
with most earnest advice not to go that way, for that it was impossible
to get along. The roads were represented as so bad; the floods so much
out; the hills and bogs so dangerous; that, really, I began to *doubt*;
and, if I had not been brought up amongst the clays of the Holt Forest
and the bogs of the neighbouring heaths, I should certainly have
turned off to my right, to go over Hindhead, great as was my objection
to going that way. "Well, then," said my friend at Bower, "If you *will*
go that way, by G——, you must go down *Hawkley Hanger;*" of which
he then gave me *such* a description! But, even this I found to fall
short of the reality. I inquired simply whether *people were in the habit*
of going down it; and the answer being in the affirmative, on I went
through green lanes and bridleways till I came to the turnpike-road
from Petersfield to Winchester, which I crossed, going into a narrow
and almost untrodden green-lane, on the side of which I found a cot-

tage. Upon my asking the way to *Hawkley*, the woman at the cottage said, "Right up the lane, Sir: you'll come to a *hanger* presently: you must take care, sir: you can't ride down: will your horses go *alone?*"

On we trotted up this pretty green lane; and, indeed, we had been coming gently and generally up hill for a good while. The lane was between highish banks and pretty high stuff growing on the banks, so that we could see no distance from us, and could receive not the smallest hint of what was so near at hand. The lane had a little turn towards the end; so that, out we came, all in a moment, at the very edge of the hanger! And, never, in all my life, was I so surprised and so delighted! I pulled up my horse, and sat and looked; and it was like looking from the top of a castle down into the sea, except that the valley was land and not water. I looked at my servant, to see what effect this unexpected sight had upon him. His surprise was as great as mine, though he had been bred amongst the North Hampshire hills. Those who had so strenuously dwelt on the dirt and dangers of this route, had said not a word about beauties, the matchless beauties of the scenery. These hangers are woods on the sides of very steep hills. The trees and underwood *hang*, in some sort, to the ground, instead of *standing on* it. Hence these places are called *Hangers*. From the summit of that which I had now to descend, I looked down upon the villages of Hawkley, Greatham, Selborne and some others.

From the south-east, round, southward, to the north-west, the main valley has cross-valleys running out of it, the hills on the sides of which are very steep, and, in many parts, covered with wood. The hills that form these cross-valleys run out into the main valley, like piers into the sea. Two of these promontories, of great height, are on the west side of the main valley, and were the first objects that struck my sight when I came to the edge of the hanger, which was on the south. The ends of these promontories are nearly perpendicular, and their tops so high in the air, that you cannot look at the village below without something like a feeling of apprehension. The leaves are all off, the hop-poles are in stack, the fields have little verdure; but, while the spot is beautiful beyond description even now, I must leave to imagination to suppose what it is, when the trees and hangers and hedges are in leaf, the corn waving, the meadows bright, and the hops upon the poles!

From the south-west, round, eastward, to the north, lie the *heaths*, of which Woolmer Forest makes a part, and these go gradually rising up to Hindhead, the crown of which is to the north-west, leaving the

rest of the circle (the part from north to north-west) to be occupied
by a continuation of the valley towards Headley, Binstead, Frensham
and the Holt Forest. So that even the *contrast* in the view from the
top of the hanger is as great as can possibly be imagined. Men, however, are not to have such beautiful views as this without some trouble.
We had had the view; but we had to go down the hanger. We had,
indeed, some roads to get along as well as we could, afterwards; but,
we had to get down the hanger first. The horses took the lead, and
crept partly down upon their feet, and partly upon their hocks. It was
extremely slippery too; for the soil is a sort of marl, or, as they call it
here, maume, or mame, which is, when wet, very much like *grey soap*.
In such a case it was likely that I should keep in the rear, which I
did, and I descended by taking hold of the branches of the underwood, and so letting myself down. When we got to the bottom, I bade
my man, when he should go back to Uphusband, tell the people there,
that *Ashmansworth Lane* is not the *worst* piece of road in the world.
Our worst, however, was not come yet, nor had we by any means seen
the most novel sights.

After crossing a little field and going through a farmyard, we came
into a lane, which was, at once, road and river. We found a hard bottom, however; and when we got out of the water, we got into a lane
with high banks. The banks were quarries of white stone, like Port-
land-stone, and the bed of the road was of the same stone; and the
rains having been heavy for a day or two before, the whole was as
clean and as white as the steps of a fund-holder or dead-weight doorway in one of the Squares of the *Wen*. Here were we, then, going
along a stone road with stone banks, and yet the underwood and trees
grew well upon the tops of the banks. In the solid stone beneath us,
there were a horse-track and wheel-tracts, the former about three, and
the latter about six inches deep. How many many ages it must have
taken the horses' feet, the wheels, and the water, to wear down this
stone, so as to form a hollow way! The horses seemed alarmed at their
situation; they trod with fear; but they took us along very nicely, and,
at last, got us safe into the indescribable dirt and mire of the road
from Hawkley Green to Greatham. Here the bottom of all the land
is this solid white stone, and the top is that *mame*, which I have before
described. The hop-roots penetrate down into this stone. How deep
the stone may be I know not; but, when I came to look up at the
end of one of the piers, or promontories, mentioned above, I found
that it was all of this same stone.

At Hawkley Green, I asked a farmer the way to Thursley. He pointed to one of two roads going from the green; but, it appearing to me, that that would lead me up to the London road and over Hindhead, I gave him to understand that I was resolved to get along, some how or other, through the "low countries." He besought me not to think of it. However, finding me resolved, he got a man to go a little way to put me into the Greatham road. The man came, but the farmer could not let me go off without renewing his entreaties, that I would go away to Liphook, in which entreaties the man joined, though he was to be paid very well for his trouble.

Off we went, however, to Greatham. I am thinking, whether I ever did see *worse* roads. Upon the whole, I think, I have; though I am not sure that the roads of New Jersey, between Trenton and Elizabeth-Town, at the breaking up of winter, be worse. Talk of *shows*, indeed! Take a piece of this road; just a cut across, and a rod long, and carry it up to London. That would be something like a *show!*

Upon leaving Greatham we came out upon Woolmer Forest. Just as we were coming out of Greatham, I asked a man the way to Thursley. "You *must* go to *Liphook*, Sir," said he. "But," I said, "I *will not* go to Liphook." These people seemed to be posted at all these stages, to turn me aside from my purpose, and to make me go over that *Hindhead*, which I had resolved to avoid. I went on a little further, and asked another man the way to Headley, which, as I have already observed, lies on the western foot of Hindhead, whence I knew there must be a road to Thursley (which lies at the North East foot) without going over that miserable hill. The man told me, that I must go across the *forest*. I asked him whether it was a *good* road: "It is a *sound* road," said he, laying a weighty emphasis upon the word *sound*. "Do people go it?" said I. "Ye-es," said he. "Oh then," said I, to my man, "as it is a *sound* road, keep you close to my heels, and do not attempt to go aside, not even for a foot." Indeed, it was a *sound* road. The rain of the night had made the fresh horse tracks visible. And we got to Headley in a short time, over a sand-road, which seemed so delightful after the flints and stone and dirt and sloughs that we had passed over and through since the morning. This road was not, if we had been benighted, without its dangers, the forest being full of quags and quicksands. This is a tract of Crown-lands, or, properly speaking, *public-lands*, on some parts of which our Land Steward, Mr. Huskis-son, is making some plantations of trees, partly fir, and partly other trees. What he can plant the *fir* for, God only knows, seeing that the country is already over-stocked with that rubbish. But, this *public-land* concern is a very great concern.

If I were a Member of Parliament I *would* know what timber has been cut down, and what it has been sold for, since year 1790. However, this matter must be *investigated*, first or last. It never can be omitted in the winding up of the concern; and that winding up must come out of wheat at four shillings a bushel. It is said, hereabouts, that a man who lives near Liphook, and who is so mighty a hunter and game pursuer, that they call him *William Rufus*; it is said that this man is *Lord of the Manor of Woolmer Forest*. This he cannot be without *a grant* to that effect; and, if there be a grant, there must have been a *reason* for the grant. This *reason* I should very much like to know; and this I would know, if I were a member of Parliament. That the people call him the *Lord of the Manor* is certain; but he can hardly make preserves of the plantations; for it is well known how marvellously *hares* and *young trees* agree together! This is a matter of great public importance; and yet, how, in the present state of things, is an *investigation* to be obtained? Is there a man in Parliament that will call for it? Not one. Would a dissolution of Parliament mend the matter? No: for the same men would be there still. They are the same men that have been there for these thirty years; and the *same men* they will be, and they *must be*, until there be *a reform*. To be sure, when one dies, or cuts his throat (as in the case of Castlereagh), another *one* comes; but it is the *same body*. And, as long as it is that same body, things will always go on as they now go on. However, as Mr. Canning says the body "*works well*," we must not say the contrary.

The soil of this tract is, generally, a black sand, which, in some places, becomes *peat*, which makes very tolerable fuel. In some parts there is clay at bottom; and there the *oaks* would grow; but not while there are *hares* in any number on the forest. If trees be to grow here, there ought to be no hares, and as little hunting as possible.

We got to Headley, the sign of the Holly-Bush, just at dusk, and just as it began to rain. I had neither eaten nor drunk since eight o'clock in the morning; and as it was a nice little public-house, I at first intended to stay all night, an intention that I afterwards very indiscreetly gave up. I had *laid my plan*, which included the getting to Thursley that night. When, therefore, I had got some cold bacon and bread, and some milk, I began to feel ashamed of stopping short of my *plan*, especially after having so heroically persevered in the "stern

path," and so disdainfully scorned to go over Hindhead. I knew that
my road lay through a hamlet called *Churt,* where they grow such fine
bennet-grass seed. There was a moon; but there was also a hazy rain.
I had heaths to go over, and I might go into quags. Wishing to execute
my plan, however, I at last brought myself to quit a very comfortable
turf-fire, and to set off in the rain, having bargained to give a man
three shillings to guide me out to the Northern foot of Hindhead.
I took care to ascertain that my guide knew the road perfectly well;
that is to say, I took care to ascertain it as far as I could, which was,
indeed, no farther than his word would go. Off we set, the guide
mounted on his own or master's horse, and with a white smock frock,
which enabled us to see him clearly. We trotted on pretty fast for
about half an hour: and I perceived, not without some surprise, that
the rain, which I knew to be coming from the *South,* met me full in
the face, when it ought, according to my reckoning, to have beat upon
my right cheek. I called to the guide repeatedly to ask him if he was
sure that he was right, to which he always answered "Oh! yes, Sir, I
know the road." I did not like this, *"I know the road."* At last, after
going about six miles in nearly a Southern direction, the guide turned
short to the left. That brought the rain upon my right cheek, and,
though I could not very well account for the long stretch to the South,
I thought, that, at any rate, we were *now* in the right track; and, after
going about a mile in this new direction, I began to ask the guide
how much further we had to go; for I had got a pretty good soaking,
and was rather impatient to see the foot of Hindhead. Just at this
time, in raising my head and looking forward as I spoke to the guide,
what should I see, but a long, high, and steep *hanger* arising before
us, the trees along the top of which I could easily distinguish! The
fact was, we were just getting to the outside of the heath, and were
on the brow of a steep hill, which faced this hanging wood. The guide
had begun to descend; and I had called to him to stop; for the hill
was so steep, that, rain as it did and wet as my saddle must be, I got
off my horse in order to walk down. But now, behold, the fellow discovered that he *had lost his way!*—Where we were I could not even
guess. There was but one remedy, and that was to get back, if we
could. I became guide now; and did as Mr. Western is advising the
Ministers to do, *retraced* my steps. We went back about half the way
that we had come, when we saw two men, who showed us the way
that we ought to go. At the end of about a mile, we fortunately found
the turnpike-road; not, indeed, at the *foot,* but on the *tip-top* of that

very Hindhead, on which I had so repeatedly *vowed* I would not go! We came out on the turnpike some hundred yards on the Liphook side of the buildings called *the Hut*; so that we had the whole of three miles of hill to come down at not much better than a foot pace, with a good pelting rain at our backs.

It is odd enough how differently one is affected by the same sight, under different circumstances. At the *"Holly Bush"* at Headley there was a room full of fellows in white smock frocks, drinking and smoking and talking, and I, who was then dry and warm, *moralized* within myself on their *folly* in spending their time in such a way. But, when I got down from Hindhead to the public-house at Road-Lane, with my skin soaking and my teeth chattering, I thought just such another group, whom I saw through the window sitting round a good fire with pipes in their mouths, the *wisest assembly* I had ever set my eyes on. A real *Collective Wisdom*. And I most solemnly declare, that I felt a greater veneration for them than I have ever felt even for the *Privy Council*, notwithstanding the Right Honourable Charles Wynn and the Right Honourable Sir John Sinclair belong to the latter.

It was now but a step to my friend's house, where a good fire and a change of clothes soon put all to rights, save and except the having come over Hindhead after all my resolutions. This mortifying circumstance; this having been *beaten*, lost the guide the *three shillings* that I had agreed to give him. "Either," said I, "you did not know the way well, or you did; if the former, it was dishonest in you to undertake to guide me: if the latter, you have wilfully led me miles out of my way." He grumbled; but off he went. He certainly deserved nothing; for he did not know the way, and he prevented some other man from earning and receiving the money. But, had he not caused me to *get upon Hindhead*, he would have had the three shillings. I had, at one time, got my hand in my pocket; but the thought of having been *beaten* pulled it out again.

Thus ended the most interesting day, as far as I know, that I ever passed in all my life. Hawkley-hangers, promontories, and stone-roads will always come into my mind when I see, or hear of, picturesque views. I forgot to mention, that, in going from Hawkley to Greatham, the man, who went to show me the way, told me at a certain fork, "that road goes to *Selborne*." This put me in mind of a book, which was once recommended to me, but which I never saw, entitled *"The History and Antiquities of Selborne,"* (or something of that sort) written, I think, by a parson of the name of *White*, brother of Mr. *White*,

so long a Bookseller in Fleet-street. This parson had, I think, the living
of the parish of Selborne. The book was mentioned to me as a work
of great curiosity and interest. But, at that time, the THING was biting
so very sharply that one had no attention to bestow on antiquarian
researches. Wheat at 39s. a quarter, and South-Down ewes at 12s. 6d.
have so weakened the THING's jaws and so filed down its teeth, that
I shall now certainly read this book if I can get it. By-the-bye if *all
the parsons* had, for the last thirty years, employed their leisure time
in writing the histories of their several parishes, instead of living, as
many of them have, engaged in pursuits that I need not here name,
neither their situation, nor that of their flocks would, perhaps, have
been the worse for it at this day.

THE CHAMBERED NAUTILUS

This is the ship of pearl, which, poets feign,
    Sails the unshadowed main,—
    The venturous bark that flings
On the sweet summer wind its purpled wings
In gulfs enchanted, where the Siren sings,
    And coral reefs lie bare,
Where the cold sea-maids rise to sun their streaming hair.

Its webs of living gauze no more unfurl;
    Wrecked is the ship of pearl!
    And every chambered cell,
Where its dim dreaming life was wont to dwell,
As the frail tenant shaped his growing shell,
    Before thee lies revealed,—
Its irised ceiling rent, its sunless crypt unsealed!

Year after year beheld the silent toil
    That spread his lustrous coil;
    Still, as the spiral grew,
He left the past year's dwelling for the new,
Stole with soft step its shining archway through,
    Built up its idle door,
Stretched in his last-found home, and knew the old no more.

Thanks for the heavenly message brought by thee,
     Child of the wandering sea,
     Cast from her lap, forlorn!
From thy dead lips a clearer note is born
Than ever Triton blew from wreathèd horn!
     While on mine ear it rings,
Through the deep caves of thought I hear a voice that sings—

Build thee more stately mansions, O my soul,
     As the swift seasons roll!
     Leave thy low-vaulted past!
Let each new temple, nobler than the last,
Shut thee from heaven with a dome more vast,
     Till thou at length art free,
Leaving thine outgrown shell by life's unresting sea!

OLIVER WENDELL HOLMES

CAPTURING A CAYMAN

by Charles Waterton

Charles Waterton was one of the landed gentry of England, and his handsome estate, Walton Hall in Yorkshire, where he was born June 3, 1782, served as a game preserve and wildlife sanctuary during his tenure of the ancestral acres. On one occasion he found that his gamekeeper had shot an owl, whereupon he threatened to strangle the man if he ever shot another. Early in life he went to British Guiana, where his family had a plantation on which coffee, sugar cane, and cotton were grown. The young man was high-spirited and adventurous to the point of rashness. He didn't care for plantation life. He longed to explore South American jungles. When he was thirty years old he plunged into the Brazilian wilderness to visit the native tribes that made the deadly poison, curare, with which they tipped their arrows. He discovered the vegetable source of the poison, how the natives manufactured it, and what ingredients were added to make it stick on the arrowheads. However, he was more interested in excitement than he was in science, and when he wrote or spoke of what he found or saw on his travels, he embellished the stories to the point where sober scientists wondered whether they were fact or fiction. The judgment of posterity seems to be that the stories were mostly fact, garnished with some lighthearted exaggeration. The reader can render his own verdict after perusing this piece concerning a wrestling bout with a sulky saurian, taken from Wanderings In South America, *which Waterton published in 1825.*

Aside from that, Waterton was at least slightly eccentric and often as hot-tempered as he was lighthearted. He quarreled with MacGillivray and Swainson, noted British scientists. When he visited the United States in 1824 he became acquainted with George Ord, who completed Alexander Wilson's work and was a

*rather violent partisan on Wilson's side in the famous dispute
with Audubon. Waterton, of course, jumped in because of Ord
and denounced Audubon later as an "ornithological imposter."
One thing in which Waterton was outstanding was taxidermy. He
devised a method of preparing and preserving specimens that was
a real benefit to collectors. He took "the pledge" as a youth,
never touched hard liquor, and, out of grief over the death of his
young wife in childbirth in 1830, never slept in a bed—he slept
on the floor—the remainder of his long life. He died on his
estate, Walton Hall, May 22, 1865, in his eighty-third year.*

I HAD long wished to examine the native haunts of the Cayman;
but as the river Demerara did not afford a specimen of the large
kind, I was obliged to go to the river Essequibo to look for one.
I got the canoe ready, and went down in it to George-town;
where, having put in the necessary articles for the expedition, not
forgetting a couple of large shark-hooks, with chains attached to them,
and a coil of strong new rope, I hoisted a little sail, which I had got
made on purpose, and at six o'clock in the morning shaped our course
for the river Essequibo. I had put a pair of shoes on to prevent the
tar at the bottom of the canoe from sticking to my feet. The sun was
flaming hot, and from eleven o'clock till two beat perpendicularly
upon the top of my feet, betwixt the shoes and the trousers. Not
feeling it disagreeable, or being in the least aware of painful consequences, as I had been barefoot for months, I neglected to put on a
pair of short stockings which I had with me. I did not reflect that sitting still in one place with your feet exposed to the sun was very different from being exposed to the sun while in motion.

We went ashore in the Essequibo, about three o'clock in the afternoon, to choose a place for the night's residence, to collect firewood,
and to set the fish-hooks. It was then that I first began to find my
legs very painful: they soon became much inflamed and red and
blistered; and it required considerable caution not to burst the blisters,
otherwise sores would have ensued. I immediately got into the hammock, and there passed a painful and sleepless night, and for two
days after I was disabled from walking.

About midnight, as I was lying awake, and in great pain, I heard the
Indian say, "Massa, massa, you no hear tiger?" I listened attentively,

and heard the softly sounding tread of his feet as he approached us. The moon had gone down; but every now and then we could get a glance of him by the light of our fire: he was the jaguar, for I could see the spots on his body. Had I wished to have fired at him, I was not able to take a sure aim, for I was in such pain that I could not turn myself in my hammock. The Indian would have fired, but I would not allow him to do so, as I wanted to see a little more of our new visitor; for it is not every day or night that the traveller is favoured with an undisturbed sight of the jaguar in his own forests.

Whenever the fire got low, the jaguar came a little nearer, and when the Indian renewed it, he retired abruptly; sometimes he would come within twenty yards, and then we had a view of him, sitting on his hind legs like a dog; sometimes he moved slowly to and fro, and at other times we could hear him mend his pace, as if impatient. At last the Indian, not relishing the idea of having such company in the neighbourhood, could contain himself no longer, and set up a most tremendous yell. The jaguar bounded off like a race-horse, and returned no more; it appeared by the print of his feet the next morning that he was a full-grown jaguar.

About an hour before sunset, we reached the place which the two men who had joined us at the falls pointed out as a proper one to find a Cayman. There was a large creek close by, and a sand-bank gently sloping to the water. Just within the forest on this bank, we cleared a place of brushwood, suspended the hammocks from the trees, and then picked up enough of decayed wood for fuel.

We now baited a shark-hook with a large fish, and put it upon a board about a yard long, and one foot broad, which we had brought on purpose. This board was carried out in the canoe, about forty yards into the river. By means of a string, long enough to reach the bottom of the river, and at the end of which string was fastened a stone, the board was kept, as it were, at anchor. One end of the new rope I had bought in town was reeved through the chain of the shark-hook, and the other end fastened to a tree on the sand-bank.

It was now an hour after sunset. The sky was cloudless, and the moon shone beautifully bright. There was not a breath of wind in the heavens, and the river seemed like a large plain of quicksilver. Every now and then a huge fish would strike and plunge in the water; then the owls and goatsuckers would continue their lamentations, and the

sound of these was lost in the prowling tiger's growl. Then all was
still again, and silent as midnight.

The caymen were now upon the stir, and at intervals their noise
could be distinguished amid that of the jaguar, the owls, the goatsuckers, and frogs. It was a singular and awful sound. It was like a
suppressed sigh, bursting forth all of a sudden, and so loud that you
might hear it above a mile off. First one emitted this horrible noise,
and then another answered him; and on looking at the countenances
of the people around me, I could plainly see that they expected to
have a cayman that night.

We were at supper, when the Indian, who seemed to have had one
eye on the turtle-pot and the other on the bait in the river, said he
saw the cayman coming.

Upon looking towards the place, there appeared something on the
water like a black log of wood. It was so unlike anything alive, that I
doubted if it were a cayman; but the Indian smiled, and said he was
sure it was one, for he remembered seeing a cayman, some years ago,
when he was in the Essequibo.

At last it gradually approached the bait, and the board began to
move. The moon shone so bright that we could distinctly see him
open his huge jaws, and take in the bait. We pulled the rope. He
immediately let drop the bait; and then we saw his black head retreating from the board, to the distance of a few yards, and there it
remained quite motionless.

He did not seem inclined to advance again; and so we finished our
supper. In about an hour's time he again put himself in motion, and
took hold of the bait. But, probably, suspecting that he had to deal
with knaves and cheats, he held it in his mouth but did not swallow
it. We pulled the rope again, but with no better success than the first
time.

He retreated as usual, and came back again in about an hour. We
paid him every attention till three o'clock in the morning; when, worn
out with disappointment, we went to the hammocks, turned in, and
fell asleep.

When day broke, we found that he had contrived to get the bait
from the hook, though we had tied it on with string. We had now no
more hopes of taking a cayman till the return of night.

The second night's attempt upon the cayman was a repetition of the
first, quite unsuccessful. We went a-fishing the day after, had excellent
sport, and returned to experience a third night's disappointment. We

spent the best part of the fourth night in trying for the cayman, but all to no purpose. I was now convinced that something was materially wrong. We ought to have been successful, considering our vigilance and attention, and that we had repeatedly seen the cayman. It was useless to tarry here any longer; moreover, the coloured man began to take airs, and fancied that I could not do without him. I never admit of this in any expedition where I am commander; and so I convinced the man, to his sorrow, that I could do without him; for I paid him what I had agreed to give him, which amounted to eight dollars, and ordered him back in his own curial to Mrs. Peterson's, on the hill at the first falls. I then asked the negro if there were any Indian settlements in the neighbourhood; he said he knew of one, a day and a half off. We went in quest of it, and about one o'clock the next day the negro showed us the creek where it was.

The entrance was so concealed by thick bushes that a stranger would have passed it without knowing it to be a creek. In going up it we found it dark, winding, and intricate beyond any creek that I had ever seen before.

When we had got about two-thirds up it, we met the Indians going a-fishing. I saw, by the way their things were packed in the curial, that they did not intend to return for some days. However, on telling them what we wanted, and by promising handsome presents of powder, shot, and hooks, they dropped their expedition, and invited us up to the settlement they had just left, and where we laid in a provision of cassava.

After resting here, we went back to the river. The Indians, three in number, accompanied us in their own curial, and, on entering the river, pointed to a place a little way above, well calculated to harbour a cayman. The water was deep and still, and flanked by an immense sand-bank; there was also a little shallow creek close by.

On this sand-bank, near the forest, the people made a shelter for the night. My own was already made; for I always take with me a painted sheet, about twelve feet by ten. This, thrown over a pole, supported betwixt two trees, makes you a capital roof with very little trouble.

We showed one of the Indians the shark-hook. He shook his head and laughed at it, and said it would not do. When he was a boy, he had seen his father catch the caymen, and on the morrow he would make something that would answer.

In the meantime, we set the shark-hook, but it availed us nought; a cayman came and took it, but would not swallow it.

Seeing it was useless to attend the shark-hook any longer, we left it for the night, and returned to our hammocks.

Ere I fell asleep, a reflection or two broke in upon me. I considered, that as far as the judgment of civilized man went, everything had been procured and done to ensure success. We had hooks, and lines, and baits, and patience; we had spent nights in watching, had seen the cayman come and take the bait, and after our expectations had been wound up to the highest pitch, all ended in disappointment. Probably this poor wild man of the woods would succeed by means of a very simple process; and thus prove to his more civilized brother that, notwithstanding books and schools, there is a vast deal of knowledge to be picked up at every step, whichever way we turn ourselves.

In the morning, as usual, we found the bait gone from the shark-hook. The Indians went into the forest to hunt, and we took the canoe to shoot fish and get another supply of turtle's eggs, which we found in great abundance on this large sand-bank.

We went to the little shallow creek, and shot some young caymen, about two feet long. It was astonishing to see what spite and rage these little things showed when the arrow struck them; they turned round and bit it, and snapped at us when we went into the water to take them up. Daddy Quashi boiled one of them for his dinner, and found it very sweet and tender. I do not see why it should not be as good as frog or veal.

The day was now declining apace, and the Indian had made his instrument to take the cayman. It was very simple. There were four pieces of tough hard wood, a foot long, and about as thick as your little finger, and barbed at both ends; they were tied round the end of the rope, in such a manner, that if you conceive the rope to be an arrow, these four sticks would form the arrow's head; so that one end of the four united sticks answered to the point of the arrow-head, while the other ends of the sticks expanded at equal distances round the rope. Now it is evident, that if the cayman swallowed this (the other end of the rope, which was thirty yards long, being fastened to a tree), the more he pulled, the faster the barbs would stick into his stomach. This wooden hook, if you may so call it, was well baited with the flesh of the acouri, and the entrails were twisted round the rope for about a foot above it.

Nearly a mile from where we had our hammocks, the sand-bank was steep and abrupt, and the river very still and deep; there the Indian pricked a stick into the sand. It was two feet long, and on its extremity was fixed the machine; it hung suspended about a foot from the water, and the end of the rope was made fast to a stake driven well into the sand.

The Indian then took the empty shell of a land tortoise and gave it some heavy blows with an axe. I asked him why he did that. He said it was to let the cayman hear that something was going on. In fact the Indian meant it as the cayman's dinner-bell.

Having done this, we went back to the hammocks, not intending to visit it again till morning. During the night, the jaguars roared and grumbled in the forest, as though the world was going wrong with them, and at intervals we could hear the distant cayman. The roaring of the jaguars was awful; but it was music to the dismal noise of these hideous and malicious reptiles.

About half-past five in the morning, the Indian stole off silently to take a look at the bait. On arriving at the place he set up a tremendous shout. We all jumped out of our hammocks, and ran to him. The Indians got there before me, for they had no clothes to put on, and I lost two minutes in looking for my trousers and in slipping into them.

We found a cayman, ten feet and a half long, fast to the end of the rope. Nothing now remained to do, but to get him out of the water without injuring his scales, "hoc opus, hic labor." We mustered strong: there were three Indians from the creek, there was my own Indian Yan, Daddy Quashi, the negro from Mrs. Peterson's, James, Mr. R. Edmonstone's man, whom I was instructing to preserve birds, and lastly, myself.

I informed the Indians that it was my intention to draw him quietly out of the water, and then secure him. They looked and stared at each other, and said I might do it myself; but they would have no hand in it; the cayman would worry some of us. On saying this, "consedere duces," they squatted on their hams with the most perfect indifference.

The Indians of these wilds have never been subject to the least restraint; and I knew enough of them to be aware, that if I tried to force them against their will, they would take off, and leave me and my presents unheeded and never return.

Daddy Quashi was for applying to our guns, as usual, considering them our best and safest friends. I immediately offered to knock him down for his cowardice, and he shrunk back, begging that I would be cautious, and not get myself worried; and apologizing for his own want of resolution. My Indian was now in conversation with the others, and they asked if I would allow them to shoot a dozen arrows into him, and thus disable him. This would have ruined all. I had come above three hundred miles on purpose to get a cayman uninjured, and not to carry back a mutilated specimen. I rejected their proposition with firmness, and darted a disdainful eye upon the Indians.

Daddy Quashi was again beginning to remonstrate, and I chased him on the sand-bank for a quarter of a mile. He told me afterwards, he thought he should have dropped down dead with fright, for he was firmly persuaded, if I had caught him, I should have bundled him into the cayman's jaws. Here then we stood, in silence, like a calm before a thunder-storm. "Hoc res summa loco. Scinditur in contraria vulgus." They wanted to kill him, and I wanted to take him alive.

I now walked up and down the sand, revolving a dozen projects in my head. The canoe was at a considerable distance, and I ordered the people to bring it round to the place where we were. The mast was eight feet long, and not much thicker than my wrist. I took it out of the canoe, and wrapped the sail round the end of it. Now it appeared clear to me that if I went down upon one knee, and held the mast in the same position as the soldier holds his bayonet when rushing to the charge, I could force it down the cayman's throat, should he come open-mouthed at me. When this was told to the Indians, they brightened up, and said they would help me to pull him out of the river.

"Brave squad!" said I to myself, "'Audax omnia perpeti,' now that you have got me betwixt yourselves and danger." I then mustered all hands for the last time before the battle. We were, four South American savages, two negroes from Africa, a creole from Trinidad, and myself a white man from Yorkshire. In fact, a little tower of Babel group, in dress, no dress, address, and language.

Daddy Quashi hung in the rear; I showed him a large Spanish knife, which I always carried in the waistband of my trousers: it spoke volumes to him, and he shrugged up his shoulders in absolute despair. The sun was just peeping over the high forests on the eastern hills, as if coming to look on, and bid us act with becoming fortitude. I placed all the people at the end of the rope, and ordered them to pull till the cayman appeared on the surface of the water; and then, should he plunge, to slacken the rope and let him go again into the deep.

I now took the mast of the canoe in my hand (the sail being tied round the end of the mast) and sunk down upon one knee, about four yards from the water's edge, determining to thrust it down his throat, in case he gave me an opportunity. I certainly felt somewhat uncomfortable in this situation, and I thought of Cerberus on the other side of the Styx ferry. The people pulled the cayman to the surface; he plunged furiously as soon as he arrived in these upper regions, and immediately went below again on their slackening the rope. I saw enough not to fall in love at first sight. I now told them we would run all risks, and have him on land immediately. They pulled again, and out he came,—"monstrum horrendum, informe." This was an interesting moment. I kept my position firmly, with my eye fixed steadfast on him.

By this time the cayman was within two yards of me. I saw he was in a state of fear and perturbation; I instantly dropped the mast, sprang up, and jumped on his back, turning half round as I vaulted, so that I gained my seat with my face in a right position. I immediately seized his forelegs, and, by main force, twisted them on his back; thus they served me for a bridle.

He now seemed to have recovered from his surprise, and probably fancying himself in hostile company, he began to plunge furiously, and lashed the sand with his long and powerful tail. I was out of reach of the strokes of it, by being near his head. He continued to plunge and strike, and made my seat very uncomfortable. It must have been a fine sight for an unoccupied spectator.

The people roared out in triumph, and were so vociferous, that it was some time before they heard me tell them to pull me and my beast of burden farther inland. I was apprehensive the rope might break, and then there would have been every chance of going down to the regions under water with the cayman.

The people now dragged us above forty yards on the sand: it was the first and last time I was ever on a cayman's back. Should it be asked, how I managed to keep my seat, I would answer,—I hunted some years with Lord Darlington's fox-hounds.

After repeated attempts to regain his liberty, the cayman gave in, and became tranquil through exhaustion. I now managed to tie up his jaws, and firmly secured his fore-feet in the position I had held them. We had now another severe struggle for superiority, but he was soon overcome and again remained quiet. While some of the people were pressing upon his head and shoulders, I threw myself on his tail, and by keeping it down to the sand, prevented him from kicking up another dust. He was finally conveyed to the canoe, and then to the place where we had suspended our hammocks. There I cut his throat; and, after breakfast was over, commenced the dissection.

The back of the cayman may be said to be almost impenetrable to a musket-ball, but his sides are not near so strong, and are easily pierced with an arrow; indeed, were they as strong as the back and the belly, there would be no part of the cayman's body soft and elastic enough to admit of expansion after taking in a supply of food.

The cayman has no grinders; his teeth are entirely made for snatch and swallow; there are thirty-two in each jaw. Perhaps no animal in existence bears more decided marks in his countenance of cruelty and malice than the cayman. He is the scourge and terror of all the large rivers in South America near the line.

I was a day and a half in dissecting our cayman, and then we all got ready to return to Demerara.

THE EAGLE

He clasps the crag with hookèd hands:
Close to the sun in lonely lands,
Ring'd with the azure world, he stands.

The wrinkled sea beneath him crawls;
He watches from his mountain walls,
And like a thunderbolt he falls.

ALFRED TENNYSON

THE GREAT BIRD OF PARADISE

by Alfred Russel Wallace

The name Alfred Russel Wallace inevitably brings to mind one of the most remarkable coincidences in human history. When Charles Darwin, in June, 1858, was preparing a paper setting forth his famous theory of natural selection, he received by mail from the far-off Moluccas a treatise setting forth his own theory in almost identical terms. Darwin was thunderstruck. Two men half a world apart had come to an epoch-making conclusion in the field of science at the same time. One of them was lying fever-ridden in the Moluccas. The other was to present his theory in a paper to be read before the Linnaean Society of London on July 1, 1858. On the advice of some of the "elder statesmen" of science to whom Darwin revealed the news, the theory was presented on the date scheduled but it was offered to the Linnaean Society as a "joint paper" by Darwin and Wallace. Darwin gave Wallace equal credit. Posterity has denied it to him.

Wallace was born in Usk, Monmouthshire, England, January 8, 1823. He was an engineer and architect by training, but he turned from that to natural history and went off with H. W. Bates to explore the jungles of South America. In 1853 he published a book on his travels along the Amazon. Then he went off to the Malay Archipelago and wandered that region for eight years. The literary result was another book, titled The Malay Archipelago, *published in 1869. The account of the great bird of paradise is taken from that book. The world traveler finally settled down in his native England, and in his old age—he lived to be ninety—he dismayed some of his scientific cronies by turning to spiritualism. He died at Broadstone, in Dorset, November 7, 1913.*

THE Great Bird of Paradise (*Paradisea apoda* of Linnaeus) is the largest species known, being generally seventeen or eighteen inches from the beak to the tip of the tail. The body, wings, and tail are of a rich coffee-brown, which deepens on the breast to a blackish-violet or purple-brown. The whole top of the head and neck is of an exceedingly delicate straw-yellow, the feathers being short and close set, so as to resemble plush or velvet; the lower part of the throat up to the eye is clothed with scaly feathers of an emerald green color, and with a rich metallic gloss, and velvety plumes of a still deeper green extend in a band across the forehead and chin as far as the eye, which is bright yellow. The beak is pale lead blue; and the feet, which are rather large and very strong and well formed, are of a pale ashy-pink. The two middle feathers of the tail have no webs, except a very small one at the base and at the extreme tip, forming wire-like cirrhi, which spread out in an elegant double curve, and vary from twenty-four to thirty-four inches long. From each side of the body, beneath the wings, springs a dense tuft of long and delicate plumes, sometimes two feet in length of the most intense golden-orange color and very glossy, but changing toward the tips into a pale brown. This tuft of plumage can be elevated and spread out at pleasure, so as almost to conceal the body of the bird.

These splendid ornaments are entirely confined to the male sex, while the female is really a very plain and ordinary-looking bird of a uniform coffee-brown color which never changes; neither does she possess the long tail wires, nor a single yellow or green feather about the head.

The Great Bird of Paradise is very active and vigorous, and seems to be in constant motion all day long. It is very abundant, small flocks of females and young males being constantly met with; and though the full-plumaged birds are less plentiful, their loud cries, which are heard daily, show that they also are very numerous. Their note is "Wawk-wawk-wawk—Wŏk, wŏk-wŏk," and is so loud and shrill as to be heard a great distance, and to form the most prominent and characteristic animal sound in the Aru Islands. The mode of nidification is unknown; but the natives told me that the nest was formed of leaves placed on an ant's nest, or on some projecting limb of a very lofty tree, and they believe that it contains only one young bird. The egg is quite unknown, and the natives declared they had never seen it; and a very high reward offered for one by a Dutch official did not meet with success. They moult about January or February, and in May, when they are in full plumage, the males assemble early in the morning to exhibit themselves in dancing-parties, in certain trees in the forest, which are not fruit-trees, as I at first imagined, but which have an immense head of spreading branches and large but scattered leaves, giving a clear space for the birds to play and exhibit their plumes. On one of these trees a dozen or twenty full-plumaged male birds assemble together, raise up their wings, stretch out their necks, and elevate their exquisite plumes, keeping them in a continual vibration. Between whiles they fly across from branch to branch in great excitement, so that the whole tree is filled with waving plumes in every variety of attitude and motion. The bird itself is nearly as large as a crow, and is of a rich coffee-brown color. The head and neck is of a pure straw yellow above, and rich metallic green beneath. The long plumy tufts of golden-orange feathers spring from the sides beneath each wing, and when the bird is in repose are partly concealed by them. At the time of its excitement, however, the wings are raised vertically over the back, the head is bent down and stretched out, and the long plumes are raised up and expanded till they form two magnificent golden fans, striped with deep red at the base, and fading off into the pale brown tint of the finely divided and softly waving points. The whole bird is then overshadowed by them, the crouching body, yellow head, and emerald-green throat forming but the foundation and setting to the golden glory which waves above. When seen in this attitude, the bird of paradise really deserves its name, and must be ranked as one of the most beautiful and most wonderful of living things.

This habit enables the native to obtain specimens with comparative ease. As soon as they find that the birds have fixed upon a tree on which to assemble, they build a little shelter of palm leaves in a convenient place among the branches, and the hunter ensconces himself in it before daylight, armed with his bow and a number of arrows terminating in a round knob. A boy waits at the foot of the tree, and when the birds come at sunrise, and a sufficient number have assembled, and have begun to dance, the hunter shoots with his blunt arrow so strongly as to stun the bird, which drops down, and is secured and killed by the boy without its plumage being injured by a drop of blood. The rest take no notice, and fall one after another till some of them take the alarm.

The native mode of preserving them is to cut off the wings and feet, and then skin the body up to the beak, taking out the skull. A stout stick is then run up through the specimen coming out at the mouth. Round this some leaves are stuffed, and the whole is wrapped up in a palm spathe and dried in the smoky hut. By this plan the head, which is really large, is shrunk up almost to nothing, the body is much reduced and shortened, and the greater prominence is given to the flowing plumage. Some of these native skins are very clean, and often have wings and feet left on; others are dreadfully stained with smoke, and all give a most erroneous idea of the proportions of the living bird.

The true paradise birds are omnivorous, feeding on fruits and in-sects—of the former preferring the small figs; of the latter, grasshop-pers, locusts, and phasmas, as well as cockroaches and caterpillars. When I returned home, in 1862, I was so fortunate as to find two adult males of this species in Singapore; and as they seemed healthy, and fed voraciously on rice, bananas, and cockroaches, I determined on giving the very high price asked for them—£100—and to bring them to England by the overland route under my own care. On my way home I staid a week at Bombay, to break the journey, and to lay in a fresh stock of bananas for my birds. I had great difficulty, however, in supplying them with insect food, for in the Peninsular and Oriental steamers cockroaches were scarce, and it was only by setting traps in the storerooms, and by hunting an hour every night in the forecastle, that I could secure a few dozen of these creatures—scarcely enough for a single meal. At Malta, where I staid a fortnight, I got plenty of cockroaches from a bakehouse, and when I left, took with me several biscuit-tins full, as provision for the voyage home. We came through the Mediterranean in March, with a very cold wind; and the only place on board the mail-steamer where their large cage could be accommo-dated was exposed to a strong current of air down a hatchway which stood open day and night, yet the birds never seemed to feel the cold. During the night journey from Marseilles to Paris it was a sharp frost; yet they arrived in London in perfect health, and lived in the Zoölogical Gardens for one, and two years, often displaying their beautiful plumes to the admiration of the spectators.

TIERRA DEL FUEGO

by Charles Darwin

The uncivil war that disrupted British social, scientific, and religious circles upon the announcement of what is loosely called "the Darwinian Theory" in 1858 has died away to less than a whisper of debate now, but one curious aftermath of the fighting was that it fixed Darwin in mind as a "theorist" only, and obscured the fact that his five-year, globe-circling trip on the good ship Beagle, *1831 to 1836, entitled him to rank as one of the great collectors and field naturalists of history.*

It's true that he was a thinker and a deep one, and the theory that he put forward in his work On the Origin of Species by Means of Natural Selection *meant a complete break with the past and proposed a new outlook on biology in the future, but all this was based on observations he had made and evidence he had gathered as he went from continent to continent, from ocean to ocean, from coast to coast, and from island to island on his long voyage. The notes that he made aboard ship and the reports he sent back from time to time have been sifted often and published in annotated form in different editions under the title of* The Voyage of the Beagle. *The selection that follows is taken from Darwin's account of the natives of Tierra del Fuego. The characters York Minster and Jemmy Button mentioned in the text were Fuegians who had been captured and carried to England some years earlier and were being returned to their native country aboard the* Beagle.

December 21st. (1832)

THE *Beagle* got under weigh: and on the succeeding day, favoured to an uncommon degree by a fine easterly breeze, we closed in with the Barnevelts, and running past Cape Deceit with its stony peaks, about three o'clock doubled the weather-beaten Cape Horn. The evening was calm and bright, and we enjoyed a fine view of the surrounding isles. Cape Horn, however, demanded his tribute, and before night sent us a gale of wind directly in our teeth. We stood out to sea, and on the second day again made the land, when we saw on our weather-bow this notorious promontory in its proper form—veiled in a mist, and its dim outline surrounded by a storm of wind and water. Great black clouds were rolling across the heavens, and squalls of rain, with hail, swept by us with such extreme violence, that the Captain determined to run into Wigwam Cove. This is a snug little harbour, not far from Cape Horn; and here, at Christmas-eve, we anchored in smooth water. The only thing which reminded us of the gale outside, was every now and then a puff from the mountains, which made the ship surge at her anchors.

December 25th.—Close by the cove, a pointed hill, called Kater's Peak, rises to the height of 1700 feet. The surrounding islands all consist of conical masses of greenstone, associated sometimes with less regular hills of baked and altered clay-slate. This part of Tierra del Fuego may be considered as the extremity of the submerged chain of mountains already alluded to. The cove takes its name of "Wigwam" from some of the Fuegian habitations; but every bay in the neighbourhood might be so called with equal propriety. The inhabitants, living chiefly upon shell-fish, are obliged constantly to change their place of residence; but they return at intervals to the same spots, as is evident from the piles of old shells, which must often amount to many tons in weight. These heaps can be distinguished at a long distance by the bright green colour of certain plants, which invariably grow on them. Among these may be enumerated the wild celery and scurvy grass, two very serviceable plants, the use of which has not been discovered by the natives.

The Fuegian wigwam resembles, in size and dimensions, a haycock. It merely consists of a few broken branches stuck in the ground, and very imperfectly thatched on one side with a few tufts of grass and rushes. The whole cannot be the work of an hour, and it is only used for a few days. At Goeree Roads I saw a place where one of these naked men had slept, which absolutely offered no more cover than the form of a hare. The man was evidently living by himself, and York Minster said he was "very bad man," and that probably he had stolen something. On the west coast, however, the wigwams are rather better, for they are covered with sealskins. We were detained here several days by the bad weather. The climate is certainly wretched: the summer solstice was now passed, yet every day snow fell on the hills, and in the valleys there was rain, accompanied by sleet. The thermometer generally stood about 45°, but in the night fell to 38° or 40°. From the damp and boisterous state of the atmosphere, not cheered by a gleam of sunshine, one fancied the climate even worse than it really was.

While going one day on shore near Wollaston Island, we pulled alongside a canoe with six Fuegians. These were the most abject and miserable creatures I anywhere beheld. On the east coast the natives, as we have seen, have guanaco cloaks, and on the west, they possess sealskins. Amongst these central tribes the men generally have an otter-skin, or some small scrap about as large as a pocket-handkerchief, which is barely sufficient to cover their backs as low down as their loins. It is laced across the breast by strings, and according as the wind blows, it is shifted from side to side. But these Fuegians in the canoe were quite naked, and even one full-grown woman was absolutely so. It was raining heavily, and the fresh water, together with the spray, trickled down her body. In another harbour not far distant, a woman, who was suckling a recently-born child, came one day alongside the vessel, and remained there out of mere curiosity, whilst the sleet fell and thawed on her naked bosom, and on the skin of her naked baby! These poor wretches were stunted in their growth, their hideous faces bedaubed with white paint, their skins filthy and greasy, their hair entangled, their voices discordant, and their gestures violent. Viewing such men, one can hardly make oneself believe that they are fellow-creatures, and inhabitants of the same world. It is a common subject of conjecture what pleasure in life some of the lower animals can enjoy: how much more reasonably the same question may be asked with respect to these barbarians! At night, five or six human beings, naked and scarcely protected from the wind and rain of this tempestuous climate, sleep on the wet ground coiled up like animals. Whenever it is low water, winter or summer, night or day, they must rise to pick shell-fish from the rocks; and the women either dive to collect sea-eggs, or sit patiently in their canoes, and with a baited hair-line without any hook, jerk out little fish. If a seal is killed, or the floating carcass of a putrid whale is discovered, it is a feast; and such miserable food is assisted by a few tasteless berries and fungi.

They often suffer from famine: I heard Mr. Low, a sealing-master intimately acquainted with the natives of this country, give a curious account of the state of a party of one hundred and fifty natives on the west coast, who were very thin and in great distress. A succession of gales prevented the women from getting shell-fish on the rocks, and they could not go out in their canoes to catch seal. A small party of these men one morning set out, and the other Indians explained to him, that they were going a four days' journey for food: on their return, Low went to meet them, and he found them excessively tired, each man carrying a great square piece of putrid whales-blubber with a hole in the middle, through which they put their heads, like the Gauchos do through their ponchos or cloaks. As soon as the blubber was brought into a wigwam, an old man cut off thin slices, and muttering over them, broiled them for a minute, and distributed them to the famished party, who during this time preserved a profound silence. Mr. Low believes that whenever a whale is cast on shore, the natives bury large pieces of it in the sand, as a resource in time of famine; and a native boy, whom he had on board, once found a stock thus buried. The different tribes when at war are cannibals. From the concurrent, but quite independent evidence of the boy taken by Mr. Low, and of Jemmy Button, it is certainly true, that when pressed in winter by hunger, they kill and devour their old women before they kill their dogs: the boy, being asked by Mr. Low why they did this, answered, "Doggies catch otters, old women no." This boy described the manner in which they are killed by being held over smoke and thus choked; he imitated their screams as a joke, and described the parts of their bodies which are considered best to eat. Horrid as such a death by the hands of their friends and relatives must be, the fears of the old women, when hunger begins to press, are more painful to think of; we were told that they then often run away into the mountains, but that they are pursued by the men and brought back to the slaughter-house at their own fire-sides!

Captain Fitz Roy could never ascertain that the Fuegians have any distinct belief in a future life. They sometimes bury their dead in caves, and sometimes in the mountain forests; we do not know what ceremonies they perform. Jemmy Button would not eat land-birds, because "eat dead men:" they are unwilling even to mention their dead friends. We have no reason to believe that they perform any sort of religious worship; though perhaps the muttering of the old man before he distributed the putrid blubber to his famished party, may be of this nature. Each family or tribe has a wizard or conjuring doctor, whose office we could never clearly ascertain. Jemmy believed in dreams, though not, as I have said, in the devil: I do not think that our Fuegians were much more superstitious than some of the sailors;

for an old quarter-master firmly believed that the successive heavy gales, which we encountered off Cape Horn, were caused by our having the Fuegians on board. The nearest approach to a religious feeling which I heard of, was shown by York Minster, who, when Mr. Bynoe shot some very young ducklings as specimens, declared in the most solemn manner, "Oh Mr. Bynoe, much rain, snow, blow much." This was evidently a retributive punishment for wasting human food. In a wild and excited manner he also related, that his brother, one day whilst returning to pick up some dead birds which he had left on the coast, observed some feathers blown by the wind. His brother said (York imitating his manner), "What that?" and crawling onwards, he peeped over the cliff, and saw "wild man" picking his birds; he crawled a little nearer, and then hurled down a great stone and killed him. York declared for a long time afterwards storms raged, and much rain and snow fell. As far as we could make out, he seemed to consider the elements themselves as the avenging agents: it is evident in this case, how naturally, in a race a little more advanced in culture, the elements would become personified. What the "bad wild men" were, has always appeared to me most mysterious: from what York said, when we found the place like the form of a hare, where a single man had slept the night before, I should have thought that they were thieves who had been driven from their tribes; but other obscure speeches made me doubt this; I have sometimes imagined that the most probable explanation was that they were insane.

The different tribes have no government or chief; yet each is surrounded by other hostile tribes, speaking different dialects, and separated from each other only by a deserted border or neutral territory: the cause of their warfare appears to be the means of subsistence. Their country is a broken mass of wild rocks, lofty hills, and useless forests: and these are viewed through mists and endless storms. The habitable land is reduced to the stones on the beach; in search of food they are compelled unceasingly to wander from spot to spot, and so steep is the coast, that they can only move about in their wretched canoes. They cannot know the feeling of having a home, and still less that of domestic affection; for the husband is to the wife a brutal master to a laborious slave. Was a more horrid deed ever perpetrated, than that witnessed on the west coast by Byron, who saw a wretched mother pick up her bleeding dying infant-boy, whom her husband had mercilessly dashed on the stones for dropping a basket of sea-eggs! How little can the higher powers of the mind be brought into play:

what is there for imagination to picture, for reason to compare, for judgment to decide upon? to knock a limpet from the rock does not require even cunning, that lowest power of the mind. Their skill in some respects may be compared to the instinct of animals; for it is not improved by experience: the canoe, their most ingenious work, poor as it is, has remained the same, as we know from Drake, for the last two hundred and fifty years.

Whilst beholding these savages, one asks, whence have they come? What could have tempted, or what change compelled a tribe of men, to leave the fine regions of the north, to travel down the Cordillera or backbone of America, to invent and build canoes, which are not used by the tribes of Chile, Peru, and Brazil, and then to enter on one of the most inhospitable countries within the limits of the globe? Although such reflections must at first seize on the mind, yet we may feel sure that they are partly erroneous. There is no reason to believe that the Fuegians decrease in number; therefore we must suppose that they enjoy a sufficient share of happiness, of whatever kind it may be, to render life worth having. Nature by making habit omnipotent, and its effects hereditary, has fitted the Fuegian to the climate and the productions of his miserable country.

THE KING OF THE VIPERS

by George Borrow

George Borrow, traveler, linguist, author, was born in Dere-ham, a town in Norfolk, England, July 5, 1803. At the age of twenty-one he went up to London to try his hand at free-lance writing and found it hard going. After two years of desperate ef-fort without much success, he took to the road in gypsy fashion. He made friends with gypsies, camped with them, studied their language and customs, and eventually wrote books about them, their language, and their literature. Even in his famous novels, Lavengro *and* The Romany Rye, *which are partly autobiographi-cal, he incorporated much gypsy lore that he gained through traveling the countryside with members of the tribe.*

Borrow was more than six feet tall and something of an ath-lete. He was a fine horseman as well as a great walker, and his writings indicate that he was well up on boxing. He was a self-taught scholar who lived and wrote with vigor, made positive statements, and offered many dissenting opinions. He was, in addition, courageous and adventurous. He took a job as book agent for the Bible Society and traveled—mostly on horseback—through Spain, Portugal, and Morocco hawking his wares. Any "heretic" peddling Protestant bibles in Catholic Spain circa 1837 needed courage and was bound to run into sundry difficulties and stirring adventures. He described all this in his book The Bible in Spain, *published in 1843, and it made him famous. However, his reputation rests largely on* Lavengro, *from which the selec-tion offered below is taken, and on* The Romany Rye. *Under separate titles, these books are really one entrancing story of George Borrow and his gypsy friends. Borrow died at Oulton, England, July 26, 1881.*

IT was midsummer when we arrived at this place, and the weather, which had for a long time been wet and gloomy, now became bright and glorious; I was subjected to but little control, and passed my time pleasantly enough, principally in wandering about the neighbouring country. It was flat and somewhat fenny, a district more of pasture than agriculture, and not very thickly inhabited. I soon became well acquainted with it. At the distance of two miles from the station was a large lake, styled in the dialect of the country "a mere," about whose borders tall reeds were growing in abundance, this was a frequent haunt of mine; but my favourite place of resort was a wild sequestered spot at a somewhat greater distance. Here, surrounded with woods and thick groves, was the seat of some ancient family, deserted by the proprietor, and only inhabited by a rustic servant or two. A place more solitary and wild could scarcely be imagined; the garden and walks were overgrown with weeds and briars, and the unpruned woods were so tangled as to be almost impervious. About this domain I would wander till overtaken by fatigue, and then I would sit down with my back against some beech, elm, or stately alder tree, and, taking out my book, would pass hours in a state of unmixed enjoyment, my eyes now fixed on the wondrous pages, now glancing at the sylvan scene around; and sometimes I would drop the book and listen to the voice of the rooks and wild pigeons, and not unfrequently to the croaking of multitudes of frogs from the neighbouring swamps and fens.

In going to and from this place I frequently passed a tall elderly individual, dressed in rather a quaint fashion, with a skin cap on his head and stout gaiters on his legs; on his shoulders hung a moderate sized leathern sack; he seemed fond of loitering near sunny banks, and of groping amidst furze and low scrubby bramble bushes, of which there were plenty in the neighbourhood of Norman Cross. Once I saw him standing in the middle of a dusty road, looking intently at a large mark which seemed to have been drawn across it, as if by a walking-stick. "He must have been a large one," the old man muttered half to himself, "or he would not have left such a trail, I wonder if he is near; he seems to have moved this way." He then went behind some bushes which grew on the right side of the road, and appeared to be in quest of something, moving behind the bushes with his head downwards, and occasionally striking their roots with his foot: at length he exclaimed, "Here he is!" and forthwith I saw him dart amongst the bushes. There was a kind of scuffling noise, the rustling of branches, and the crackling of dry sticks. "I have him!" said the man at last; "I have got him!" and presently he made his appearance about twenty yards down the road, holding a large viper in his hand. "What do you think of that, my boy?" said he, as I went up to him; "what do you think of catching such a thing as that with the naked hand?" "What do I think?" said I. "Why, that I could do as much myself." "You do," said the man, "do you? Lord! how the young people in these days are given to conceit; it did not use to be so in my time: when I was a child, childer knew how to behave themselves; but the childer of these days are full of conceit, full of froth, like the mouth of this viper;" and with his forefinger and thumb he squeezed a considerable quantity of foam from the jaws of the viper down upon the road. "The childer of these days are a generation of— God forgive me, what was I about to say!" said the old man; and opening his bag he thrust the reptile into it, which appeared far from empty. I passed on. As I was returning, towards the evening, I overtook the old man, who was wending in the same direction. "Good evening to you, sir," said I, taking off a cap which I wore on my head. "Good evening," said the old man; and then, looking at me, "How's this?" said he, "you ar'n't, sure, the child I met in the morning?" "Yes," said I, "I am; what makes you doubt it?" "Why, you were then all froth and conceit," said the old man, "and now you take off your cap to me." "I beg your pardon," said I, "if I was frothy and conceited, it ill becomes a child like me to be so." "That's true, dear," said the old man; "well; as you have begged my pardon, I truly forgive you." "Thank you," said I; "have you caught any more of those things?" "Only four or five," said the old man; "they are getting scarce, though this used to be a great neighbourhood for them." "And what do you do with them?" said I; "do you carry them home and play with them!" "I sometimes play with one or two that I tame," said the old man; "but I hunt them mostly for the fat which they contain, out of which I make unguents which are good for various sore troubles, especially for the rheumatism." "And do you get your living by hunting these creatures?" I demanded. "Not altogether," said the old man; "besides being a viper-hunter, I am what they call a herbalist, one who knows the virtue of particular herbs; I gather them at the proper season, to make medicines with for the sick." "And do you live in the neighbourhood?" I demanded. "You seem very fond of asking questions, child.

No, I do not live in this neighbourhood in particular, I travel about; I have not been in this neighbourhood till lately for some years."

From this time the old man and myself formed an acquaintance; I often accompanied him in his wanderings about the neighbourhood, and on two or three occasions assisted him in catching the reptiles which he hunted. He generally carried a viper with him which he had made quite tame, and from which he had extracted the poisonous fangs; it would dance and perform various kinds of tricks. He was fond of telling me anecdotes connected with his adventures with the reptile species. "But," said he one day, sighing, "I must shortly give up this business, I am no longer the man I was, I am become timid, and when a person is timid in viper-hunting he had better leave off, as it is quite clear his virtue is leaving him. I got a fright some years ago, which I am quite sure I shall never get the better of; my hand has been shaky more or less ever since." "What frightened you?" said I. "I had better not tell you," said the old man, "or you may be frightened too, lose your virtue, and be no longer good for the business." "I don't care," said I; "I don't intend to follow the business: I dare say I shall be an officer, like my father." "Well," said the old man, "I once saw the king of the vipers, and since then——" "The king of the vipers!" said I, interrupting him; "have the vipers a king?" "As sure as we have," said the old man, "as sure as we have King George to rule over us, have these reptiles a king to rule over them." "And where did you see him?" said I. "I will tell you," said the old man, "though I don't like talking about the matter. It may be about seven years ago that I happened to be far down yonder to the west, on the other side of England, nearly two hundred miles from here, following my business. It was a very sultry day, I remember, and I had been out several hours catching creatures. It might be about three o'clock in the afternoon, when I found myself on some heathy land near the sea, on the ridge of a hill, the side of which, nearly as far down as the sea, was heath; but on the top there was arable ground, which had been planted, and from which the harvest had been gathered— oats or barley, I know not which—but I remember that the ground was covered with stubble. Well, about three o'clock, as I told you before, what with the heat of the day and from having walked about for hours in a lazy way, I felt very tired; so I determined to have a sleep, and I laid myself down, my head just on the ridge of the hill, towards the field, and my body over the side down amongst the heath; my bag, which was nearly filled with creatures, lay at a little distance

from my face; the creatures were struggling in it, I remember, and I
thought to myself, how much more comfortably off I was than they;
I was taking my ease on the nice open hill, cooled with the breezes,
whilst they were in the nasty close bag, coiling about one another, and
breaking their very hearts all to no purpose: and I felt quite comfortable and happy in the thought, and little by little closed my eyes,
and fell into the sweetest snooze that ever I was in in all my life; and
there I lay over the hill's side, with my head half in the field, I don't
know how long, all dead asleep. At last it seemed to me that I heard a
noise in my sleep, something like a thing moving, very faint, however,
far away; then it died, and then it came again upon my ear as I slept,
and now it appeared almost as if I heard crackle, crackle; then it died
again, or I became yet more dead asleep than before, I know not
which, but I certainly lay some time without hearing it. All of a sudden
I became awake, and there was I, on the ridge of the hill, with my
cheek on the ground towards the stubble, with a noise in my ear like
that of something moving towards me, among the stubble of the field;
well, I lay a moment or two listening to the noise, and then I became
frightened, for I did not like the noise at all, it sounded so odd; so I
rolled myself on my belly and looked towards the stubble. Mercy
upon us! there was a huge snake, or rather a dreadful viper, for it was
all yellow and gold, moving towards me, bearing its head about a foot
and a half above the ground, the dry stubble crackling beneath its
outrageous belly. It might be about five yards off when I first saw it,
making straight towards me, child, as if it would devour me. I lay
quite still, for I was stupefied with horror, whilst the creature came
still nearer; and now it was nearly upon me, when it suddenly drew
back a little, and then—what do you think?—it lifted its head and
chest high in the air, and high over my face as I looked up, flickering at
me with its tongue as if it would fly at my face. Child, what I felt at
that moment I can scarcely say, but it was a sufficient punishment for
all the sins I ever committed; and there we two were, I looking up at
the viper, and the viper looking down upon me, flickering at me with
its tongue. It was only the kindness of God that saved me: all at once
there was a loud noise, the report of a gun, for a fowler was shooting
at a covey of birds, a little way off in the stubble. Whereupon the
viper sunk its head and immediately made off over the ridge of the
hill, down in the direction of the sea. As it passed by me, however—
and it passed close by me—it hesitated a moment, as if it was doubtful
whether it should not seize me; it did not, however, but made off down

the hill. It has often struck me that he was angry with me, and came upon me unawares for presuming to meddle with his people, as I have always been in the habit of doing."

"But," said I, "how do you know that it was the king of the vipers?"

"How do I know?" said the old man, "who else should it be? There was as much difference between it and other reptiles as between King George and other people."

"Is King George, then, different from other people?" I demanded.

"Of course," said the old man; "I have never seen him myself, but I have heard people say that he is a ten times greater man than other folks; indeed, it stands to reason that he must be different from the rest, else people would not be so eager to see him. Do you think, child, that people would be fools enough to run a matter of twenty or thirty miles to see the king, provided King George——"

"Haven't the French a king?" I demanded.

"Yes," said the old man, "or something much the same, and a queer one he is; not quite so big as King George, they say, but quite as terrible a fellow. What of him?"

"Suppose he should come to Norman Cross!"

"What should he do at Norman Cross, child?"

"Why, you were talking about the vipers in your bag breaking their hearts, and so on, and their king coming to help them. Now, suppose the French king should hear of his people being in trouble at Norman Cross, and——"

"He can't come, child," said the old man, rubbing his hands, "the water lies between them. The French don't like the water; neither vipers nor Frenchmen take kindly to the water, child."

When the old man left the country, which he did a few days after the conversation which I have just related, he left me the reptile which he had tamed and rendered quite harmless by removing the fangs. I was in the habit of feeding it with milk, and frequently carried it abroad with me in my walks.

NATURE

by Ralph Waldo Emerson

Some readers may think it strange to find one of Emerson's essays in a book largely concerned with natural history and indeed offered for sale on that basis. For that matter, some persons find Emerson hard to read—and harder still to swallow and digest— on any subject. Nevertheless, the Sage of Concord, like most New England scholars and writers, had an innate love of Nature and a fair working knowledge of the general subject as it applied to the woods, streams, lakes, pastures, and cultivated fields of his native New England soil. There is no disguising the fact, however, that in this essay he has soared far above Concord farms and far beyond the accepted limits of natural history to give us his ideas of Nature in relation to Man. It is not natural history; it is natural philosophy. If it is urged that a little bit of natural philosophy goes a long way, then by all means let's get our supply from Ralph Waldo Emerson. Everything he ever said or wrote was meant to go a long way.

P.S. No money refunded to those who won't have Emerson at any price.

INTRODUCTION

OUR age is retrospective. It builds the sepulchers of the fathers. It writes biographies, histories, and criticism. The foregoing generations beheld God and nature face to face; we, through their eyes. Why should not we also enjoy an original relation to the universe? Why should not we have a poetry and philosophy of insight and not of tradition, and a religion by revelation to us and not the history of theirs? Embosomed for a season in nature, whose floods of life stream around and through us and invite us by the powers they supply to action proportioned to nature, why should we grope among the dry bones of the past or put the living generation into masquerade out of its faded wardrobe? The sun shines today also. There is more wool and flax in the fields. There are new lands, new men, new thoughts. Let us demand our own works and laws and worship.

Undoubtedly we have no questions to ask which are unanswerable. We must trust the perfection of the creation so far as to believe that whatever curiosity the order of things has awakened in our minds, the order of things can satisfy. Every man's condition is a solution in hieroglyphic to those inquiries he would put. He acts it as life before he apprehends it as truth. In like manner, nature is already in its forms and tendencies describing its own design. Let us interrogate the great apparition that shines so peacefully around us. Let us inquire, to what end is nature?

All science has one aim, namely, to find a theory of nature. We have theories of races and of functions, but scarcely yet a remote approach to an idea of creation. We are now so far from the road to truth that religious teachers dispute and hate each other, and speculative men are esteemed unsound and frivolous. But to a sound judgment, the most abstract truth is the most practical. Whenever a true theory appears, it will be its own evidence. Its test is that it will explain all phenomena. Now many are thought not only unexplained but inexplicable; as language, sleep, madness, dreams, beasts, sex.

Philosophically considered, the universe is composed of Nature and the Soul. Strictly speaking, therefore, all that is separate from us, all which Philosophy distinguishes as the NOT ME, that is, both nature and art, all other men and my own body, must be ranked under this name, NATURE. In enumerating the values of nature and casting up their sum, I shall use the word in both senses—in its common and in its philosophical import. In inquiries so general as our present one, the inaccuracy is not material; no confusion of thought will occur. *Nature*, in the common sense, refers to essences unchanged by man: space, the air, the river, the leaf. *Art* is applied to the mixture of his will with the same things, as in a house, a canal, a statue, a picture. But his operations taken together are so insignificant, a little chipping, baking, patching, and washing, that in an impression so grand as that of the world on the human mind, they do not vary the result.

I. NATURE

To go into solitude, a man needs to retire as much from his chamber as from society. I am not solitary whilst I read and write, though nobody is with me. But if a man would be alone, let him look at the stars. The rays that come from those heavenly worlds will separate between him and what he touches. One might think the atmosphere was made transparent with this design, to give man, in the heavenly bodies, the perpetual presence of the sublime. Seen in the streets of cities, how great they are! If the stars should appear one night in a thousand years, how would men believe and adore; and preserve for many generations the remembrance of the city of God which had been shown! But every night come out these envoys of beauty and light the universe with their admonishing smile.

The stars awaken a certain reverence because, though always present, they are inaccessible; but all natural objects make a kindred impression, when the mind is open to their influence. Nature never wears a mean appearance. Neither does the wisest man extort her secret and lose his curiosity by finding out all her perfection. Nature never became a toy to a wise spirit. The flowers, the animals, the mountains reflected the wisdom of his best hour as much as they had delighted the simplicity of his childhood.

When we speak of nature in this manner, we have a distinct but most poetical sense of the mind. We mean the integrity of impression made by manifold natural objects. It is this which distinguishes the stick of timber of the woodcutter from the tree of the poet. The charming landscape which I saw this morning is indubitably made up of some twenty or thirty farms. Miller owns this field, Locke that, and Manning the woodland beyond. But none of them owns the landscape. There is a property in the horizon which no man has but he whose eye can integrate all the parts, that is, the poet. This is the best part of these men's farms, yet to this their warranty-deeds give no title.

To speak truly, few adult persons can see nature. Most persons do not see the sun. At least they have a very superficial seeing. The sun illuminates only the eye of the man, but shines into the eye and the heart of the child. The lover of nature is he whose inward and outward senses are still truly adjusted to each other, who has retained the spirit of infancy even into the era of manhood. His intercourse with heaven and earth becomes part of his daily food. In the presence of nature a wild delight runs through the man, in spite of real sorrows. Nature says, He is my creature, and, maugre all his impertinent griefs, he shall be glad with me. Not the sun or the summer alone but every hour and season yields its tribute of delight; for every hour and change corresponds to and authorizes a different state of the mind from breathless noon to grimmest midnight. Nature is a setting that fits equally well a comic or a mourning piece. In good health, the air is a cordial of incredible virtue. Crossing a bare common in snow puddles at twilight under a clouded sky, without having in my thoughts any occurrence of special good fortune, I have enjoyed a perfect exhilaration. I am glad to the brink of fear. In the woods, too, a man casts off his years as the snake his slough, and at what period soever of life is always a child. In the woods is perpetual youth. Within these plantations of God a decorum and sanctity reign, a perennial festival is dressed, and the guest sees not how he should tire of them in a thousand years. In the woods we return to reason and faith. There I feel that nothing can befall me in life—no disgrace, no calamity (leaving me my eyes) which nature cannot repair. Standing on the bare ground—my head bathed by the blithe air and uplifted into infinite space—all mean egotism vanishes. I become a transparent eyeball; I am nothing; I see all; the currents of the Universal Being circulate through me; I am part or parcel of God. The name of the nearest friend sounds then foreign and accidental: to be brothers, to be acquaintances, master or servant, is then a trifle and a disturbance. I am the lover of uncontained and immortal beauty. In the wilderness I find something more dear and connate than in streets or villages. In the tranquil landscape, and especially in the distant line of the horizon, man beholds something as beautiful as his own nature.

The greatest delight which the fields and woods minister is the suggestion of an occult relation between man and the vegetable. I am not alone and unacknowledged. They nod to me, and I to them. The waving of the boughs in the storm is new to me and old. It takes me by surprise and yet is not unknown. Its effect is like that of a higher thought or a better emotion coming over me when I deemed I was thinking justly or doing right.

Yet it is certain that the power to produce this delight does not reside in nature but in man, or in a harmony of both. It is necessary to use these pleasures with great temperance. For nature is not always tricked in holiday attire, but the same scene which yesterday breathed perfume and glittered as for the frolic of the nymphs is overspread

with melancholy today. Nature always wears the colors of the spirit.
To a man laboring under calamity, the heat of his own fire hath sadness in it. Then there is a kind of contempt of the landscape felt by
him who has just lost by death a dear friend. The sky is less grand as
it shuts down over less worth in the population.

II. COMMODITY

Whoever considers the final cause of the world will discern a multitude of uses that enter as parts into that result. They all admit of
being thrown into one of the following classes: Commodity; Beauty;
Language; and Discipline.

Under the general name of commodity I rank all those advantages
which our senses owe to nature. This, of course, is a benefit which is
temporary and mediate, not ultimate, like its service to the soul. Yet
although low, it is perfect in its kind and is the only use of nature
which all men apprehend. The misery of man appears like childish
petulance when we explore the steady and prodigal provision that
has been made for his support and delight on this green ball which
floats him through the heavens. What angels invented these splendid
ornaments, these rich conveniences, this ocean of air above, this ocean
of water beneath, this firmament of earth between, this zodiac of lights,
this tent of dropping clouds, this striped coat of climates, this four-
fold year? Beasts, fire, water, stones and corn serve him. The field is at
once his floor, his work-yard, his playground, his garden, and his bed.

> *More servants wait on man*
> *Than he'll take notice of.*

Nature, in its ministry to man, is not only the material but is also
the process and the result. All the parts incessantly work into each
other's hands for the profit of man. The wind sows the seed; the sun
evaporates the sea; the wind blows the vapor to the field; the ice on the
other side of the planet condenses rain on this; the rain feeds the
plant; the plant feeds the animal; and thus the endless circulations of
the divine charity nourish man.

The useful arts are reproductions or new combinations by the wit
of man of the same natural benefactors. He no longer waits for favor-
ing gales, but by means of steam he realizes the fable of Aeolus's
bag and carries the two and thirty winds in the boiler of his boat. To
diminish friction, he paves the road with iron bars and, mounting a

coach with a shipload of men, animals and merchandise behind him, he darts through the country, from town to town, like an eagle or a swallow through the air. By the aggregate of these aids, how is the face of the world changed, from the era of Noah to that of Napoleon! The private poor man hath cities, ships, canals, bridges built for him. He goes to the post office, and the human race run on his errands; to the bookshop, and the human race read and write of all that happens, for him; to the courthouse, and nations repair his wrongs. He sets his house upon the road, and the human race go forth every morning and shovel out the snow and cut a path for him.

But there is no need of specifying particulars in this class of uses. The catalogue is endless, and the examples so obvious that I shall leave them to the reader's reflection, with the general remark that this mercenary benefit is one which has respect to a farther good. A man is fed, not that he may be fed, but that he may work.

III. BEAUTY

A nobler want of man is served by nature, namely, the love of Beauty.

The ancient Greeks called the world *Cosmos*, beauty. Such is the constitution of all things, or such the plastic power of the human eye, that the primary forms, as the sky, the mountain, the tree, the animal, give us a delight *in and for themselves*; a pleasure arising from outline, color, motion, and grouping. This seems partly owing to the eye itself. The eye is the best of artists. By the mutual action of its structure and of the laws of light, perspective is produced which integrates every mass of objects, of what character soever, into a well colored and shaded globe, so that where the particular objects are mean and unaffecting, the landscape which they compose is round and symmetrical. And as the eye is the best composer, so light is the first of painters. There is no object so foul that intense light will not make beautiful. And the stimulus it affords to the sense and a sort of infinitude which it hath, like space and time, make all matter gay. Even the corpse has its own beauty. But besides this general grace diffused over nature, almost all the individual forms are agreeable to the eye, as is proved by our endless imitations of some of them, as the acorn, the grape, the pine cone, the wheat ear, the egg, the wings and forms of most birds, the lion's claw, the serpent, the butterfly, sea shells, flames, clouds, buds, leaves, and the forms of many trees, as the palm.

For better consideration, we may distribute the aspects of Beauty in a threefold manner.

1. First, the simple perception of natural forms is a delight. The influence of the forms and actions in nature is so needful to man that, in its lowest functions, it seems to lie on the confines of commodity and beauty. To the body and mind which have been cramped by noxious work or company, Nature is medicinal and restores their tone. The tradesman, the attorney, comes out of the din and craft of the street and sees the sky and the woods and is a man again. In their eternal calm he finds himself. The health of the eye seems to demand a horizon. We are never tired so long as we can see far enough.

But in other hours Nature satisfies by its loveliness, and without any mixture of corporeal benefit. I see the spectacle of morning from the hilltop over against my house, from daybreak to sunrise, with emotions which an angel might share. The long slender bars of cloud float like fishes in the sea of crimson light. From the earth, as a shore, I look out into that silent sea. I seem to partake its rapid transformations; the active enchantment reaches my dust, and I dilate and conspire with the morning wind. How does Nature deify us with a few and cheap elements! Give me health and a day, and I will make the pomp of emperors ridiculous. The dawn is my Assyria, the sunset and moonrise my Paphos and unimaginable realms of faerie; broad noon shall be my England of the senses and the understanding; the night shall be my Germany of mystic philosophy and dreams.

Not less excellent, except for our less susceptibility in the afternoon, was the charm, last evening, of a January sunset. The western clouds divided and subdivided themselves into pink flakes, modulated with tints of unspeakable softness, and the air had so much life and sweetness that it was a pain to come within doors. What was it that Nature would say? Was there no meaning in the live repose of the valley behind the mill, and which Homer or Shakespeare could not re-form for me in words? The leafless trees become spires of flame in the sunset, with the blue east for their background, and the stars of the dead calices of flowers and every withered stem and stubble rimed with frost contribute something to the mute music.

The inhabitants of cities suppose that the country landscape is pleasant only half the year. I please myself with the graces of the winter scenery and believe that we are as much touched by it as by the genial influences of summer. To the attentive eye, each moment of the year has its own beauty, and in the same field it beholds every hour a picture which was never seen before and which shall never be seen again. The heavens change every moment and reflect their glory or gloom on the plains beneath. The state of the crop in the surrounding farms alters the expression of the earth from week to week. The succession of native plants in the pastures and roadsides, which makes the silent clock by which time tells the summer hours, will make even the divisions of the day sensible to a keen observer. The tribes of birds and insects, like the plants punctual to their time, follow each other, and the year has room for all. By watercourses, the variety is greater. In July the blue pontederia or pickerel-weed blooms in large beds in the shallow parts of our pleasant river and swarms with yellow butterflies in continual motion. Art cannot rival this pomp of purple and gold. Indeed the river is a perpetual gala and boasts each month a new ornament.

But this beauty of Nature which is seen and felt as beauty is the least part. The shows of day, the dewy morning, the rainbow, mountains, orchards in blossom, stars, moonlight, shadows in still water, and the like, if too eagerly hunted, become shows merely, and mock us with their unreality. Go out of the house to see the moon, and 'tis mere tinsel; it will not please as when its light shines upon your necessary journey. The beauty that shimmers in the yellow afternoons of October, who ever could clutch it? Go forth to find it, and it is gone; 'tis only a mirage as you look from the windows of diligence.

2. The presence of a higher, namely, of the spiritual element is essential to its perfection. The high and divine beauty which can be loved without effeminacy is that which is found in combination with the human will. Beauty is the mark God sets upon virtue. Every natural action is graceful. Every heroic act is also decent and causes the place and the bystanders to shine. We are taught by great actions that the universe is the property of every individual in it. Every rational creature has all nature for his dowry and estate. It is his, if he will. He may divest himself of it; he may creep into a corner and abdicate his kingdom as most men do; but he is entitled to the world by his constitution. In proportion to the energy of his thought and will, he takes up the world into himself. "All those things for which men plough, build, or sail, obey virtue," said Sallust. "The winds and waves," said Gibbon, "are always on the side of the ablest navigators." So are the sun and moon and all the stars of heaven. When a noble act is done—perchance in a scene of great natural beauty: when Leonidas and his three hundred martyrs consume one day in dying, and the sun and

moon come each and look at them once in the steep defile of Ther-
mopylae; when Arnold Winkelried, in the high Alps under the shadow
of the avalanche, gathers in his side a sheaf of Austrian spears to
break the line for his comrades—are not these heroes entitled to add
the beauty of the scene to the beauty of the deed? When the bark of
Columbus nears the shore of America—before it the beach lined with
savages fleeing out of all their huts of cane; the sea behind; and the
purple mountains of the Indian Archipelago around—can we separate
the man from the living picture? Does not the New World clothe his
form with her palm-groves and savannahs as fit drapery? Ever does
natural beauty steal in like air and envelope great actions. When Sir
Harry Vane was dragged up the Tower hill, sitting on a sled, to suffer
death as the champion of the English laws, one of the multitude cried
out to him, "You never sate on so glorious a seat!" Charles II, to
intimidate the citizens of London, caused the patriot Lord Russell to
be drawn in an open coach through the principal streets of the city
on his way to the scaffold. "But," his biographer says, "the multitude
imagined they saw liberty and virtue sitting by his side." In private
places, among sordid objects, an act of truth or heroism seems at once
to draw to itself the sky as its temple, the sun as its candle. Nature
stretches out her arms to embrace man, only let his thoughts be of
equal greatness. Willingly does she follow his steps with the rose and
the violet and bend her lines of grandeur and grace to the decoration
of her darling child. Only let his thoughts be of equal scope and the
frame will suit the picture. A virtuous man is in unison with her
works and makes the central figure of the visible sphere. Homer,
Pindar, Socrates, Phocion, associate themselves fitly in our memory
with the geography and climate of Greece. The visible heavens and
earth sympathize with Jesus. And in common life whosoever has seen a
person of powerful character and happy genius will have remarked how
easily he took all things along with him—the persons, the opinions,
and the day, and Nature became ancillary to a man.

3. There is still another aspect under which the beauty of the world
may be viewed, namely, as it becomes an object of the intellect. Beside
the relation of things to virtue, they have a relation to thought. The
intellect searches out the absolute order of things as they stand in the
mind of God and without the colors of affection. The intellectual and
the active powers seem to succeed each other, and the exclusive activity
of the one generates the exclusive activity of the other. There is something unfriendly in each to the other, but they are like the alternate

periods of feeding and working in animals; each prepares and will be
followed by the other. Therefore does beauty, which, in relation to
actions, as we have seen, comes unsought, and comes because it is
unsought, remain for the apprehension and pursuit of the intellect;
and then again, in its turn, of the active power. Nothing divine dies.
All good is eternally reproductive. The beauty of Nature re-forms itself in the mind, and not for barren contemplation but for new creation.

All men are in some degree impressed by the face of the world,
some men even to delight. This love of beauty is Taste. Others have
the same love in such excess that, not content with admiring, they
seek to embody it in new forms. The creation of beauty is Art.

The production of a work of art throws a light upon the mystery
of humanity. A work of art is an abstract or epitome of the world. It
is the result or expression of Nature in miniature. For although the
works of Nature are innumerable and all different, the result or the
expression of them all is similar and single. Nature is a sea of forms
radically alike and even unique. A leaf, a sunbeam, a landscape, the
ocean, make an analogous impression on the mind. What is common
to them all—that perfectness and harmony—is beauty. The standard of
beauty is the entire circuit of natural forms, the totality of Nature,
which the Italians expressed by defining beauty "*il piu nell' uno.*"
Nothing is quite beautiful alone, nothing but is beautiful in the whole.
A single object is only so far beautiful as it suggests this universal
grace. The poet, the painter, the sculptor, the musician, the architect,
seek each to concentrate this radiance of the world on one point, and
each in his several work to satisfy the love of beauty which stimulates
him to produce. Thus is Art a Nature passed through the alembic of
man. Thus in art does Nature work through the will of a man filled
with the beauty of her first works.

The world thus exists to the soul to satisfy the desire of beauty.
This element I call an ultimate end. No reason can be asked or given
why the soul seeks beauty. Beauty, in its largest and profoundest sense,
is one expression for the universe. God is the all-fair. Truth and goodness and beauty are but different faces of the same All. But beauty in
Nature is not ultimate. It is the herald of inward and eternal beauty
and is not alone a solid and satisfactory good. It must stand as a part,
and not as yet the last or highest expression of the final cause of
Nature.

CONCERNING WHALES

by Herman Melville

Born in New York, August 1, 1819, Herman Melville shipped
aboard a merchant vessel as a junior hand at the age of nineteen
and made a trip to Liverpool and return. Two years later he
signed articles as a member of the crew of the New Bedford
whaler Acushnet, which was heading for the South Pacific. That
was early in 1841. After about a year and a half of sailing and
whaling with the Acushnet crew, he jumped ship when it
touched at Nuku Hiva, one of the Marquesas Islands, and lived
on that and other islands of the group with Polynesian natives
for some months. He signed aboard other whaling ships in the
area for brief hitches, visited the Society Islands, lived in Honolulu for a spell, and finally returned to the United States in 1844
as a member of the crew of a United States Navy ship.

His experiences among the natives of the South Pacific islands
gave him the material for his first book, Typee, published in 1846.
This book found immediate favor with the reading public, and
the author followed it with another, Omoo, in much the same
vein. Melville was launched as a popular author and turned out
three more tales of adventure in the next three years. In 1850 he
moved to Pittsfield, Massachusetts, and the following year he published Moby Dick, a book that found little favor. In fact, it rather
spoiled his reputation, and practically all of his fairly numerous
later books were neglected to the point where he was glad to accept a position as a customs inspector in New York to earn a living. He had sunk to obscurity as an author and, when he died in
New York, September 28, 1891, he was remembered only as the
author of Typee and Omoo. A score or more years after his death
Moby Dick was exhumed from its literary grave and hailed for
what it is—a masterly and magnificent description of the whaling
industry in the days of sailing ships, a thrilling tale of adventure

with a wealth of symbolic imagery and mystical overtones, the story of a relentless spirit of revenge and appalling retribution. It is now accepted as an American classic. In the following excerpt the author discourses in lordly fashion on the whale group and assorted relatives. This is natural history with a considerable flourish and also cetology as it was known a century ago. Since that time scientists have added to their knowledge of the subject, but not enough to render unfit for publication this paean in print of the whale family, great and small. Out of respect to Melville it should be remembered that the blue whale, which may run to one hundred feet in length and weigh more than a ton to the running foot, is not only the largest animal extant but the largest that ever lived on the surface of the earth or in the waters thereof.

ALREADY we are boldly launched upon the deep; but soon we shall be lost in its unshored harborless immensities. Ere that come to pass; ere the Pequod's weedy hull rolls side by side with the barnacled hulls of the leviathan; at the outset it is but well to attend to a matter almost indispensable to a thorough appreciative understanding of the more special leviathanic revelations and allusions of all sorts which are to follow.

It is some systematized exhibition of the whale in his broad genera, that I would now fain put before you. Yet is it no easy task. The classification of the constituents of a chaos, nothing less is here essayed. Listen to what the best and latest authorities have laid down.

"No branch of Zoology is so much involved as that which is entitled Cetology," says Captain Scoresby, A.D. 1820.

"It is not my intention, were it in my power, to enter into the inquiry as to the true method of dividing the cetacea into groups and families. . . . Utter confusion exists among the historians of this animal" (sperm whale), says Surgeon Beale, A.D. 1839.

"Unfitness to pursue our research in the unfathomable waters." "Impenetrable veil covering our knowledge of the cetacea." "A field strewn with thorns." "All these incomplete indications but serve to torture us naturalists."

Thus speak of the whale, the great Cuvier, and John Hunter, and Lesson, those lights of zoology and anatomy. Nevertheless, though of real knowledge there be little, yet of books there are a plenty; and so in some small degree, with cetology, or the science of whales. Many are the men, small and great, old and new, landsmen and seamen, who have at large or in little, written of the whale. Run over a few: —The Authors of the Bible; Aristotle; Pliny; Aldrovandi; Sir Thomas Browne; Gesner; Ray; Linnaeus; Rondeletius; Willoughby; Green; Artedi; Sibbald; Brisson; Marten; Lacépède; Bonneterre; Desmarest; Baron Cuvier; Frederick Cuvier; John Hunter; Owen; Scoresby; Beale; Bennett; J. Ross Browne; the Author of Miriam Coffin; Olmstead; and the Rev. T. Cheever. But to what ultimate generalizing purpose all these have written, the above cited extracts will show.

Of the names in this list of whale authors only those following Owen ever saw living whales; and but one of them was a real professional harpooneer and whaleman. I mean Captain Scoresby. On the separate subject of the Greenland or right-whale, he is the best existing authority. But Scoresby knew nothing and says nothing of the great sperm whale, compared with which the Greenland whale is almost unworthy mentioning. And here be it said, that the Greenland whale is an usurper upon the throne of the seas. He is not even by any means the largest of the whales. Yet, owing to the long priority of his claims, and the profound ignorance which till some seventy years back, invested the then fabulous or utterly unknown sperm whale, and which ignorance to this present day still reigns in all but some few scientific retreats and whale-ports; this usurpation has been every way complete. Reference to nearly all the leviathanic allusions in the great poets of past days, will satisfy you that the Greenland whale, without one rival, was to them the monarch of the seas. But the time has at last come for a new proclamation. This is Charing Cross; hear ye! good people all,—the Greenland whale is deposed,—the great sperm whale now reigneth!

There are only two books in being which at all pretend to put the living sperm whale before you, and at the same time, in the remotest degree succeed in the attempt. Those books are Beale's and Bennett's; both in their time surgeons to the English South-Sea whale-ships, and both exact and reliable men. The original matter touching the sperm whale to be found in their volumes is necessarily small; but so far as it goes, it is of excellent quality, though mostly confined to scientific description. As yet, however, the sperm whale, scientific or poetic, lives not complete in any literature. Far above all other hunted whales, his is an unwritten life.

Now the various species of whales need some sort of popular comprehensive classification, if only an easy outline one for the present, hereafter to be filled in all its departments by subsequent laborers. As no better man advances to take this matter in hand, I hereupon offer my own poor endeavors. I promise nothing complete; because any human thing supposed to be complete must for that very reason infallibly be faulty. I shall not pretend to a minute anatomical description of the various species, or—in this space at least—to much of any description. My object here is simply to project the draught of a systematization of cetology. I am the architect, not the builder.

But it is a ponderous task; no ordinary letter-sorter in the Post-Office is equal to it. To grope down into the bottom of the sea after them; to have one's hands among the unspeakable foundations, ribs, and very pelvis of the world; this is a fearful thing. What am I that I should essay to hook the nose of this leviathan! The awful tauntings in Job might well appal me. "Will he (the leviathan) make a covenant with thee? Behold the hope of him is vain!" But I have swam through libraries and sailed through oceans; I have had to do with whales with these visible hands; I am in earnest; and I will try. There are some preliminaries to settle.

First: The uncertain, unsettled condition of this science of Cetology is in the very vestibule attested by the fact, that in some quarters it still remains a moot point whether a whale be a fish. In his System of Nature, A.D. 1776, Linnaeus declares, "I hereby separate the whales from the fish." But of my own knowledge, I know that down to the year 1850, sharks and shad, alewives and herring, against Linnaeus's express edict, were still found dividing the possession of the same seas with the Leviathan.

The grounds upon which Linnaeus would fain have banished the whales from the waters, he states as follows: "On account of their warm bilocular heart, their lungs, their moveable eyelids, their hollow ears, penem intrantem feminam mammis lactantem," and finally, "ex lege naturae jure meritoque." I submitted all this to my friends Simeon Macey and Charley Coffin, of Nantucket, both messmates of mine in a certain voyage, and they united in the opinion that the reasons set forth were altogether insufficient. Charley profanely hinted they were humbug.

Be it known that, waiving all argument, I take the good old-fashioned ground that the whale is a fish, and call upon holy Jonah to back me. This fundamental thing settled, the next point is, in what internal respect does the whale differ from other fish. Above, Linnaeus has given you those items. But in brief they are these: lungs and warm blood; whereas, all other fish are lungless and cold-blooded.

Next: how shall we define the whale, by his obvious externals, so as conspicuously to label him for all time to come. To be short, then, a whale is a *spouting fish with a horizontal tail*. There you have him. However contracted, that definition is the result of expanded meditation. A walrus spouts much like a whale, but the walrus is not a fish, because he is amphibious. But the last term of the definition is still more cogent, as coupled with the first. Almost any one must have noticed that all the fish familiar to landsmen have not a flat, but a vertical, or up-and-down tail. Whereas, among spouting fish the tail, though it may be similarly shaped, invariably assumes a horizontal position.

By the above definition of what a whale is, I do by no means exclude from the leviathanic brotherhood any sea creature hitherto identified with the whale by the best informed Nantucketers; nor, on the other hand, link with it any fish hitherto authoritatively regarded as alien.* Hence, all the smaller, spouting and horizontal-tailed fish must be included in this ground-plan of cetology. Now, then, come the grand divisions of the entire whale host.

First: According to magnitude I divide the whales into three primary BOOKS (Subdivisible into Chapters), and these shall comprehend them all, both small and large.

I. The Folio Whale; II. the Octavo Whale; III. the Duodecimo Whale.

As the type of the Folio I present the *Sperm Whale*; of the Octavo, the *Grampus*; of the Duodecimo, the *Porpoise*.

FOLIOS. Among these I here include the following chapters:—
I. The *Sperm Whale*; II. the *Right Whale*; III. the *Fin Back Whale*; IV. the *Humpbacked Whale*; V. the *Razor Back Whale*; VI. the *Sulphur Bottom Whale*.

BOOK I. (*Folio*), Chapter I. (*Sperm Whale*).—This whale, among the English of old vaguely known as the Trumpa whale and the Physeter whale, and the Anvil-headed whale, is the present Cachalot of the French, and the Pottsfisch of the Germans, and the Macrocephalus of the Long Words. He is, without doubt, the largest inhabitant

* I am aware that down to the present time, the fish styled Lamatins and Dugongs (Pig-fish and Sow-fish of the Coffins of Nantucket) are included by many naturalists among the whales. But as these pig-fish are a noisy, contemptible set, mostly lurking in the mouths of rivers, and feeding on wet hay, and especially as they do not spout, I deny their credentials as whales; and have presented them with their passports to quit the Kingdom of Cetology.

of the globe; the most formidable of all whales to encounter; the most
majestic in aspect; and lastly, by far the most valuable in commerce;
he being the only creature from which that valuable substance, spermaceti, is obtained. All his peculiarities will, in many other places, be
enlarged upon. It is chiefly with his name that I now have to do.
Philologically considered, it is absurd. Some centuries ago, when the
sperm whale was almost wholly unknown in his own proper individuality, and when his oil was only accidentally obtained from the
stranded fish; in those days spermaceti, it would seem, was popularly
supposed to be derived from a creature identical with the one then
known in England as the Greenland or Right Whale. It was the idea
also, that this same spermaceti was that quickening humor of the
Greenland Whale which the first syllable of the word literally expresses. In those times, also, spermaceti was exceedingly scarce, not
being used for light, but only as an ointment and medicament. It was
only to be had from the druggists as you nowadays buy an ounce of
rhubarb. When, as I opine, in the course of time, the true nature of
spermaceti became known, its original name was still retained by the
dealers; no doubt to enhance its value by a notion so strangely significant of its scarcity. And so the appellation must at last have come to
be bestowed upon the whale from which this spermaceti was really
derived.

BOOK I. (*Folio*), Chapter II. (*Right Whale*).—In one respect this
is the most venerable of the leviathans, being the one first regularly
hunted by man. It yields the article commonly known as whalebone
or baleen; and the oil specially known as "whale oil," an inferior article
in commerce. Among the fishermen, he is indiscriminately designated
by all the following titles: The Whale; the Greenland Whale; the
Black Whale; the Great Whale; the True Whale; the Right Whale.
There is a deal of obscurity concerning the identity of the species thus
multitudinously baptized. What then is the whale, which I include in
the second species of my Folios? It is the Great Mysticetus of the
English naturalists; the Greenland Whale of the English whaleman;
the Baleine Ordinaire of the French whaleman; the Growlands Wal-
fish of the Swedes. It is the whale which for more than two centuries
past has been hunted by the Dutch and English in the Arctic seas; it is
the whale which the American fishermen have long pursued in the
Indian ocean, on the Brazil Banks, on the Nor' West Coast, and various other parts of the world, designated by them Right Whale Cruis-
ing Grounds.

Some pretend to see a difference between the Greenland Whale of the English and the Right Whale of the Americans. But they precisely agree in all their grand features; nor has there yet been presented a single determinate fact upon which to ground a radical distinction. It is by endless subdivisions based upon the most inconclusive differences, that some departments of natural history become so repellingly intricate. The Right Whale will be elsewhere treated of at some length, with reference to elucidating the sperm whale.

Book I. (*Folio*), Chapter III. (*Fin-Back*).—Under this head I reckon a monster which, by the various names of Fin-Back, Tall-Spout, and Long-John, has been seen almost in every sea and is commonly the whale whose distant jet is so often descried by passengers crossing the Atlantic, in the New York packet-tracks. In the length he attains, and in his baleen, the Fin-Back resembles the Right Whale, but is of a less portly girth, and a lighter color, approaching to olive. His great lips present a cable-like aspect, formed by the intertwisting, slanting folds of large wrinkles. His grand distinguishing feature, the fin, from which he derives his name, is often a conspicuous object. This fin is some three or four feet long, growing vertically from the hinder part of the back, of an angular shape, and with a very sharp pointed end. Even if not the slightest other part of the creature be visible, this isolated fin will, at times, be seen plainly projecting from the surface. When the sea is moderately calm, and slightly marked with spherical ripples, and this gnomon-like fin stands up and casts shadows upon the wrinkled surface, it may well be supposed that the watery circle surrounding it somewhat resembles a dial, with its style and wavy hour-lines graved on it. On that Ahaz-dial the shadow often goes back. The Fin-Back is not gregarious. He seems a whale-hater, as some men are man-haters. Very shy; always going solitary; unexpectedly rising to the surface in the remotest and most sullen waters; his straight and single lofty jet rising like a tall misanthropic spear upon a barren plain; gifted with such wondrous power and velocity in swimming, as to defy all present pursuit from man; this leviathan seems the banished and unconquerable Cain of his race, bearing for his mark that style upon his back. From having the baleen in his mouth, the Fin-Back is sometimes included with the Right Whale, among a theoretic species denominated *Whalebone whales*, that is, whales with baleen. Of these so-called Whalebone whales, there would seem to be several varieties, most of which, however, are little known. Broad-nosed whales and beaked whales; pike-headed whales; bunched whales; under-jawed whales and rostrated whales, are the fisherman's names for a few sorts.

In connexion with this appellative of "Whalebone whales," it is of great importance to mention, that however such a nomenclature may be convenient in facilitating allusions to some kind of whales, yet it is in vain to attempt a clear classification of the Leviathan, founded upon either his baleen, or hump, or fin, or teeth; notwithstanding that those marked parts or features very obviously seem better adapted to afford the basis for a regular system of Cetology than any other detached bodily distinctions, which the whale, in his kinds, presents. How then? The baleen, hump, back-fin, and teeth; these are things whose peculiarities are indiscriminately dispersed among all sorts of whales, without any regard to what may be the nature of their structure in other and more essential particulars. Thus, the Sperm Whale and the Humpbacked Whale, each has a hump; but there the similitude ceases. Then this same Humpbacked Whale and the Greenland Whale, each of these has baleen; but there again the similitude ceases. And it is just the same with the other parts above mentioned. In various sorts of whales, they form such irregular combinations, or, in the case of any one of them detached, such an irregular isolation as utterly to defy all general methodization formed upon such a basis. On this rock every one of the whale-naturalists has split.

But it may possibly be conceived that, in the internal parts of the whale, in his anatomy—there, at least, we shall be able to hit the right classification. Nay; what thing, for example, is there in the Greenland Whale's anatomy more striking than his baleen? Yet we have seen that by his baleen it is impossible correctly to classify the Greenland Whale. And if you descend into the bowels of the various leviathans, why there you will not find distinctions a fiftieth part as available to the systematizer as those external ones already enumerated. What then remains? nothing but to take hold of the whales bodily, in their entire liberal volume, and boldly sort them that way. And this is the Bibliographical system here adopted; and it is the only one that can possibly succeed, for it alone is practicable. To proceed.

Book I. (*Folio*), Chapter IV. (*Hump Back*).—This whale is often seen on the northern American coast. He has been frequently captured there, and towed into harbor. He has a great pack on him like a peddler; or you might call him the Elephant and Castle whale. At any rate, the popular name for him does not sufficiently distinguish him, since the Sperm Whale also has a hump though a smaller one. His oil is not very valuable. He has baleen. He is the most gamesome and light-hearted of all the whales, making more gay foam and white water generally than any other of them.

Book I. (*Folio*), Chapter V. (*Razor Back*).—Of this whale little is known but his name. I have seen him at a distance off Cape Horn. Of a retiring nature, he eludes both hunters and philosophers. Though no coward, he has never yet shown any part of him but his back, which rises in a long sharp ridge. Let him go. I know little more of him, nor does anybody else.

Book I. (*Folio*), Chapter VI. (*Sulphur Bottom*).—Another retiring gentleman, with a brimstone belly, doubtless got by scraping along the Tartarian tiles in some of his profounder divings. He is seldom seen; at least I have never seen him except in the remoter southern seas, and then always at too great a distance to study his countenance. He is never chased; he would run away with rope-walks of line. Prodigies are told of him. Adieu, Sulphur Bottom! I can say nothing more that is true of ye, nor can the oldest Nantucketer.

Thus ends Book I. (*Folio*), and now begins Book II. (*Octavo*).

OCTAVOES.* These embrace the whales of middling magnitude, among which at present may be numbered:—I., the *Grampus*; II., the *Black Fish*; III., the *Narwhale*; IV., the *Thrasher*; V., the *Killer*.

Book II. (*Octavo*), Chapter I. (*Grampus*).—Though this fish, whose loud sonorous breathing, or rather blowing, has furnished a proverb to landsmen, is so well known a denizen of the deep, yet he is not popularly classed among whales. But possessing all the grand distinctive features of the leviathan, most naturalists have recognised him for one. He is of moderate octavo size, varying from fifteen to twenty-five feet in length, and of corresponding dimensions round the waist. He swims in herds; he is never regularly hunted, though his oil is considerable in quantity, and pretty good for light. By some fishermen his approach is regarded as premonitory of the advance of the great sperm whale.

Book II. (*Octavo*), Chapter II. (*Black Fish*).—I give the popular fishermen's names for all these fish, for generally they are the best. Where any name happens to be vague or inexpressive, I shall say so, and suggest another. I do so now touching the Black Fish, so called because blackness is the rule among almost all whales. So, call him

---

* Why this book of whales is not denominated the Quarto is very plain. Because, while the whales of this order, though smaller than those of the former order, nevertheless retain a proportionate likeness to them in figure, yet the bookbinder's Quarto volume in its dimensioned form does not preserve the shape of the Folio volume, but the Octavo volume does.

the Hyena Whale, if you please. His voracity is well known and from
the circumstance that the inner angles of his lips are curved upwards,
he carries an everlasting Mephistophelean grin on his face. This whale
averages some sixteen or eighteen feet in length. He is found in almost
all latitudes. He has a peculiar way of showing his dorsal hooked fin
in swimming, which looks something like a Roman nose. When not
more profitably employed, the sperm whale hunters sometimes capture the Hyena Whale, to keep up the supply of cheap oil for domestic
employment—as some frugal housekeepers, in the absence of company, and quite alone by themselves, burn unsavory tallow instead of
odorous wax. Though their blubber is very thin, some of these whales
will yield you upwards of thirty gallons of oil.

Book II. (*Octavo*), Chapter III. (*Narwhale*), that is, *Nostril Whale*.
—Another instance of a curiously named whale, so named I suppose
from his peculiar horn being originally mistaken for a peaked nose.
The creature is some sixteen feet in length, while its horn averages
five feet, though some exceed ten, and even attain to fifteen feet.
Strictly speaking, this horn is but a lengthened tusk, growing out from
the jaw in a line a little depressed from the horizontal. But it is only
found on the sinister side, which has an ill effect, giving its owner
something analogous to the aspect of a clumsy left-handed man. What
precise purpose this ivory horn or lance answers, it would be hard to
say. It does not seem to be used like the blade of the sword-fish and
bill-fish; though some sailors tell me that the Narwhale employs it for
a rake in turning over the bottom of the sea for food. Charley Coffin
said it was used for an ice-piercer; for the Narwhale, rising to the surface of the Polar Sea, and finding it sheeted with ice, thrusts his horn
up, and so breaks through. But you cannot prove either of these
surmises to be correct. My own opinion is, that however this one-
sided horn may really be used by the Narwhale—however that may
be—it would certainly be very convenient to him for a folder in reading
pamphlets. The Narwhale I have heard called the Tusked Whale, the
Horned Whale, and the Unicorn Whale. He is certainly a curious example of the Unicornism to be found in almost every kingdom of
animated nature. From certain cloistered old authors I have gathered
that this same sea-unicorn's horn was in ancient days regarded as the
great antidote against poison, and as such, preparations of it brought
immense prices. It was also distilled to a volatile salts for fainting
ladies the same way that the horns of the male deer are manufactured
into hartshorn. Originally it was in itself accounted an object of great
curiosity. Black Letter tells me that Sir Martin Frobisher on his return

from that voyage, when Queen Bess did gallantly wave her jewelled hand to him from a window of Greenwich Palace, as his bold ship sailed down the Thames; "when Sir Martin returned from that voyage," saith Black Letter, "on bended knees he presented to her highness a prodigious long horn of the Narwhale, which for a long period after hung in the castle at Windsor." An Irish author avers that the Earl of Leicester, on bended knees, did likewise present to her highness another horn, pertaining to a land beast of the unicorn nature.

The Narwhale has a very picturesque, leopard-like look, being of a milk-white ground color, dotted with round and oblong spots of black. His oil is very superior, clear and fine; but there is little of it, and he is seldom hunted. He is mostly found in the circumpolar seas.

Book II. (Octavo), Chapter IV. (Killer).—Of this whale little is precisely known to the Nantucketer, and nothing at all to the professed naturalists. From what I have seen of him at a distance, I should say that he was about the bigness of a grampus. He is very savage—a sort of Feegee fish. He sometimes takes the great Folio whales by the lip, and hangs there like a leech, till the mighty brute is worried to death. The Killer is never hunted. I never heard what sort of oil he has. Exception might be taken to the name bestowed upon this whale, on the ground of its indistinctness. For we are all killers, on land and on sea; Bonapartes and Sharks included.

Book II. (Octavo), Chapter V. (Thrasher).—This gentleman is famous for his tail which he uses for a ferule in thrashing his foes. He mounts the Folio Whale's back, and as he swims, he works his passage by flogging him; as some schoolmasters get along in the world by a similar process. Still less is known of the Thrasher than of the Killer. Both are outlaws, even in the lawless seas.

Thus ends Book II. (Octavo), and begins Book III. (Duodecimo).

Duodecimoes.—These include the smaller whales. I. The Huzza Porpoise. II. The Algerine Porpoise. III. The Mealy-mouthed Porpoise.

To those who have not chanced specially to study the subject, it may possibly seem strange, that fishes not commonly exceeding four or five feet should be marshalled among WHALES—a word, which, in the popular sense, always conveys an idea of hugeness. But the creatures set down above as Duodecimoes are infallibly whales, by the terms of my definition of what a whale is—i.e., a spouting fish, with a horizontal tail.

Book III. (Duodecimo), Chapter I. (Huzza Porpoise).—This is the common porpoise found all over the globe. The name is of my own bestowal; for there are more than one sort of porpoises, and something must be done to distinguish them. I call him thus, because he always swims in hilarious shoals, which upon the broad sea keep tossing themselves to heaven like caps in a Fourth-of-July crowd. Their appearance is generally hailed with delight by the mariner. Full of fine spirits, they invariably come from the breezy billows to windward. They are the lads that always live before the wind. They are accounted a lucky omen. If you yourself can withstand three cheers at beholding these vivacious fish, then heaven help ye; the spirit of godly gamesomeness is not in ye. A well-fed, plump Huzza Porpoise will yield you one good gallon of good oil. But the fine and delicate fluid extracted from his jaws is exceedingly valuable. It is in request among jewellers and watchmakers. Sailors put it on their hones. Porpoise meat is good eating, you know. It may never have occurred to you that a porpoise spouts. Indeed, his spout is so small that it is not very readily discernible. But the next time you have a chance, watch him; and you will then see the great Sperm Whale himself in miniature.

Book III. (*Duodecimo*), Chapter II. (*Algerine Porpoise*).—A pirate. Very savage. He is only found, I think, in the Pacific. He is somewhat larger than the Huzza Porpoise, but much of the same general make. Provoke him, and he will buckle to a shark. I have lowered for him many times, but never yet saw him captured.

Book III. (*Duodecimo*), Chapter III. (*Mealy-mouthed Porpoise*). —The largest kind of Porpoise; and only found in the Pacific, so far as it is known. The only English name, by which he has hitherto been designated, is that of the fisher—Right-Whale Porpoise, from the circumstance that he is chiefly found in the vicinity of that Folio. In shape, he differs in some degree from the Huzza Porpoise, being of a less rotund and jolly girth; indeed, he is of quite a neat and gentleman-like figure. He has no fins on his back (most other porpoises have), he has a lovely tail, and sentimental Indian eyes of a hazel hue. But his mealy-mouth spoils him. Though his entire back down to his side fins is of a deep sable, yet a boundary line, distinct as the mark in a ship's hull, called the "bright waist," that line streaks him from stem to stern, with two separate colors, black above and white below. The white comprises part of his head, and the whole of his mouth, which makes him look as if he had just escaped from a felonious visit to a meal-bag. A most mean and mealy aspect! His oil is much like that of the common porpoise.

*   *   *   *

Beyond the Duodecimo, this system does not proceed, inasmuch as the Porpoise is the smallest of the whales. Above, you have all the Leviathans of note. But there are a rabble of uncertain, fugitive, half-fabulous whales, which, as an American whaleman, I know by reputation, but not personally. I shall enumerate them by their fore-castle appellations; for possibly such a list may be valuable to future investigators, who may complete what I have here but begun. If any of the following whales, shall hereafter be caught and marked, then he can readily be incorporated into this System, according to his Folio, Octavo, or Duodecimo magnitude:—The Bottle-Nose Whale; the Junk Whale; the Pudding-Headed Whale; the Cape Whale; the Leading Whale; the Cannon Whale; the Scragg Whale; the Coppered Whale; the Elephant Whale; the Iceberg Whale; the Quog Whale; the Blue Whale; &c. From Icelandic, Dutch, and old English authorities, there might be quoted other lists of uncertain whales, blessed with all manner of uncouth names. But I omit them as altogether obsolete; and can hardly help suspecting them for mere sounds, full of Leviathanism, but signifying nothing.

Finally: It was stated at the outset, that this system would not be here, and at once perfected. You cannot but plainly see that I have kept my word. But I now leave my cetological System standing thus unfinished, even as the great Cathedral of Cologne was left, with the cranes still standing upon the top of the uncompleted tower. For small erections may be finished by their first architects; grand ones, true ones, ever leave the copestone to posterity. God keep me from ever completing anything. This whole book is but a draught—nay, but the draught of a draught. Oh, Time, Strength, Cash, and Patience!

SIGHTS, SOUNDS AND REFLECTIONS
AT WALDEN POND

by Henry David Thoreau

The first dip into Walden *is a red-letter day in the life of any thinking young person. It startles most of us out of our complacency, if not out of our wits. Thoreau took his stand on firm ground and then dug down to bedrock. In a world customarily bound by conformity, he fearlessly filed his minutes of dissent with a vigor and clarity that command attention. In a region where property and propriety were held in reverence that amounted almost to worship, he had little use for either. He defied the tax collector, another heresy in the eyes of his New England neighbors. He was relentless in the defense of what he believed to be his rights and in the pursuit of what he firmly stated were his aims. For all that, he was such a quiet revolutionist that he and his writings were largely ignored in his lifetime. His only admirers were his literate Concord neighbors, notably Ralph Waldo Emerson, who gave aid and comfort to his young friend in many ways. But today there are volumes of Thoreau's writings in homes and libraries in many lands and languages.*

That, however, is not the reason for his inclusion here. In this collection Thoreau appears as a true lover of Nature and a remarkably keen observer in that field, particularly during the two years he spent in his little house on the side of Walden Pond, where he had a greater opportunity to observe and more leisure to write than at any other period of his too short life. He was born at Concord, Massachusetts, July 12, 1817, and died there May 6, 1862, at the age of forty-four. The excerpts here are from Walden, *a book that has attained the stature of a classic.*

ECONOMY

IF I should attempt to tell how I have desired to spend my life in past years, it would probably surprise those of my readers who are somewhat acquainted with its actual history; it would certainly astonish those who know nothing about it. I will only hint at some of the enterprises which I have cherished.

In any weather, at any hour of the day or night, I have been anxious to improve the nick of time, and notch it on my stick, too; to stand on the meeting of two eternities, the past and future, which is precisely the present moment; to toe that line. You will pardon some obscurities, for there are more secrets in my trade than in most men's, and yet not voluntarily kept, but inseparable from its very nature. I would gladly tell all that I know about it, and never paint "No admittance" on my gate.

I long ago lost a hound, a bay horse, and a turtledove, and am still on their trail. Many are the travellers I have spoken concerning them, describing their tracks and what calls they answered to. I have met one or two who had heard the hound, and the tramp of the horse, and even seen the dove disappear behind a cloud, and they seemed as anxious to recover them as if they had lost them themselves.

To anticipate, not the sunrise and the dawn merely, but, if possible, Nature herself! How many mornings, summer and winter, before yet any neighbor was stirring about his business, have I been about mine! No doubt, many of my townsmen have met me returning from this enterprise, farmers starting for Boston in the twilight, or woodchoppers going to their work. It is true, I never assisted the sun materially in his rising, but, doubt not, it was of the last importance only to be present at it.

So many autumn, ay, and winter days, spent outside the town, trying to hear what was in the wind, to hear and carry it express! I wellnigh sunk all my capital in it, and lost my own breath into the bargain, running in the face of it. If it had concerned either of the political parties, depend upon it, it would have appeared in the Gazette with the earliest intelligence. At other times watching from the observatory of some cliff or tree, to telegraph any new arrival; or waiting at evening on the hill-tops for the sky to fall, that I might catch something, though I never caught much, and that manna-wise, would dissolve again in the sun.

For a long time I was reporter to a journal, of no very wide circulation, whose editor has never yet seen fit to print the bulk of my contributions, and, as is too common with writers, I got only my labor for my pains. However, in this case my pains were their own reward.

For many years I was self-appointed inspector of snow-storms and rain-storms, and did my duty faithfully; surveyor, if not of highways, then of forest paths and all across-lot routes, keeping them open, and ravines bridged and passable at all seasons, where the public heel had testified to their utility.

I have looked after the wild stock of the town, which give a faithful herdsman a good deal of trouble by leaping fences; and I have had an eye to the unfrequented nooks and corners of the farm; though I did not always know whether Jonas or Solomon worked in a particular field to-day; that was none of my business. I have watered the red huckleberry, the sand cherry and the nettle-tree, the red pine and the black ash, the white grape and the yellow violet, which might have withered else in dry seasons.

In short, I went on thus for a long time (I may say it without boasting), faithfully minding my business, till it became more and more evident that my townsmen would not after all admit me into the list of town officers, nor make my place a sinecure with a moderate allowance. My accounts, which I can swear to have kept faithfully, I have, indeed, never got audited, still less accepted, still less paid and settled. However, I have not set my heart on that.

*   *   *   *

SOUNDS

I did not read books the first summer; I hoed beans. Nay, I often did better than this. There were times when I could not afford to sacrifice the bloom of the present moment to any work, whether of the head or hands. I love a broad margin to my life. Sometimes, in a summer morning, having taken my accustomed bath, I sat in my sunny doorway from sunrise till noon, rapt in a revery, amidst the pines and hickories and sumachs, in undisturbed solitude and stillness, while the birds sang around or flitted noiseless through the house, until by the sun falling in at my west window, or the noise of some traveller's wagon on the distant highway, I was reminded of the lapse of time. I grew in those seasons like corn in the night, and they were far better than any work of the hand would have been. They were not time subtracted from my life, but so much over and above my usual allowance. I realized what the Orientals mean by contemplation and the forsaking of works. For the most part, I minded not how the hours went. The day advanced as if to light some work of mine; it was morning, and lo, now it is evening, and nothing memorable is accomplished. Instead of singing like the birds, I silently smiled at my incessant good fortune. As the sparrow had its trill, sitting on the hickory before my door, so had I my chuckle or suppressed warble which he might hear out of my nest. My days were not days of the week, bearing the stamp of any heathen deity, nor were they minced into hours and fretted by the ticking of a clock; for I lived like the Puri Indians, of whom it is said that "for yesterday, to-day, and to-morrow they have only one word, and they express the variety of meaning by pointing backward for yesterday, forward for to-morrow, and overhead for the passing day." This was sheer idleness to my fellow-townsmen, no doubt; but if the birds and flowers had tried me by their standard, I should not have been found wanting. A man must find his occasions in himself, it is true. The natural day is very calm, and will hardly reprove his indolence.

I had this advantage, at least, in my mode of life, over those who were obliged to look abroad for amusement, to society and the theatre, that my life itself was become my amusement and never ceased to be novel. It was a drama of many scenes and without an end. If we were always, indeed, getting our living, and regulating our lives according to the last and best mode we had learned, we should never be troubled with ennui. Follow your genius closely enough, and it will not fail to show you a fresh prospect every hour. Housework was a pleasant pastime. When my floor was dirty, I rose early, and setting all my furniture out of doors on the grass, bed and bedstead making but one budget, dashed water on the floor, and sprinkled white sand from the pond on it, and then with a broom scrubbed it clean and white; and by the time the villagers had broken their fast, the morning sun had dried my house sufficiently to allow me to move in again, and my meditations were almost uninterrupted. It was pleasant to see my whole household effects out on the grass, making a little pile like a gypsy's pack, and my three-legged table, from which I did not remove the books and pen and ink, standing amid the pines and hickories. They seemed glad to get out themselves, and as if unwilling to be brought in. I was sometimes tempted to stretch an awning over them and take my seat there. It was worth the while to see the sun shine on these things, and hear the free wind blow on them; so much more interesting most familiar objects look out of doors than in the house. A bird sits on the next bough, life-everlasting grows under the table, and blackberry vines run round its legs; pine cones, chestnut burs, and strawberry leaves are strewn about. It looked as if this was the way these forms came to be transferred to our furniture, to tables, chairs, and bedsteads,—because they once stood in their midst.

My house was on the side of a hill, immediately on the edge of the larger wood, in the midst of a young forest of pitch pines and hickories, and half a dozen rods from the pond, to which a narrow footpath led down the hill. In my front yard grew the strawberry, blackberry, and life-everlasting, johnswort and goldenrod, shrub oaks and sand cherry, blueberry and groundnut. Near the end of May, the sand cherry (*Cerasus pumila*) adorned the sides of the path with its delicate flowers arranged in umbels cylindrically about its short stems, which last, in the fall, weighed down with good-sized and handsome cherries, fell over in wreaths like rays on every side. I tasted them out of compliment to Nature, though they were scarcely palatable. The sumach (*Rhus glabra*) grew luxuriantly about the house, pushing up through the embankment which I had made, and growing five or six feet the first season. Its broad pinnate tropical leaf was pleasant though strange to look on. The large buds, suddenly pushing out late in the spring from dry sticks which had seemed to be dead, developed themselves as by magic into graceful green and tender boughs, an inch in diameter; and sometimes, as I sat at my window, so heedlessly did they grow and tax their weak joints, I heard a fresh and tender bough suddenly fall like a fan to the ground, when there was not a breath of air stirring, broken off by its own weight. In August, the large masses of berries, which, when in flower, had attracted many wild bees, gradually assumed their bright velvety crimson hue, and by their weight again bent down and broke the tender limbs.

As I sit at my window this summer afternoon, hawks are circling about my clearing; the tantivy of wild pigeons, flying by twos and threes athwart my view, or perching restless on the white pine boughs behind my house, gives a voice to the air; a fish hawk dimples the glassy surface of the pond and brings up a fish; a mink steals out of the marsh before my door and seizes a frog by the shore; the sedge is bending under the weight of the reed-birds flitting hither and thither; and for the last half-hour I have heard the rattle of railroad cars, now dying away and then reviving like the beat of a partridge, conveying travellers from Boston to the country. For I did not live so out of the world as that boy who, as I hear, was put out to a farmer in the east part of the town, but ere long ran away and came home again, quite down at the heel and homesick. He had never seen such a dull and out-of-the-way place; the folks were all gone off; why, you couldn't even hear the whistle! I doubt if there is such a place in Massachusetts now:—

> "In truth, our village has become a butt
>   For one of those fleet railroad shafts, and o'er
>   Our peaceful plain its soothing sound is—Concord."

The Fitchburg Railroad touches the pond about a hundred rods south of where I dwell. I usually go to the village along its causeway, and am, as it were, related to society by this link. The men on the freight trains, who go over the whole length of the road, bow to me as to an old acquaintance, they pass me so often, and apparently they take me for an employee; and so I am. I too would fain be a track-repairer somewhere in the orbit of the earth.

The whistle of the locomotive penetrates my woods summer and winter, sounding like the scream of a hawk sailing over some farmer's yard, informing me that many restless city merchants are arriving within the circle of the town, or adventurous country traders from the other side. As they come under one horizon, they shout their warning to get off the track to the other, heard sometimes through the circles of two towns. Here come your groceries, country; your rations, countrymen! Nor is there any man so independent on his farm that he can say them nay. And here's your pay for them! screams the country-man's whistle; timber like long battering-rams going twenty miles an hour against the city's walls, and chairs enough to seat all the weary and heavy-laden that dwell within them. With such huge and lumbering civility the country hands a chair to the city. All the Indian huckleberry hills are stripped, all the cranberry meadows are raked into the city. Up comes the cotton, down goes the woven cloth; up comes the silk, down goes the woollen; up come the books, but down goes the wit that writes them.

When I meet the engine with its train of cars moving off with planetary motion,—or, rather, like a comet, for the beholder knows not if with that velocity and with that direction it will ever revisit this system, since its orbit does not look like a returning curve,—with its steam cloud like a banner streaming behind in golden and silver wreaths, like many a downy cloud which I have seen, high in the heavens, unfolding its masses to the light,—as if this travelling demigod, this cloud-compeller, would ere long take the sunset sky for the livery of his train; when I hear the iron horse make the hills echo with his snort like thunder, shaking the earth with his feet, and breathing fire and smoke from his nostrils (what kind of winged horse or fiery dragon they will put into the new Mythology I don't know), it seems as if the earth had got a race now worthy to inhabit it. If all were as it seems, and men made the elements their servants for noble ends! If the cloud that hangs over the engine were the perspiration of heroic deeds, or as beneficent as that which floats over the farmer's fields, then the elements and Nature herself would cheerfully accompany men on their errands and be their escort.

*   *   *   *

Now that the cars are gone by and all the restless world with them, and the fishes in the pond no longer feel their rumbling, I am more alone than ever. For the rest of the long afternoon, perhaps, my meditations are interrupted only by the faint rattle of a carriage or team along the distant highway.

Sometimes, on Sundays, I heard the bells, the Lincoln, Acton, Bedford, or Concord bell, when the wind was favorable, a faint, sweet, and, as it were, natural melody, worth importing into the wilderness. At a sufficient distance over the woods this sound acquires a certain vibratory hum, as if the pine needles in the horizon were the strings of a harp which it swept. All sound heard at the greatest possible distance produces one and the same effect, a vibration of the universal lyre, just as the intervening atmosphere makes a distant ridge of earth interesting to our eyes by the azure tint it imparts to it. There came to me in this case a melody which the air had strained, and which had conversed with every leaf and needle of the wood, that portion of the sound which the elements had taken up and modulated and echoed from vale to vale. The echo is, to some extent, an original sound, and therein is the magic and charm of it. It is not merely a repetition of what was worth repeating in the bell, but partly the voice of the wood; the same trivial words and notes sung by a wood-nymph.

At evening, the distant lowing of some cow in the horizon beyond the woods sounded sweet and melodious and at first I would mistake it for the voices of certain minstrels by whom I was sometimes serenaded, who might be straying over hill and dale; but soon I was not unpleasantly disappointed when it was prolonged into the cheap and natural music of the cow. I do not mean to be satirical, but to express my appreciation of those youths' singing, when I state that I perceived clearly that it was akin to the music of the cow, and they were at length one articulation of Nature.

Regularly at half-past seven, in one part of the summer, after the evening train had gone by, the whip-poor-wills chanted their vespers for half an hour, sitting on a stump by my door, or upon the ridge-pole of the house. They would begin to sing almost with as much precision as a clock, within five minutes of a particular time, referred to the setting of the sun, every evening. I had a rare opportunity to become acquainted with their habits. Sometimes I heard four or five at once in different parts of the wood, by accident one a bar behind another, and so near me that I distinguished not only the cluck after each note, but often that singular buzzing sound like a fly in a spider's web, only proportionally louder. Sometimes one would circle round and round me in the woods a few feet distant as if tethered by a string, when probably I was near its eggs. They sang at intervals throughout the night, and were again as musical as ever just before and about dawn.

When other birds are still, the screech owls take up the strain, like mourning women their ancient u-lu-lu. Their dismal scream is truly Ben Jonsonian. Wise midnight hags! It is no honest and blunt tu-whit tu-who of the poets, but, without jesting, a most solemn graveyard ditty, the mutual consolations of suicide lovers remembering the pangs and the delights of supernal love in the infernal groves. Yet I love to hear their wailing, their doleful responses, trilled along the wood-side; reminding me sometimes of music and singing birds; as if it were the dark and tearful side of music, the regrets and sighs that would fain be sung. They are the spirits, the low spirits and melancholy fore-bodings, of fallen souls that once in human shape night-walked the earth and did the deeds of darkness, now expiating their sins with their wailing hymns or threnodies in the scenery of their transgressions. They give me a new sense of the variety and capacity of that nature which is our common dwelling. *Oh-o-o-o-o that I never had been bor-r-r-rn!* sighs one on this side of the pond, and circles with the rest-lessness of despair to some new perch on the gray oaks. Then—*that I never had been bor-r-r-rn!* echoes another on the farther side with tremulous sincerity, and—*bor-r-r-r-n!* comes faintly from far in the Lincoln woods.

I was also serenaded by a hooting owl. Near at hand you could fancy it the most melancholy sound in Nature, as if she meant by this to stereotype and make permanent in her choir the dying moans of a human being,—some poor weak relic of mortality who has left hope behind, and howls like an animal, yet with human sobs, on entering the dark valley, made more awful by a certain gurgling melodiousness,—I find myself beginning with the letters *gl* when I try to imitate it,—expressive of a mind which has reached the gelatinous, mildewy stage in the mortification of all healthy and courageous thought. It reminded me of ghouls and idiots and insane howlings. But now one answers from far woods in a strain made really melodious by distance,—*Hoo hoo hoo, hooer hoo*; and indeed for the most part it suggested only pleasing associations, whether heard by day or night, summer or winter.

I rejoice that there are owls. Let them do the idiotic and maniacal hooting for men. It is a sound admirably suited to swamps and twilight woods which no day illustrates, suggesting a vast and undeveloped nature which men have not recognized. They represent the stark twilight and unsatisfied thoughts which all have. All day the sun has shone on the surface of some savage swamp, where the single spruce stands hung with usnea lichens, and small hawks circulate above, and the chickadee lisps amid the evergreens, and the partridge and rabbit skulk beneath; but now a more dismal and fitting day dawns, and a different race of creatures awakes to express the meaning of Nature there.

Late in the evening I heard the distant rumbling of wagons over bridges,—a sound heard farther than almost any other at night,—the baying of dogs, and sometimes again the lowing of some disconsolate cow in a distant barn-yard. In the meanwhile all the shore rang with the trump of bullfrogs, the sturdy spirits of ancient wine-bibbers and wassailers, still unrepentant, trying to sing a catch in their Stygian lake,—if the Walden nymphs will pardon the comparison, for though there are almost no weeds, there are frogs there,—who would fain keep up the hilarious rules of their old festal tables, though their voices have waxed hoarse and solemnly grave, mocking at mirth, and the wine has lost its flavor, and become only liquor to distend their paunches, and sweet intoxication never comes to drown the memory of the past, but mere saturation and waterloggedness and distention. The most aldermanic, with his chin upon a heart-leaf, which serves for a napkin to his drooling chops, under this northern shore quaffs a deep draught of the once scorned water, and passes round the cup with the ejaculation *tr-r-r-oonk, tr-r-r-oonk, tr-r-r-oonk!* and straightway comes over the water from some distant cove the same password repeated, where the next in seniority and girth has gulped down to his mark; and when this observance has made the circuit of the shores, then ejaculates the master of ceremonies, with satisfaction, *tr-r-r-oonk!* and each in his turn repeats the same down to the least distended, leakiest, and flabbiest paunched, that there be no mistake; and then the bowl goes round again and again, until the sun disperses the morning mist, and only the patriarch is not under the pond, but vainly bellowing *troonk* from time to time, and pausing for a reply.

I am not sure that I ever heard the sound of cock-crowing from my clearing, and I thought that it might be worth the while to keep a cockerel for his music merely, as a singing bird. The note of this once wild Indian pheasant is certainly the most remarkable of any bird's, and if they could be naturalized without being domesticated, it would soon become the most famous sound in our woods, surpassing the clangor of the goose and the hooting of the owl; and then imagine the cackling of the hens to fill the pauses when their lords' clarions rested! No wonder that Man added this bird to his tame stock,—to say nothing of the eggs and drumsticks. To walk in a winter morning in a wood where these birds abounded, their native woods, and hear the wild cockerels crow on the trees, clear and shrill for miles over the resounding earth, drowning the feebler notes of other birds,— think of it! It would put nations on the alert. Who would not be early to rise, and rise earlier and earlier every successive day of his life, till he became unspeakably healthy, wealthy, and wise? This foreign bird's note is celebrated by the poets of all countries along with the notes of their native songsters. All climates agree with brave Chanticleer. He is more indigenous even than the natives. His health is ever good, his lungs are sound, his spirits never flag. Even the sailor on the Atlantic and Pacific is awakened by his voice; but its shrill sound never roused me from my slumbers. I kept neither dog, cat, cow, pig, nor hens, so that you would have said there was a deficiency of domestic sounds; neither the churn, nor the spinning-wheel, nor even the singing of the kettle, nor the hissing of the urn, nor children crying, to comfort one. An old-fashioned man would have lost his senses or died of ennui before this. Not even rats in the wall, for they were starved out, or rather were never baited in,—only squirrels on the roof and under the floor, a whip-poor-will on the ridge-pole, a blue jay screaming beneath the window, a hare or woodchuck under the house, a screech owl or a cat owl behind it, a flock of wild geese or a laughing loon on the pond, and a fox to bark in the night. Not even a lark or an oriole, those mild plantation birds, ever visited my clearing. No cockerels to crow nor hens to cackle in the yard. No yard! but unfenced nature reaching up to your very sills. A young forest growing up under your windows, and wild sumachs and blackberry vines breaking through into your cellar; sturdy pitch pines rubbing and creaking against the shingles for want of room, their roots reaching quite under the house. Instead of a scuttle or a blind blown off in the gale,—a pine tree snapped off or torn up by the roots behind your house for fuel. Instead of no path to the front-yard gate in the Great Snow,—no gate—no front-yard,—and no path to the civilized world.

BRUTE NEIGHBORS

The mice which haunted my house were not the common ones, which are said to have been introduced into the country, but a wild native kind not found in the village. I sent one to a distinguished naturalist, and it interested him much. When I was building, one of these had its nest underneath the house, and before I had laid the second floor, and swept out the shavings, would come out regularly at lunch time and pick up the crumbs at my feet. It probably had never seen a man before; and it soon became quite familiar, and would run over my shoes and up my clothes. It could readily ascend the sides of the room by short impulses, like a squirrel, which it resembled in its motions. At length, as I leaned with my elbow on the bench one day, it ran up my clothes, and along my sleeve, and round and round the paper which held my dinner, while I kept the latter close, and dodged and played at bopeep with it; and when at last I held still a piece of cheese between my thumb and finger, it came and nibbled it, sitting in my hand, and afterward cleaned its face and paws, like a fly, and walked away.

A phoebe soon built in my shed, and a robin for protection in a pine which grew against the house. In June the partridge (*Tetrao umbellus*), which is so shy a bird, led her brood past my windows, from the woods in the rear to the front of my house, clucking and calling to them like a hen, and in all her behavior proving herself the hen of the woods. The young suddenly disperse on your approach, at a signal from the mother, as if a whirlwind had swept them away, and they so exactly resemble the dried leaves and twigs that many a traveller has placed his foot in the midst of a brood, and heard the whir of the old bird as she flew off, and her anxious calls and mewing, or seen her trail her wings to attract his attention, without suspecting their neighborhood. The parent will sometimes roll and spin round before you in such a dishabille, that you cannot, for a few moments, detect what kind of creature it is. The young squat still and flat, often running their heads under a leaf, and mind only their mother's directions given from a distance, nor will your approach make them run again and betray themselves. You may even tread on them, or have your eyes on them for a minute, without discovering them. I have held them in my open hand at such a time, and still their only care, obedient to their mother and their instinct, was to squat there without fear or trembling. So perfect is this instinct, that once, when I had laid them on the leaves again, and one accidentally fell on its side, it was found with the rest in exactly the same position ten minutes afterward. They are not callow like the young of most birds, but more perfectly developed and precocious even than chickens. The remarkably adult yet innocent expression of their open and serene eyes is very memorable. All intelligence seems reflected in them. They suggest not merely the purity of infancy, but a wisdom clarified by experience. Such an eye was not born when the bird was, but is coeval with the sky it reflects. The woods do not yield another such a gem. The traveller does not often look into such a limpid well. The ignorant or reckless sportsman often shoots the parent at such a time, and leaves these innocents to fall a prey to some prowling beast or bird, or gradually mingle with the decaying leaves which they so much resemble. It is said that when hatched by a hen they will directly disperse on some alarm, and so are lost, for they never hear the mother's call which gathers them again. These were my hens and chickens.

It is remarkable how many creatures live wild and free though secret in the woods, and still sustain themselves in the neighborhood of towns, suspected by hunters only. How retired the otter manages to live here! He grows to be four feet long, as big as a small boy, perhaps without any human being getting a glimpse of him. I formerly saw the raccoon in the woods behind where my house is built, and probably still heard their whinnering at night. Commonly I rested an hour or two in the shade at noon, after planting, and ate my lunch, and read a little by a spring which was the source of a swamp and of a brook, oozing from under Brister's Hill, half a mile from my field. The approach to this was through a succession of descending grassy hollows, full of young pitch pines, into a larger wood about the swamp. There, in a very secluded and shaded spot, under a spreading white pine, there was yet a clean, firm sward to sit on. I had dug out the spring and made a well of clear gray water, where I could dip up a pailful without roiling it, and thither I went for this purpose almost every day in midsummer, when the pond was warmest. Thither, too, the woodcock led her brood, to probe the mud for worms, flying but a foot above them down the bank, while they ran in a troop beneath; but at last, spying me, she would leave her young and circle round and round me, nearer and nearer till within four or five feet, pretending broken wings and legs to attract my attention, and get off her young, who would already have taken up their march, with faint, wiry peep, single file through the swamp, as she directed. Or I heard the peep of the young when I could not see the parent bird. There too the turtle doves sat over the spring, or fluttered from bough to bough of the soft white pines over my head; or the red squirrel, coursing down the nearest bough, was particularly familiar and inquisitive. You only need sit still long enough in some attractive spot in the woods that all its inhabitants may exhibit themselves to you by turns.

I was witness to events of a less peaceful character. One day when I went out to my wood-pile, or rather my pile of stumps, I observed two large ants, the one red, the other much larger, nearly half an inch long, and black, fiercely contending with one another. Having once got hold they never let go, but struggled and wrestled and rolled on the chips incessantly. Looking farther, I was surprised to find that the chips were covered with such combatants, that it was not a *duellum*, but a *bellum*, a war between two races of ants, the red always pitted against the black, and frequently two red ones to one black. The legions of these Myrmidons covered all the hills and vales in my wood-yard, and the ground was already strewn with the dead and dying, both red and black. It was the only battle which I have ever witnessed, the only battle-field I ever trod while the battle was raging; intercine war; the red republicans on the one hand, and the black imperialists on the other. On every side they were engaged in deadly combat, yet without any noise that I could hear, and human soldiers never fought so resolutely. I watched a couple that were fast locked in each other's embraces, in a little sunny valley amid the chips, now at noonday prepared to fight till the sun went down, or life went out. The smaller red champion had fastened himself like a vice to his adversary's front, and through all the tumblings on that field never for an instant ceased to gnaw at one of his feelers near the root, having already caused the other to go by the board; while the stronger black one dashed him from side to side, and, as I saw on looking nearer, had already divested him of several of his members. They fought with more pertinacity than bulldogs. Neither manifested the least disposition to retreat. It was evident that their battle-cry was "Conquer or die." In the meanwhile there came along a single red ant on the hillside of this valley, evidently full of excitement, who either had despatched his foe, or had not yet taken part in the battle; probably the latter, for he had lost none of his limbs; whose mother had charged him to return with his shield or upon it. Or perchance he was some Achilles, who had nourished his wrath apart, and had now come to avenge or rescue his Patroclus. He saw this unequal combat from afar, —for the blacks were nearly twice the size of the red,—he drew near with rapid pace till he stood on his guard within half an inch of the combatants; then, watching his opportunity, he sprang upon the black warrior, and commenced his operations near the root of his right fore leg, leaving the foe to select among his own members; and so there were three united for life, as if a new kind of attraction had been invented which put all other locks and cements to shame. I should not have wondered by this time to find that they had their respective musical bands stationed on some eminent chip, and playing their national airs the while, to excite the slow and cheer the dying combatants. I was myself excited somewhat even as if they had been men. The more you think of it, the less the difference. And certainly there is not the fight recorded in Concord history, at least, if in the history of America, that will bear a moment's comparison with this, whether for the numbers engaged in it, or for the patriotism and heroism displayed. For numbers and for carnage it was an Austerlitz or Dresden. Concord Fight! Two killed on the patriots' side, and Luther Blanchard wounded! Why here every ant was a Buttrick,—"Fire! for God's sake fire!"—and thousands shared the fate of Davis and Hosmer. There was not one hireling there. I have no doubt that it was a principle they fought for, as much as our ancestors, and not to avoid a threepenny tax on their tea; and the results of this battle will be as important and memorable to those whom it concerns as those of the battle of Bunker Hill, at least.

I took up the chip on which the three I have particularly described were struggling, carried into my house, and placed it under a tumbler on my window-sill, in order to see the issue. Holding a microscope to the first-mentioned red ant, I saw that, though he was assiduously gnawing at the near fore leg of his enemy, having severed his remaining feeler, his own breast was all torn away, exposing what vitals he had there to the jaws of the black warrior, whose breastplate was apparently too thick for him to pierce; and the dark carbuncles of the sufferer's eyes shone with ferocity such as war only could excite. They struggled half an hour longer under the tumbler, and when I looked again the black soldier had severed the heads of his foes from their bodies, and the still living heads were hanging on either side of him like ghastly trophies at his saddle-bow, still apparently as firmly fastened as ever, and he was endeavoring with feeble struggles, being without feelers and with only the remnant of a leg, and I know not how many other wounds, to divest himself of them; which at length, after half an hour more, he accomplished. I raised the glass, and he went off over the window-sill in that crippled state. Whether he finally survived that combat, and spent the remainder of his days in some Hotel des Invalides, I do not know; but I thought that his industry would not be worth much thereafter. I never learned which party was victorious, nor the cause of the war; but I felt for the rest of that day as if I had had my feelings excited and harrowed by witnessing the struggle, the ferocity and carnage, of a human battle before my door.

Kirby and Spence tell us that the battles of ants have long been celebrated and the date of them recorded, though they say that Huber is the only modern author who appears to have witnessed them. "Aeneas Sylvius," say they, "after giving a very circumstantial account of one contested with great obstinacy by a great and small species on the trunk of a pear tree," adds that "'this action was fought in the pontificate of Eugenius the Fourth, in the presence of Nicholas Pistoriensis, an eminent lawyer, who related the whole history of the battle with the greatest fidelity.' A similar engagement between great and small ants is recorded by Olaus Magnus, in which the small ones, being victorious, are said to have buried the bodies of their own soldiers, but left those of their giant enemies a prey to the birds. This event happened previous to the expulsion of the tyrant Christiern the Second from Sweden." The battle which I witnessed took place in the Presidency of Polk, five years before the passage of Webster's Fugitive-Slave Bill.

Many a village Bose, fit only to course a mud-turtle in a victualling cellar, sported his heavy quarters in the woods, without the knowledge of his master, and ineffectually smelled at old fox burrows and wood-chuck's holes; led perchance by some slight cur which nimbly threaded the wood, and might still inspire a natural terror in its denizens;—now far behind his guide, barking like a canine bull toward some small squirrel which had treed itself for scrutiny, then, cantering off, bending the bushes with his weight, imagining that he is on the track of some stray member of the jerbilla family. Once I was surprised to see a cat walking along the stony shore of the pond, for they rarely wander so far from home. The surprise was mutual. Nevertheless the most domestic cat, which has lain on a rug all her days, appears quite at home in the woods, and, by her sly and stealthy behavior, proves herself more native there than the regular inhabitants. Once, when berrying, I met with a cat with young kittens in the woods, quite wild, and they all, like their mother, had their backs up and were fiercely spitting at me. A few years before I lived in the woods there was what was called a "winged cat" in one of the farm-houses in Lincoln nearest the pond, Mr. Gilian Baker's. When I called to see her in June, 1842, she was gone a-hunting in the woods, as was her wont (I am not sure whether it was a male or female, and so use the more common pronoun), but her mistress told me that she came into the neighborhood a little more than a year before, in April, and was finally taken into their house; that she was of a dark brownish-gray color, with a white spot on her throat, and white feet, and had a large bushy tail like a fox; that in the winter the fur grew thick and flatted out along her sides, forming strips ten or twelve inches long by two and a half wide, and under her chin like a muff, the upper side loose, the under matted like felt, and in the spring these appendages dropped off. They gave me a pair of her "wings," which I keep still. There is no appearance of a membrane about them. Some thought it was part flying squirrel or some other wild animal, which is not impossible, for, according to naturalists, prolific hybrids have been produced by the union of the marten and domestic cat. This would have been the right kind of cat for me to keep, if I had kept any, for why should not a poet's cat be winged as well as his horse?

In the fall the loon (*Colymbus glacialis*) came, as usual, to moult and bathe in the pond, making the woods ring with his wild laughter before I had risen. At rumor of his arrival all the Mill-dam sportsmen are on the alert, in gigs and on foot, two by two and three by three, with patent rifles and conical balls and spy-glasses. They come rustling through the woods like autumn leaves, at least ten men to one loon. Some station themselves on this side of the pond, some on that, for the poor bird cannot be omnipresent; if he dive here he must come up there. But now the kind October wind rises, rustling the leaves and rippling the surface of the water, so that no loon can be heard or seen, though his foes sweep the pond with spy-glasses, and make the woods resound with their discharges. The waves generously rise and dash angrily, taking sides with all water-fowl, and our sportsmen must beat a retreat to town and shop and unfinished jobs. But they were too often successful. When I went to get a pail of water early in the morning I frequently saw this stately bird sailing out of my cove within a few rods. If I endeavored to overtake him in a boat, in order to see how he would manoeuvre, he would dive and be completely lost, so that I did not discover him again, sometimes, till the latter part of the day. But I was more than a match for him on the surface. He commonly went off in a rain.

As I was paddling along the north shore one very calm afternoon, for such days especially they settle on to the lakes, like the milkweed down, having looked in vain over the pond for a loon, suddenly one, sailing out from the shore toward the middle a few rods in front of me, set up his wild laugh and betrayed himself. I pursued with a paddle and he dived, but when he came up I was nearer than before. He dived again, but I miscalculated the direction he would take, and we were fifty rods apart when he came to the surface this time, for I had helped to widen the interval; and again he laughed long and loud, and with more reason than before. He manoeuvred so cunningly that I could not get within half a dozen rods of him. Each time, when he came to the surface, turning his head this way and that, he coolly surveyed the water and the land, and apparently chose his course so that he might come up where there was the widest expanse of water and at the greatest distance from the boat. It was surprising how quickly he made up his mind and put his resolve into execution. He led me at once to the widest part of the pond, and could not be driven from it. While he was thinking one thing in his brain, I was endeavoring to divine his thought in mine. It was a pretty game, played on the smooth surface of the pond, a man against a loon. Suddenly your adversary's checker disappears beneath the board, and the problem is to place yours nearest to where his will appear again. Sometimes he would come up unexpectedly on the opposite side of me, having apparently passed directly under the boat. So long-winded was he and so un-weariable, that when he had swum farthest he would immediately plunge again, nevertheless; and then no wit could divine where in the deep pond, beneath the smooth surface, he might be speeding his way like a fish, for he had time and ability to visit the bottom of the pond in its deepest part. It is said that loons have been caught in the New York lakes eighty feet beneath the surface, with hooks set for trout,—though Walden is deeper than that. How surprised must the fishes be to see this ungainly visitor from another sphere speeding his way amid their schools! Yet he appeared to know his course as surely under water as on the surface, and swam much faster there. Once or twice I saw a ripple where he approached the surface, just put his head out to reconnoitre, and instantly dived again. I found that it was as well for me to rest on my oars and wait his reappearing as to endeavor to calculate where he would rise; for again and again, when I was straining my eyes over the surface one way, I would suddenly be star-tled by his unearthly laugh behind me. But why, after displaying so much cunning, did he invariably betray himself the moment he came up by that loud laugh? Did not his white breast enough betray him? He was indeed a silly loon, I thought. I could commonly hear the plash of the water when he came up, and so also detected him. But after an hour he seemed as fresh as ever, dived as willingly, and swam yet farther than at first. It was surprising to see how serenely he sailed off without unruffled breast when he came to the surface, doing all the work with his webbed feet beneath. His usual note was this de-moniac laughter, yet somewhat like that of a waterfowl; but occasion-ally, when he had balked me most successfully and come up a long way off, he uttered a long-drawn unearthly howl, probably more like that of a wolf than any bird; as when a beast puts his muzzle to the ground and deliberately howls. This was his looning,—perhaps the wildest sound that is ever heard here, making the woods ring far and wide. I concluded that he laughed in derision of my efforts, confident of his own resources. Though the sky was by this time overcast, the pond was so smooth that I could see where he broke the surface when I did not hear him. His white breast, the stillness of the air, and the smoothness of the water were all against him. At length, having come up fifty rods off, he uttered one of those prolonged howls, as if calling on the god of loons to aid him, and immediately there came a wind from the east and rippled the surface, and filled the whole air with misty rain, and I was impressed as if it were the prayer of the loon answered, and his god was angry with me; and so I left him disappearing far away on the tumultuous surface.

For hours, in fall days, I watched the ducks cunningly tack and veer and hold the middle of the pond, far from the sportsman; tricks which they will have less need to practise in Louisiana bayous. When compelled to rise they would sometimes circle round and round and over the pond at a considerable height, from which they could easily see to other ponds and the river, like black motes in the sky; and, when I thought they had gone off thither long since, they would settle down by a slanting flight of a quarter of a mile on to a distant part which was left free; but what beside safety they got by sailing in the middle of Walden I do not know, unless they love its water for the same reason that I do.

THANATOPSIS

To him who, in the love of Nature, holds
Communion with her visible forms, she speaks
A various language: for his gayer hours
She has a voice of gladness, and a smile
And eloquence of beauty; and she glides
Into his darker musings with a mild
And gentle sympathy, that steals away
Their sharpness, ere he is aware. When thoughts
Of the last bitter hour come like a blight
Over thy spirit, and sad images
Of the stern agony, and shroud, and pall,
And breathless darkness, and the narrow house,
Make thee to shudder, and grow sick at heart,—
Go forth under the open sky, and list
To Nature's teachings, while from all around—
Earth and her waters, and the depths of air—
Comes a still voice,—Yet a few days, and thee
The all-beholding sun shall see no more
In all his course; nor yet in the cold ground,
Where thy pale form was laid with many tears,
Nor in the embrace of ocean, shall exist
Thy image. Earth, that nourished thee, shall claim
Thy growth, to be resolved to earth again;
And, lost each human trace, surrendering up

Thine individual being, shalt thou go
To mix forever with the elements;
To be a brother to the insensible rock,
And to the sluggish clod, which the rude swain
Turns with his share and treads upon. The oak
Shall send his roots abroad, and pierce thy mould.

Yet not to thine eternal resting-place
Shalt thou retire alone,—nor couldst thou wish
Couch more magnificent. Thou shalt lie down
With patriarchs of the infant world,—with kings,
The powerful of the earth,—the wise, the good,
Fair forms, and hoary seers of ages past,
All in one mighty sepulchre. The hills,
Rock-ribbed, and ancient as the sun; the vales
Stretching in pensive quietness between;
The venerable woods; rivers that move
In majesty, and the complaining brooks,
That make the meadows green; and, poured round all,
Old ocean's gray and melancholy waste,—
Are but the solemn decorations all
Of the great tomb of man! The golden sun,
The planets, all the infinite host of heaven,
Are shining on the sad abodes of death
Through the still lapse of ages. All that tread
The globe are but a handful to the tribes
That slumber in its bosom. Take the wings
Of morning, and the Barcan desert pierce,
Or lose thyself in the continuous woods
Where rolls the Oregon, and hears no sound
Save its own dashings,—yet the dead are there!
And millions in those solitudes, since first
The flight of years began, have laid them down
In their last sleep,—the dead reign there alone!
So shalt thou rest; and what if thou withdraw
In silence from the living, and no friend
Take note of thy departure? All that breathe
Will share thy destiny. The gay will laugh
When thou art gone, the solemn brood of care
Plod on, and each one, as before, will chase
His favorite phantom; yet all these shall leave
Their mirth and their employments, and shall come
And make their bed with thee. As the long train
Of ages glide away, the sons of men—

The youth in life's green spring, and he who goes
In the full strength of years, matron and maid,
And the sweet babe, and the gray-headed man—
Shall, one by one, be gathered to thy side
By those who in their turn shall follow them.

So live, that when thy summons comes to join
The innumerable caravan that moves
To that mysterious realm where each shall take
His chamber in the silent halls of death,
Thou go not like the quarry-slave at night,
Scourged to his dungeon, but, sustained and soothed
By an unfaltering trust, approach thy grave
Like one who wraps the drapery of his couch
About him, and lies down to pleasant dreams.

WILLIAM CULLEN BRYANT

ON THE BEACH AT SAN DIEGO

by Richard Henry Dana

---

*The brutalities to which seamen were subjected in the days of
sailing ships were known to all. Dr. Samuel Johnson said nearly
two centuries ago of sailor life: "Being in a ship is being in jail,
with the chance of being drowned." For all that, the book from
which the following selection was taken,* Two Years Before The
Mast, *created a sensation when it was published in 1840 because
of the author's eyewitness account of his captain's barbarous mis-
treatment of some of his shipmates. Most of the ordinary seamen
of sailing days were illiterate, and usually an "X" marked the
spot where a signature should have been when a man signed articles. Richard Henry Dana, born in Cambridge, Massachusetts,
August 1, 1815, was a college student at Harvard when he decided to go to sea in the hope of improving his health, particularly his eyesight, which weakened under his studying. He was
nineteen when he signed aboard the brig* Pilgrim *of Boston for
a voyage to California that began in August, 1834, and ended
when the ship arrived back in Boston Harbor in September, 1836.*

*In more than one way the voyage was a success. Young Dana
returned much improved in health. The shipowners made a profit
on the voyage. And four years later when Dana, then a young
lawyer, published his book, public indignation forced the enact-
ment of laws to better the lot of men before the mast. Dana went
on to considerable success at the bar and became an authority on
international law. He died in Rome, Italy, January 6, 1882. His
factual account of his two-year voyage is a classic of its kind, and
his story of his experiences ashore and afloat still makes fascinating reading. The cargo they sought in California was bullock
hides for the leather trade back in New England. Dana's description of the duties and diversions of the shore party at San*

Diego will give the reader an idea of what the California countryside was like a century and a quarter ago.

THE morning after my landing I began the duties of hide-curing. In order to understand these, it will be necessary to give the whole history of a hide, from the time it is taken from a bullock until it is put on board the vessel to be carried to Boston. When the hide is taken from the bullock, holes are cut round it, near the edge, by which it is staked out to dry. In this manner it dries without shrinking. After the hides are thus dried in the sun, and doubled with the skin out, they are received by the vessels at the different ports on the coast, and brought down to the depot at San Diego. The vessels land them, and leave them in large piles near the houses. Then begins the hide-curer's duty.

The first thing is to put them in soak. This is done by carrying them down at low tide, and making them fast, in small piles, by ropes, and letting the tide come up and cover them. Every day we put in soak twenty-five for each man, which, with us, made a hundred and fifty. There they lie forty-eight hours, when they are taken out, and rolled up in wheelbarrows, and thrown into the vats. These vats contain brine, made very strong—being sea-water, with great quantities of salt thrown in. This pickles the hides, and in this they lie forty-eight hours; the use of the sea-water, into which they are first put, being merely to soften and clean them. From these vats they are taken, and lie on a platform for twenty-four hours, and then are spread upon the ground, and carefully stretched and staked out, with the skin up, that they may dry smooth. After they had been staked, and while yet wet and soft, we used to go upon them with our knives, and carefully cut off all the bad parts—the pieces of meat and fat, which would corrupt and infect the whole if stowed away in a vessel for many months, the large *flippers*, the ears, and all other parts which would prevent close stowage. This was the most difficult part of our duty, as it required much skill to take off everything that ought to come off, and not to cut or injure the hide. It was also a long process, as six of us had to clean a hundred and fifty, most of which required a great deal to be done to them, as the Spaniards are very careless in skinning their cattle. Then, too, as we cleaned them while they were staked out, we were obliged to kneel down upon them, which always gives beginners the backache. The first day I was so slow and awkward that I cleaned only eight; at the end of a few days I doubled my number; and in a fortnight or three weeks could keep up with the others, and clean my twenty-five.

This cleaning must be got through with before noon, for by that time the hides get too dry. After the sun has been upon them a few hours they are carefully gone over with scrapers, to get off all the grease which the sun brings out. This being done, the stakes are pulled up, and the hides carefully doubled, with the hair side out, and left to dry. About the middle of the afternoon they are turned over, for the other side to dry, and at sundown piled up and covered over. The next day they are spread out and opened again, and at night, if fully dry, are thrown upon a long, horizontal pole, five at a time, and beaten with flails. This takes all the dust from them. Then, having been salted, scraped, cleaned, dried, and beaten, they are stowed away in the house. Here ends their history, except that they are taken out again when the vessel is ready to go home, beaten, stowed away on board, carried to Boston, tanned, made into shoes and other articles for which leather is used, and many of them, very probably, in the end, are brought back again to California in the shape of shoes, and worn out in pursuit of other bullocks, or in the curing of other hides.

By putting a hundred and fifty in soak every day, we had the same number at each stage of curing on each day; so that we had, every day, the same work to do upon the same number—a hundred and fifty to put in soak, a hundred and fifty to wash out and put in the vat, the same number to haul from the vat and put on the platform to drain, the same number to spread and stake out and clean, the same number to beat and stow away in the house. I ought to except Sunday; for, by a prescription which no captain or agent has yet ventured to break in upon, Sunday has been a day of leisure on the beach for years. On Saturday night the hides, in every stage of process, are carefully covered up, and not uncovered until Monday morning. On Sundays we had absolutely no work to do, unless it might be to kill a bullock, which was sent down for our use about once a week, and sometimes came on Sunday. Another advantage of the hide-curing life was, that we had just so much work to do, and when that was through, the time was our own. Knowing this, we worked hard, and needed no driving. We "turned out" every morning with the first signs of daylight, and allowing a short time, at about eight o'clock, for breakfast, generally got through our labour between one and two o'clock, when we dined, and had the rest of the time to ourselves, until just before sundown, when we beat the dry hides and put them in the house, and covered over all the others. By this means we had about three hours to ourselves every afternoon, and at sundown we had our supper, and our work was done for the day. There was no watch to stand, and no topsails to reef. The evenings we generally spent at one another's houses, and I often went up and spent an hour or so at the oven, which was called the "Kanaka Hotel," and the "Oahu Coffee-house." Immediately after dinner we usually took a short siesta, to make up for our early rising, and spent the rest of the afternoon according to our own fancies. I generally read, wrote, and made or mended clothes; for necessity, the mother of invention, had taught me these two latter arts. The Kanakas went up to the oven, and spent the time in sleeping, talking, and smoking, and my mess-mate, Nicholas, who neither knew how to read nor write, passed away the time by a long siesta, two or three smokes with his pipe, and a *paseo* to the other houses. This leisure time is never interfered with, for the captains know that the men earn it by working hard and fast, and that, if they interfered with it, the men could easily make their twenty-five hides apiece last through the day. We were pretty independent, too; for the master of the house —"capitan de la casa"—had nothing to say to us except when we were at work on the hides; and although we could not go up to town without his permission, this was seldom or never refused.

The great weight of the wet hides, which we were obliged to roll about in wheelbarrows; the continual stooping upon those which were pegged out to be cleaned; and the smell of the nasty vats, into which we were often obliged to wade, knee-deep, to press down the hides— all made the work disagreeable and fatiguing: but we soon became hardened to it, and the comparative independence of our life reconciled us to it, for there was nobody to *haze* us and find fault; and when we were through for the day we had only to wash and change our clothes, and our time was our own. There was, however, one exception to the time being our own, which was, that on two afternoons of every week we were obliged to go off for wood for the cook to use in the galley. Wood is very scarce in the vicinity of San Diego, there being no trees of any size for miles. In the town, the inhabitants burn the small wood which grows in thickets, and for which they send out Indians in large numbers, every few days. Fortunately the climate is so fine that they have no need of a fire in their houses, and only use it for cooking. With us, the getting of wood was a great trouble; for all that in the vicinity of the houses had been cut down, and we were obliged to go off a mile or two, and to carry it some distance on our backs, as we could not get the hand-cart up the hills and over the uneven places. Two afternoons in the week, generally Monday and Thursday, as soon as we were through dinner, we started off for the bush, each of us furnished with a hatchet and a long piece of rope, and dragging the hand-cart behind us, and followed by the whole colony of dogs, which were always ready for the bush, and were half mad whenever they saw our preparations. We went with the hand-cart as far as we could conveniently drag it, and, leaving it in an open, conspicuous space, separated ourselves, each taking his own course, and looking about for some good place to begin upon. Frequently we had to go nearly a mile from the hand-cart before we could find any fit place. Having lighted upon a good thicket, the next thing was to clear away the underbrush, and have fair play at the trees. These trees are seldom more than five or six feet high, and the highest that I ever saw in these expeditions could not have been more than twelve, so that, with lopping off the branches and clearing away the underwood, we had a good deal of cutting to do for a very little wood. Having cut enough for a "back-load," the next thing was to make it well fast with the rope, and heaving the bundle upon our backs, and taking the hatchet in hand, to walk off, up hill and down dale, to the hand-cart. Two good back-loads apiece filled the hand-cart, and that was each one's proportion. When each had brought down his second load, we filled the hand-cart, and took our way again slowly back to the beach. It was generally sundown when we got back; and unloading, covering the hides for the night, and getting our supper, finished the day's work.

These wooding excursions had always a mixture of something rather pleasant in them. Roaming about in the woods with hatchet in hand, like a backwoodsman, followed by a troop of dogs, starting up birds, snakes, hares, and foxes, and examining the various kinds of trees, flowers, and birds'-nests, was, at least, a change from the monotonous drag and pull on shipboard. Frequently, too, we had some amusement and adventure. The coyotes, of which I have before spoken—a sort of mixture of the fox and wolf breeds—fierce little animals, with bushy tails and large heads, and a quick, sharp bark, abound here, as in all other parts of California. These the dogs were very watchful for, and, whenever they saw them, started off in full run after them. We had many fine chases; yet, although our dogs ran finely, the rascals generally escaped. They are a match for the dog—one to one—but as the dogs generally went in squads, there was seldom a fair fight. A smaller dog, belonging to us, once attacked a coyote singly, and was considerably worsted, and might, perhaps, have been killed, had we not come to his assistance. We had, however, one dog which gave them a good deal of trouble and many hard runs. He was a fine, tall fellow, and united strength and agility better than any dog that I have ever seen. He was born at the islands, his father being an English mastiff, and his mother a greyhound. He had the high head, long legs, narrow body, and springing gait of the latter, and the heavy jaw, thick jowls, and strong fore-quarters of the mastiff. When he was brought to San Diego, an English sailor said that he looked about the face like the Duke of Wellington, whom he had once seen at the Tower; and, indeed, there was something about him which resembled the portraits of the Duke. From this time he was christened "Welly," and became the favourite and bully of the beach. He always led the dogs by several yards in the chase, and had killed two coyotes at different times in single combats. We often had fine sport with these fellows. A quick, sharp bark from a coyote, and in an instant every dog was at the height of his speed. A few minutes made up for an unfair start, and gave each dog his right place. Welly, at the head, seemed almost to skim over the bushes, and after him came Fanny, Feliciana, Childers, and the other fleet ones—the spaniels and terriers; and then, behind, followed the heavy corps—bull-dogs, etc., for we had every breed. Pursuit by us was in vain, and in about half an hour the dogs would begin to come panting and straggling back.

Besides the coyotes, the dogs sometimes made prizes of rabbits and hares, which are plentiful here, and numbers of which we often shot for our dinners. Among the other animals there was a reptile I was not so much disposed to find amusement from, the rattlesnake. These snakes are very abundant here, especially during the spring of the year. The latter part of the time that I was on shore I did not meet with so many, but for the first two months we seldom went into "the bush" without one of our number starting some of them. I remember perfectly well the first one that I ever saw. I had left my companions, and was beginning to clear away a fine clump of trees, when, just in the midst of the thicket, but a few yards from me, one of these fellows set up his hiss. It is a sharp, continuous sound, and resembles very much the letting off of the steam from the small pipe of a steamboat, except that it is on a smaller scale. I knew, by the sound of an axe, that one of my companions was near, and called out to him, to let him know what I had fallen upon. He took it very lightly, and as he seemed inclined to laugh at me for being afraid, I determined to keep my place. I knew that so long as I could hear the rattle I was safe, for these snakes never make a noise when they are in motion. Accordingly I continued my work, and the noise which I made with cutting and breaking the trees kept him in alarm; so that I had the rattle to show me his whereabouts. Once or twice the noise stopped for a short time, which gave me a little uneasiness, and retreating a few steps, I threw something into the bush, at which he would set his rattle a-going, and, finding that he had not moved from his first place, I was easy again. In this way I continued at my work until I had cut a full load, never suffering him to be quiet for a moment. Having cut my load, I strapped it together, and got everything ready for starting. I felt that I could now call the others without the imputation of being afraid, and went in search of them. In a few minutes we were all collected, and began an attack upon the bush. The big Frenchman, who was the one that I had called to at first, I found as little inclined to approach the snake as I had been. The dogs, too, seemed afraid of the rattle, and kept up a barking at a safe distance; but the Kanakas showed no fear, and getting long sticks, went into the bush, and keeping a bright lookout, stood within a few feet of him. One or two blows struck near him, and a few stones thrown, started him, and we lost his track, and had the pleasant consciousness that he might be directly under our feet. By throwing stones and chips in different directions we made him spring his rattle again, and began another attack. This time we drove him into the clear ground, and saw him gliding off, with head and tail erect, when a stone, well aimed, knocked him over the bank, down a declivity of fifteen or twenty feet, and stretched him at his length. Having made sure of him by a few more stones, we went down, and one of the Kanakas cut off his rattle. These rattles vary in number, it is said, according to the age of the snake; though the Indians think they indicate the number of creatures they have killed. We always preserved them as trophies, and at the end of the summer had a considerable collection. None of our people were bitten by them, but one of our dogs died of a bite, and another was supposed to have been bitten, but recovered. We had no remedy for a bite, though it was said that the Indians of the country had, and the Kanakas professed to have an herb which would cure it, but it was fortunately never brought to the test.

Hares and rabbits, as I said before, were abundant, and during the winter months the waters are covered with wild ducks and geese. Crows, too, abounded, and frequently alighted in great numbers upon our hides, picking up the pieces of dried meat and fat. Bears and wolves are numerous in the upper parts of the coast, and in the interior (and, indeed, a man was killed by a bear within a few miles of San Pedro, while we were there), but there were none in our immediate neighbourhood. The only other animals were horses. Over a dozen of these were owned by men on the beach, and were allowed to run loose among the hills, with a long lasso attached to them, to pick up feed wherever they could find it. We were sure of seeing them once a day, for there was no water among the hills, and they were obliged to come down to the well which had been dug upon the beach. These horses were bought at from two to six and eight dollars apiece, and were held very much as common property. We generally kept one fast to one of the houses, so that we could mount him and catch any of the others. Some of them were really fine animals, and gave us many good runs up to the presidio and over the country.

NATURE

The world is too much with us; late and soon,
Getting and spending, we lay waste our powers:
Little we see in Nature that is ours;
We have given our hearts away, a sordid boon!
The Sea that bares her bosom to the moon;
The winds that will be howling at all hours,
And are up-gathered now like sleeping flowers;
For this, for everything, we are out of tune;
It moves us not.—Great God! I'd rather be
A Pagan, suckled in a creed outworn,
So might I, standing on this pleasant lea,
Have glimpses that would make me less forlorn;
Have sight of Proteus rising from the sea;
Or hear old Triton blow his wreathèd horn.

WILLIAM WORDSWORTH

A DISSERTATION ON
NEW ENGLAND ELMS

by Oliver Wendell Holmes

This is taken from The Autocrat of the Breakfast Table, *a noble volume of kindly sentiment and genial philosophy. As has been mentioned elsewhere, every New Englander either inherits or absorbs at least a modicum of interest in Nature. A century ago there was also, throughout the same region, something of a tribal enthusiasm for harness "hosses" that could step a mile in 2:40 or better, and the genial Autocrat owned to it himself in verse. He was an exception, however, among New Englanders in extending his sporting experiences as far as the English Turf. He probably was the only New Englander, and certainly the only New England eminent author and anatomist, to witness the running of two Epsom Derbies that were more than fifty years apart. He saw Plenipotentiary win at Epsom Downs in 1834 when he was a young man of twenty-five, and he saw Ormonde win in 1886 when he was three times that age, a literary celebrity, and the guest of the Prince of Wales at the running of the Derby. In the same book in which Oliver Wendell Holmes boasts of these sporting expeditions,* Our Hundred Days in Europe, *he includes some comment on English elms and other trees, but it's quite evident that he remained faithful to his first love, the favorite elm of New England, "Ulmus americana," the subject of the following selection.*

I WONDER how my great trees are coming on this summer.
—Where are your great trees, Sir?—said the divinity-student.
Oh, all round about New England. I call all trees mine that I have put my wedding-ring on, and I have as many tree-wives as Brigham Young has human ones.

—One set's as green as the other,—exclaimed a boarder, who has never been identified.

They're all Bloomers,—said the young fellow called John.

[I should have rebuked this trifling with language, if our landlady's daughter had not asked me just then what I meant by putting my wedding-ring on a tree.]

Why, measuring it with my thirty-foot tape, my dear,—said I,—I have worn a tape almost out on the rough barks of our old New England elms and other big trees.—Don't you want to hear me talk trees a little now? That is one of my specialties.

[So they all agreed that they should like to hear me talk about trees.]

I want you to understand, in the first place, that I have a most intense, passionate fondness for trees in general, and have had several romantic attachments to certain trees in particular. Now, if you expect me to hold forth in a "scientific" way about my tree-loves,—to talk, for instance, of the Ulmus Americana, and describe the ciliated edges of its samara, and all that,—you are an anserine individual, and I must refer you to a dull friend who will discourse to you of such matters. What should you think of a lover who should describe the idol of his heart in the language of science, thus: Class, Mammalia; Order, Primates; Genus, Homo; Species, Europeus; Variety, Brown; Individual, Ann Eliza; Dental Formula,

$$i\frac{2-2}{2-2} \quad c\frac{1-1}{1-1} \quad p\frac{2-2}{2-2} \quad m\frac{3-3}{3-3}, \text{ and so on?}$$

No, my friends, I shall speak of trees as we see them, love them, adore them in the fields, where they are alive, holding their green sunshades over our heads, talking to us with their hundred thousand whispering tongues, looking down on us with that sweet meekness which belongs to huge, but limited organisms,—which one sees in the brown eyes of oxen, but most in the patient posture, the outstretched arms, and the heavy-drooping robes of these vast beings endowed with life, but not with soul,—which outgrow us and outlive us, but stand helpless,—poor things!—while Nature dresses and undresses them, like so many full-sized, but under-witted children.

Did you ever read old Daddy Gilpin? Slowest of men, even of English men; yet delicious in his slowness, as is the light of a sleepy eye in woman. I always supposed "Dr. Syntax" was written to make fun of him. I have a whole set of his works, and am very proud of it, with

its gray paper, and open type, and long *ff*, and orange-juice landscapes.
Père Gilpin had the kind of science I like in the study of Nature,—
a little less observation than White of Selborne, but a little more poetry.—Just think of applying the Linnaean system to an elm! Who
cares how many stamens or pistils that little brown flower, which
comes out before the leaf, may have to classify it by? What we want
is the meaning, the character, the expression of a tree, as a kind and
as an individual.

There is a mother-idea in each particular kind of tree, which, if well
marked, is probably embodied in the poetry of every language. Take
the oak, for instance, and we find it always standing as a type of
strength and endurance. I wonder if you ever thought of the single
mark of supremacy which distinguishes this tree from those around
it? The others shirk the work of resisting gravity; the oak defies it. It
chooses the horizontal direction for its limbs so that their whole weight
may tell,—and then stretches them out fifty or sixty feet, so that the
strain may be mighty enough to be worth resisting. You will find, that,
in passing from the extreme downward droop of the branches of the
weeping-willow to the extreme upward inclination of those of the poplar, they sweep nearly half a circle. At 90° the oak stops short; to slant
upward another degree would mark infirmity of purpose; to bend
downwards, weakness of organization. The American elm betrays
something of both; yet sometimes, as we shall see, puts on a certain
resemblance to its sturdier neighbor.

It won't do to be exclusive in our taste about trees. There is hardly
one of them which has not peculiar beauties in some fitting place for
it. I remember a tall poplar of monumental proportions and aspect, a
vast pillar of glossy green, placed on the summit of a lofty hill, and a
beacon to all the country round. A native of that region saw fit to
build his house very near it, and, having a fancy that it might blow
down some time or other, and exterminate himself and any incidental
relatives who might be "stopping" or "tarrying" with him,—also laboring under the delusion that human life is under all circumstances to
be preferred to vegetable existence,—had the great poplar cut down.
It is so easy to say, "It is only a poplar," and so much harder to re-
place its living cone than to build a granite obelisk!

I must tell you about some of my tree-wives. I was at one period
of my life much devoted to the young lady-population of Rhode Island, a small but delightful State in the neighborhood of Pawtucket.
The number of inhabitants being not very large, I had leisure, during

my visits to the Providence Plantations, to inspect the face of the country in the intervals of more fascinating studies of physiognomy. I heard some talk of a great elm a short distance from the locality just mentioned. "Let us see the great elm,"—I said, and proceeded to find it,—knowing that it was on a certain farm in a place called Johnston, if I remember rightly. I shall never forget my ride and my introduction to the great Johnston elm.

I always tremble for a celebrated tree when I approach it for the first time. Provincialism has no *scale* of excellence in man or vegetable; it never knows a first-rate article of either kind when it has it, and is constantly taking second and third rate ones for Nature's best. I have often fancied the tree was afraid of me, and that a sort of shiver came over it as over a betrothed maiden when she first stands before the unknown to whom she has been plighted. Before the measuring tape the proudest tree of them all quails and shrinks into itself. All those stories of four or five men stretching their arms around it and not touching each other's fingers, of one's pacing the shadow at noon and making it so many hundred feet, die upon its leafy lips in the presence of the awful ribbon which has strangled so many false pretensions.

As I rode along the pleasant way, watching eagerly for the object of my journey, the rounded tops of the elms rose from time to time at the road-side. Wherever one looked taller and fuller than the rest, I asked myself,—"Is this it?" But as I drew nearer, they grew smaller, —or it proved, perhaps, that two standing in a line had looked like one, and so deceived me. At last, all at once, when I was not thinking of it, —I declare to you it makes my flesh creep when I think of it now,— all at once I saw a great green cloud swelling in the horizon, so vast, so symmetrical, of such Olympian majesty and imperial supremacy among the lesser forest-growths, that my heart stopped short, then jumped at my ribs as a hunter springs at a five-barred gate, and I felt all through me, without need of uttering the words,—"This is it!"

You will find this tree described, with many others, in the excellent Report upon the Trees and Shrubs of Massachusetts. The author has given my friend the Professor credit for some of his measurements, but measured this tree himself, carefully. It is a grand elm for size of trunk, spread of limbs, and muscular development,—one of the first, perhaps the first, of the first class of New England elms.

The largest actual girth I have ever found at five feet from the ground is in the great elm lying a stone's throw or two north of the main road (if my points of compass are right) in Springfield. But this has much the appearance of having been formed by the union of two trunks growing side by side.

The West-Springfield elm and one upon Northampton meadows belong also to the first class of trees.

There is a noble old wreck of an elm at Hatfield, which used to spread its claws out over a circumference of thirty-five feet or more before they covered the foot of its bole up with earth. This is the American elm most like an oak of any I have ever seen.

The Sheffield elm is equally remarkable for size and perfection of form. I have seen nothing that comes near it in Berkshire County, and few to compare with it anywhere. I am not sure that I remember any other first-class elms in New England, but there may be many.

—What makes a first-class elm?—Why, size, in the first place, and chiefly. Anything over twenty feet of clear girth, five feet above the ground, and with a spread of branches a hundred feet across, may claim that title, according to my scale. All of them, with the questionable exception of the Springfield tree above referred to, stop, so far as my experience goes, at about twenty-two or twenty-three feet of girth and a hundred and twenty of spread.

Elms of the second class, generally ranging from fourteen to eighteen feet, are comparatively common. The queen of them all is that glorious tree near one of the churches in Springfield. Beautiful and stately she is beyond all praise. The "great tree" on Boston common comes in the second rank, as does the one at Cohasset, which used to have, and probably has still, a head as round as an apple-tree, and that at Newburyport, with scores of others which might be mentioned. These last two have perhaps been over-celebrated. Both, however, are pleasing vegetables. The poor old Pittsfield elm lives on its past reputation. A wig of false leaves is indispensable to make it presentable.

[I don't doubt there may be some monster-elm or other, vegetating green, but inglorious, in some remote New England village, which only wants a sacred singer to make it celebrated. Send us your measurements,—(certified by the postmaster, to avoid possible imposition),—circumference five feet from soil, length of line from bough-end to bough-end, and we will see what can be done for you.]

—I wish somebody would get us up the following work:—

SYLVA NOVANGLICA.

Photographs of New England Elms and other Trees, taken upon the Same Scale of Magnitude. With Letter-Press Descriptions, by a Distinguished Literary Gentleman. Boston —— —— & Co. 185 . . .

The same camera should be used,—so far as possible,—at a fixed distance. Our friend, who has given us so many interesting figures in his "Trees of America," must not think this Prospectus invades his province; a dozen portraits, with lively descriptions, would be a pretty complement to his large work, which, so far as published, I find excellent. If my plan were carried out, and another series of a dozen English trees photographed on the same scale, the comparison would be charming.

It has always been a favorite idea of mine to bring the life of the Old and the New World face to face, by an accurate comparison of their various types of organization. We should begin with man, of course; institute a large and exact comparison between the development of *la pianta umana*, as Alfieri called it, in different sections of each country, in the different callings, at different ages, estimating height, weight, force by the dynamometer and the spirometer, and finishing off with a series of typical photographs, giving the principal national physiognomies. Mr. Hutchinson has given us some excellent English data to begin with.

Then I would follow this up by contrasting the various parallel forms of life in the two continents. Our naturalists have often referred to this incidentally or expressly; but the *animus* of Nature in the two half globes of the planet is so momentous a point of interest to our race, that it should be made a subject of express and elaborate study. Go out with me into that walk which we call *the Mall*, and look at the English and American elms. The American elm is tall, graceful, slender-sprayed, and drooping as if from languor. The English elm is compact, robust, holds its branches up, and carries its leaves for weeks longer than our own native tree.

Is this typical of the creative force on the two sides of the ocean, or not? Nothing but a careful comparison through the whole realm of life can answer this question.

There is a parallelism without identity in the animal and vegetable life of the two continents, which favors the task of comparison in an extraordinary manner. Just as we have two trees alike in many ways, yet not the same, both elms, yet easily distinguishable, just so we have a complete flora and a fauna, which, parting from the same ideal, embody it with various modifications. Inventive power is the only quality of which the Creative Intelligence seems to be economical; just as with our largest human minds, that is the divinest of faculties, and the one that most exhausts the mind which exercises it. As the same patterns have very commonly been followed, we can see which is worked out in the largest spirit, and determine the exact limitations under which the Creator places the movement of life in all its manifestations in either locality. We should find ourselves in a very false position, if it should prove that Anglo-Saxons can't live here, but die out, if not kept up by fresh supplies, as Dr. Knox and other more or less wise persons have maintained. It may turn out the other way, as I have heard one of our literary celebrities argue,—and though I took the other side, I liked his best,—that the American is the Englishman reinforced.

> Under the greenwood tree
> Who loves to lie with me,
> And tunc his merry note
> Unto the sweet bird's throat.
> Come hither! come hither! come hither!
> Here shall he see
> No enemy
> But winter and rough weather.
>
> Who doth ambition shun
> And loves to live i' the sun,
> Seeking the food he eats
> And pleased with what he gets,
> Come hither! come hither! come hither!
> Here shall he see
> No enemy
> But winter and rough weather.

SHAKESPEARE, *As You Like It*

THE WATER OUZEL

by John Muir

A remarkable man, John Muir. After making a study of his life
and works, Edwin Way Teale gave as his opinion: "Of those who
have written of nature surpassingly well—Gilbert White, Henry
Thoreau, Richard Jefferies, W. H. Hudson—John Muir was the
wildest. He was the most active, the most at home in the wilderness, the most daring, the most self-reliant." It rings true. He
walked from Wisconsin to the Gulf of Mexico. He turned his
back on civilization and took to the wilderness without a gun.
He came to know every square yard of the Yosemite and to love
all the trees of the Sierra. He explored Alaska. His preparations
for an expedition consisted in putting some bread and tea in a
sack and hopping over the back fence. An immigrant boy, he lived
to hobnob with the rich and the powerful on his own terms; they
came to him in the woods to learn something about the land of
their birth.

John Muir, born in Dunbar, Scotland, April 21, 1838, the third
child and the first boy of a family of seven children, was eleven
years old when he came to the United States. The family settled
on a farm in Wisconsin. It was hard work, and the father was a
stern taskmaster, but young John somehow found time enough to
read good books and learn much about wildlife in the vicinity. As
he grew up he revealed a remarkable aptitude for mechanics and
with his own hands put together many labor-saving devices. He
probably could have made a fortune in that field, but he wanted
something more than money out of life. Later, in California, he
amassed a sum of $100,000 in ten years as a fruit-grower and de-
cided that he had enough of it—enough money and enough of
fruit-growing. That was when he literally took to the woods for
the remainder of his life. One day somebody spoke to him of
E. H. Harriman, the railroad builder and multimillionaire. "I'm

richer than he is," declared John Muir, "I have all the money I want—and he hasn't."

Four years at the University of Wisconsin brought Muir no bachelor degree because he had taken only the courses in which he was interested, mostly the natural sciences and some Greek and Latin. He was later to receive honorary degrees from four universities, Wisconsin, California, Yale, and Harvard. When he left college he said that he was leaving the University of Wisconsin for the University of the Wilderness and strolled away on his thousand-mile trip to the Gulf that later became a book. He was thirty years old when his wanderings carried him to California, where he discovered the mountains among which he was to live and roam for so many years. It was love at first sight. He took any kind of job to be near them. He became a ranch hand. He herded sheep. He explored the canyons and scaled the peaks. The only reason he settled down to fruit-growing for a spell was that he was married in 1880 and thought that, as a family man, he should make sure that his family would never starve.

John Muir succeeded in everything he tried. He beat his neighbors at growing and packing and selling fruit, and, when he felt he had accumulated enough money to secure the future of his family, he quit growing fruit and went back to his mountains again. There he was king, and men came to do homage. Ralph Waldo Emerson visited him in the Yosemite in April, 1871. Asa Gray, the great botanist, camped with him on Mount Shasta in 1877. Theodore Roosevelt, then President of the United States, spent three days and three nights camping with John Muir in the Yosemite in May, 1903, and mildly complained that Muir was interested only in big things—big trees, glaciers, and mountains. But both men were interested in wildlife refuges and national parks, and Roosevelt was in a position to do something about it. The meeting of these men and minds was of profit to all of us.

John Muir wrote more than half a dozen books about his mountains. This chapter on the water ouzel is taken from The Mountains of California. A chill that turned into pneumonia brought about the death of "John o' the Mountains" in a Los Angeles hospital on Christmas Eve, 1914, when he was in his seventy-seventh year.

THE waterfalls of the Sierra are frequented by only one bird—the Ouzel or Water Thrush (*Cinclus Mexicanus,* Sw.). He is a singularly joyous and lovable little fellow, about the size of a robin, clad in a plain water-proof suit of bluish gray, with a tinge of chocolate on the head and shoulders. In form he is about as smoothly plump and compact as a pebble that has been whirled in a pot-hole, the flowing contour of his body being interrupted only by his strong feet and bill, the crisp wing-tips, and the up-slanted wren-like tail.

Among all the countless waterfalls I have met in the course of ten years' exploration in the Sierra, whether among the icy peaks, or warm foot-hills, or in the profound yosemitic cañons of the middle region, not one was found without its Ouzel. No cañon is too cold for this little bird, none too lonely, provided it be rich in falling water. Find a fall, or cascade, or rushing rapid, anywhere upon a clear stream, and there you will surely find its complementary Ouzel, flitting about in the spray, diving in foaming eddies, whirling like a leaf among beaten foam-bells; ever vigorous and enthusiastic, yet self-contained, and neither seeking nor shunning your company.

If disturbed while dipping about in the margin shallows, he either sets off with a rapid whir to some other feeding-ground up or down the stream, or alights on some half-submerged rock or snag out in the current, and immediately begins to nod and courtesy like a wren, turning his head from side to side with many other odd dainty movements that never fail to fix the attention of the observer.

He is the mountain streams' own darling, the hummingbird of blooming waters, loving rocky ripple-slopes and sheets of foam as a bee loves flowers, as a lark loves sunshine and meadows. Among all the mountain birds, none has cheered me so much in my lonely wanderings,—none so unfailingly. For both in winter and summer he sings, sweetly, cheerily, independent alike of sunshine and of love, requiring no other inspiration than the stream on which he dwells. While water sings, so must he, in heat or cold, calm or storm, ever attuning his voice in sure accord; low in the drought of summer and the drought of winter, but never silent.

What may be regarded as the separate songs of the Ouzel are exceedingly difficult of description, because they are so variable and at the same time so confluent. Though I have been acquainted with my favorite ten years, and during most of this time have heard him sing nearly every day, I still detect notes and strains that seem new to me. Nearly all of his music is sweet and tender, lapsing from his round breast like water over the smooth lip of a pool, then breaking farther on into a sparkling foam of melodious notes, which glow with subdued enthusiasm, yet without expressing much of the strong, gushing ecstasy of the bobolink or skylark.

The more striking strains are perfect arabesques of melody, composed of a few full, round, mellow notes, embroidered with delicate trills which fade and melt in long slender cadences. In a general way his music is that of the streams refined and spiritualized. The deep booming notes of the falls are in it, the trills of rapids, the gurgling of margin eddies, the low whispering of level reaches, and the sweet tinkle of separate drops oozing from the ends of mosses and falling into tranquil pools.

The Ouzel never sings in chorus with other birds, nor with his kind, but only with the streams. And like flowers that bloom beneath the surface of the ground, some of our favorite's best song-blossoms never rise above the surface of the heavier music of the water. I have often observed him singing in the midst of beaten spray, his music completely buried beneath the water's roar; yet I knew he was surely singing by his gestures and the movements of his bill.

His food, as far as I have noticed, consists of all kinds of water insects, which in summer are chiefly procured along shallow margins. Here he wades about ducking his head under water and deftly turning over pebbles and fallen leaves with his bill, seldom choosing to go into deep water where he has to use his wings in diving.

He seems to be especially fond of the larvae of mosquitoes, found in abundance attached to the bottom of smooth rock channels where the current is shallow. When feeding in such places he wades upstream, and often while his head is under water the swift current is deflected upward along the glossy curves of his neck and shoulders, in the form of a clear, crystalline shell, which fairly incloses him like a bell-glass, the shell being broken and re-formed as he lifts and dips his head; while ever and anon he sidles out to where the too powerful current carries him off his feet; then he dexterously rises on the wing and goes gleaning again in shallower places.

The Ouzel is usually found singly; rarely in pairs, excepting during the breeding season, and *very* rarely in threes or fours. I once observed three thus spending a winter morning in company, upon a small glacier lake, on the Upper Merced, about 7,500 feet above the level of the sea.

A storm had occurred during the night, but the morning sun shone unclouded, and the shadowy lake, gleaming darkly in its setting of fresh snow, lay smooth and motionless as a mirror. My camp chanced to be within a few feet of the water's edge, opposite a fallen pine, some of the branches of which leaned out over the lake. Here my three dearly welcome visitors took up their station, and at once began to embroider the frosty air with their delicious melody, doubly delightful to me that particular morning, as I had been somewhat apprehensive of danger in breaking my way down through the snow-choked cañons to the lowlands.

The portion of the lake bottom selected for a feeding-ground lies at a depth of fifteen or twenty feet below the surface, and is covered with a short growth of algae and other aquatic plants—facts I had previously determined while sailing over it on a raft. After alighting on the glassy surface, they occasionally indulged in a little play, chasing one another round about in small circles; then all three would suddenly dive together, and then come ashore and sing.

The Ouzel seldom swims more than a few yards on the surface, for, not being web-footed, he makes rather slow progress, but by means of his strong, crisp wings he swims, or rather flies, with celerity under the surface, often to considerable distances. But it is in withstanding the force of heavy rapids that his strength of wing in this respect is most strikingly manifested. The following may be regarded as a fair illustration of his power of subaquatic flight. One stormy morning in winter when the Merced River was blue and green with unmelted snow, I observed one of my ouzels perched on a snag out in the midst of a swift-rushing rapid, singing cheerily, as if everything was just to his mind; and while I stood on the bank admiring him, he suddenly plunged into the sludgy current, leaving his song abruptly broken off. After feeding a minute or two at the bottom, and when one would suppose that he must inevitably be swept far downstream, he emerged just where he went down, alighted on the same snag, showered the water-beads from his feathers, and continued his unfinished song, seemingly in tranquil ease as if it had suffered no interruption.

The Ouzel alone of all birds dares to enter a white torrent. And though strictly terrestrial in structure, no other is so inseparably related to water, not even the duck, or the bold ocean albatross, or the stormy-petrel. For ducks go ashore as soon as they finish feeding in undisturbed places, and very often make long flights overland from lake to lake or field to field. The same is true of most other aquatic birds. But the Ouzel, born on the brink of a stream, or on a snag or boulder in the midst of it, seldom leaves it for a single moment. For, notwithstanding he is often on the wing, he never flies overland, but whirs with rapid, quail-like beat above the stream, tracing all its windings. Even when the stream is quite small, say from five to ten feet wide, he seldom shortens his flight by crossing a bend, however abrupt it may be; and even when disturbed by meeting some one on the bank, he prefers to fly over one's head, to dodging out over the ground. When, therefore, his flight along a crooked stream is viewed endwise, it appears most strikingly wavered—a description on the air of every curve with lightning-like rapidity.

The vertical curves and angles of the most precipitous torrents he traces with the same rigid fidelity, swooping down the inclines of cascades, dropping sheer over dizzy falls amid the spray, and ascending with the same fearlessness and ease, seldom seeking to lessen the steepness of the acclivity by beginning to ascend before reaching the base of the fall. No matter though it may be several hundred feet in height he holds straight on, as if about to dash headlong into the throng of booming rockets, then darts abruptly upward, and, after alighting at the top of the precipice to rest a moment, proceeds to feed and sing. His flight is solid and impetuous, without any intermission of wing-beats,—one homogeneous buzz like that of a laden bee on its way home. And while thus buzzing freely from fall to fall, he is frequently heard giving utterance to a long outdrawn train of unmodulated notes, in no way connected with his song, but corresponding closely with his flight in sustained vigor.

The Ouzel's nest is one of the most extraordinary pieces of bird architecture I ever saw, odd and novel in design, perfectly fresh and beautiful, and in every way worthy of the genius of the little builder. It is about a foot in diameter, round and bossy in outline, with a neatly arched opening near the bottom, somewhat like an old-fashioned brick oven, or Hottentot's hut. It is built almost exclusively of green and yellow mosses, chiefly the beautiful fronded hypnum that covers the rocks and old drift-logs in the vicinity of waterfalls. These are deftly interwoven, and felted together into a charming little hut; and so situated that many of the outer mosses continue to flourish as if they had not been plucked. A few fine, silky-stemmed grasses are occasionally found interwoven with the mosses, but, with the exception of a thin layer lining the floor, their presence seems accidental, as they are of a species found growing with the mosses and are probably plucked with them. The site chosen for this curious mansion is usually some little rock-shelf within reach of the lighter particles of the spray of a waterfall, so that its walls are kept green and growing, at least during the time of high water.

In choosing a building-spot, concealment does not seem to be taken into consideration; yet notwithstanding the nest is large and guilelessly exposed to view, it is far from being easily detected, chiefly because it swells forward like any other bulging moss-cushion growing naturally in such situations. This is more especially the case where the nest is kept fresh by being well sprinkled. Sometimes these romantic little huts have their beauty enhanced by rock-ferns and grasses that spring up around the mossy walls, or in front of the door-sill, dripping with crystal beads.

Furthermore, at certain hours of the day, when the sunshine is poured down at the required angle, the whole mass of the spray enveloping the fairy establishment is brilliantly irised; and it is through so glorious a rainbow atmosphere as this that some of our blessed ouzels obtain their first peep at the world.

In these moss huts three or four eggs are laid, white like foam-bubbles; and well may the little birds hatched from them sing water songs, for they hear them all their lives, and even before they are born.

I have often observed the young just out of the nest making their odd gestures, and seeming in every way as much at home as their experienced parents, like young bees on their first excursions to the flower fields. No amount of familiarity with people and their ways seems to change them in the least. To all appearance their behavior is just the same on seeing a man for the first time, as when they have seen him frequently.

On the lower reaches of the rivers where mills are built, they sing on through the din of the machinery, and all the noisy confusion of dogs, cattle, and workmen. On one occasion, while a wood-chopper was at work on the river-bank, I observed one cheerily singing within reach of the flying chips. Nor does any kind of unwonted disturbance put him in bad humor, or frighten him out of calm self-possession. In passing through a narrow gorge, I once drove one ahead of me from rapid to rapid, disturbing him four times in quick succession where he could not very well fly past me on account of the narrowness of the channel. Most birds under similar circumstances fancy themselves pursued, and become suspiciously uneasy; but, instead of growing nervous about it, he made his usual dippings, and sang one of his most tranquil strains. When observed within a few yards their eyes are seen to express remarkable gentleness and intelligence; but they seldom allow so near a view unless one wears clothing of about the same color as the rocks and trees, and knows how to sit still. On one occasion, while rambling along the shore of a mountain lake, where the birds, at least those born that season, had never seen a man, I sat down to rest on a large stone close to the water's edge, upon which it seemed the ouzels and sandpipers were in the habit of alighting when they came to feed on that part of the shore, and some of the other birds also, when they came down to wash or drink. In a few minutes, along came a whirring Ouzel and alighted on the stone beside me, within reach of my hand. Then suddenly observing me, he stooped nervously as if about to fly on the instant, but as I remained as motionless as the stone, he gained confidence, and looked me steadily in the face for about a minute, then flew quietly to the outlet and began to sing. Next came a sandpiper and gazed at me with much the same guileless expression of eye as the Ouzel. Lastly, down with a swoop came a Steller's jay out of a fir-tree, probably with the intention of moistening his noisy throat. But instead of sitting confidingly as my other visitors had done, he rushed off at once, nearly tumbling heels over head into the lake in his suspicious confusion, and with loud screams roused the neighborhood.

Even so far north as icy Alaska, I have found my glad singer. When I was exploring the glaciers between Mount Fairweather and the Stikeen River, one cold day in November, after trying in vain to force a way through the innumerable icebergs of Sum Dum Bay to the great glaciers at the head of it, I was weary and baffled and sat resting in my canoe convinced at last that I would have to leave this part of my work for another year. Then I began to plan my escape to open water before the young ice which was beginning to form should shut me in. While I thus lingered drifting with the bergs, in the midst of these gloomy forebodings and all the terrible glacial desolation and grandeur, I suddenly heard the well-known whir of an Ouzel's wings, and, looking up, saw my little comforter coming straight across the ice from the shore. In a second or two he was with me, flying three times round my head with a happy salute, as if saying, "Cheer up, old friend; you see I'm here, and all's well." Then he flew back to the shore, alighted on the top-most jag of a stranded iceberg, and began to nod and bow as though he were on one of his favorite boulders in the midst of a sunny Sierra cascade.

Such, then, is our little cinclus, beloved of every one who is so fortunate as to know him. Tracing on strong wing every curve of the most precipitous torrents from one extremity of the Sierra to the other; not fearing to follow them through their darkest gorges and coldest snow-tunnels; acquainted with every waterfall, echoing their divine music; and throughout the whole of their beautiful lives interpreting all that we in our unbelief call terrible in the utterances of torrents and storms, as only varied expressions of God's eternal love.

TO THE SKYLARK

Ethereal minstrel! pilgrim of the sky!
    Dost thou despise the earth where cares abound?
Or, while the wings aspire, are heart and eye
    Both with thy nest upon the dewy ground?
Thy nest, which thou canst drop into at will,
Those quivering wings composed, that music still!

To the last point of vision, and beyond,
    Mount, daring warbler!—that love-prompted strain,
'Twixt thee and thine a never-failing bond,
    Thrills not the less the bosom of the plain;
Yet mightst thou seem, proud privilege! to sing
All independent of the leafy spring.

Leave to the nightingale her shady wood;
    A privacy of glorious light is thine,
Whence thou dost pour upon the world a flood
    Of harmony, with instinct more divine;
Type of the wise, who soar, but never roam,—
True to the kindred points of Heaven and Home!

WILLIAM WORDSWORTH

THE BURROWING OWL

by Elliott Coues

The author of this article on that odd bird, the burrowing owl, was something of an odd bird himself. Elliott Coues was born in Portsmouth, New Hampshire, September 9, 1842, and grew up in Washington, D.C., where he was graduated from Washington University in 1861 and from the medical school of the same institution in 1863. He became an army doctor in 1864 and remained in the service until he resigned in 1881 to become professor of anatomy at the medical school of his alma mater.

The curious part of the career of this particular army surgeon was that, during his seventeen years in the service, he was chiefly noted—and is still remembered—for what might be called his extracurricular activities. It was as a naturalist, and chiefly an ornithologist, that he was famous. Even before he was graduated from college he had published a paper on the sandpiper group. Through being shifted from one army post to another in the western section of the country, he came to know the region and its wildlife. In the eighth year of his military service in the West he produced, in 1872, a book titled Key to North American Birds, *something new in the ornithological field and a volume that was recognized immediately as a scientific achievement of the first order.*

Somebody in the upper echelon of army command must have taken note of this because, in 1873, this particular army surgeon was appointed naturalist and secretary to the United States Northern Border Commission, an undertaking that lasted three years and gave him an intimate knowledge of the border terrain and its plant and animal inhabitants from Lake Superior to the Pacific Ocean. When that task was completed in 1876 he was assigned a similar position in a larger program. He was appointed naturalist and secretary to the United States Geological and Geo-

graphical Survey of Territories. The "Territories" to be surveyed covered most of the western part of the country and later were legally carved into seventeen sovereign states of the Union. The survey lasted some four years, and by that time our army doctor had gained such a knowledge of the country that he later was able to put out an annotated edition of the Lewis and Clark journals, which remains a valuable reference work to this day and a boon to historians.

But ornithology was his chief interest. He was one of the founders of the American Ornithological Union in 1883, and in 1887 he resigned from his teaching position in medical school to devote the remainder of his life to the study of birds. A contemporary described him as a tall, full-bearded man, impressive in appearance and bearing, and one who usually became the center of attention when he joined any group. In the selection that follows he exposes the fable of owls, prairie dogs, and rattlesnakes living together in perfect harmony in underground apartments. But a legend dies hard. They still believe this one in the cactus country. At least they tell it to the tourists.

THE Burrowing Owl is the only bird of its family inhabiting, in any numbers, the entirely treeless regions of the West. Wherever it can find shelter in the holes of such animals as wolves, foxes, and badgers, and especially of the various species of marmot squirrels, there it is found in abundance; and in not a few instances small colonies are observed living apart from their ordinary associates, in holes apparently dug by themselves. They constitute a notable exception to the general rule of arboricole habits in this family, being specially fitted by their conformation for the subterranean mode of life for which they are designed, and are furthermore exceptional in their gregarious disposition, here carried to the extreme.

Having been noticed by the earlier writers in special connection with the singular settlements of the prairie-dog (*Cynomys ludovicianus*), and the life relations of the two creatures being really intimate in very many localities, an almost inseparable association of ideas has been brought about, which is only partly true; and it was a long time before the whole truth in the case became apparent. When competent observers, familiar with the animals, disagree, as they have, respecting the kind and degree of relation between the bird and the mammals, we need not be surprised at conflict of opinion in the books of naturalists who never saw either of them alive. The case is further complicated by the introduction of the rattlesnakes; and no little pure bosh is in type respecting the harmonious and confidential relations, imagined to subsist between the trio, which, like the "happy family" of Barnum, lead Utopian existences. According to the dense bathos of such nursery tales, in this underground Elysium the snakes give their rattles to the puppies to play with, the old dogs cuddle the Owlets, and farm out their own litters to the grave and careful birds; when an Owl and a dog come home, paw-in-wing, they are often mistaken by their respective progeny, the little dogs nosing the Owls in search of the maternal font, and the old dogs left to wonder why the baby Owls will not nurse. It is a pity to spoil a good story for the sake of a few facts, but as the case stands, it would be well for the Society for the Prevention of Cruelty to Animals to take it up. First, as to the reptiles, it may be observed that they are like other rattlesnakes, dangerous, venomous creatures; they have no business in the burrows, and are after no good when they do enter. They wriggle into the holes, partly because there is no other place for them to crawl into on the bare, flat plain, and partly in search of Owls' eggs, Owlets, and puppies, to eat. Next, the Owls themselves are simply attracted to the villages of prairie-dogs as the most convenient places for shelter and nidification, where they find eligible ready-made burrows, and are spared the trouble of digging for themselves. Community of interest makes them gregarious to an extent unusual among rapacious birds; while the exigencies of life on the plains cast their lot with the rodents. That the Owls live at ease in the settlements, and on familiar terms with their four-footed neighbors, is an undoubted fact; but that they inhabit the same burrows, or have any intimate domestic relations, is quite another thing. It is no proof that the quadruped and the birds live together, that they are often seen to scuttle at each other's heels into the same hole when alarmed; for in such a case the two simply seek the nearest shelter, independently of each other. The probability is, that young dogs often furnish a meal to the Owls, and that, in return, the latter are often robbed of their eggs; while certainly the young of both, and the Owls' eggs, are eaten by the snakes. In the larger settlements there are thousands upon thousands of burrows, many occupied by the dogs, but more, perhaps, vacant. These latter are the homes of the Owls. Moreover, the ground below is honeycombed with communicating passages, leading in every direction. If the underground plan could be mapped, it would resemble the city of Boston, with its tortuous and devious streets. The dogs are continually busy in fair weather in repairing and extending their establishments; the main entrances may be compared to the stump of a hollow tree, the interior of which communicates with many hollow branches that moreover intersect, these passages finally ending in little pockets, the real home of the animals. It is quite possible that the respective retreats of a dog and an Owl may have but one vestibule, but even this does not imply that they nest together. It is strong evidence in point, that usually there are the fewest Owls in the towns most densely populated by the dogs, and conversely. Scarcity of food, of water, or some obscure cause, often makes the dogs emigrate from one locality to another; it is in such "deserted villages" that the Owls are usually seen in the greatest numbers. I have never seen them so numerous as in places where there are plenty of holes, but where scarcely a stray dog remained.

I never undertook to unearth the nest of a Burrowing Owl, but others have been more zealous in the pursuit of knowledge under difficulties. Dr. Cooper says that he once dug two fresh eggs out of a burrow, which he followed down for three feet, and then traced five feet horizontally, at the end of which he found an enlarged chamber, where the eggs were deposited on a few feathers. In his interesting note in the *American Naturalist*, Dr. C. S. Canfield gives a more explicit account of the nesting: "I once took pains to dig out a nest of the *Athene cunicularia*. I found that the burrow was about four feet long, and the nest was only about two feet from the surface of the ground. The nest was made in a cavity of the ground, of about a foot in diameter, well filled with dry, soft horse-dung, bits of an old blanket, and fur of a coyote (*Canis latrans*) that I had killed a few days before. One of the parent birds was on the nest, and I captured it. It had no intention of leaving the nest, even when entirely uncovered with the shovel and exposed to the open air. It fought bravely with beak and claws. I found *seven* young ones, perhaps eight or ten days old, well covered with down, but without any feathers. There are very few birds that carry more rubbish into the nest than the *Athene*; and even the Vultures are not much more filthy. I am satisfied that the A. *cunicularia* lays a larger number of eggs than is attributed to it. I have frequently seen, late in the season, six, seven, or eight young birds standing around the mouth of a burrow, isolated from others in such a manner that I could not suppose that they belonged to two or more families."

The notes of the Burrowing Owl are peculiar. The birds do not "hoot," nor is there anything lugubrious or foreboding in their cry. Sometimes they chuckle, chatter, and squeal in an odd way, as if they had caught a habit of barking from the "dogs" they live with, and were trying to imitate the sound. But their natural cry is curiously similar to that of the Rain Crow, or Cuckoo of America—so much so, that more than one observer has been deceived. They scream hoarsely when wounded and caught, though this is but seldom, since, if any life remains, they scramble quickly into a hole and are not easy to recover. The flight is perfectly noiseless, like that of other Owls, owing to the peculiar downy texture of the plumage. By day they seldom fly far from the entrance of their burrow, and rarely, if ever, mount in the air. I never saw one on wing more than a few moments at a time, just long enough for it to pass from one hillock to another, as it does by skimming low over the surface of the ground in a rapid, easy, and rather graceful manner. They live chiefly upon insects, especially grasshoppers; they also feed upon lizards, as I once determined by dissection, and there is no doubt that young prairie-dogs furnish them many a meal. As commonly observed, perched on one of the innumerable little eminences that mark a dog-town, amid their curious surroundings, they present a spectacle not easily forgotten. Their figure is peculiar, with their long legs and short tail; the element of the grotesque is never wanting; it is hard to say whether they look most ludicrous as they stand stiffly erect and motionless, or when they suddenly turn tail to duck into the hole, or when engaged in their various antics. Bolt upright, on what may be imagined their rostrum, they gaze about with a bland and self-satisfied, but earnest air, as if about to address an audience upon a subject of great pith and moment. They suddenly bow low, with profound gravity, and rising as abruptly, they begin to twitch their face and roll their eyes about in the most mysterious manner, gesticulating wildly, every now and then bending forward till the breast almost touches the ground, to propound the argument with more telling effect. Then they face about to address the rear, that all may alike feel the force of their logic; they draw themselves up to their fullest height, outwardly calm and self-contained, pausing in the discourse to note its effect upon the audience, and collect their wits for the next rhetorical flourish. And no distant likeness between these frothy orators and others is found in the celerity with which they subside and seek their holes on the slightest intimation of danger.

NATURE AND BOOKS

by Richard Jefferies

*There is a haunting quality to the prose of Richard Jefferies.
He spent most of his short adult life looking backward from a
London flat to the sights and sounds of the English countryside
around "the old house at Coate" in which he had been born
November 6, 1848, and which he had left as a young man to try
his hand at newspaper writing in London.*

*He soon displayed his talent as a writer—on an agricultural
subject. It had to do with the hard life of the farm laborers in his
native Wiltshire. He had attempted novels, but they were failures.
His ordinary newspaper work was just that—ordinary. But when
he wrote of farms and farmers, of cattle and other farm animals, of
birds and beasts, of days on the Wiltshire Downs, he wrote with
a sure hand and a magic touch. He produced essays, magazine
articles, books, all on the topic that he knew and loved.*

*He rose from obscurity and near-poverty in London—with a
wife and child on his hands—to widespread acclaim and something approaching modest financial success through his articles,
essays, and such books as* The Gamekeeper at Home, Wild Life
in a Southern County, Wood Magic, Life in the Fields, Bevis,
and The Story of My Heart. *But his days were numbered. He
had been writing under sentence of death—a slow, wracking death
by tuberculosis. He died August 14, 1887, four months before his
fortieth birthday, in the little town of Goring in Berkshire, almost within walking distance of the Wiltshire Downs and "the
old house at Coate."*

WHAT is the colour of the dandelion? There are many dandelions: that which I mean flowers in May, when the meadow-grass has started and the hares are busy by daylight. That which flowers very early in the year has a thickness of hue, and is not interesting; in autumn the dandelions quite change their colour and are pale. The right dandelion for this question is the one that comes about May with a very broad disc, and in such quantities as often to cover a whole meadow. I used to admire them very much in the fields by Surbiton (strong clay soil), and also on the towing-path of the Thames where the sward is very broad, opposite Long Ditton; indeed, I have often walked up that towing-path on a beautiful sunny morning, when all was quiet except the nightingales in the Palace hedge, on purpose to admire them. I dare say they are all gone now for evermore; still, it is a pleasure to look back on anything beautiful. What colour is this dandelion? It is not yellow, nor orange, nor gold; put a sovereign on it and see the difference. They say the gipsies call it the Queen's great hairy dog-flower—a number of words to one stalk; and so, to get a colour to it, you may call it the yellow-gold-orange plant. In the winter, on the black mud under a dark, dripping tree, I found a piece of orange peel, lately dropped—a bright red orange speck in the middle of the blackness. It looked very beautiful, and instantly recalled to my mind the great dandelion discs in the sunshine of summer. Yet certainly they are not red-orange. Perhaps, if ten people answered this question, they would each give different answers. Again, a bright day or a cloudy, the presence of a slight haze, or the juxtaposition of other colours, alters it very much; for the dandelion is not a glazed colour, like the buttercup, but sensitive. It is like a sponge, and adds to its own hue that which is passing, sucking it up.

The shadows of the trees in the wood, why are they blue? Ought they not to be dark? Is it really blue, or an illusion? And what is their colour when you see the shadow of a tall trunk aslant in the air like a leaning pillar? The fallen brown leaves wet with dew have a different brown from those that are dry, and the upper surface of the green growing leaf is different from the under surface. The yellow butterfly, if you meet one in October, has so toned down his spring yellow that you might fancy him a pale green leaf floating along the road. There is a shining, quivering, gleaming; there is a changing, fluttering, shifting; there is a mixing, weaving—varnished wings, translucent wings, wings with dots and veins, all playing over the purple heath; a very tangle of many-toned lights and hues. Then come the apples: if you look upon them from an upper window, so as to glance along the level plane of the fruit, delicate streaks of scarlet, like those that lie parallel to the eastern horizon before sunrise; golden tints under bronze, and apple-green, and some that the wasps have hollowed, more glowingly beautiful than the rest; sober leaves and black and white swallows: to see it you must be high up, as if the apples were strewn on a sward of foliage. So have I gone in three steps from May dandelion to September apple; an immense space measured by things beautiful, so filled that ten folio volumes could not hold the description of them, and I have left out the meadows, the brooks, and hills. Often in writing about these things I have felt very earnestly my own incompetence to give the least idea of their brilliancy and many-sided colours. My gamut was so very limited in its terms, and would not give a note to one in a thousand of those I saw. At last I said, I will have more words; I will have more terms; I will have a book on colour, and I will find and use the right technical name for each one of these lovely tints. I was told that the very best book was by Chevreul, which had tinted illustrations, chromatic scales, and all that could be desired.

Quite true, all of it; but for me it contained nothing. There was a good deal about assorted wools, but nothing about leaves; nothing by which I could tell you the difference between the light scarlet of one poppy and the deep purple-scarlet of another species. The dandelion remained unexplained; as for the innumerable other flowers, and wings, and sky-colours, they were not even aproached. The book, in short, dealt with the artificial and not with nature. Next I went to science—works on optics, such a mass of them. Some I had read in old time, and turned to again; some I read for the first time, some translated from the German, and so on. It appeared that, experimenting with physical colour, tangible paint, they had found out that red, yellow, and blue were the three primary colours; and then, experimenting with light itself, with colours not tangible, they found out that red, green, and violet were the three primary colours; but neither of these would do for the dandelion. Once upon a time I had taken an interest in spectrum analysis, and the theory of the polarisation of light was fairly familiar; any number of books, but not what I wanted to know. Next the idea occurred to me of buying all the colours used in painting, and tinting as many pieces of paper a separate hue, and so comparing these with petals, and wings, and grass, and trifolium. This did not answer at all; my unskilful hands made a very poor wash, and the yellow paper set by a yellow petal did not agree, the scientific reason of which I cannot enter into now. Secondly, the names attached to many of these paints are unfamiliar to general readers; it is doubtful if bistre, Leitch's blue, oxide of chromium, and so on, would convey an idea. They might as well be Greek symbols: no use to attempt to describe hues of heath or hill in that way. These, too, are only distinct colours. What was to be done with all the shades and tones? Still there remained the language of the studio; without doubt a master of painting could be found who would quickly supply the technical term of anything I liked to show him; but again no use, because it would be technical. And a still more insurmountable difficulty occurs: in so far as I have looked at pictures, it seems as if the artists had met with the same obstacle in paints as I have in words—that is to say, a deficiency. Either painting is incompetent to express the extreme beauty of nature, or in some way the canons of art forbid the attempt. Therefore I had to turn back, throw down my books with a bang, and get me a bit of fallen timber in the open air to meditate.

Would it be possible to build up a fresh system of colour language by means of natural objects? Could we say pine-wood green, larch green, spruce green, wasp yellow, humble-bee amber? And there are fungi that have marked tints, but the Latin names of these agarics are not pleasant. Butterfly blue—but there are several varieties; and this plan is interfered with by two things: first, that almost every single item of nature, however minute, has got a distinctly different colour, so that the dictionary of tints would be immense; and next, so very few would know the object itself that the colour attached to it would have no meaning. The power of language has been gradually enlarging for a great length of time, and I venture to say that the English language at the present time can express more, and is more subtle, flexible, and, at the same time, vigorous, than any of which we possess a record. When people talk to me about studying Sanscrit, or Greek, or Latin, or German, or, still more absurd, French, I feel as if I could fell them with a mallet happily. Study the English, and you will find everything there, I reply. With such a language I fully anticipate, in years to come, a great development in the power of expressing thoughts and feelings which are now thoughts and feelings only. How many have said of the sea, 'It makes me feel something I cannot say'! Hence it is clear there exists in the intellect a layer, if I may so call it, of thought yet dumb—chambers within the mind which require the key of new words to unlock. Whenever that is done a fresh impetus is given to human progress. There are a million books, and yet with all their aid I cannot tell you the colour of the May dandelion. There are three greens at this moment in my mind: that of the leaf of the flower-de-luce, that of the yellow iris leaf, and that of the bayonet-like leaf of the common flag. With admission to a million books, how am I to tell you the difference between these tints? So many, many books, and such a very, very little bit of nature in them! Though we have been so many thousand years upon the earth we do not seem to have done any more as yet than walk along beaten footpaths, and sometimes really it would seem as if there were something in the minds of many men quite artificial, quite distinct from the sun and trees and hills—altogether house people, whose gods must be set in four-cornered buildings. There is nothing in books that touches my dandelion.

It grows, ah yes, it grows! How does it grow? Builds itself up somehow of sugar and starch, and turns mud into bright colour and dead earth into food for bees, and some day perhaps for you, and knows when to shut its petals, and how to construct the brown seeds to float with the wind, and how to please the children, and how to puzzle me. Ingenious dandelion! If you find out that its correct botanical name is *Leontodon taraxacum*, or *Leontodon densleonis*, that will bring it into botany; and there is a place called Dandelion Castle in Kent, and a bell with the inscription—

> John de Dandelion with his great dog
> Brought over this bell on a mill cog—

which is about as relevant as the mere words *Leontodon taraxacum*. Botany is the knowledge of plants according to the accepted definition; naturally, therefore, when I began to think I would like to know a little more of flowers than could be learned by seeing them in the fields, I went to botany. Nothing could be more simple. You buy a book which first of all tells you how to recognise them, how to classify them; next instructs you in their uses, medical or economical; next tells you about the folk-lore and curious associations; next enters into a lucid explanation of the physiology of the plant and its relation to other creatures; and finally, and most important, supplies you with the ethical feeling, the ideal aspiration to be identified with each particular flower. One moderately thick volume would probably suffice for such a modest round as this.

Lo! now the labour of Hercules when he set about bringing up Cerberus from below, and all the work done by Apollo in the years when he ground corn, are but a little matter compared with the attempt to master botany. Great minds have been at it these two thousand years, and yet we are still only nibbling at the edge of the leaf, as the ploughboys bite the young hawthorn in spring. The mere classification—all plant-lore was a vast chaos till there came the man of Sweden, the great Linnaeus, till the sexes were recognised, and everything was ruled out and set in place again. A wonderful man! I think it would be true to say it was Linnaeus who set the world on its present twist of thinking, and levered our mental globe a little more perpendicular to the ecliptic. He actually gathered the dandelion and took it to bits like a scientific child; he touched nature with his fingers instead of sitting looking out of window—perhaps the first man who had ever done so for seventeen hundred years or so, since superstition blighted the progress of pagan Rome. The work he did! But no one reads Linnaeus now; the folios, indeed, might moulder to dust without loss, because his spirit has got into the minds of men, and the text is of little consequence. The best book he wrote to read now is the delightful 'Tour in Lapland,' with its quaint pen-and-ink sketches, so realistically vivid, as if the thing sketched had been banged on the paper and so left its impress. I have read it three times, and I still cherish the old yellow pages; it is the best botanical book, written by the greatest of botanists, specially sent on a botanical expedition, and it contains nothing about botany. It tells you about the canoes, and the hard cheese, and the Laplander's warehouse on top of a pole, like a pigeon-house; and the innocent way in which the maiden helped the traveller in his bath, and how the aged men ran so fast that the devil could not catch them; and, best of all, because it gives a smack in the face to modern pseudo-scientific medical cant about hygiene, showing how the Laplanders break every 'law,' human and 'divine,' ventilation, bath, and diet—all the trash—and therefore enjoy the most excellent health, and live to a great old age. Still I have not succeeded in describing the immense labour there was in learning to distinguish plants on the Linnaean system. Then comes in order of time the natural system, the geographical distribution; then there is the geological relationship, so to say, to Pliocene plants, natural selection and evolution. Of that let us say nothing; let sleeping dogs lie, and evolution is a very weary dog. Most charming, however, will be found the later studies of naturalists on the interdependence of flowers and insects; there is another work the dandelion has got to do—endless,

endless botany! Where did the plants come from at first? Did they come creeping up out of the sea at the edge of the estuaries, and gradually run their roots into the ground, and so make green the earth? Did Man come out of the sea, as the Greeks thought? There are so many ideas in plants. Flora, with a full lap, scattering knowledge and flowers together; everything good and sweet seems to come out of flowers, up to the very highest thoughts of the soul, and we carry them daily to the very threshold of the other world. Next you may try the microscope and its literature, and find the crystals in the rhubarb.

I remember taking sly glances when I was a very little boy at an old Culpepper's Herbal, heavily bound in leather and curiously illustrated. It was so deliciously wicked to read about the poisons; and I thought perhaps it was a book like that, only in papyrus rolls, that was used by the sorceress who got ready the poisoned mushrooms in old Rome. Youth's ideas are so imaginative, and bring together things that are so widely separated. Conscience told me I had no business to read about poisons; but there was a fearful fascination in hemlock, and I recollect tasting a little bit—it was very nasty. At this day, nevertheless, if any one wishes to begin a pleasant, interesting, unscientific acquaintance with English plants, he would do very well indeed to get a good copy of Culpepper. Grey hairs had insisted in showing themselves in my beard when, all those weary years afterwards, I thought I would like to buy the still older Englishman, Gerard, who had no Linnaeus to guide him, who walked about our English lanes centuries ago. What wonderful scenes he must have viewed when they were all a tangle of wild flowers, and plants that are now scarce were common, and the old ploughs, and the curious customs, and the wild red-deer— it would make a good picture, it really would, Gerard studying English orchids! Such a volume!—hundreds of pages, yellow of course, close type, and marvellously well printed. The minute care they must have taken in those early days of printing to get up such a book—a wonderful volume both in bodily shape and contents. Just then the only copy I could hear of was much damaged. The cunning old bookseller said he could make it up; but I have no fancy for patched books, they are not genuine; I would rather have them deficient; and the price was rather long, and so I went Gerardless. Of folk-lore and medicinal use and history and associations here you have hints. The bottom of the sack is not yet; there are the monographs, years of study expended upon one species of plant growing in one locality, perhaps; some made up into thick books and some into broad quarto pamphlets, with most beautiful plates, that, if you were to see them, would tempt you to cut them out and steal them, all sunk and lost like dead ships under the sand: piles of monographs. There are warehouses in London that are choked to the beams of the roof with them, and every fresh exploration furnishes another shelf-load. The source of the Nile was unknown a very few years ago, and now, I have no doubt, there are dozens of monographs on the flowers that flourish there. Indeed, there is not a thing that grows that may not furnish a monograph. The author spends perhaps twenty years in collecting his material, during which time he must of course come across a great variety of amusing information, and then he spends another ten years writing out a fair copy of his labours. Then he thinks it does not quite do in that form, so he snips a paragraph out of the beginning and puts it at the end; next he shifts some more matter from the middle to the preface; then he thinks it over. It seems to him that it is too big, it wants condensation. The scientific world will say he has made too much of it; it ought to read very slight, and present the facts while concealing the labour. So he sets about removing the superfluous—leaves out all the personal observations, and all the little adventures he has met with in his investigations; and so, having got it down to the dry bones and stones thereof, and omitted all the mortar that stuck them together, he sends for the engraver, and the next three years are occupied in working up the illustrations. About this time some new discovery is made by a foreign observer, which necessitates a complete revision of the subject; and so having shifted the contents of the book about hither and thither till he does not know which is the end and which is the beginning, he pitches the much-mutilated copy into a drawer and turns the key. Farewell, no more of this; his declining days shall be spent in peace. A few months afterwards a work is announced in Leipsic which 'really trenches on my favourite subject, and really after spending a lifetime I can't stand it.' By this time his handwriting has become so shaky he can hardly read it himself, so he sends in despair for a lady who works a type-writer, and with infinite patience she makes a clean manuscript of the muddled mass. To the press at last, and the proofs come rapidly. Such a relief! How joyfully easy a thing is when you set about it! but by-and-by this won't do. Sub-section A ought to be in a foot-note, family B is doubtful; and so the corrections grow and run over the margin in a thin treble hand, till they approach the bulk of the original book—a good profit for the printer; and so after about forty years the monograph is published—the work of a life is accomplished. Fifty copies are sent round to as many public libraries and learned societies, and the rest of the impression lies on the shelves till dust and time and spiders' webs have buried it. Splendid work in it too. Looked back upon from to-day with the key of modern thought, these monographs often contain a whole chest of treasure. And still there are the periodicals, a century of magazines and journals and reviews and notices that have been coming out these hundred years and dropping to the ground like dead leaves unnoticed. And then there are the art works—books about shape and colour and ornament, and a naturalist lately has been trying to see how the leaves of one tree look fitted on the boughs of another. Boundless is the wealth of Flora's lap; the ingenuity of man has been weaving wreaths out of it for ages, and still the bottom of the sack is not yet. Nor have we got much news of the dandelion. For I sit on the thrown timber under the trees and meditate, and I want something more: I want the soul of the flowers.

The bee and the butterfly take their pollen and their honey, and the strange moths so curiously coloured, like the curious colouring of the owls, come to them by night, and they turn towards the sun and live their little day, and their petals fall, and where is the soul when the body decays? I want the inner meaning and the understanding of the wild flowers in the meadow. Why are they? What end? What purpose? The plant knows, and sees, and feels; where is its mind when the petal falls? Absorbed in the universal dynamic force, or what? They make no shadow of pretence, these beautiful flowers, of being beautiful for my sake, of bearing honey for me; in short, there does not seem to be any kind of relationship between us, and yet— as I said just now—language does not express the dumb feelings of the mind any more than the flower can speak. I want to know the soul of the flowers, but the word soul does not in the smallest degree convey the meaning of my wish. It is quite inadequate; I must hope that you will grasp the drift of my meaning. All these life-laboured monographs, these classifications, works of Linnaeus, and our own classic Darwin, microscope, physiology, and the flower has not given us its message yet. There are a million books; there are no books: all the books have to be written. What a field! A whole million of books have got to be written. In this sense there are hardly a dozen of them done, and these mere primers. The thoughts of man are like the foraminifera, those minute shells which build up the solid chalk hills and lay the level plain of endless sand; so minute that, save with a powerful lens, you would never imagine the dust on your fingers to be more than dust. The thoughts of man are like these: each to him seems great in his day, but the ages roll, and they shrink till they become triturated dust, and you might, as it were, put a thousand on your thumb-nail. They are not shapeless dust for all that; they are organic, and they build and weld and grow together, till in the passage of time they will make a new earth and a new life. So I think I may say there are no books; the books are yet to be written.

Let us get a little alchemy out of the dandelions. They were not precise, the Arabian sages, with their flowing robes and handwriting; there was a large margin to their manuscripts, much imagination. Therein they failed, judged by the monograph standard, but gave a subtle food for the mind. Some of this I would fain see now inspiring the works and words of our great men of science and thought—a little alchemy. A great change is slowly going forward all over the printing-press world, I mean wherever men print books and papers. The Chinese are perhaps outside that world at present, and the other Asian races; the myriads, too, of the great southern islands and of Africa. The change is steadily, however, proceeding wherever the printing-press is used. Nor Pope, nor Kaiser, nor Czar, nor Sultan, nor fanatic monk, nor muezzin, shouting in vain from his minaret, nor, most fanatic of all, the fanatic shouting in vain in London, can keep it out—all powerless against a bit of printed paper. Bits of printed paper that listen to no command, to which none can say, 'Stand back; thou shalt not enter.' They rise on the summer whirlwinds from the very dust of the road, and float over the highest walls; they fall on the well-kept lawns—monastery, prison, palace—there is no fortress against a bit of printed paper. They penetrate where even Danaë's gold cannot go. Our Darwins, our Lyalls, Herschels, Faradays—all the immense army of those that go down to nature with considering eye— are steadfastly undermining and obliterating the superstitious past, literally burying it under endless loads of accumulated facts; and the printing-presses, like so many Argos, take these facts on their voyage round the world. Over go temples, and minarets, and churches, or rather there they stay, the hollow shells, like the snail shells which thrushes have picked clean; there they stay like Karnac, where there is no more incense, like the stone circles on our own hills, where there are no more human sacrifices. Thus men's minds all over the printing-press world are unlearning the falsehoods that have bound them down so long; they are unlearning, the first step to learn. They are going down to nature and taking up the clods with their own hands, and so coming to have touch of that which is real. As yet we are in the fact stage; by-and-by we shall come to the alchemy, and get the honey for the inner mind and soul. I found, therefore, from the dandelion that there were no books, and it came upon me, believe me, as a great surprise, for I had lived quite certain that I was surrounded with them. It is nothing but unlearning, I find now; five thousand books to unlearn.

Then to unlearn the first ideas of history, of science, of social institutions, to unlearn one's own life and purpose; to unlearn the old mode of thought and way of arriving at things; to take off peel after peel, and so get by degrees slowly towards the truth—thus writing as it were, a sort of floating book in the mind, almost remaking the soul. It seems as if the chief value of books is to give us something to unlearn. Sometimes I feel indignant at the false views that were instilled into me in early days, and then again I see that that very indignation gives me a moral life. I hope in the days to come future thinkers will unlearn us, and find ideas infinitely better. How marvellous it seems that there should be found communities furnished with the printing-press and fully convinced they are more intelligent than ants, and yet deliberately refusing by a solid 'popular' vote to accept free libraries! They look with scorn on the mediaeval times, when volumes were chained in the college library or to the desk at church. Ignorant times those! A good thing it would be if only three books were chained to a desk, open and free in every parish throughout the kingdom now. So might the wish to unlearn be at last started in the inert mind of the mass. Almost the only books left to me to read, and not to unlearn very much, are my first books—the graven classics of Greece and Rome, cut with a stylus so deeply into the tablet they cannot be erased. Little of the monograph or of classification, no bushel baskets full of facts, no minute dissection of nature, no attempt to find the soul under the scalpel. Thoughts which do not exactly deal with nature direct in a mechanical way, as the chemist labels all his gums and spices and earths in small boxes—I wonder if anybody at Athens ever made a collection of the coleoptera? Yet in some way they had got the spirit of the earth and sea, the soul of the sun. This never dies; this I wish not to unlearn; this is ever fresh and beautiful as a summer morning:—

Such the golden crocus,
Fair flower of early spring; the gopher white,
And fragrant thyme, and all the unsown beauty
Which in moist grounds the verdant meadows bear;
The ox-eye, the sweet-smelling flower of Jove,

The chalca, and the much-sung hyacinth,
And the low-growing violet, to which
Dark Proserpine a darker hue has given.

They come nearest to our own violets and cowslips—the unsown
beauty of our meadows—to the hawthorn leaf and the high pinewood.
I can forget all else that I have read, but it is difficult to forget these
even when I will. I read them in English. I had the usual Latin and
Greek instruction, but I read them in English deliberately. For the
inflexion of the vowel I care nothing; I prize the idea. Scholars may
regard me with scorn. I reply with equal scorn. I say that a great
classic thought is greater to an English mind in English words than
in any other form, and therein fits best to this our life and day. I read
them in English first, and intend to do so to the end. I do not know
what set me on these books, but I began them when about eighteen.
The first of all was Diogenes Laertius's 'Lives of the Philosophers.'
It was a happy choice; my good genius, I suppose, for you see I was
already fairly well read in modern science, and these old Greek philoso-
phies set me thinking backwards, unwinding and unlearning, and getting at that eidolon which is not to be found in the mechanical heavens
of this age. I still read him. I still find new things, quite new, because
they are so very, very old, and quite true; and with his help I seem
in a measure to look back upon our thoughts now as if I had projected myself a thousand years forward in space. An imperfect book,
say the critics. I do not know about that; his short paragraphs and
chapters in their imperfect state convey more freshness to the mind
than the thick, laboured volumes in which modern scholarship pro-
fesses to describe ancient philosophy. I prefer the imperfect original
records. Neither can I read the ponderous volumes of modern history,
which are nothing but words. I prefer the incomplete and shattered
chronicles themselves, where the swords shine and the armour rings,
and all is life though but a broken frieze. Next came Plato (it took me
a long time to read Plato, and I have had to unlearn much of him)
and Xenophon. Socrates' dialectic method taught me how to write,
or rather how to put ideas in sequence. Sophocles, too; and last, that
wonderful encyclopaedia of curious things, Athenaeus. So that I
found, when the idea of the hundred best books came out, that between seventy and eighty of them had been my companions almost
from boyhood, those lacking to complete the number being chiefly
ecclesiastical or Continental. Indeed, some years before the hundred

books were talked of, the idea had occurred to me of making up a
catalogue of books that could be bought for ten pounds. In an article
in the 'Pall Mall Gazette' on 'The Pigeons at the British Museum'
I said, 'It seems as if all the books in the world—really books—can be
bought for 10£. Man's whole thought is purchasable at that small
price—for the value of a watch, of a good dog.' The idea of making a
10£ catalogue was in my mind—I did make a rough pencil one—and
I still think that a 10£ library is worth the notice of the publishing
world. My rough list did not contain a hundred. These old books of
nature and nature's mind ought to be chained up, free for every man
to read in every parish. These are the only books I do not wish to unlearn, one item only excepted, which I shall not here discuss. It is
curious, too, that the Greek philosophers, in the more rigid sense of
science, anticipated most of the drift of modern thought. Two chapters
in Aristotle might almost be printed without change as summaries of
our present natural science. For the facts of nature, of course, neither
one hundred books nor a 10£ library would be worth mentioning;
say five thousand, and having read those, then go to Kew, and spend
a year studying the specimens of wood only stored there, such a little
slice after all of the whole. You will then believe what I have advanced, that there are no books as yet; they have got to be written;
and if we pursue the idea a little further, and consider that these are
all about the crude clods of life—for I often feel what a very crude
and clumsy clod I am—only of the earth, a minute speck among one
hundred millions of stars, how shall we write what is *there?* It is only
to be written by the mind or soul, and that is why I strive so much to
find what I have called the alchemy of nature. Let us not be too
entirely mechanical, Baconian, and experimental only; let us let the
soul hope and dream and float on these oceans of accumulated facts,
and feel still greater aspiration than it has ever known since first a
flint was chipped before the glaciers. Man's mind is the most important fact with which we are yet acquainted. Let us not turn then
against it and deny its existence with too many brazen instruments,
but remember these are but a means, and that the vast lens of the
Californian refractor is but glass—it is the infinite speck upon which
the ray of light will fall that is the one great fact of the universe. By
the mind, without instruments, the Greeks anticipated almost all
our thoughts; by-and-by, having raised ourselves up upon these huge
mounds of facts, we shall begin to see still greater things; to do so we
must look not at the mound under foot, but at the starry horizon.

IN THE HEMLOCKS

by John Burroughs

The important fact in the long and happy life of John Burroughs was that, in his writings, he bridged the gap that ordinarily separates the naturalist from the Nature-lover. He was not a scientist; he was an artist, a writer who painted what he saw in clear words and poetic phrases. He loved poetry and wrote some very good verse. His first book had nothing to do with birds or natural history. He had met Walt Whitman in Washington, D.C., during the Civil War, became a Whitman admirer at a time when this was a somewhat risky business, and in 1867 produced his first literary offering to the book trade under the title Notes on Walt Whitman, Poet and Person. *In return, it was Walt Whitman who suggested the title for the second Burroughs book,* Wake-Robin, *that launched him on a lifelong career as an interpreter of Nature to the general public.*

John Burroughs was born on a farm in the town of Roxbury, Delaware County, New York, on April 3, 1837. Though he received scant formal education in local schools himself, he was teaching a rural school at the age of eighteen, and continued to teach until he went to Washington in 1863 as a civilian employee of the Quartermaster Corps. The success of his book Wake-Robin *encouraged him to quit Washington in 1873 and settle on a fruit farm at West Park, New York. He called the place Riverby because, to the east, he could view the Hudson River from his own acres. Raising fruit there, of course, was to be a secondary affair. John Burroughs was going to write. An early meeting with Ralph Waldo Emerson—it was when Burroughs was teaching school near West Point before he went to Washington—fired him with a great admiration for the Sage of Concord as a writer, poet, and philosopher, and the Emersonian influence can be detected, especially in the earlier Burroughs books. But it was late in his career*

*that he wrote: "The most precious things of life are near at hand,
without money and without price. Each of you has the whole
wealth of the universe at your very door. All that I ever had, and
still have, may be yours by stretching forth your hand and taking
it." One is tempted to say that the voice is that of Emerson,
though the hand is the hand of Burroughs.*

*As success came to the Riverby writer, the great and the small
came to visit him and learn something about Nature from him on
his home ground. He was forced to build a retreat called "Slab-
sides" a few miles off where he could work and write undisturbed.
He welcomed many visitors, to be sure, and among them John
Muir, Theodore Roosevelt, and Frank M. Chapman. He lived to
become a picturesque personage with a white mane and a long
white beard, a famous Nature writer who went to Florida in the
winter with Thomas A. Edison, Harvey Firestone and Henry
Ford. He was on a train returning from a trip to California when
he died on March 29, 1921, just short of his eighty-fourth birthday. The selection that follows is a chapter from his first book
about Nature, Wake-Robin. It will be noted that Burroughs uses
the name "red-eyed fly-catcher" (for the red-eyed vireo), and other
bird names and terms long out of date.*

I DESCEND a steep hill, and approach the hemlocks through a
large sugar-bush. When twenty rods distant, I hear all along the
line of the forest the incessant warble of the red-eyed fly-catcher,
cheerful and happy as the merry whistle of a school-boy. He is
one of our most common and widely distributed birds. Approach any
forest at any hour of the day, in any kind of weather, from May to
August, in any of the Middle or Eastern districts, and the chances
are that the first note you hear will be his. Rain or shine, before noon
or after, in the deep forest or in the village grove,—when it is too hot
for the thrushes or too cold and windy for the warblers,—it is never
out of time or place for this little minstrel to indulge his cheerful
strain. In the deep wilds of the Adirondac, where few birds are seen
and fewer heard, his note was almost constantly in my ear. Always
busy, making it a point never to suspend for one moment his occupation to indulge his musical taste, his lay is that of industry and contentment. There is nothing plaintive or especially musical in his

performance, but the sentiment expressed is eminently that of cheerfulness. Indeed, the songs of most birds have some human significance, which, I think, is the source of the delight we take in them. The song of the bobolink to me expresses hilarity; the song-sparrow's, faith; the bluebird's, love; the cat-bird's, pride; the white-eyed fly-catcher's, self-consciousness; that of the hermit thrush, spiritual serenity: while there is something military in the call of the robin.

The vireosylvia is classed among the fly-catchers by some writers, but is much more of a worm-eater, and has few of the traits or habits of the *Muscicapa* or the true *Sylvia*. He resembles somewhat the warbling vireo, and the two birds are often confounded by careless observers. Both warble in the same cheerful strain, but the latter more continuously and rapidly. The red-eye is a larger, slimmer bird, with a faint bluish crown, and a light line over the eye. His movements are peculiar. You may see him hopping among the limbs, exploring the under side of the leaves, peering to the right and left, now flitting a few feet, now hopping as many, and warbling incessantly, occasionally in a subdued tone, which sounds from a very indefinite distance. When he has found a worm to his liking, he turns lengthwise of the limb, and bruises its head with his beak before devouring it.

As I enter the woods the slate-colored snow-bird starts up before me and chirps sharply. His protest when thus disturbed is almost metallic in its sharpness. He breeds here, and is not esteemed a snow-bird at all, as he disappears at the near approach of winter, and returns again in spring, like the song-sparrow, and is not in any way associated with the cold and the snow. So different are the habits of birds in different localities. Even the crow does not winter here, and is seldom seen after December or before March.

The snow-bird, or "black chipping-bird," as it is known among the farmers, is the finest architect of any of the ground-builders known to me. The site of its nest is usually some low bank by the roadside, near a wood. In a slight excavation, with a partially concealed entrance, the exquisite structure is placed. Horse and cow hair are plentifully used, imparting to the interior of the nest great symmetry and firmness as well as softness.

Passing down through the maple arches, barely pausing to observe the antics of a trio of squirrels,—two gray ones and a black one,—I cross an ancient brush fence and am fairly within the old hemlocks, and in one of the most primitive, undisturbed nooks. In the deep moss I tread as with muffled feet, and the pupils of my eyes dilate in the dim, almost religious light. The irreverent red squirrels, how-ever, run and snicker at my approach, or mock the solitude with their ridiculous chattering and frisking.

This nook is the chosen haunt of the winter wren. This is the only place and these the only woods in which I find him in this vicinity. His voice fills these dim aisles, as if aided by some marvellous sounding-board. Indeed, his song is very strong for so small a bird, and unites in a remarkable degree brilliancy and plaintiveness. I think of a tremulous, vibrating tongue of silver. You may know it is the song of a wren, from its gushing, lyrical character: but you must needs look sharp to see the little minstrel, especially while in the act of sing-ing. He is nearly the color of the ground and the leaves; he never ascends the tall trees, but keeps low, flitting from stump to stump and from root to root, dodging in and out of his hiding-places, and watching all intruders with a suspicious eye. He has a very pert, almost comical look. His tail stands more than perpendicular: it points straight toward his head. He is the least ostentatious singer I know of. He does not strike an attitude, and lift up his head in preparation, and, as it were, clear his throat; but sits there on a log and pours out his music, looking straight before him, or even down at the ground. As a songster, he has but few superiors. I do not hear him after the first week in July.

While sitting on this soft-cushioned log, tasting the pungent acidu-lous wood-sorrel, the blossoms of which, large and pink-veined, rise everywhere above the moss, a rufous-colored bird flies quickly past, and alighting on a low limb a few rods off, salutes me with "Whew! Whew!" or "Whoit! Whoit!" almost as you would whistle for your dog. I see by his impulsive, graceful movements, and his dimly speckled breast, that it is a thrush. Presently he utters a few soft, mellow, flute-like notes, one of the most simple expressions of melody to be heard, and scuds away, and I see it is the veery, or Wilson's thrush. He is the least of the thrushes in size, being about that of the common blue-bird, and he may be distinguished from his relatives by the dimness of the spots upon his breast. The wood thrush has very clear, distinct oval spots on a white ground; in the hermit, the spots run more into lines, on a ground of a faint bluish-white; in the veery, the marks are almost obsolete, and a few rods off his breast presents only a dull yellowish appearance. To get a good view of him you have only to sit down in his haunts, as in such cases he seems equally anxious to get a good view of you.

From those tall hemlocks proceeds a very fine insect-like warble, and occasionally I see a spray tremble, or catch the flit of a wing. I watch and watch, till my head grows dizzy and my neck is in danger of permanent displacement, and still do not get a good view. Presently the bird darts, or, as it seems, falls down a few feet in pursuit of a fly or a moth, and I see the whole of it, but in the dim light am undecided. It is for such emergencies that I have brought my gun. A bird in the hand is worth half a dozen in the bush, even for ornithological purposes; and no sure and rapid progress can be made in the study without taking life, without procuring specimens. This bird is a warbler, plainly enough, from his habits and manner; but what kind of warbler? Look on him and name him: a deep orange or flame-colored throat and breast; the same color showing also in a line over the eye and in his crown; back variegated black and white. The female is less marked and brilliant. The orange-throated warbler would seem to be his right name, his characteristic cognomen; but no, he is doomed to wear the name of some discoverer, perhaps the first who robbed his nest or rifled him of his mate,—Blackburn; hence, Blackburnian warbler. The *burn* seems appropriate enough, for in these dark evergreens his throat and breast show like flame. He has a very fine warble, suggesting that of the redstart, but not especially musical. I find him in no other woods in this vicinity.

I am attracted by another warble in the same locality, and experience a like difficulty in getting a good view of the author of it. It is quite a noticeable strain, sharp and sibilant, and sounds well amid the old trees. In the upland woods of beech and maple it is a more familiar sound than in these solitudes. On taking the bird in hand, one cannot help exclaiming, "How beautiful!" So tiny and elegant, the smallest of the warblers; a delicate blue back, with a slight bronze-colored triangular spot between the shoulders; upper mandible black; lower mandible yellow as gold; throat yellow, becoming a dark bronze on the breast. Blue yellow-back he is called, though the yellow is much nearer a bronze. He is remarkably delicate and beautiful,—the handsomest as he is the smallest of the warblers known to me. It is never without surprise that I find amid these rugged, savage aspects of nature creatures so fairy and delicate. But such is the law. Go to the sea, or climb the mountain, and with the ruggedest and the savagest you will find likewise the fairest and the most delicate. The greatness and the minuteness of nature pass all understanding.

Ever since I entered the woods, even while listening to the lesser songsters, or contemplating the silent forms about me, a strain has reached my ears from out the depths of the forest that to me is the finest sound in nature,—the song of the hermit thrush. I often hear him thus a long way off, sometimes over a quarter of a mile away, when only the stronger and more perfect parts of his music reach me; and through the general chorus of wrens and warblers I detect this sound rising pure and serene, as if a spirit from some remote height were slowly chanting a divine accompaniment. This song appeals to the sentiment of the beautiful in me, and suggests a serene religious beatitude as no other sound in nature does. It is perhaps more of an evening than a morning hymn, though I hear it at all hours of the day. It is very simple, and I can hardly tell the secret of its charm. "O spheral, spheral!" he seems to say; "O holy, holy! O clear away, clear away! O clear up, clear up!" interspersed with the finest trills and the most delicate preludes. It is not a proud, gorgeous strain, like the tanager's or the grossbeak's; suggests no passion or emotion,— nothing personal,—but seems to be the voice of that calm, sweet solemnity one attains to in his best moments. It realizes a peace and a deep, solemn joy that only the finest souls may know. A few nights ago I ascended a mountain to see the world by moonlight; and, when near the summit, the hermit commenced his evening hymn a few rods from me. Listening to this strain on the lone mountain, with the full moon just rounded from the horizon, the pomp of your cities and the pride of your civilization seemed trivial and cheap.

I have seldom known two of these birds to be singing at the same time in the same locality, rivalling each other, like the wood thrush or the veery. Shooting one from a tree, I have observed another take up the strain from almost the identical perch, in less than ten minutes afterward. Later in the day, when I had penetrated the heart of the old "Bark-peeling," I came suddenly upon one singing from a low stump, and for a wonder he did not seem alarmed, but lifted up his divine voice as if his privacy was undisturbed. I open his beak, and find the inside yellow as gold. I was prepared to find it inlaid with pearls and diamonds, or to see an angel issue from it.

He is not much in the books. Indeed, I am acquainted with scarcely any writer on ornithology whose head is not muddled on the subject of our three prevailing songthrushes, confounding either their figures or their songs. A writer in the "Atlantic" gravely tells us the wood thrush is sometimes called the hermit, and then, after describing the song of the hermit with great beauty and correctness, coolly ascribes it to the veery! The new Cyclopaedia, fresh from the study of Audubon, says the hermit's song consists of a single plaintive note, and that the veery's resembles that of the wood thrush! These observations are as wide of the mark as that of the author of "Outdoor Papers," whose usually accurate pen slips badly when he tells us that the trill of the hair-bird is produced by the bird fluttering its wings upon its sides! The hermit thrush may be easily identified by his color; his back being a clear olive-brown, becoming rufous on his rump and tail. A quill from his wing placed beside one from his tail on a dark ground presents quite a marked contrast.

I walk along the old road, and note the tracks in the thin layer of mud. When do these creatures travel here? I have never yet chanced to meet one. Here a partridge has set its foot; there, a woodcock; here, a squirrel or mink; there, a skunk; there, a fox. What a clear, nervous track Reynard makes! how easy to distinguish it from that of a little dog,—it is so sharply cut and defined! A dog's track is coarse and clumsy beside it. There is as much wildness in the track of an animal as in its voice. Is a deer's track like a sheep's, or a goat's? What winged-footed fleetness and agility may be inferred from the sharp, braided track of the gray squirrel upon the new snow! Ah! in nature is the best discipline. How wood-life sharpens the senses, giving a new power to the eye, the ear, the nose! And are not the rarest and most exquisite songsters wood-birds?

Everywhere in these solitudes I am greeted with the pensive, almost pathetic note of the wood-pewee. The pewees are the true fly-catchers, and are easily identified. They are very characteristic birds, have strong family traits, and pugnacious dispositions. They are the least attractive or elegant birds of our fields or forest. Sharp-shouldered, big-headed, short-legged, of no particular color, of little elegance in flight or movement, with a disagreeable flirt of the tail, always quarrelling with their neighbors and with one another, no birds are so little calculated to excite pleasurable emotions in the beholder, or to become objects of human interest and affection. The king-bird is the best dressed member of the family, but he is a braggart; and, though always snubbing his neighbors, is an arrant coward, and shows the white feather at the slightest display of pluck in his antagonist. I have seen him turn tail to a swallow, and have known the little pewee in question to whip him beautifully. From the great crested to the little green fly-catcher, their ways and general habits are the same. Slow in flying from point to point, they yet have a wonderful quickness, and snap up the fleetest insects with little apparent effort. There is a constant play of quick, nervous movements underneath their outer show of calmness and stolidity. They do not scour the limbs and trees like the warblers, but, perched upon the middle branches, wait like true hunters, for the game to come along. There is often a very audible snap of the beak as they seize their prey.

The wood-pewee, the prevailing species in this locality, arrests your attention by his sweet, pathetic cry. There is room for it also in the deep woods, as well as for the more prolonged and elevated strains.

Its relative, the phoebe-bird, builds an exquisite nest of moss on the side of some shelving cliff or overhanging rock. The other day, passing by a ledge near the top of a mountain in a singularly desolate locality, my eye rested upon one of these structures, looking precisely as if it grew there, so in keeping was it with the mossy character of the rock, and I have had a growing affection for the bird ever since. The rock seemed to love the nest and to claim it as its own. I said, What a lesson in architecture is here! Here is a house that was built, but with such loving care and such beautiful adaptation of the means to the end, that it looks like a product of nature. The same wise economy is noticeable in the nests of all birds. No bird would paint its house white or red, or add aught for show.

At one point in the grayest, most shaggy part of the woods, I come suddenly upon a brood of screech-owls, full grown, sitting together upon a dry, moss-draped limb, but a few feet from the ground. I pause within four or five yards of them and am looking about me, when my eye alights upon these gray, motionless figures. They sit perfectly upright, some with their backs and some with their breasts toward me, but every head turned squarely in my direction. Their eyes are closed to a mere black line; through this crack they are watching me, evidently thinking themselves unobserved. The spectacle is weird and grotesque, and suggests something impish and uncanny. It is a new effect, the night side of the woods by daylight. After observing them a moment I take a single step toward them, when, quick as thought, their eyes fly wide open, their attitude is changed, they bend, some this way, some that, and, instinct with life and motion, stare wildly around them. Another step, and they all take flight but one, which stoops low on the branch, and with the look of a frightened cat regards me for a few seconds over its shoulder. They fly swiftly and softly, and disperse through the trees. I shoot one, which is of a tawny red tint, like that figured by Wilson, who mistook a young bird for an old one. The old birds are a beautiful ashen gray mottled with black. In the present instance, they were sitting on the branch with the young.

Coming to a drier and less mossy place in the woods, I am amused with the golden-crowned thrush,—which, however, is no thrush at all, but a warbler, like the nightingale. He walks on the ground ahead of me with such an easy, gliding motion, and with such an unconscious, preoccupied air, jerking his head like a hen or a partridge, now hurrying, now slackening his pace, that I pause to observe him. If I sit down, he pauses to observe me, and extends his pretty ramblings on all sides, apparently very much engrossed with his own affairs, but never losing sight of me. But few of the birds are walkers, most being hoppers, like the robin.

Satisfied that I have no hostile intentions, the pretty pedestrian mounts a limb a few feet from the ground, and gives me the benefit of one of his musical performances, a sort of accelerating chant. Commencing in a very low key, which makes him seem at a very uncertain distance, he grows louder and louder, till his body quakes and his chant runs into a shriek, ringing in my ear with a peculiar sharpness. This lay may be represented thus: "Teacher, *teacher*, Teacher, TEACHER, *TEACHER!*"—the accent on the first syllable and each word uttered with increased force and shrillness. No writer with whom I am acquainted gives him credit for more musical ability than is displayed in this strain. Yet in this the half is not told. He has a far rarer song, which he reserves for some nymph whom he meets in the air. Mounting by easy flights to the top of the tallest tree, he launches into the air with a sort of suspended, hovering flight, like certain of the finches, and bursts into a perfect ecstasy of song,—clear, ringing, copious, rivalling the goldfinch's in vivacity, and the linnet's in melody. This strain is one of the rarest bits of bird-melody to be heard, and is oftenest indulged in late in the afternoon or after sundown. Over the woods, hid from view, the ecstatic singer warbles his finest strain. In this song you instantly detect his relationship to the water-wagtail,—erroneously called water-thrush,—whose song is likewise a sudden burst, full and ringing, and with a tone of youthful joyousness in it, as if the bird had just had some unexpected good fortune. For nearly two years this strain of the pretty walker was little more than a disembodied voice to me, and I was puzzled by it as Thoreau by his mysterious night-warbler, which, by the way, I suspect was no new bird at all, but one he was otherwise familiar with. The little bird himself seems disposed to keep the matter a secret, and improves every opportunity to repeat before you his shrill, accelerating lay, as if this were quite enough and all he laid claim to. Still, I trust I am betraying no confidence in making the matter public here. I think this is preeminently his love-song, as I hear it oftenest about the mating season. I have caught half-suppressed bursts of it from two males chasing each other with fearful speed through the forest.

Turning to the left from the old road, I wander over soft logs and gray yielding *debris*, across the little trout brook, until I emerge in the overgrown "Bark-peeling,"—pausing now and then on the way to admire a small, solitary white flower which rises above the moss, with radical, heart-shaped leaves, and a blossom precisely like the liverwort except in color, but which is not put down in my botany,—or to observe the ferns, of which I count six varieties, some gigantic ones nearly shoulder-high.

At the foot of a rough, scraggy yellow birch, on a bank of club-moss, so richly inlaid with partridge-berry and curious shining leaves—with here and there in the bordering a spire of the false wintergreen strung with faint pink flowers and exhaling the breath of a May orchard—that it looks too costly a couch for such an idler, I recline to note what transpires. The sun is just past the meridian, and the afternoon chorus is not yet in full tune. Most birds sing with the greatest spirit and vivacity in the forenoon, though there are occasional bursts later in the day, in which nearly all voices join; while it is not till the twilight that the full power and solemnity of the thrush's hymn is felt.

My attention is soon arrested by a pair of humming-birds, the ruby-throated, disporting themselves in a low bush a few yards from me. The female takes shelter amid the branches, and squeaks exultingly, as the male, circling above, dives down as if to dislodge her. Seeing me, he drops like a feather on a slender twig, and in a moment both are gone. Then, as if by a preconcerted signal, the throats are all atune. I lie on my back with eyes half closed, and analyze the chorus of warblers, thrushes, finches, and fly-catchers; while, soaring above all, a little withdrawn and alone, rises the divine soprano of the hermit. That richly modulated warble proceeding from the top of yonder birch, and which unpractised ears would mistake for the voice of the scarlet tanager, comes from that rare visitant, the rose-breasted grossbeak. It is a strong, vivacious strain, a bright noonday song, full of health and assurance, indicating fine talents in the performer, but not genius. As I come up under the tree he casts his eye down at me, but continues his song. This bird is said to be quite common in the Northwest, but he is rare in the Eastern districts. His beak is disproportionately large and heavy, like a huge nose, which slightly mars his good looks; but Nature has made it up to him in a blush rose upon his breast, and the most delicate of pink linings to the under side of his wings. His back is variegated black and white, and when flying low the white shows conspicuously. If he passed over your head, you would note the delicate flush under his wings.

That bit of bright scarlet on yonder dead hemlock, glowing like a live coal against the dark background, seeming almost too brilliant for the severe northern climate, is his relative, the scarlet tanager. I occasionally meet him in the deep hemlocks, and know no stronger contrast in nature. I almost fear he will kindle the dry limb on which he alights. He is quite a solitary bird, and in this section seems to prefer the high, remote woods, even going quite to the mountain's top. Indeed, the event of my last visit to the mountain was meeting one of these brilliant creatures near the summit, in full song. The breeze carried the notes far and wide. He seemed to enjoy the elevation, and I imagine his song had more scope and freedom than usual. When he had flown far down the mountain-side, the breeze still brought me his finest notes. In plumage he is the most brilliant bird we have. The bluebird is not entirely blue; nor will the indigo-bird bear a close inspection, nor the goldfinch, nor the summer redbird. But the tanager loses nothing by a near view; the deep scarlet of his body and the black of his wings and tail are quite perfect. This is his holiday suit; in the fall he becomes a dull yellowish-green,—the color of the female the whole season.

One of the leading songsters in this choir of the old Bark-peeling is the purple finch or linnet. He sits somewhat apart, usually on a dead hemlock, and warbles most exquisitely. He is one of our finest songsters, and stands at the head of the finches, as the hermit at the head of the thrushes. His song approaches an ecstasy, and, with the exception of the winter-wren's, is the most rapid and copious strain to be heard in these woods. It is quite destitute of the trills and the liquid, silvery, bubbling notes that characterize the wren's; but there runs through it a round, richly modulated whistle, very sweet and very pleasing. The call of the robin is brought in at a certain point with marked effect, and, throughout, the variety is so great and the strain so rapid that the impression is as of two or three birds singing at the same time. He is not common here, and I only find him in these or similar woods. His color is peculiar, and looks as if it might have been imparted by dipping a brown bird in diluted pokeberry juice. Two or three more dippings would have made the purple complete. The female is the color of the song-sparrow, a little larger, with heavier beak, and tail much more forked.

In a little opening quite free from brush and trees, I step down to bathe my hands in the brook, when a small, light slate-colored bird flutters out of the bank, not three feet from my head, as I stoop down, and as if severely lamed or injured, flutters through the grass and into the nearest bush. As I do not follow, but remain near the nest, she *chips* sharply, which brings the male, and I see it is the speckled Canada warbler. I find no authority in the books for this bird to build upon the ground, yet here is the nest, made chiefly of dry grass, set in a slight excavation in the bank, not two feet from the water, and looking a little perilous to anything but ducklings or sandpipers. There are two young birds and one little speckled egg, just pipped. But how is this? What mystery is here? One nestling is much larger than the other, monopolizes most of the nest, and lifts its open mouth far above that of its companion, though obviously both are of the same age, not more than a day old. Ah! I see; the old trick of the cow-bunting, with a stinging human significance. Taking the interloper by the nape of the neck, I deliberately drop it into the water, but not without a pang, as I see its naked form, convulsed with chills, float down stream. Cruel? So is Nature cruel. I take one life to save two. In less than two days this pot-bellied intruder would have caused the death of the two rightful occupants of the nest; so I step in and turn things into their proper channel again.

It is a singular freak of Nature, this instinct which prompts one bird to lay its eggs in the nests of others, and thus shirk the responsibility of rearing its own young. The cow-buntings always resort to this cunning trick; and when one reflects upon their numbers, it is evident that these little tragedies are quite frequent. In Europe the parallel case is that of the cuckoo, and occasionally our own cuckoo imposes upon a robin or a thrush in the same manner. The cow-bunting seems to have no conscience about the matter, and, so far as I have observed, invariably selects the nest of a bird smaller than itself. Its egg is usually the first to hatch; its young overreaches all the rest when food is brought; it grows with great rapidity, spreads and fills the nest, and the starved and crowded occupants soon perish, when the parent bird removes their dead bodies, giving its whole energy and care to the foster-child.

The warblers and smaller fly-catchers are generally the sufferers, though I sometimes see the slate-colored snow-bird unconsciously duped in like manner; and the other day, in a tall tree in the woods, I discovered the black-throated green-backed warbler devoting itself to this dusky, overgrown foundling. An old farmer to whom I pointed out the fact was much surprised that such things should happen in his woods without his knowledge.

These birds may be seen prowling through all parts of the woods at this season, watching for an opportunity to steal their egg into some nest. One day, while sitting on a log I saw one moving by short flights through the trees and gradually nearing the ground. Its movements were hurried and stealthy. About fifty yards from me it disappeared behind some low brush and had evidently alighted upon the ground.

After waiting a few moments I cautiously walked in the direction. When about half way I accidentally made a slight noise, when the bird flew up, and seeing me, hurried off out of the woods. Arrived at the place, I found a simple nest of dry grass and leaves partially concealed under a prostrate branch. I took it to be the nest of a sparrow. There were three eggs in the nest and one lying about a foot below it, as if it had been rolled out, as of course it had. It suggested the thought that perhaps when the cow-bird finds the full complement of eggs in a nest, it throws out one and deposits its own instead. I revisited the nest a few days afterward and found an egg again cast out, but none had been put in its place. The nest had been abandoned by its owner and the eggs were stale.

In all cases where I have found this egg, I have observed both male and female of the cow-bird lingering near, the former uttering his peculiar liquid, glassy note from the tops of the trees.

In July, the young which have been reared in the same neighborhood, and which are now of a dull fawn color, begin to collect in small flocks, which grow to be quite large in autumn.

The speckled Canada is a very superior warbler, having a lively, animated strain, reminding you of certain parts of the canary's, though quite broken and incomplete; the bird, the while, hopping amid the branches with increased liveliness, and indulging in fine sibilant chirps, too happy to keep silent.

His manners are quite marked. He has a habit of courtesying when he discovers you, which is very pretty. In form he is an elegant bird, somewhat slender, his back of a bluish lead-color, becoming nearly black on his crown: the under part of his body, from his throat down, is of a light, delicate yellow, with a belt of black dots across his breast. He has a fine eye, surrounded by a light-yellow ring.

The parent birds are much disturbed by my presence, and keep up a loud emphatic chirping, which attracts the attention of their sympathetic neighbors, and one after another they come to see what has happened. The chestnut-sided and the Blackburnian come in company. The black and yellow warbler pauses a moment and hastens away; the Maryland yellow-throat peeps shyly from the lower bushes and utters his "Fip! fip!" in sympathy; the wood-pewee comes straight to the tree overhead, and the red-eyed vireo lingers and lingers, eying me with a curious, innocent look, evidently much puzzled. But all disappear again, one by one, apparently without a word of condolence or encouragement to the distressed pair. I have often noticed among birds this show of sympathy,—if indeed it be sympathy, and not merely curiosity, or desire to be forewarned of the approach of a common danger.

An hour afterward I approach the place, find all still, and the mother bird upon the nest. As I draw near she seems to sit closer, her eyes growing large with an inexpressibly wild, beautiful look. She keeps her place till I am within two paces of her, when she flutters away as at first. In the brief interval the remaining egg has hatched, and the two little nestlings lift their heads without being jostled or overreached by any strange bedfellow. A week afterward and they were flown away,—so brief is the infancy of birds. And the wonder is that they escape, even for this short time, the skunks and minks and muskrats that abound here, and that have a decided partiality for such tidbits.

I pass on through the old Bark-peeling, now threading an obscure cow-path or an overgrown wood-road; now clambering over soft and decayed logs, or forcing my way through a network of briers and hazels; now entering a perfect bower of wild-cherry, beech, and soft-maple; now emerging into a little grassy lane, golden with buttercups or white with daisies, or wading waist-deep in the red raspberry-bushes.

Whir! whir! whir! and a brood of half-grown grouse start up like an explosion, a few paces from me, and, scattering, disappear in the bushes on all sides.

Passing along one of the old Bark-peelers' roads which wander aimlessly about, I am attracted by a singularly brilliant and emphatic warble, proceeding from the low bushes, and quickly suggesting the voice of the Maryland yellow-throat. Presently the singer hops up on a dry twig and gives me a good view. Lead-colored head and neck, becoming nearly black on the breast; clear olive-green back, and yellow belly. From his habit of keeping near the ground, even hopping upon it occasionally, I know him to be a ground-warbler; from his dark breast, the ornithologist has added the expletive mourning, hence the mourning ground-warbler.

Of this bird both Wilson and Audubon confessed their comparative ignorance, neither ever having seen its nest or become acquainted with its haunts and general habits. Its song is quite striking and novel, though its voice at once suggests the class of warblers to which it belongs. It is very shy and wary, flying but a few feet at a time, and studiously concealing itself from your view. I discover but one pair here. The female has food in her beak, but carefully avoids betraying the locality of her nest. The ground-warblers all have one notable feature,—very beautiful legs, as white and delicate as if they had always worn silk stockings and satin slippers. High tree warblers have dark-brown or black legs and more brilliant plumage, but less musical ability.

The chestnut-sided belongs to the latter class. He is quite common in these woods, as in all the woods about. He is one of the rarest and handsomest of the warblers; his white breast and throat, chestnut sides, and yellow crown show conspicuously. But little is known of his habits or haunts. Last year I found the nest of one in an uplying beechwood, in a low bush near the roadside, where cows passed and browsed daily. Things went on smoothly till the cow-bunting stole her egg into it, when other mishaps followed, and the nest was soon empty. A characteristic attitude of the male during this season is a slight drooping of the wings, and tail a little elevated, which gives him a very smart, bantam-like appearance. His song is fine and hurried, and not much of itself, but has its place in the general chorus.

A far sweeter strain, falling on the ear with the true sylvan cadence, is that of the black-throated green-backed warbler, whom I meet at various points. He has no superiors among the true *Sylvia*. His song is very plain and simple, but remarkably pure and tender, and might be indicated by straight lines thus ―― ―― v ――; the first two marks representing two sweet, silvery notes, in the same pitch of voice, and quite unaccented; the latter marks, the concluding notes, wherein the tone and inflection are changed. The throat and breast of the male are a rich black, like velvet, his face yellow, and his back a yellowish green.

Beyond the Bark-peeling, where the woods are mingled hemlock, beech, and birch, the languid midsummer note of the black-throated blue-back falls on my ear. "Twea, twea, twea-e-e!" in the upward slide, and with the peculiar *z-ing* of summer insects, but not destitute of a certain plaintive cadence. It is one of the most languid, unhurried sounds in all the woods. I feel like reclining upon the dry leaves at once. Audubon says he has never heard his love-song; but this is all the love-song he has, and he is evidently a very plain hero with his little brown mistress. He assumes few attitudes, and is not a bold and striking gymnast, like many of his kindred. He has a preference for dense woods of beech and maple, moves slowly amid the lower branches and smaller growths, keeping from eight to ten feet from the ground, and repeats now and then his listless, indolent strain. His back and crown are dark blue; his throat and breast, black; his belly, pure white; and he has a white spot on each wing.

Here and there I meet the black and white creeping-warbler, whose fine strain reminds me of hair-wire. It is unquestionably the finest bird-song to be heard. Few insect strains will compare with it in this respect; while it has none of the harsh, brassy character of the latter, being very delicate and tender.

That sharp, uninterrupted, but still continued warble, which, before one has learned to discriminate closely, he is apt to confound with the red-eyed vireo's, is that of the solitary warbling vireo; a bird slightly larger, much rarer, and with a louder, less cheerful and happy strain. I see him hopping along lengthwise of the limbs, and note the orange tinge of his breast and sides and the white circle around his eye.

But the declining sun and the deepening shadows admonish me that this ramble must be brought to a close, even though only the leading characters in this chorus of forty songsters have been described, and only a small portion of the venerable old woods explored. In a secluded, swampy corner of the old Bark-peeling, where I find the great purple orchis in bloom, and where the foot of man or beast seems never to have trod, I linger long, contemplating the wonderful display of lichens and mosses that overrun both the smaller and the larger growths. Every bush and branch and sprig is dressed up in the most rich and fantastic of liveries; and, crowning all, the long bearded moss festoons the branches or sways gracefully from the limbs. Every twig looks a century old, though green leaves tip the end of it. A young yellow birch has a venerable, patriarchal look, and seems ill at ease under such premature honors. A decayed hemlock is draped as if by hands for some solemn festival.

Mounting toward the upland again, I pause reverently, as the hush and stillness of twilight come upon the woods. It is the sweetest, ripest hour of the day. And as the hermit's evening hymn goes up from the deep solitude below me, I experience that serene exaltation of sentiment of which music, literature, and religion are but the faint types and symbols.

TO A MOUSE

On Turning Her Up in Her Nest with the Plough, November 1785

Wee, sleekit, cowrin, tim'rous beastie,
O, what a panic's in thy breastie!
Thou need na start awa sae hasty,
    Wi' bickering brattle!
I wad be laith to rin an' chase thee,
    Wi' murd'ring pattle!

I'm truly sorry man's dominion,
Has broken nature's social union,
An' justifies that ill opinion,
    Which makes thee startle
At me, thy poor, earth-born companion,
    An' fellow-mortal!

I doubt na, whiles, but thou may thieve;
What then? poor beastie, thou maun live!
A daimen icker in a thrave
    'S a sma' request;
I'll get a blessin wi' the lave,
    An' never miss't!

Thy wee bit housie, too, in ruin!
It's silly wa's the win's are strewin!
An' naething, now, to big a new ane,
    O' foggage green!

An' bleak December's winds ensuin,
    Baith snell an' keen!

Thou saw the fields laid bare an' waste,
An' weary winter comin fast,
An' cozie here, beneath the blast,
    Thou thought to dwell—
Till crash! the cruel coulter past
    Out thro' thy cell.

That wee bit heap o' leaves an' stibble,
Has cost thee mony a weary nibble!
Now thou's turn'd out, for a' thy trouble,
    But house or hald,
To thole the winter's sleety dribble,
    An' cranreuch cauld!

But Mousie, thou art no thy lane,
In proving foresight may be vain;
The best-laid schemes o' mice an' men
    Gang aft agley,
An' lea'e us nought but grief an' pain,
    For promis'd joy!

Still thou art blest, compar'd wi' me;
The present only toucheth thee:
But och! I backward cast my e'e,
    On prospects drear!
An' forward, tho' I canna see,
    I guess an' fear!

                  ROBERT BURNS

TURTLE EGGS FOR AGASSIZ

by Dallas Lore Sharp

Dallas Lore Sharp was born in Haleyville, New Jersey, December 13, 1870, and died in Hingham, Massachusetts, November 29, 1929. He was a teacher and author, and for years the head of the English Department at Boston University. In addition to many magazine articles on Nature, he wrote a number of books including Wild Life Near Home *(1901),* A Watcher in the Woods *(1903),* The Face of the Fields *(1911)—from which this story is taken—and* Beyond the Pasture Bars *(1914). It isn't often that the report of a scientific expedition verges on the hilarious. Not often enough.*

I T is one of the wonders of the world that so few books are written. With every human being a possible book, and with many a human being capable of becoming more books than the world could contain, is it not amazing that the books of men are so few? And so stupid!

I took down, recently, from the shelves of a great public library, the four volumes of Agassiz's "Contributions to the Natural History of the United States." I doubt if anybody but the charwoman, with her duster, had touched those volumes for twenty-five years. They are an excessively learned, a monumental, an epoch-making work, the fruit of vast and heroic labors, with colored plates on stone, showing the turtles of the United States, and their embryology. The work was published more than half a century ago (by subscription); but it looked old beyond its years—massive, heavy, weathered, as if dug from the rocks. It was difficult to feel that Agassiz could have written it—could have built it, grown it, for the laminated pile had required for its growth the patience and painstaking care of a process of nature, as if it were a kind of printed coral reef. Agassiz do this? The big, human, magnetic man at work upon these pages of capital letters, Roman figures, brackets, and parentheses in explanation of the pages of diagrams and plates! I turned away with a sigh from the weary learning, to read the preface.

When a great man writes a great book he usually flings a preface after it, and thereby saves it, sometimes, from oblivion. Whether so or not, the best things in most books are their prefaces. It was not, however, the quality of the preface to these great volumes that interested me, but rather the wicked waste of durable book-material that went to its making. Reading down through the catalogue of human names and of thanks for help received, I came to a sentence beginning:—

"In New England I have myself collected largely; but I have also received valuable contributions from the late Rev. Zadoc Thompson of Burlington; . . . from Mr. D. Henry Thoreau of Concord; . . . and from Mr. J. W. P. Jenks of Middleboro'." And then it hastens on with the thanks in order to get to the turtles, as if turtles were the one and only thing of real importance in all the world.

Turtles no doubt are important, extremely important, embryologically, as part of our genealogical tree; but they are away down among the roots of the tree as compared with the late Rev. Zadoc Thompson of Burlington. I happen to know nothing about the Rev. Zadoc, but to me he looks very interesting. Indeed, any reverend gentleman of his name and day who would catch turtles for Agassiz must have been interesting. And as for D. Henry Thoreau, we know he was interesting. The rarest wood-turtle in the United States was not so rare a specimen as this gentleman of Walden Woods and Concord. We are glad even for this line in the preface about him; glad to know that he tried, in this untranscendental way, to serve his day and generation. If Agassiz had only put a chapter in his turtle book about it! But this is the material he wasted, this and more of the same human sort; for the "Mr. J. W. P. Jenks of Middleboro'" (at the end of the quotation) was, some years later, an old college professor of mine, who told me a few of the particulars of his turtle contributions, particulars which Agassiz should have found a place for in his big book. The preface, in another paragraph, says merely that this gentleman sent turtles to Cambridge by the thousands—brief and scanty recognition! For that is not the only thing this gentleman did. On one occasion he sent, not turtles, but turtle *eggs* to Cambridge—and brought them, I should say; and all there is to show for it, so far as I could discover, is a sectional drawing of a bit of the mesoblastic layer of one of the eggs!

Of course, Agassiz wanted to make that mesoblastic drawing, or some other equally important drawing, and had to have the fresh turtle egg to draw it from. He had to have it, and he got it. A great man, when he wants a certain turtle egg, at a certain time, always gets it, for he gets some one else to get it. I am glad he got it. But what makes me sad and impatient is that he did not think it worth while to tell about the getting of it, and so made merely a learned turtle book of what might have been an exceedingly interesting human book.

It would seem, naturally, that there could be nothing unusual or interesting about the getting of turtle eggs when you want them. Nothing at all, if you should chance to want the eggs as you chance to find them. So with anything else,—good copper stock, for instance, if you should want it, and should chance to be along when they chance to be giving it away. But if you want copper stock, say of C & H quality, *when* you want it, and are bound to have it, then you must command more than a college professor's salary. And likewise, precisely, when it is turtle eggs that you are bound to have.

Agassiz wanted those turtle eggs when he wanted them—not a minute over three hours from the minute they were laid. Yet even that does not seem exacting, hardly more difficult than the getting of hen eggs only three hours old. Just so, provided the professor could have had his private turtle-coop in Harvard Yard; and provided he could have made his turtles lay. But turtles will not respond, like hens, to meat-scraps and the warm mash. The professor's problem was not to get from a mud turtle's nest in the back yard to the table in the laboratory; but to get from the laboratory in Cambridge to some pond when the turtles were laying, and back to the laboratory within the limited time. And this, in the days of Darius Green, might have called for nice and discriminating work—as it did.

Agassiz had been engaged for a long time upon his "Contributions." He had brought the great work nearly to a finish. It was indeed, finished but for one small yet very important bit of observation; he had carried the turtle egg through every stage of its development with the single exception of one—the very earliest—that stage of first cleavages, when the cell begins to segment, immediately upon its being laid. That beginning stage had brought the "Contributions" to a halt. To get eggs that were fresh enough to show the incubation at this period had been impossible.

There were several ways that Agassiz might have proceeded: he might have got a leave of absence for the spring term, taken his laboratory to some pond inhabited by turtles, and there camped until he could catch the reptile digging out her nest. But there were difficulties in all of that—as those who are college professors and naturalists know. As this was quite out of the question, he did the easiest thing—asked Mr. Jenks of Middleboro to get him the eggs. Mr. Jenks got them. Agassiz knew all about his getting of them; and I say the strange and irritating thing is, that Agassiz did not think it worth while to tell us about it, at least in the preface to his monumental work.

It was many years later that Mr. Jenks, then a gray-haired college professor, told me how he got those eggs to Agassiz.

"I was principal of an academy, during my younger days," he says, "and was busy one day with my classes, when a large man suddenly filled the doorway of the room, smiled to the four corners of the room, and called out with a big, quick voice that he was Professor Agassiz.

"Of course he was. I knew it, even before he had had time to shout about it to me across the room.

"Would I get him some turtle eggs? he called. Yes, I would. And would I get them to Cambridge within three hours from the time they were laid? Yes, I would. And I did. And it was worth the doing. But I did it only once.

"When I promised Agassiz those eggs I knew where I was going to get them. I had got turtle eggs there before—at a particular patch of sandy shore along a pond, a few miles distant from the academy.

"Three hours was the limit. From my railroad station to Boston was thirty-five miles; from the pond to the station was perhaps three or four miles; from Boston to Cambridge we called about three miles. Forty miles in round numbers! We figured it all out before he returned, and got the trip down to two hours,—record time: driving from the pond to the station; from the station by express train to Boston; from Boston, by cab to Cambridge. This left an easy hour for accidents and delays.

"Cab and car we reckoned into our time-table; but what we didn't figure on was the turtle." And he paused abruptly.

"Young man, when *you* go after turtle eggs, take into account the turtle! No! no! that's bad advice. Youth never reckons on the turtle —and youth seldom ought to. Old age does that; and old age would never have got those turtle eggs to Agassiz.

"It was in the early spring that Agassiz came to the academy, long

before there was any likelihood of the turtles laying. But I was eager
for the quest, and so fearful of failure, that I started out to watch at
the pond fully two weeks ahead of the time that the turtles might be
expected to lay. I remember the date clearly: it was May 14.

"A little before dawn—along near three o'clock—I would drive over
to the pond, hitch my horse near by, settle myself quietly among some
thick cedars close to the sandy shore, and there I would wait, my kettle
of sand ready, my eye covering the whole sleeping pond. Here among
the cedars I would eat my breakfast, and then get back in good season
to open the academy for the morning session.

"And so the watch began.

"I soon came to know individually the dozen or more turtles that
kept to my side of the pond. Shortly after the cold mist would lift
and melt away, they would stick up their heads through the quiet water; and as the sun slanted down over the ragged rim of treetops, the
slow things would float into the warm, lighted spots, or crawl out and
doze comfortably on the hummocks and snags.

"What fragrant mornings those were! How fresh and new and un-
breathed! The pond odors, the woods odors, the odors of the ploughed
fields—of water-lily, and wild grape, and the dew-laid soil! I can taste
them yet, and hear them yet—the still, large sounds of the waking
day—the pickerel breaking the quiet with his swirl; the kingfisher dropping anchor; the stir of feet and wings among the trees. And then
the thought of the great book being held up for me! Those were rare
mornings!

"But there began to be a good many of them, for the turtles showed
no desire to lay. They sprawled in the sun, and never one came out
upon the sand as if she intended to help on the great professor's book.
The embryology of her eggs was of small concern to her; her Contribution to the Natural History of the United States could wait.

"And it did wait. I began my watch on the 14th of May; June 1st
found me still among the cedars, still waiting, as I had waited every
morning, Sundays and rainy days alike. June 1st was a perfect morning, but every turtle slid out upon her log, as if egg-laying might be
a matter strictly of next year.

"I began to grow uneasy,—not impatient yet, for a naturalist learns
his lesson of patience early, and for all his years; but I began to fear
lest, by some subtle sense, my presence might somehow be known to
the creatures; that they might have gone to some other place to lay,
while I was away at the schoolroom.

"I watched on to the end of the first week, on to the end of the second week in June, seeing the mists rise and vanish every morning, and along with them vanish, more and more, the poetry of my early morning vigil. Poetry and rheumatism cannot long dwell together in the same clump of cedars, and I had begun to feel the rheumatism. A month of morning mists wrapping me around had at last soaked through to my bones. But Agassiz was waiting, and the world was waiting, for those turtle eggs; and I would wait. It was all I could do, for there is no use bringing a china nest-egg to a turtle; she is not open to any such delicate suggestion.

"Then came the mid-June Sunday morning, with dawn breaking a little after three; a warm, wide-awake dawn, with the level mist lifted from the level surface of the pond a full hour higher than I had seen it any morning before.

"This was the day. I knew it. I have heard persons say that they can hear the grass grow; that they know by some extra sense when danger is nigh. That we have these extra senses I fully believe, and I believe they can be sharpened by cultivation. For a month I had been brooding over this pond, and now I knew. I felt a stirring of the pulse of things that the cold-hearted turtles could no more escape than could the clods and I.

"Leaving my horse unhitched, as if he, too, understood, I slipped eagerly into my covert for a look at the pond. As I did so, a large pickerel ploughed a furrow out through the spatter-docks, and in his wake rose the head of an enormous turtle. Swinging slowly around, the creature headed straight for the shore, and without a pause scrambled out on the sand.

"She was about the size of a big scoop-shovel; but that was not what excited me, so much as her manner, and the gait at which she moved; for there was method in it and fixed purpose. On she came, shuffling over the sand and toward the higher open fields, with a hurried, determined see-saw that was taking her somewhere in particular, and that was bound to get her there on time.

"I held my breath. Had she been a dinosaurian making Mesozoic footprints, I could not have been more fearful. For footprints in the Mesozoic mud, or in the sands of time, were as nothing to me when compared with fresh turtle eggs in the sands of this pond.

"But over the strip of sand, without a stop, she paddled, and up a narrow cow-path into the high grass along a fence. Then up the narrow cow-path on all fours, just like another turtle, I paddled, and into the high wet grass along the fence.

"I kept well within sound of her, for she moved recklessly, leaving a trail of flattened grass a foot and a half wide. I wanted to stand up,— and I don't believe I could have turned her back with a rail,—but I was afraid if she saw me that she might return indefinitely to the pond; so on I went, flat to the ground, squeezing through the lower rails of the fence, as if the field beyond were a melon-patch. It was nothing of the kind, only a wild, uncomfortable pasture, full of dewberry vines, and very discouraging. They were excessively wet vines and briery. I pulled my coat-sleeves as far over my fists as I could get them, and with the tin pail of sand swinging from between my teeth to avoid noise, I stumped fiercely but silently on after the turtle.

"She was laying her course, I thought, straight down the length of this dreadful pasture, when, not far from the fence, she suddenly hove to, warped herself short about, and came back, barely clearing me, at a clip that was thrilling. I warped about, too, and in her wake bore down across the corner of the pasture, across the powdery public road, and on to a fence along a field of young corn.

"I was somewhat wet by this time, but not so wet as I had been before wallowing through the deep dry dust of the road. Hurrying up behind a large tree by the fence, I peered down the corn-rows and saw the turtle stop, and begin to paw about in the loose soft soil. She was going to lay!

"I held on to the tree and watched, as she tried this place, and that place, and the other place—the eternally feminine!—but *the* place, evidently, was hard to find. What could a female turtle do with a whole field of possible nests to choose from? Then at last she found it, and whirling about, she backed quickly at it, began to bury herself before my staring eyes.

"Those were not the supreme moments of my life; perhaps those moments came later that day; but those certainly were among the slowest, most dreadfully mixed up moments that I ever experienced. They were hours long. There she was, her shell just showing, like some old hulk in the sand along shore. And how long would she stay there? and how should I know if she had laid an egg?

"I could still wait. And so I waited, when, over the freshly awakened fields, floated four mellow strokes from the distant town clock.

"Four o'clock! Why, there was no train until seven! No train for three hours! The eggs would spoil! Then with a rush it came over me that this was Sunday morning, and there was no regular seven o'clock train,—none till after nine.

"I think I should have fainted had not the turtle just then begun

crawling off. I was weak and dizzy; but there, there in the sand, were
the eggs! and Agassiz! and the great book! And I cleared the fence,
and the forty miles that lay between me and Cambridge, at a single
jump. He should have them, trains or no. Those eggs should go to
Agassiz by seven o'clock if I had to gallop every mile of the way. Forty
miles! Any horse could cover it in three hours if he had to; and un-
setting the astonished turtle, I scooped out her round white eggs.

"On a bed of sand in the bottom of the pail I laid them, with what
care my trembling fingers allowed; filled in between them with more
sand; so with another layer to the rim; and covering all smoothly with
more sand, I ran back for my horse.

"That horse knew, as well as I, that the turtles had laid, and that he
was to get those eggs to Agassiz. He turned out of the field into the
road on two wheels, a thing he had not done for twenty years,
doubling me up before the dashboard, the pail of eggs miraculously
lodged between my knees.

"I let him out. If only he could keep this pace all the way to Cambridge! or even halfway there; and I would have time to finish the
trip on foot. I shouted him on, holding to the dasher with one hand,
the pail of eggs with the other, not daring to get off my knees, even
though the bang on them, as we pounded down the wood-road, was
terrific. But nothing must happen to the eggs; they must not be jarred,
or even turned over in the sand before they came to Agassiz.

"In order to get out on the pike it was necessary to drive back away
from Boston toward the town. We had nearly covered the distance,
and were rounding a turn from the woods into the open fields, when,
ahead of me, at the station it seemed, I heard the quick sharp whistle
of a locomotive.

"What did it mean? Then followed the PUFF, PUFF, PUFF, of a starting train. But what train? Which way going? And jumping to my feet
for a longer view, I pulled into a side road that paralleled the track
and headed hard for the station.

"We reeled along. The station was still out of sight, but from behind the bushes that shut it from view, rose the smoke of a moving
engine. It was perhaps a mile away, but we were approaching, head
on, and topping a little hill I swept down upon a freight train, the
black smoke pouring from the stack, as the mighty creature got itself
together for its swift run down the rails.

"My horse was on the gallop, going with the track, and straight toward the coming train. The sight of it almost maddened me—the bare

thought of it, on the road to Boston! On I went; on it came, a half—a quarter of a mile between us, when suddenly my road shot out along an unfenced field with only a level stretch of sod between me and the engine.

"With a pull that lifted the horse from his feet, I swung him into the field and sent him straight as an arrow for the track. That train should carry me and my eggs to Boston!

"The engineer pulled the rope. He saw me standing up in the rig, saw my hat blow off, saw me wave my arms, saw the tin pail swing in my teeth, and he jerked out a succession of sharp halts! But it was he who should halt, not I; and on we went, the horse with a flounder landing the carriage on top of the track.

"The train was already grinding to a stop; but before it was near a standstill, I had backed off the track, jumped out, and, running down the rails with the astonished engineers gaping at me, swung aboard the cab.

"They offered no resistance; they hadn't had time. Nor did they have the disposition, for I looked strange, not to say dangerous. Hatless, dew-soaked, smeared with yellow mud, and holding, as if it were a baby or a bomb, a little tin pail of sand.

" 'Crazy,' the fireman muttered, looking to the engineer for his cue.

"I had been crazy, perhaps, but I was not crazy now.

" 'Throw her wide open,' I commanded, 'Wide open! These are fresh turtle eggs for Professor of Agassiz of Cambridge. He must have them before breakfast.'

"Then they knew I was crazy, and evidently thinking it best to humor me, threw the throttle wide open, and away we went.

"I kissed my hand to the horse, grazing unconcernedly in the open field, and gave a smile to my crew. That was all I could give them, and hold myself and my eggs together. But the smile was enough. And they smiled through their smut at me, though one of them held fast to his shovel, while the other kept his hand upon a big ugly wrench. Neither of them spoke to me, but above the roar of the swaying engine I caught enough of their broken talk to understand that they were driving under a full head of steam, with the intention of handing me over to the Boston police, as perhaps the safest way of disposing of me.

"I was only afraid that they would try it at the next station. But that station whizzed past without a bit of slack, and the next, and the next; when it came over me that this was the through freight, which should have passed in the night, and was making up lost time.

"Only the fear of the shovel and the wrench kept me from shaking hands with both men at this discovery. But I beamed on them; and they at me. I was enjoying it. The unwonted jar beneath my feet was wrinkling my diaphragm with spasms of delight. And the fireman beamed at the engineer, with a look that said, 'See the lunatic grin; he likes it!'

"He did like it. How the iron wheels sang to me as they took the rails! How the rushing wind in my ears sang to me! From my stand on the fireman's side of the cab I could catch a glimpse of the track just ahead of the engine, where the ties seemed to leap into the throat of the mile-devouring monster. The joy of it! of seeing space swallowed by the mile!

"I shifted the eggs from hand to hand and thought of my horse, of Agassiz, of the great book, of my great luck,—luck—luck,—until the multitudinous tongues of the thundering train were all chiming 'luck! luck! luck!' They knew! they understood! This beast of fire and tireless wheels was doing its best to get the eggs to Agassiz!

"We swung out past the Blue Hills, and yonder flashed the morning sun from the towering dome of the State House. I might have leaped from the cab and run the rest of the way on foot, had I not caught the eye of the engineer watching me narrowly. I was not in Boston yet, nor in Cambridge either. I was an escaped lunatic, who had held up a train, and forced it to carry me to Boston.

"Perhaps I had overdone the lunacy business. Suppose these two men should take it into their heads to turn me over to the police, whether I would or not? I could never explain the case in time to get the eggs to Agassiz. I looked at my watch. There were still a few minutes left, in which I might explain to these men, who, all at once, had become my captors. But it was too late. Nothing could avail against my actions, my appearance, and my little pail of sand.

"I had not thought of my appearance before. Here I was, face and clothes caked with yellow mud, my hair wild and matted, my hat gone, and in my full-grown hands a tiny tin pail of sand, as if I had been digging all night with a tiny tin shovel on the shore! And thus to appear in the decent streets of Boston of a Sunday morning!

"I began to feel like a lunatic. The situation was serious, or might be, and rather desperately funny at its best. I must in some way have shown my new fears, for both men watched me more sharply.

TURTLE EGGS FOR AGASSIZ

"Suddenly, as we were nearing the outer freight-yard, the train slowed down and came to a stop. I was ready to jump, but I had no chance. They had nothing to do, apparently, but to guard me. I looked at my watch again. What time we had made! It was only six o'clock, with a whole hour to get to Cambridge.

"But I didn't like this delay. Five minutes—ten—went by.

" 'Gentlemen,' I began, but was cut short by an express train coming past. We were moving again, on—into a siding; on—on to the main track; and on with a bump and a crash and a succession of crashes, running the length of the train; on at a turtle's pace, but on,—when the fireman quickly jumping for the bell-rope, left the way to the step free, and—the chance had come!

"I never touched the step, but landed in the soft sand at the side of the track, and made a line for the yard fence.

"There was no hue or cry. I glanced over my shoulder to see if they were after me. Evidently their hands were full, and they didn't know I had gone.

"But I had gone; and was ready to drop over the high board-fence, when it occurred to me that I might drop into a policeman's arms. Hanging my pail in a splint on top of a post, I peered cautiously over —a very wise thing to do before you jump a high board-fence. There, crossing the open square toward the station, was a big burly fellow with a club—looking for me.

"I flattened for a moment, when some one in the yard yelled at me. I preferred the policeman, and grabbing my pail I slid over to the street. The policeman moved on past the corner of the station out of sight! The square was free, and yonder stood a cab!

"Time was flying now. Here was the last lap. The cabman saw me coming and squared away. I waved a paper dollar at him, but he only stared the more. A dollar can cover a good deal, but I was too much for one dollar. I pulled out another, thrust them both at him, and dodged into the cab, calling, 'Cambridge!'

"He would have taken me straight to the police station, had I not said, 'Harvard College. Professor Agassiz's house! I've got eggs for Agassiz'; and pushed another dollar up at him through the hole.

"It was nearly half-past six.

" 'Let him go!' I ordered, 'Here's another dollar if you make Agassiz' house in twenty minutes. Let him out. Never mind the police!'

"He evidently knew the police, or there were few around at that time on a Sunday morning. We went down the sleeping streets, as

I had gone down the wood-roads from the pond two hours before, but with the rattle and crash now of a fire brigade. Whirling a corner into Cambridge Street, we took the bridge at a gallop, the driver shouting out something in Hibernian to a pair of waving arms and a belt and brass buttons.

"Across the bridge with a rattle and jolt that put the eggs in jeopardy, and on over the cobblestones we went. Half-standing, to lessen the jar, I held the pail in one hand and held myself in the other, not daring to let go even to look at my watch.

"But I was afraid to look at the watch. I was afraid to see how near to seven o'clock it might be. The sweat was dropping from my nose, so close was I running to the limit of my time.

"Suddenly there was a lurch, and I dove forward, ramming my head into the front of the cab, coming up with a rebound that landed me across the small of my back on the seat, and sent half of my pail of eggs helter-skelter over the floor.

"We had stopped. Here was Agassiz' house; and not taking time to pick up the scattered eggs, I tumbled out, and pounded at the door.

"No one was astir in the house. But I would stir them. And I did. Right in the midst of the racket the door opened. It was the maid.

"'Agassiz,' I gasped, 'I want Professor Agassiz, quick!' And I pushed by her into the hall.

"'Go 'way, sir. I'll call the police. Professor Agassiz is in bed. Go 'way, sir.'

"'Call him—Agassiz—instantly, or I'll call him myself!'

"But I didn't; for just then a door overhead was flung open, a white-robed figure appeared on the dim landing above, and a quick loud voice called excitedly,—

"'Let him in! Let him in! I know him. He has my turtle eggs!'

"And the apparition, slipperless, and clad in anything but an academic gown, came sailing down the stairs.

"The maid fled. The great man, his arms extended, laid hold of me with both hands, and dragging me and my precious pail into his study, with a swift, clean stroke laid open one of the eggs, as the watch in my trembling hands ticked its way to seven—as if nothing unusual were happening to the history of the world."

"You were in time then?" I said.

"To the tick. There stands my copy of the great book. I am proud of the humble part I had in it."

SEEN AND LOST

by W. H. Hudson

Many of the selections in this book were chosen largely for their subject matter, a sensible enough procedure in compiling a book designed to offer a wide range of good writing on Nature in her visible forms; but, when we come to W. H. Hudson, we are moving into the realm of great literature. This tall, gaunt, bearded man, who never laid eyes on England until he was twenty-eight years old, was a master of English prose. It is lucky for us that he loved Nature, was a keen observer, and had a passionate interest in everything outdoors; he would have written "wildly well" on any subject that engaged the interest of his rather melancholy mind and brooding spirit. It is too bad that many literate persons know Hudson only as the author of Green Mansions, that enchanting romance wrapped in fantasy and jungle scenery, or perhaps as the author of The Purple Land, a picaresque novel of wild days in the Argentine. These are delightful stories, but who reads only those books has missed the best of Hudson, the distillation of his searching soul and somber thoughts set forth in flawless phrasing. Poor health and—during most of his adult years—grim poverty in London colored his outlook on life. In Nature only did he find "respite, respite and Nepenthe."

The vital statistics about Hudson are important. His father was born in Marblehead, Massachusetts, and his mother was a Maine woman. They migrated to the Argentine, and William Henry Hudson was born at Quilmes, about ten miles from Buenos Aires, August 4, 1841. The boy grew up there on his father's sheep ranch and showed a deep interest in wildlife at an early age. When he was fifteen years old he had an attack of rheumatic fever that affected his heart, and the doctors who were called in said that the boy would not live long. For that reason he was allowed to do as he pleased, and he pleased to indulge his love of Nature to the

*greatest possible extent. He was outdoors at all seasons, observing,
collecting, reflecting, and writings notes on what he found. He
roamed the Argentine, and he wandered as far as Patagonia. He
was particularly fond of birds, and soon was writing and mailing
off such exceptional reports on his findings that he was elected a
corresponding member of the Zoological Society in London.*

*When he was twenty-one his mother died, and that was a heavy
blow. Eight years later his father died, and William Henry Hudson left the Argentine for the land of his forefathers, England.
His weak heart made it impossible for him to take any position
that required physical exertion, so he tried to make a living by
writing after he landed in England in 1869. He wandered up to
London, took what odd jobs of writing he could get, barely
scraped along, and, in 1876, married a singer who was no better
off than he was. His wife gave singing lessons and piano lessons,
but pupils were few. Mrs. Hudson opened a boarding house. It
failed. Mrs. Hudson's sister died and left her a house. The Hud-
sons moved into the garret of the house and rented the lower
floors to eke out their income.*

*All this poverty-stricken time Hudson had been studying Na-
ture in the London public parks and the surrounding countryside
and writing a book about "the purple land that England lost."
The book was published in 1885. It gained Hudson a reputation
but little money. He wrote more books, some about his youthful
days in South America and some about the English countryside
and country life, but general recognition and financial success
were long in coming, and when they came he was too old and
sick to care. Of publishers who had refused to accept a book or
an article of his at any price, he later wrote in a letter to his
friend Morley Roberts, "And now when I don't want the beastly
money and care nothing for fame and am sick and tired of the
whole thing, they actually come and beg a book or article from
me."* Such was the life of the man who gave us The Purple Land,
The Naturalist in La Plata, Idle Days in Patagonia, Green Mansions, Far Away and Long Ago, Nature in Downland, The Land's
End, A Traveller in Little Things, and A Hind in Richmond
Park. *His wife died shortly before he did, and he was too weak
to go to her funeral. He died August 18, 1922, in London, at the
age of 81, and was buried beside his wife in the Broadwater Cemetery in Worthing on the south coast of England. Nearby in the*

same cemetery is the grave of a kindred spirit, Richard Jefferies.
The longer selection that follows is from The Naturalist in La
Plata. *The shorter bit about his friend the pig is from a gathering*
of his essays and magazine articles published in 1919 as The Book
of a Naturalist. *It shows that the darker musings of Hudson were*
now and then lightened by inner laughter. This is the mood that,
in The Purple Land, *gave us Anselmo's priceless story of how he*
purchased the cream-nosed horses of Manuel, also called the Fox.

WE can imagine what the feelings of a lapidary would be—an enthusiast whose life is given to the study of precious stones, and whose sole delight is in the contemplation of their manifold beauty—if a stranger should come in to him, and, opening his hand, exhibit a new unknown gem, splendid as ruby or as sapphire, yet manifestly no mere variety of any familiar stone, but differing as widely from all others as diamond from opal or cat's eye; and then, just when he is beginning to rejoice in that strange exquisite loveliness, the hand should close and the stranger, with a mocking smile on his lips, go forth and disappear from sight in the crowd. A feeling such as that would be is not unfrequently experienced by the field naturalist whose favoured lot it is to live in a country not yet "thoroughly worked out," with its every wild inhabitant scientifically named, accurately described, and skilfully figured in some colossal monograph. One swift glance of the practised eye, ever eagerly searching for some new thing, and he knows that here at length is a form never previously seen by him; but his joy is perhaps only for a few minutes, and the prize is snatched from sight forever. The lapidary might have some doubts; he might think that the stranger had, after all, only mocked him with the sight of a wonderful artificial gem, and that a close examination would have proved its worthlessness; but the naturalist can have no doubts; if he is an enthusiast, well acquainted with the fauna of his district, and has good eyesight, he knows that there is no mistake; for there it is, the new strange form, photographed by instantaneous process on his mind, and there it will remain a tantalizing image, its sharp lines and fresh colouring unblurred by time.

Walking in some open forest glade, he may look up just in time to see a great strange butterfly—a blue Morpho, let us say, wandering in some far country where this angel insect is unknown—passing athwart his vision with careless, buoyant flight, the most sylph-like thing in nature, and all blue and pure like its aerial home, but with a more delicate and wonderful brilliance in its cerulean colour, giving such unimaginable glory to its broad airy wings; and then, almost before his soul has had time to feel its joy, it may soar away unloitering over the tall trees, to be seen no more.

But the admiration, the delight, and the desire are equally great, and the loss just as keenly felt, whether the strange species seen happens to be one surpassingly beautiful or not. Its newness is to the naturalist its greatest attraction. How beautiful beyond all others seems a certain small unnamed brown bird to my mind! so many years have passed and its image has not yet grown dim; yet I saw it only for a few moments, when it hopped out from the thick foliage and perched within two or three yards of me, not afraid, but only curious; and after peering at me first with one eye and then the other, and wiping its small dagger on a twig, it flew away and was seen no more. For many days I sought for it, and for years waited its reappearance, and it was more to me than ninety and nine birds which I had always known; yet it was very modest, dressed in a brown suit, very pale on the breast and white on the throat, and for distinction a straw-coloured stripe over the eye—that ribbon which Queen Nature bestows on so many of her feathered subjects, in recognition, I suppose, of some small and common kind of merit. If I should meet with it in a collection I should know it again; only, in that case it would look plain and homely to me—this little bird that for a time made all others seem unbeautiful.

Even a richer prize may come in sight for a brief period—one of the nobler mammalians, which are fewer in number, and bound to earth like ourselves, and therefore so much better known than the wandering children of the air. In some secluded spot, resting amidst luxuriant herbage or forest undergrowth, a slight rustling makes us start, and, lo! looking at us from the clustering leaves, a strange face; the leaf-like ears erect, the dark eyes round with astonishment, and the sharp black nose twitching and sniffing audibly, to take in the unfamiliar flavour of a human presence from the air, like the pursed-up and smacking lips of a wine-drinker tasting a new vintage. No sooner seen than gone, like a dream, a phantom, the quaint furry face to be thereafter only an image in memory.

Sometimes the prize may be a very rich one, and actually within reach of the hand—challenging the hand, as it were, to grasp it, and yet presently slip away to be seen no more, although it may be sought for day after day, with a hungry longing comparable to that of some poor tramp who finds a gold doubloon in the forest, and just when he is beginning to realize all that it means to him drops it in the grass and cannot find it again. There is not the faintest motion in the foliage, no rustle of any dry leaf, and yet we know that something has moved—something has come or has gone; and, gazing fixedly at one spot, we suddenly see that it is still there, close to us, the pointed ophidian head and long neck, not drawn back and threatening, but sloping forward, dark and polished as the green and purple weed-stems springing from marshy soil, and with an irregular chain of spots extending down the side. Motionless, too, as the stems it is; but presently the tongue, crimson and glistening, darts out and flickers, like a small jet of smoke and flame, and is withdrawn; then the smooth serpent head drops down, and the thing is gone.

One of my earliest experiences of seeing and losing relates to a hummingbird—a veritable "jewel of ornithology." I was only a boy at the time, but already pretty well acquainted with the birds of the district I lived in, near La Plata River, and among them were three species of the hummingbird. One spring day I saw a fourth—a wonderful little thing, only half as big as the smallest of the other three—the well-known *Phaithornis splendens*—and scarcely larger than a bumble-bee. I was within three feet of it as it sucked at the flowers, suspended motionless in the air, the wings appearing formless and mist-like from their rapid vibratory motion, but the rest of the upper plumage was seen distinctly as anything can be seen. The head and neck and upper part of the back were emerald green, with the metallic glitter usually seen in the burnished scale-like feathers of these small birds; the lower half of the back was velvet-black; the tail and tail-coverts white as snow. On two other occasions, at intervals of a few days, I saw this brilliant little stranger, always very near, and tried without success to capture it, after which it disappeared from the plantation. Four years later I saw it once again not far from the same place. It was late in summer, and I was out walking on the level plain where the ground was carpeted with short grass, and nothing else grew there except a solitary stunted cardoon thistle-bush with one flower on its central stem above the grey-green artichoke-like leaves. The disc of the great thorny blossom was as broad as that of a sunflower, purple in colour, delicately frosted with white; on this flat disc several insects were feeding—flies, fireflies, and small wasps—and I paused for a few minutes in my walk to watch them. Suddenly a small misty object flew swiftly downwards past my face, and paused motionless in the air an inch or two above the rim of the flower. Once more my lost hummingbird, which I remembered so well! The exquisitely graceful form, half circled by the misty moth-like wings, the glittering green and velvet-black mantle, and snow-white tail spread open like a fan—there it hung like a beautiful bird-shaped gem suspended by an invisible gossamer thread. One—two—three moments passed, while I gazed, trembling with rapturous excitement, and then, before I had time to collect my faculties and make a forlorn attempt to capture it with my hat, away it flew, gliding so swiftly on the air that form and colour were instantly lost, and in appearance it was only an obscure grey line traced rapidly along the low sky and fading quickly out of sight. And that was the last I ever saw of it.

The case of this small "winged gem," still wandering nameless in the wilds, reminds me of yet another bird seen and lost, also remarkable for its diminutive size. For years I looked for it, and when the wished-for opportunity came, and it was in my power to secure it, I refrained; and Fate punished me by never permitting me to see it again. On several occasions while riding on the pampas I had caught glimpses of this minute bird flitting up moth-like, with uncertain tremulous flight, and again dipping into the woods, tall grass, or thistles. Its plumage was yellowish in hue, like sere dead herbage, and its extremely slender body looked longer and slimmer than it was, owing to the great length of its tail, or of the two middle tail-feathers. I knew that it was a *Synallaxis*—a genus of small birds of the Wood-hewer family. Now, as I have said in a former chapter, these are wise little birds, more interesting—I had almost said more beautiful—in their wisdom, or wisdom-simulating instincts, than the quetzal in its resplendent green or the cock-of-the-rock in its vivid scarlet and orange mantle. Wrens and mockingbirds have melody for their chief attraction, and the name of each kind is, to our minds, also the name of a certain kind of sweet music; we think of swifts and swallows in connection with the mysterious migration instinct; and hummingbirds have a glittering display and the miraculous motions necessary to display their ever-changing iridescent beauty. In like manner, the homely Dendrocolaptidae possess the genius for building, and an account of one of these small birds without its nest would be like a biography of Sir Christopher Wren that made no mention of his works. It was not strange then, that when I saw this small bird the question rose to my mind, What kind of nest does it build?

One morning in the month of October, the great breeding-time for birds in the Southern Hemisphere, while cautiously picking my way through a bed of cardoon bushes, the mysterious little creature flitted up and perched among the clustering leaves quite near to me. It uttered a feeble grasshopper-like chirp; and then a second individual, smaller, paler-coloured, and if possible shyer than the first, showed itself for two or three seconds, after which both birds dived once more into concealment. How glad I was to see them! for there they were, male and female, in a suitable spot in my own fields, where they evidently meant to breed. Every day after that I paid them one cautious visit, and by waiting from five to fifteen minutes, standing motionless among the thistles, I always succeeded in getting them to show themselves for a few moments. I could easily have secured them then, but my wish was to discover their nesting habits; and after watching for some days, I was rewarded by finding their nest; then for three days more I watched it slowly progressing towards completion, and each time I approached it one of the small birds would flit out to vanish into the herbage. The structure was about six inches long, and not more than two inches in diameter, and was placed horizontally on a broad stiff cardoon leaf, sheltered by other leaves above. It was made of the finest dry grass loosely woven, and formed a simple perfectly straight tube, open at both ends. The aperture was so small that I could only insert my little finger, and the bird could not, of course, have turned round in so narrow a passage, and so always went in at one end and left by the other. On visiting the spot on the fourth day I found, to my intense chagrin, that the delicate fabric had been broken and thrown down by some animal; also that the birds had utterly vanished—for I sought them in vain, both there and in every weedy and thistly spot in the neighbourhood. The bird without the nest had seemed a useless thing to possess; now, for all my pains, I had only a wisp of fine dry grass in my hand, and no bird. The shy, modest little creature, dwelling violet-like amidst clustering leaves, and even when showing itself still "half-hidden from the eye," was thereafter to be only a tantalizing image in memory. Still, my case was not so hopeless as that of the imagined lapidary; for however rare a species may be, and near to its final extinction, there must always be many individuals existing, and I was cheered by the thought that I might yet meet with one at some future time. And, even if this particular

species was not to gladden my sight again, there were others, scores
and hundreds more, and at any moment I might expect to see one
shining, a living gem, on Nature's open extended palm.

Sometimes it has happened that an animal would have been overlooked or passed by with scant notice, to be forgotten, perhaps, but
for some singular action or habit which has instantly given it a strange
importance, and made its possession desirable.

I was once engaged in the arduous and monotonous task of driving
a large number of sheep a distance of two hundred and fifty miles,
in excessively hot weather, when sheep prefer standing still to travelling. Five or six gauchos were with me, and we were on the southern
pampas of Buenos Ayres, near to a long precipitous stony sierra which
rose to a height of five or six hundred feet above the plain. Who that
has travelled for eighteen days on a dead level in a broiling sun can
resist a hill? That sierra was more sublime to us than Conondagua,
than Illimani.

Leaving the sheep, I rode to it with three of the men; and after
securing our horses on the lower slope, we began our laborious ascent.
Now the gaucho when taken from his horse, on which he lives like
a kind of parasite, is a very slow-moving creature, and I soon left my
friends far behind. Coming to a place where ferns and flowering herbage grew thick, I began to hear all about me sounds of a character
utterly unlike any natural sound I was acquainted with—innumerable
low clear voices tinkling or pealing like minute sweet-toned, resonant
bells—for the sounds were purely metallic and perfectly bell-like. I
was completely ringed round with the mysterious music, and as I
walked it rose and sank rhythmically, keeping time to my steps. I stood
still, and immediately the sounds ceased. I took a step forwards, and
again the fairy-bells were set ringing, as if at each step my foot touched
a central meeting point of a thousand radiating threads, each thread
attached to a peal of little bells hanging concealed among the herbage.
I waited for my companions, and called their attention to the phenomenon, and to them also it was a thing strange and perplexing. "It
is the bell-snake!" cried one excitedly. This is the rattlesnake; but although at that time I had no experience of this reptile, I knew that he
was wrong. Yet how natural the mistake! The Spanish name of "bell-
snake" had made him imagine that the whirring sound of the vibrating
rattles, resembling muffled cicada music, is really bell-like in character.
Eventually we discovered that the sound was made by grasshoppers;
but they were seen only to be lost, for I could not capture one, so

excessively shy and cunning had the perpetual ringing of their own little tocsins made them. And presently I had to return to my muttons; and afterwards there was no opportunity of revisiting the spot to observe so singular a habit again and collect specimens. It was a very slender grasshopper, about an inch and a half long, of a uniform, tawny, protective colour—the colour of an old dead leaf. It also possessed a protective habit common to most grasshoppers, of embracing a slender vertical stem with its four fine front legs, and moving cunningly round so as to keep the stem always in front of it to screen itself from sight. Only other grasshoppers are silent when alarmed, and the silence and masking action are related, and together prevent the insect from being detected. But this particular species, or race, or colony, living on the sides of the isolated sierra, had acquired a contrary habit, resembling a habit of gregarious birds and mammals. For this informing sound (unless it mimicked some *warning-sound*, as of a rattlesnake, which it didn't) could not possibly be beneficial to individuals living alone, as grasshoppers generally do, but, on the contrary, only detrimental; and such a habit was therefore purely for the public good, and could only have arisen in a species that always lived in communities.

On another occasion, in the middle of the hot season, I was travelling alone across-country in a locality which was new to me, a few leagues east of La Plata River, in its widest part. About eleven o'clock in the morning I came to a low-lying level plain where the close-cropped grass was vivid green, although elsewhere all over the country the vegetation was scorched and dead, and dry as ashes. The ground being so favourable, I crossed this low plain at a swinging gallop, and in about thirty minutes' time. In that half-hour I saw a vast number of snakes, all of one kind, and a species new to me; but my anxiety to reach my destination before the oppressive heat of the afternoon made me hurry on. So numerous were the snakes in that green place that frequently I had as many as a dozen in sight at one time. It looked to me like a *Coronella*—harmless colubrine snakes—but was more than twice as large as either of the two species of that genus I was already familiar with. In size they varied greatly, ranging from two to fully five feet in length, and the colour was dull yellow or tan, slightly lined and mottled with shades of brown. Among dead or partially withered grass and herbage they would have been undistinguishable at even a very short distance, but on the vivid green turf they were strangely conspicuous, some being plainly visible forty or fifty yards away; and not one was seen coiled up. They were all lying motionless, stretched out full length, and looking like dark yellow or tan-coloured ribbons, thrown on to the grass. It was most unusual to see so many snakes together, although not surprising in the circumstances. The December heats had dried up all the watercourses and killed the vegetation, and made the earth hard and harsh as burnt bricks; and at such times snakes, especially the more active non-venomous kinds, will travel long distances, in their slow way, in search of water. Those I saw during my ride had probably been attracted by the moisture from a large area of country; and although there was no water, the soft fresh grass must have been grateful to them. Snakes are seen coiled up when they are at home; when travelling and far afield, they lie as a rule extended full length, even when resting—and they are generally resting. Pausing at length, before quitting this green plain, to give my horse a minute's rest, I got off and approached a large snake; but when I was quite twelve yards from it, it lifted its head, and, turning deliberately around, came rather swiftly at me. I retreated, and it followed, until, springing on to my horse, I left it, greatly surprised at its action, and beginning to think that it must be venomous. As I rode on the feeling of surprise increased, conquering haste; and in the end, seeing more snakes, I dismounted and approached the largest, when exactly the same thing occurred again, the snake rousing itself and coming angrily at me when I was still (considering the dull lethargic character of the deadliest kinds) at an absurd distance from it. Again and again I repeated the experiment, with the same result. And at length I stunned one with a blow of my whip to examine its mouth, but found no poison-fangs in it.

I then resumed my journey, expecting to meet with more snakes of the same kind at my destination; but there were none, and very soon business called me to a distant place, and I never met with this species afterwards. But when I rode away from that green spot, and was once more on the higher, desolate, wind-swept plain surrounding it—a rustling sea of giant thistles, still erect, although dead, and red as rust, and filling the hot blue sky with silvery down—it was with a very strange feeling. The change from the green and living to the dead and dry and dusty was so great! There seemed to be something mysterious, extra-natural, in that low-level plain, so green and fresh and snaky, where my horse's hoofs had made no sound—a place where no man dwelt, and no cattle pastured, and no wild bird folded its wing. And the serpents there were not like others—the mechanical coiled-up thing we know, a mere bone-and-muscle man-trap, set by the elements, to spring and strike when trodden on: but these had a high intelligence, a lofty spirit, and were filled with a noble rage and astonishment that any other kind of creature, even a man, should venture there to disturb their sacred peace. It was a fancy, born of that sense of mystery which the unknown and the unusual in nature wakes in us—an obsolescent feeling that still links us to the savage. But the simple fact was wonderful enough, and that has been set down simply and apart from all fancies. If the reader happens not to be a naturalist, it is right to tell him that a naturalist cannot exaggerate consciously; and if he be capable of unconscious exaggeration, then he is no naturalist. He should hasten "to join the innumerable caravan that moves" to the fantastic realms of romance. Looking at the simple fact scientifically, it was a case of mimicry—the harmless snake mimicking the fierce deadly kind. Only with this difference: the venomous snake, of all the deadly things in nature, is the slowest to resentment, the most reluctant to enter into a quarrel; whereas in this species angry demonstrations were made when the intruder was yet far off, and before he had shown any hostile intentions.

My last case—the last, that is, of the few I have selected—relates to a singular variation in the human species. On this occasion I was again travelling alone in a strange district on the southern frontier of Buenos Ayres. On a bitterly cold mid-winter day, shortly before noon, I arrived, stiff and tired, at one of those pilgrims' rests on the pampas—a wayside *pulperia*, or public house, where the traveller can procure anything he may require or desire, from a tumbler of Brazilian rum to make glad his heart, to a poncho, or cloak of blue cloth with fluffy scarlet lining, to keep him warm o' nights; and, to speed him on his way, a pair of cast-iron spurs weighing six pounds avoirdupois, with rowels eight inches in diameter, manufactured in this island for the use of barbarous men beyond the sea. The wretched mud-and-grass building was surrounded by a foss crossed by a plank drawbridge; outside of the enclosure twelve or fourteen saddled horses were standing, and from the loud noise of talk and laughter in the bar I conjectured that a goodly company of rough frontiersmen were already making merry at that early hour. It was necessary for me to go in among them to see the proprietor of the place and ask permission to visit his kitchen in order to make myself a "tin of coffee," that being the refreshment I felt inclined for. When I went in and made my salutation, one man wheeled round square before me, stared straight into my eyes, and in an exceedingly high-pitched reedy or screechy voice and a sing-song tone returned my "good morning," and bade me call for the liquid I loved best at his expense. I declined with thanks, and in accordance with gaucho etiquette added that I was prepared to pay for his liquor. It was then for him to say that he had already been served and so let the matter drop, but he did not do so: he screamed out in his wild animal voice that he would take gin. I paid for his drink, and would, I think, have felt greatly surprised at his strange insolent behaviour, so unlike that of the usually courteous gaucho, but this thing affected me not at all, so profoundly had his voice and singular appearance impressed me; and for the rest of the time I remained in the place I continued to watch him narrowly. Professor Huxley has somewhere said, "A variation frequently occurs, but those who take notice of it take no care about noting down the particulars." That is not a failing of mine, and this is what I noted down while the man's appearance was still fresh in memory. He was about five feet eleven inches in height—very tall for a gaucho—straight and athletic, with exceedingly broad shoulders, which made his round head look small; long arms and huge hands. The round flat face, coarse black hair, swarthy reddish colour, and smooth hairless cheeks seemed to show that he had more Indian than Spanish blood in him, while his round black eyes were even more like those of a rapacious animal in expression than in the pure-blooded Indian. He also had the Indian or half-breed's moustache, when that natural ornament is permitted to grow, and which is composed of thick bristles standing out like a cat's whiskers. The mouth was the marvellous feature, for it was twice the size of an average mouth, and the two lips were alike in thickness. This mouth did not smile, but snarled, both when he spoke and when he should have smiled; and when he snarled the whole of his teeth and a part of the gums were displayed. The teeth were not as in other human beings—incisors, canines, and molars: they were all exactly alike, above and below, each tooth a gleaming white triangle, broad at the gum where it touched its companion teeth, and with a point sharp as the sharpest-pointed dagger. They were like the teeth of a shark or crocodile. I noticed that when he showed them, which was very often, they were not set together as in dogs, weasels, and other savage snarling animals, but apart, showing the whole terrible serration in the huge red mouth.

After getting his gin he joined in the boisterous conversation with the others, and this gave me an opportunity of studying his face for several minutes, all the time with a curious feeling that I had put

myself into a cage with a savage animal of horrible aspect, whose instincts were utterly unknown to me, and were probably not very pleasant. It was interesting to note that whenever one of the others addressed him directly, or turned to him when speaking, it was with a
curious expression, not of fear, but partly amusement and partly something else which I could not fathom. Now, one might think that this
was natural enough purely on account of the man's extraordinary appearance. I do not think that a sufficient explanation; for however
strange a man's appearance may be, his intimate friends and associates
soon lose all sense of wonder at his strangeness, and even forget that
he is unlike others. My belief is that this curiosity or whatever it was
they showed in their faces, was due to something in his character—
a mental strangeness, showing itself at unexpected times, and which
might flash out at any moment to amuse or astonish them. There
was certainly a correspondence between the snarling action of the
mouth and the dangerous form of the teeth, perfect as that in any
snarling animal; and such animals, it should be remembered, snarl
not only when angry and threatening, but in their playful moods as
well. Other and more important correspondences or correlations might
have existed; and the voice certainly was unlike any human voice I
have ever heard, whether in white, red, or black man. But the time I
had for observation was short, the conversation revealed nothing further, and by-and-by I went away in search of the odorous kitchen,
where there would be hot water for coffee, or at all events cold water
and a kettle, and materials for making a fire—to wit, bones of dead
cattle, "buffalo chips," and rancid fat.

I have never been worried with the wish or ambition to be head-
hunter in the Dyak sense, but on this one occasion I did wish that it
had been possible, without violating any law, or doing anything to a
fellow-creature which I should not like done to myself, to have obtained possession of this man's head, with its set of unique and terrible
teeth. For how, in the name of Evolution, did he come by them,
and by other physical peculiarities—the snarling habit and that high-
pitched animal voice, for instance—which made him a being different
from others—one separate and far apart? Was he, so admirably
formed, so complete and well-balanced, merely a freak of nature, to
use an old-fashioned phrase—a sport, or spontaneous individual variation—an experiment for a new human type, imagined by Nature in
some past period, inconceivably long ago, but which she had only
now, too late, found time to carry out? Or rather was he like that little
hairy maiden exhibited not long ago in London, a reproduction of the

past, the mystery called reversion—a something in the life of a species like memory in the life of an individual, the memory which suddenly brings back to the old man's mind the image of his childhood? For no dream-monster in human form ever appeared to me with so strange and terrible a face; and this was no dream but sober fact, for I saw and spoke with this man; and unless cold steel has given him his quietus, or his own horse has crushed him, or a mad bull gored him—all natural forms of death in that wild land—he is probably living and in the prime of life, and perhaps at this very moment drinking gin at some astonished traveller's expense at that very bar where I met him. The old Palaeolithic man, judging from the few remains we have of him, must have had an unspeakably savage and, to our way of thinking, repulsive and horrible aspect, with his villainous low receding forehead, broad nose, great projecting upper jaw, and retreating chin; to meet such a man face to face in Piccadilly would frighten a nervous person of the present time. But his teeth were not unlike our own, only very much larger and more powerful, and well adapted to their work of masticating the flesh, underdone and possibly raw, of mammoth and rhinoceros. If, then, this living man recalls a type of the past, it is of a remoter past, a more primitive man, the volume of whose history is missing from the geological records. To speculate on such a subject seems idle and useless; and when I coveted possession of that head it was not because I thought that it might lead to any fresh discovery. A lower motive inspired the feeling. I wished for it only that I might bring it over the sea, to drop it like a new apple of discord, suited to the spirit of the times, among the anthropologists and evolutionists generally of this old and learned world. Inscribed, of course, "To the most learned," but giving no locality and no particulars. I wished to do that for the pleasure—not a very noble kind of pleasure, I allow—of witnessing from some safe hiding-place the stupendous strife that would have ensued—a battle more furious, lasting and fatal to many a brave knight of biology, than was ever yet fought over any bone or bony fragment or fabric ever picked up, including the celebrated cranium of the Neanderthal.

*   *   *   *

MY FRIEND THE PIG

Is there a man among us who on running through a list of his friends is unable to say that there is one among them who is a perfect pig?

I think not; and if any reader says that he has no such an one for the simple reason that he would not and could not make a friend of a perfect pig, I shall maintain that he is mistaken, that if he goes over the list a second time and a little more carefully, he will find in it not only a pig, but a sheep, a cow, a fox, a cat, a stoat, and even a perfect toad.

But all this is a question I am not concerned with, seeing that the pig I wish to write about is a real one—a four-footed beast with parted hoofs. I have a friendly feeling towards pigs generally, and consider them the most intelligent of beasts, not excepting the elephant and the anthropoid ape—the dog is not to be mentioned in this connection. I also like his disposition and attitude towards all other creatures, especially man. He is not suspicious, or shrinkingly submissive, like horses, cattle, and sheep; nor an impudent devil-may-care like the goat; nor hostile like the goose; nor condescending like the cat; nor a flattering parasite like the dog. He views us from a totally different, a sort of democratic, standpoint as fellow-citizens and brothers, and takes it for granted, or grunted, that we understand his language, and without servility or insolence he has a natural, pleasant, camerados-all or hail-fellow-well-met air with us.

It may come as a shock to some of my readers when I add that I like him, too, in the form of rashers on the breakfast-table; and this I say with a purpose on account of much wild and idle talk one hears on this question even from one's dearest friends—the insincere horror expressed and denunciation of the revolting custom of eating our fellow-mortals. The other day a lady of my acquaintance told me that she went to call on some people who lived a good distance from her house, and was obliged to stay to luncheon. This consisted mainly of roast pork, and as if that was not enough, her host, when helping her, actually asked if she was fond of a dreadful thing called the crackling!

It is a common pose; but it is also something more, since we find it mostly in persons who are frequently in bad health and are restricted to a low diet; naturally at such times vegetarianism appeals to them. As their health improves they think less of their fellow-mortals. A little chicken broth is found uplifting; then follows the inevitable sole, then calves' brains, then a sweetbread, then a partridge, and so on, progressively, until they are once more able to enjoy their salmon or turbot, veal and lamb cutlets, fat capons, turkeys and geese, sirloins of beef, and, finally, roast pig. That's the limit; we have outgrown cannibalism, and are not keen about haggis, though it is still eaten by the wild

tribes inhabiting the northern portion of our island. All this should
serve to teach vegetarians not to be in a hurry. Thoreau's "handful of
rice" is not sufficient for us, and not good enough yet. It will take long
years and centuries of years before the wolf with blood on his iron
jaws can be changed into the white innocent lamb that nourishes itself
on grass.

Let us now return to my friend the pig. He inhabited a stye at the
far end of the back garden of a cottage or small farmhouse in a lonely
little village in the Wiltshire downs where I was staying. Close to the
stye was a gate opening into a long green field, shut in by high hedges,
where two or three horses and four or five cows were usually grazing.
These beasts, not knowing my sentiments, looked askance at me and
moved away when I first began to visit them, but when they made
the discovery that I generally had apples and lumps of sugar in my
coat pockets they all at once became excessively friendly and followed
me about, and would put their heads in my way to be scratched, and
licked my hands with their rough tongues to show that they liked me.
Every time I visited the cows and horses I had to pause beside the
pig-pen to open the gate into the field; and invariably the pig would
get up and coming towards me salute me with a friendly grunt. And
I would pretend not to hear or see, for it made me sick to look at his
pen in which he stood belly-deep in the fetid mire, and it made me
ashamed to think that so intelligent and good-tempered an animal, so
profitable to man, should be kept in such abominable conditions. Oh,
poor beast, excuse me, but I'm in a hurry and have no time to return
your greeting or even to look at you!

In this village, as in most of the villages in all this agricultural and
pastoral county of Wiltshire, there is a pig-club, and many of the cot-
tagers keep a pig; they think and talk a great deal about their pigs,
and have a grand pig-day gathering and dinner, with singing and even
dancing to follow, once a year. And no wonder that this is so, considering what they get out of the pig; yet in any village you will find
it kept in this same unspeakable condition. It is not from indolence
nor because they take pleasure in seeing their pig unhappy before
killing him or sending him away to be killed, but because they cherish
the belief that the filthier the state in which they keep their pig the
better the pork will be! I have met even large prosperous farmers,
many of them, who cling to this delusion. One can imagine a conversation between one of these Wiltshire pig-keepers and a Danish
farmer. "Yes," the visitor would say, "we too had the same notion at

one time, and thought it right to keep our pigs as you do; but that was a long time back, when English and Danes were practically one people, seeing that Canute was king of both countries. We have since then adopted a different system; we now believe, and the results prove that we are in the right way, that it is best to consider the animal's nature and habits and wants, and to make the artificial conditions imposed on him as little oppressive as may be. It is true that in a state of nature the hog loves to go into pools and wallow in the mire, just as stags, buffaloes, and many other beasts do, especially in the dog-days when the flies are most troublesome. But the swine, like the stag, is a forest animal, and does not love filth for its own sake, nor to be left in a miry pen, and though not as fastidious as a cat about his coat, he is naturally as clean as any other forest creature."

Here I may add that in scores of cases when I have asked a cottager why he didn't keep a pig, his answer has been that he would gladly do so, but for the sanitary inspectors, who would soon order him to get rid of it, or remove it to a distance on account of the offensive smell. It is probable that if it could be got out of the cottager's mind that there must need be an offensive smell, the number of pigs fattened in the villages would be trebled.

I hope now after all these digressions I shall be able to go on with the history of my friend the pig. One morning as I passed the pen he grunted—spoke, I may say—in such a pleasant friendly way that I had to stop and return his greeting; then, taking an apple from my pocket, I placed it in his trough. He turned it over with his snout, then looked up and said something like "Thank-you" in a series of gentle grunts. Then he bit off and ate a small piece, then another small bite, and eventually taking what was left in his mouth he finished eating it. After that he always expected me to stay a minute and speak to him when I went to the field; I knew it from his way of greeting me, and on such occasions I gave him an apple. But he never ate it greedily: he appeared more inclined to talk than to eat, until by degrees I came to understand what he was saying. What he said was that he appreciated my kind intentions in giving him apples. But, he went on, to tell the real truth, it is not a fruit I am particularly fond of. I am familiar with its taste as they sometimes give me apples, usually the small unripe or bad ones that fall from the trees. However, I don't actually dislike them. I get skim milk and am rather fond of it; then a bucket of mash, which is good enough for hunger; but what I enjoy most is a cabbage, only I don't get one very often now. I sometimes think that if they would let me out of this muddy pen to ramble like the sheep and other beasts in the field or on the downs, I should be able to pick up a number of morsels which would taste better than anything they give me. Apart from the subject of food I hope you won't mind my telling you that I'm rather fond of being scratched on the back.

So I scratched him vigorously with my stick, and made him wriggle his body and wink and blink and smile delightedly all over his face. Then I said to myself; "Now what the juice can I do more to please him?" For though under sentence of death, he had done no wrong, but was a good, honest-hearted fellow-mortal, so that I felt bound to do something to make the miry remnant of his existence a little less miserable.

I think it was the word *juice* I had just used—for that was how I pronounced it to make it less like a swear-word—that gave me an inspiration. In the garden, a few yards back from the pen, there was a large clump of old elder-trees, now overloaded with ripening fruit—the biggest clusters I had ever seen. Going to the trees I selected and cut the finest bunch I could find, as big round as my cap, and weighing over a pound. This I deposited in his trough and invited him to try it. He sniffed at it a little doubtfully, and looked at me and made a remark or two, then nibbled at the edge of the cluster, taking a few berries into his mouth, and holding them some time before he ventured to crush them. At length he did venture, then looked at me again and made more remarks, "Queer fruit this! Never tasted anything quite like it before, but I really can't say yet whether I like it or not."

Then he took another bite, then more bites, looking up at me and saying something between the bites, till, little by little, he had consumed the whole bunch; then turning round, he went back to his bed with a little grunt to say that I was now at liberty to go on to the cows and horses.

However, on the following morning he hailed my approach in such a lively manner, with such a note of expectancy in his voice, that I concluded he had been thinking a great deal about elder-berries, and was anxious to have another go at them. Accordingly I cut him another bunch, which he quickly consumed, making little exclamations the while—"Thank you, thank you, very good—very good indeed!" It was a new sensation in his life, and made him very happy, and was almost as good as a day of liberty in the fields and meadows and on the open green downs.

From that time I visited him two or three times a day to give him huge clusters of elder-berries. There were plenty for the starlings as well; the clusters on those trees would have filled a cart.

Then one morning I heard an indignant scream from the garden, and peeping out saw my friend, the pig, bound hand and foot, being lifted by a dealer into his cart with the assistance of the farmer.

"Good-bye, old boy!" said I as the cart drove off; and I thought that by and by, in a month or two, if several persons discovered a peculiar and fascinating flavour in their morning rasher, it would be due to the elder-berries I had supplied to my friend the pig, which had gladdened his heart for a week or two before receiving his quietus.

WHAT THE THRUSH SAID

O thou whose face hath felt the Winter's wind,
   Whose eye has seen the snow-clouds hung in mist,
   And the black elm tops 'mong the freezing stars,
   To thee the spring will be a harvest-time.
O thou, whose only book has been the light
   Of supreme darkness which thou feddest on
   Night after night when Phoebus was away,
   To thee the spring shall be a triple morn.
O fret not after knowledge—I have none,
   And yet my song comes native with the warmth.
O fret not after knowledge—I have none,
   And yet the Evening listens. He who saddens
At thought of idleness cannot be idle,
And he's awake who thinks himself asleep.

JOHN KEATS

SUGARING FOR MOTHS

by W. J. Holland

Half a century ago W. J. Holland (1848–1932) was the great authority on moths and butterflies, and his two hefty volumes, The Moth Book *and* The Butterfly Book, *garnished with color plates, were the standard works on the North American species. They are a bit outmoded now, but the author's honest enthusiasm for the subject shines through the text in many paragraphs, and the dog-eared volumes are worth perusing for that feature alone. Dr. Holland was an ordained minister who first preached at a Moravian church in Philadelphia and then moved to Pittsburgh, where he was pastor of the Bellefield Presbyterian Church from 1874 to 1891. He made a career of science and religion simultaneously. Wherever he was and wherever he went, he collected and described Lepidoptera. This included a trip to Japan in 1887 and a trip to Africa in 1889. In 1891 he gave up his pastorate to become the chancellor of what was then called the Western University of Pennsylvania and is now the University of Pittsburgh. He filled that post for ten years and then retired to devote himself to writing and studying in his favorite field, the world of the scale-winged insects. The selection that follows is from* The Moth Book. *Note in the second paragraph a reference to "tulip-poplars," due to the fact that, in the lumber trade the tulip tree (Lireodendron tulipifera), for no good reason, is called the yellow poplar.*

THE day has been hot and sultry. The sun has set behind great banks of clouds which are piling up on the northwestern horizon. Now that the light is beginning to fade, the great masses of cumulus, which are slowly gathering and rising higher toward the zenith, are lit up by pale flashes of sheet-lightning. As yet the storm is too far off to permit us to hear the boom of the thunder, but about ten or eleven o'clock to-night we shall probably experience all the splendor of a dashing thundershower.

Along the fringe of woodland which skirts the back pastures is a path which we long have known. Here stand long ranks of ancient beeches; sugar maples, which in fall are glorious in robes of yellow and scarlet; ash trees, the tall gray trunks of which carry skyward huge masses of light pinnated foliage; walnuts and butternuts, oaks, and tulip-poplars. On either side of the path in luxuriant profusion are saplings, sprung from the monarchs of the forest, young elm trees planted by the winds, broad-leaved papaws, round-topped hawthorns, viburnums, spreading dogwoods, and here and there in moist places clumps of willows. Where the path runs down by the creek, sycamores spread their gaunt white branches toward the sky, and drink moisture from the shallow reaches of the stream, in which duckweed, arrow-weed, and sweet pond-lilies bloom.

The woodland is the haunt of many a joyous thing, which frequents the glades and hovers over the flowers. To-night the lightning in the air, the suggestion of a coming storm which lurks in the atmosphere, will send a thrill through all the swarms, which have been hidden through the day on moss-grown trunks, or among the leaves, and they will rise, as the dusk gathers, in troops about the pathway. It is just the night upon which to take a collecting trip, resorting to the well-known method of "sugaring."

Here we have a bucket and a clean whitewash brush. We have put into the bucket four pounds of cheap sugar. Now we will pour in a bottle of stale beer and a little rum. We have stirred the mixture well. In our pockets are our cyanide jars. Here are the dark lanterns. Before the darkness falls, while yet there is light enough to see our way along the path, we will pass from tree to tree and apply the brush charged with the sweet semi-intoxicating mixture to the trunks of the trees.

The task is accomplished! Forty trees and ten stumps have been baptized with sugar-sweetened beer. Let us wash our sticky fingers in the brook and dry them with our handkerchiefs. Let us sit down on the grass beneath this tree and puff a good Havana. It is growing darker. The bats are circling overhead. A screech owl is uttering a plaintive lament, perhaps mourning the absence of the moon, which to-night will not appear. The frogs are croaking in the pond. The fire-flies soar upward and flash in sparkling multitudes where the grass grows rank near the water.

Now let us light our lamps and put a drop or two of chloroform into our cyanide jars, just enough to slightly dampen the paper which holds the lumps of cyanide in place. We will retrace our steps along the path and visit each moistened spot upon the tree-trunks.

Here is the last tree which we sugared. There in the light of the lantern we see the shining drops of our mixture clinging to the mosses and slowly trickling downward toward the ground. Turn the light of the lantern full upon the spot, advancing cautiously, so as not to break the dry twigs under foot or rustle the leaves. Ha! Thus far nothing but the black ants which tenant the hollows of the gnarled old tree appear to have recognized the offering which we have made. But they are regaling themselves in swarms about the spot. Look at them! Scores of them, hundreds of them are congregating about the place, and seem to be drinking with as much enjoyment as a company of Germans on a picnic in the wilds of Hoboken.

Let us stealthily approach the next tree. It is a beech. What is there? Oho! my beauty! Just above the moistened patch upon the bark is a great *Catocala*. The gray upper wings are spread, revealing the lower wings gloriously banded with black and crimson. In the yellow light of the lantern the wings appear even more brilliant than they do in sunlight. How the eyes glow like spots of fire! The moth is wary. He has just alighted; he has not yet drunk deep. Move cautiously! Keep the light of the lantern steadily upon him. Uncover your poisoning jar. Approach. Hold the jar just a little under the moth, for he will drop downward on the first rush to get away. Clap the jar over him! There! you have done it! You have him securely. He flutters for a moment, but the chloroform acts quickly and the flutterings cease. Put that jar into one pocket and take out another. Now let us go to the next tree. It is an old walnut. The trunk is rough, seamed, and full of knotted excrescences. See what a company has gathered! There are a dozen moths, large and small, busily at work tippling. Begin with those which are nearest to the ground. When I was young my grandfather taught me that in shooting wild turkeys resting in a tree, it is always best to shoot the lowest fowl first, and then the next. If you shoot the gobbler which perches highest, as he comes tumbling down through the flock, he will startle them all, and they will fly away together; but if you take those which are roosting well down among the branches, those above will simply raise their heads and stare about for a moment to find out the source of their peril, and you can bag three or four before the rest make up their minds to fly. I follow the same plan with my moths, unless, perchance, the topmost moth is some unusual rarity, worth all that suck the sweets below him.

Bravo! You have learned the lesson well. You succeeded admirably in bottling those *Taraches* which were sucking the moisture at the lower edge of the sweetened patch. There above them is a fine specimen of *Strenoloma lunilinea*. Aha! You have him. Now take that *Catocala*. It is *amasia*, a charming little species. Above him is a specimen of *cara*, one of the largest and most superb of the genus. Well done! You have him, too. Now wait a moment! Have your captives ceased their struggles in your jar? Yes; they seem to be thoroughly stunned. Transfer them to the other jar for the cyanide to do its work. Look at your lantern. Is the wick trimmed? Come on then.

Let us go to the next tree. This is an ash. The moist spot shows faintly upon the silvery-gray bark of the tree. Look sharply! Here below are a few *Geometers* daintily sipping the sweets. There is a little *Eustixis pupula*, with its silvery-white wings dotted with points of black. There is a specimen of *Harrisimemna*, the one with the coppery-brown spots on the fore wings. A good catch!

Stop! Hold still! Ha! I thought he would alight. That is *Catocala coccinata*—a fine moth—not overly common, and the specimen is perfect.

Well, let us try another tree. Here they are holding a general assembly. Look! See them fairly swarming about the spot. A dozen have found good places; two or three are fluttering about trying to alight. The ants have found the place as well as the moths. They are squabbling with each other. The moths do not like the ants. I do not blame them. I would not care to sit down at a banquet and have ants crawling all over the repast. There is a specimen of *Catocala relicta*, the hind wings white, banded with black. How beautiful simple colors are when set in sharp contrast and arranged in graceful lines! There is a specimen of *Catocala neogama*, which was originally described by Abbot from Georgia. It is not uncommon. There is a good *Mamestra*, and there *Pyrophila pyramidoides*. The latter is a common species; we shall find scores of them before we get through. Do not bother with those specimens of *Agrotis ypsilon*; there are choicer things to be had. It is a waste of time to take them to-night. Let them drink themselves drunk, when the flying squirrels will come and catch them. Do you see that flying squirrel there peeping around the trunk of the tree? Flying squirrels eat insects. I have seen them do it at night, and they have robbed me of many a fine specimen.

Off now to the next tree!

And so we go from tree to tree. The lightning in the west grows more vivid. Hark! I hear the thunder. It is half-past nine. The storm will be here by ten. The leaves are beginning to rustle in the tree-tops. The first pulse of the tornado is beginning to be felt. Now the wind is rising. Boom! Boom! The storm is drawing nearer. We are on our second round and are coming up the path near the pasture-gate. Our collecting jars are full. We have taken more than a hundred specimens representing thirty species. Not a bad night's work. Hurry up! Here are the draw-bars. Are you through? Put out the light in your lantern. Come quickly after me. I know the path. Here is the back garden gate. It is beginning to rain. We shall have to run if we wish to avoid a wetting. Ah! here are the steps of the veranda. Come up!

My! what a flash and a crash that was! Look back and see how the big trees are bowing their heads as the wind reaches them, and the lightning silhouettes them against the gray veil of the rain. We may be glad we are out of the storm, with a good roof overhead. To-morrow morning the sun will rise bright and clear, and we shall have work enough to fill all the morning hours in setting the captures we have made. Good-night!

This guest of summer,
The temple-haunting martlet, does approve
By his lov'd mansionry, that the heaven's breath
Smells wooingly here; no jutty, frieze, buttress,
Nor coigne of vantage, but this bird has made
His pendent bed and procreant cradle. Where they
Most breed and haunt, I have observ'd, the air
Is delicate.

                              SHAKESPEARE, *Macbeth*

But, look, the morn, in russet mantle clad,
Walks o'er the dew of yon high eastern hill.

                              SHAKESPEARE, *Hamlet*

THE PRONGHORN ANTELOPE

by Theodore Roosevelt

Of the former President of the United States and world figure,
Theodore Roosevelt, there is no need to set down a single word
here. It is Theodore Roosevelt the naturalist who is our man. At
the age of thirteen he was keeping a diary in which he wrote the
species names, both in English and Latin, of the birds, mammals,
snakes, frogs, and other creatures he encountered in the woods
and fields of the New York City suburbs. At Harvard he and his
fellow-student Henry Davis Minot joined in compiling and publishing a leaflet with the title The Summer Birds of the Adirondacks in Franklin County, N.Y. That was in October, 1877. In
short, he was a naturalist before he ever thought of going into
politics or seeking public office. As an undergraduate he joined
the Harvard Natural History Society and, even more impressive,
the Nuttall Ornithological Club of Cambridge, before which he
presented a paper on the merits and demerits of a comparative
newcomer in the country at that time, the English or house
sparrow.

At that point he was determined to make natural history his
lifework, but he changed his mind. Even so, in and out of public
office, he found time to study Nature, to live outdoors, to go on
collecting trips, to make friends and exchange correspondence
with other naturalists, and to write such books as Hunting Trips
of a Ranchman (1886), The Wilderness Hunter (1893), African
Game Trails (1910), and Through the Brazilian Wilderness
(1914). The last article he wrote was a review of Leo Miller's
In the Wilds of South America for the American Museum of Natural History Journal. The last letter he wrote was to William
Beebe on a matter of taxonomy in Beebe's notable monograph
on pheasants, which he looked forward to reviewing. As President
of the United States he was the fervid advocate and prime mover

*in the field of conservation and the establishment and mainte-
nance of our national parks system.*

*The following selection dealing with a distinctive American
quadruped, the pronghorn, is taken from* Hunting Trips of a
Ranchman. *But the truth is that, from his youthful notes on Adi-
rondack birds to the letter about pheasant classification written
to William Beebe the night before he died, the famous author-
naturalist was at heart an ornithologist and bird-lover. Incidentally, the "stout old Manitou" mentioned in the text was the
author's favorite horse, and, though we do not follow horse and
rider to the end of the hunt, the reader is herewith informed that
"stout old Manitou" carried back to the ranch not only the future
President of the United States but a supply of antelope meat for
the cookshack.*

NO antelope are found, except rarely, immediately around my
ranch house where the ground is much too broken to suit
them; but on the great prairies, ten or fifteen miles off, they
are plentiful, though far from as abundant as they were a
few years ago when they were first driven into the land. By plainsmen
they are called either pronghorn or antelope, but are most often known
by the latter and much less descriptive title. Where they are found
they are always very conspicuous figures in the landscape; for, far from
attempting to conceal itself, an antelope really seems anxious to take
up a prominent position, caring only to be able itself to see its foes.
It is the smallest in size of the plains game, even smaller than a white-
tail deer; and its hide is valueless, being thin and porous, and making
very poor buckskin. In its whole appearance and structure it is a most
singular creature. Unlike all other hollow-horned animals, it sheds its
horns annually, exactly as the deer shed their solid antlers, but the
shedding process in the pronghorn occupies but a few days—so short
a time, indeed, that many hunters stoutly deny that it takes place at
all. The hair is of a remarkable texture, very long, coarse, and brittle;
in the spring it comes off in handfuls. In strong contrast to the reddish
yellow of the other parts of the body, the rump is pure white, and
when alarmed or irritated every hair in the white patch bristles up on
end, greatly increasing the apparent area of the color. The flesh, unlike that of any other plains animal, is equally good all through the

year. In the fall it is hardly so juicy as deer venison, but in spring, when no other kind of game is worth eating, it is perfectly good, and at that time of year, if we have to get fresh meat, we would rather kill antelope than anything else; and as the bucks are always to be instantly distinguished from the does by their large horns, we confine ourselves to them, and so work no harm to the species.

The antelope is a queer looking, rather than a beautiful animal. The curious pronged horns, great bulging eyes, and strange bridle-like marks and bands on the face and throat are more striking, but less handsome, than the delicate head and branching antlers of a deer, and it entirely lacks the latter animal's grace of movement. In its form and look, when standing still, it is rather angular and goat-like, and its movements merely have the charm that comes from lightness, speed, and agility. Its gait is singularly regular and even, without any of the bounding, rolling movement of a deer; and it is, consequently, very easy to hit running, compared with other kinds of game.

Antelope have a most morbid curiosity. The appearance of anything out of the way or to which they are not accustomed, often seems to drive them nearly beside themselves with mingled fright and desire to know what it is, a combination of feeling that throws them into a perfect panic during whose continuance they will at times seem utterly unable to take care of themselves. In very remote, wild places, to which no white man often penetrates, the appearance of a white-topped wagon will be enough to excite this feeling in the pronghorn, and in such cases it is not unusual for a herd to come up and circle around the strange object, heedless of rifle-shots. This curiosity is particularly strong in the bucks during rutting time, and one method of hunting them is to take advantage of it and "flag" them up to the hunters by waving a red handkerchief or some other object to and fro in the air. In very wild places they can sometimes be flagged up, even after they have seen the man; but elsewhere the latter must keep himself carefully concealed behind a ridge or hillock or in tall grass, and keep cautiously waving the handkerchief overhead. The antelope will look fixedly at it, stamp, snort, start away, come nearer by fits and starts, and run from one side to the other, the better to see it. Sometimes a wary old buck will keep this up for half an hour, and at the end make off; but again, the attraction may prove too strong, and the antelope comes slowly on until within rifle-shot. This method of hunting, however, is not so much practiced now as formerly, as the antelope are getting continually shyer and more difficult to flag. I have never myself shot one in this manner, though I have often seen the feat performed, and have several times tried it myself, but always with the result that after I had made my arm really weak with waving the handkerchief to and fro, the antelope, which had been shifting about just out of range, suddenly took to its heels and made off.

No other kind of plains game, except the bighorn, is as shy and sharp-sighted as the antelope; and both its own habits and the open nature of the ground on which it is found render it peculiarly difficult to stalk. There is no cover, and if a man is once seen by the game the latter will not let him out of sight again, unless it decides to go off at a gait that soon puts half a dozen miles between them. It shifts its position, so as to keep the hunter continually in sight. Thus, if it is standing on a ridge, and the hunter disappears into a ravine up which he intends to crawl, the antelope promptly gallops off to some other place of observation from which its foe is again visible; and this is repeated until the animal at last makes up its mind to start for good. It keeps up an incessant watch, being ever on the lookout for danger, far or near; and as it can see an immense distance, and has its home on ground so level that a horseman can be made out a mile off, its attention is apt to be attracted when still four or five rifle-shots beyond range, and after it has once caught a glimpse of the foe, the latter might as well give up hopes of getting the game. . . .

A pronghorn is by far the fleetest animal on the plains; one can outrun and outlast a deer with the greatest of ease. . . .

In May or early June the doe brings forth her fawns, usually two in number, for she is very prolific. She makes her bed in some valley or hollow, and keeps with the rest of the band, only returning to the fawns to feed them. They lie out in the grass or under some slight bush, but are marvellously hard to find. By instinct they at once crouch down so as to be as inconspicuous as possible. Once we scared away a female pronghorn from a perfectly level hillside; and in riding along passed over the spot she had left and came upon two little fawns that could have been but a few hours old. They lay flat in the grass, with their legs doubled under them and their necks and heads stretched out on the ground. When we took them up and handled them, they soon got used to us and moved awkwardly around, but at any sudden noise or motion they would immediately squat flat down again. But at a very early age the fawns learn to shift for themselves, and can run as fast as their parents, even when no larger than a jackrabbit. Once, while we were haying, a couple of my cowboys spent half an hour in trying to run down and capture a little fawn, but were unable to catch it, it ran so fast and ducked about so quickly. Antelope fawns are very easily tamed and make most amusing pets. . . .

Young fawns seem to give out no scent, and thus many of them escape from the murderous carnivorous beasts that are ever prowling about at night over the prairie. . . .

Pronghorns perhaps prefer the rolling prairies of short grass as their home, but seem to do almost as well on the desolate and monotonous wastes where the sagebrush and prickly-pear and a few blades of coarse grass are the only signs of plant life to be seen. In such places, the pronghorn, the sage cock, the rattlesnake and the horned toad alone are able to make a living.

I never but once took a trip of any length with antelope hunting for its chief object. This was one June, when all the men were away on the roundup. As is usual during the busy half of the ranchman's year, the spring and the summer, when men have no time to hunt and game is out of condition, we had been living on salt pork, beans, potatoes, and bread, and I had hardly had a rifle in my hand for months; so, finding I had a few days to spare, I thought I should take a short trip on the prairies in the beautiful June weather, and get a little sport and a little fresh meat out of the bands of pronghorn bucks which I was sure to encounter. Intending to be gone but a couple of days, it was not necessary to take many articles. Behind my saddle I carried a blanket for bedding, and an oilskin coat to ward off the wet; a large metal cup with the handle riveted, not soldered, on, so that water could be boiled in it; a little tea and salt, and some biscuits; and a small waterproof bag containing my half-dozen personal necessaries— not forgetting a book. The whole formed a small, light pack, very little encumbrance to stout old Manitou. In June, fair weather can generally be counted on in the dry plains country.

I started in the very earliest morning, when the intense brilliance of the stars had just begun to pale before the first streak of dawn. By the time I left the river bottom and struck off up the valley of a winding creek, which led through the Bad Lands, the eastern sky was growing rosy; and soon the buttes and cliffs were lit by the level rays of the cloudless summer sun. The air was fresh and sweet, and odorous with the scents of the springtime that was but barely past; the dew lay heavy, in glittering drops, on the leaves and the blades of grass, whose vivid green, at this season, for a short time brightens the desolate and sterile-looking wastes of the lonely Western plains. The rose-bushes were all in bloom, and their pink blossoms clustered in every point and bend of the stream; and the sweet, sad songs of the hermit thrushes rose from the thickets, while the meadowlarks perched boldly in sight as they uttered their loud and more cheerful song. The roundup had passed by our ranch, and all the cattle with our brands—the Maltese cross and cut dewlap, or the elk horn and triangle had been turned loose; they had not yet worked away from the river and, as I rode by, long strings of them, walking single file off to the hills or standing in groups, looked at me as I passed.

Leaving the creek, I struck off among a region of scoria buttes, the ground rising into rounded hills, through whose grassy covering the red volcanic rock showed in places, while boulder-like fragments of it were scattered all through the valleys between. There were a few clumps of bushes here and there, and near one of them were two magpies, who lit on an old buffalo head, bleached white by sun and snow. Magpies are birds that catch the eye at once from their bold black-and-white plumage and long tails. They are very saucy and at the same time very cunning and shy. In spring we do not often see them; but in the late fall and winter they will come close around the huts and outbuildings, on the lookout for anything to eat. If a deer is hung up and they can get at it they will pick it to pieces with their sharp bills; and their carnivorous tastes and their habit of coming around hunters' camps after game that is left out call to mind their kinsman, the whiskey-jack, or moose-bird, of the Northern forests. . . .

Nowhere, not even at sea, does a man feel more lonely than when riding over the far-reaching, seemingly never-ending plains; and after a man has lived a little while on or near them, their very vastness and loneliness and their melancholy monotony have a strong fascination for him. The landscape seems always the same, and after the traveller has plodded on for miles and miles he gets to feel as if the distance was indeed boundless. As far as the eye can see there is no break; either the prairie stretches out into perfectly level flats, or else there are gentle, rolling slopes, whose crests mark the divide between the drainage systems of the different creeks; and when one of these is ascended, immediately another precisely like it takes its place in the distance, and so roll in a succession as interminable as that of the waves of the ocean. Nowhere else can one seem so far off from all mankind; the plains stretch out in death-like and measureless expanse, and as he journeys over them they will for many miles be lacking in all signs of life. Although he can see so far, yet all objects on the outermost verge of the horizon, even though within the ken of his vision, look unreal and strange; for there is no shade to take away the bright glare, and at a little distance things seem to shimmer and dance in the hot rays of the sun. The ground is scorched to a dull brown, and against its monotonous expanse any objects stand out with a prominence that makes it difficult to judge the distance at which they are. A mile off one can see, through the strange shimmering haze, the shadowy white outlines of something which looms vaguely up till it looks as large as the canvas top of a prairie wagon; but as the horseman comes nearer it shrinks and dwindles and takes clearer form, until at last it changes into the ghastly staring skull of some mighty buffalo, long dead and gone to join the rest of his vanished race.

Let me go where'er I will
I hear a sky-born music still:
It sounds from all things old,
It sounds from all things young,
From all that's fair, from all that's foul,
Peals out a cheerful song.
It is not only in the rose,
It is not only in the bird,
Not only where the rainbow glows,
Nor in the song of woman heard,
But in the darkest meanest things
There alway, alway something sings.
'Tis not in the high stars alone,
Nor in the cups of budding flowers,
Nor in the redbreast's mellow tone,
Nor in the bow that smiles in showers,
But in the mud and scum of things
There alway, alway something sings.

RALPH WALDO EMERSON

THE SERPENT'S WORLD

by Raymond L. Ditmars

For something over twoscore years—in fact, from 1899 until his death in 1942—Raymond Lee Ditmars was well known and ordinarily identified as "the snake man at the Bronx Zoo." He was all of that and more. He was the North American authority on snakes of this continent, and he knew a great deal about other forms of wildlife. But he certainly concentrated on snakes, wrote more about them than anything else, and could handle them with the ease and confidence of a "snake charmer" on a vaudeville stage. To many onlookers at his frequent lectures it seemed a dangerous business, and probably would have been in less skillful hands, because he often would spill a rattlesnake or a copperhead out of a canvas bag and somehow hold it on a curved metal hook at the end of a wooden stick while he talked about its haunts and habits.

Born in Newark, New Jersey, June 20, 1876, Raymond Lee Ditmars turned to science as a career as soon as he was graduated from Barnard School for Boys—it was then a military academy —in 1891. He obtained a position as an assistant in the entomological department of the American Museum of Natural History and worked there for half a dozen years. However, he studied stenography on the side and in 1898, he left the museum to become a court reporter on the staff of the New York Times. Incidentally, his knowledge of stenography won him some notice in the field of ornithology. He attended a meeting of the American Ornithological Union on an occasion when Elliott Coues gave a brilliant extemporaneous talk. Ditmars took it down in shorthand and thus enabled Dr. Frank Chapman, editor of Bird-Lore, to publish it later in that magazine.

Newspaper life was alluring, but zoology was more alluring, especially when Ditmars was offered the position of Curator of

Reptiles at the new home of the New York Zoological Society in
the Bronx late in 1899. Many expeditions took "the snake man"
to far places, but the Bronx Zoo was his official address to the end
of his days. Among the books he wrote were The Reptile Book
(1907), Reptiles of the World (1909), Thrills of a Naturalist's
Quest (1932), Confessions of a Scientist (1934), *and* Snakes of
the World (1931), *from which the following selection was taken.*

A LITHE black form is stretched upon the top of an old stone
wall. The long and slender body lies in slightly suggested
undulations. It appears tense and yet again soft and pliant
as its outline follows the slightly uneven surface of the
stones. Its hue is really blue-black and it glows with the luster of a
new gun-barrel. The effect upon the average observer is threefold.
The thing is startling, it is decorative, and it is wholly incongruous—
this vivid form so bold in contrast to its surroundings. The head
quivers slightly. If the observer's eyes are keen this is seen to be caused
by the rapid darting of a forked tongue. Then the black object appears
to flow over the opposite side of the wall. There is a rustling murmur
among dried leaves—a hissing-scrape—the sound so characteristic of a
rapidly moving snake, and the thing is gone.

Thus we meet the blacksnake, an inoffensive type and a useful one,
but startling, nevertheless, unless one has some knowledge of serpent
life.

The supposition may be that such creatures are aimless wanderers,
to be thus encountered now and then; that they crawl into some hole
to pass the winter and emerge the coming year to prowl again and
bob up in unexpected places.

Summing up the life history of the average blacksnake produces
an interesting picture. It gives an idea of snakes generally. The serpent is lifted from the thought of a mere gliding thing in the grass
and assumes individuality among the legions of animal life.

To begin with, the blacksnake is hatched from an egg. Some snakes
are viviparous and produce living young and others are oviparous; that
is, they lay eggs. The egg-laying kinds exceed the others in number,
but not by a great majority. But to return to the origin of the blacksnake.

A female blacksnake has been steadily searching for a suitable hollow under a large flat stone. She is seeking a stone thick enough to absorb the sun's rays and retain considerable of this heat during the night. The stone must also be thick enough not to pass too great an amount of heat directly through it to the ground. The hollow beneath must be in ground or debris soft enough to be readily shoved about with her body in forming a nest for her eggs. The ground must be moderately damp. The rock should be on a hillside. While moderate dampness is sought the ground should be well drained. A part of the necessary moisture needed to develop the eggs will come from condensation beneath the rock during the night. With these requirements to be met the search for a suitable place will take a number of days. The time is invariably during the very early summer.

Finding the proper place, the female serpent crawls beneath the rock and from the center shoves the earth outward with folds of her body. A circular or ovoid area is hollowed, with protective, sharply sloping sides and within this the eggs are laid to the number of one to two dozen. They are creamy white with a pliable, but tough covering. In form and size they are not unlike the eggs of the smaller birds. They are a bit more cylindrical perhaps, but this does not hold good with all snake eggs. Their chief difference is the pliable shell, like very thin leather.

The female blacksnake takes no further interest in her eggs, and has no further thought of her future young. She goes her way.

The eggs actually grow. They absorb moisture and from thread-like embryos the infant serpents within them increase in size until they are tightly packed within the eggs which have increased a third in diameter and may become lumpy and irregular in outline. A sharp point upon each infant's snout has developed—the "egg tooth"—this is used to slit the shell and escape. The period of incubation has covered about eight weeks.

Emerging from the eggs the little serpents stay close by their nest for a day or so. They are quite unlike the parent, being gray, with large brown blotches. Within a week they are eating insect larvae, possibly young grasshoppers. This is very different food from that which they will seek when they have grown a few inches, but that is the way with all very young snakes, the early feeding habits of many of which remain a mystery.

Growth is rapid. They increase to twice their size by autumn, but remain quite unlike the parent in retaining their gray coat, although the brownish blotches are becoming darker. With the tang of chilling nights the inclination is to seek a deep fissure among the rocks and, once it is found, not to wander far away from it during the day. This is to be the winter shelter. The young serpent has already explored it—gone deeply into it. Whether or not that force called instinct prompts the reptile to realize that the fissure is deep enough to shelter it from penetration from frost, is a question. Certain it is that its investigation leads it to shelter safe from that curious point on the thermometer we call "thirty-two" if the scale be Fahrenheit, or "zero" at Centigrade. That is a fateful point in the decrease of temperature for most snakes. They can endure, while benumbed and motionless in hibernation, a temperature of close to freezing, but at or below that point where water freezes they are likely to be killed.

Well before the first slight frosts the little serpents of the brood are safely stowed away. Possibly a few have found the same crevice. They are sleek and fat and, as during the winter sleep animation is practically suspended, they will emerge in much the same condition with the spring. Their next year's hibernation will be under quite different conditions. Not far from where they are lies the parents' den and they will find it. A few of them may have already found it.

From this point we will select the story of an individual. Possibly the story of the snake noted on the stone wall. Spring has warmed the ledgy bank and a young serpent issues from the hibernating crevice. It lurks near the sheltering fissure during the fickle weather of late April and early May, then starts afield possibly reconnoitering along the borders of a marsh—for last year's frogs, developing during the summer from tadpoles, form ideal food for a snake of this size. There is a brief rest, hiding in a pile of loose stones as the serpent's lidless eyes are becoming dim with the thickening of the old skin. The eyes become white, like bubbles filled with smoke. Then they clear as an oily secretion forms under the old epidermis, loosening it over the entire body.

The snake pushes the loose skin back over the upper jaw and lower jaw by rubbing among the rocks, then crawling forth catches the moist, tissue-like garment in the stubble and slowly crawls out of it, turning it wrongside out the entire length of the body clear to the tip of the tail. Right at the point where the skin is being turned backward there is a slight writhing of the scaly sides of the body—a contracting to the rear, where the old epidermis is still encased and a muscular expanding forward of this. The skin slips backward and, delicate as it is, there is not a tear. It is an exquisite job, skillfully and slowly performed. It may take a full half-hour. But there is a snake-skin in the grass! The whole garment is inverted. The integument that has covered the jaws gapes open and on the head-parts are the coverings of the lidless eyes like miniature, strongly concave lenses.

This early summer shedding is an event. The slim young creature glistens like new satin. It is a darker gray. The spots are fainter and will be gone after the next shedding. Wild mice are to be hunted in the nests, very young examples that are easily swallowed. With the assimilation of such prey growth is speeded. By late summer the young reptile is over two feet long and close to matching the lustrous blue-black of the parent. Only the abdominal parts are lighter—a pale, slaty gray.

A chill is again descending upon the woods at night. This is particularly apparent when the nights are still—when no breeze is stirring. On such nights there is a very heavy dew bringing into sharp evidence the webs of spiders which spin in the grass. At the very beginning of this period the blacksnake has turned its nose "homeward." But what is home? This means the parents' den. And here the snake is guided by an influence as remarkable and inexorably systematic as the autumnal migration of birds.

It may be two miles from the den when the seasons start to turn. Separating it from its goal may be marshes, undulating brooks, labyrinths of stone and tangles of vegetation. The force which appears to guide it is sense of direction. What else could there be? The topography of the ground produces hills and canyons. The vegetation is the equivalent to sightless jungle. The rocks present mazes of passages, but the serpent steadily works toward the den where its parents have hibernated for years, where their ancestors have hibernated, and their ancestors back for hundreds, and possibly much longer periods of years. The den of the adults is a specific spot—a ledge on a wild hillside, usually facing south. The whole side of the hill or mountain may be ledgy, but in that expanse of rock there is some spot where a fissure, or series of fissures lead a great distance inward and downward. The snakes found it ages ago. I have wandered over a whole mountainside and seldom found more than one den. The serpents that prowl the area for a mile or more know that spot and return to it each fall for shelter from *cold*. That word signifies the turning point in a snake's existence. Activity is influenced by the temperature of environmental air. The serpent's normal blood temperature is usually one degree higher than that of the air. A temperature of seventy to ninety is best conducive to its vivacity. Below seventy it slows down. At fifty it is nearly helpless. At forty it shows bare signs of life. Above ninety it seeks cooler shelter, undergrowth or damp ground where evaporation produces a lower temperature at the immediate surface. Even the serpents of the tropics avoid open places in the full glare of sun and desert types are averse to venturing abroad during the day unless scattered patches of vegetation offer close-lying oases of shelter from the heat.

So guided from the plight of exposure to cold, the serpent starts for the den with the autumn. It may linger at times through areas which I call "transient rocks."

These are large masses of stone retaining considerable heat from the sun as the night comes on. In such places, which are usually good feeding grounds, the snake may hesitate during a period of "Indian Summer," but moves on again after a shock or two from cool nights, warning it of frosts not far away.

A typical den is on the southerly slope of a hill or mountain of ledgy character. There may be a precipitous face of rock and at the bottom a jumbled mass of great fragments weighing tons. The spot denotes cataclysmic forces in action in dim ages past. Such forces have shattered the face of the cliff and among these shattered portions is a crevice at the bottom, or there may be several adjacent crevices. These form the den. The area is secluded and tangled. Wild grape writhes its way among the rocks. Numerous struggling trees have sought root wherever they could. "The crevice," however, is usually adjacent to a platform of broken stones or open patch, or patches, where in the spring the serpents emerge and in clusters lie intoxicated with the return of the life-giving sun with its temperature so necessary for their activity.

The blacksnake finds the hibernating lair of its parents and ancestors, ascending the slope past the first hibernating crevice of its early youth, where now with its stouter body it could barely squeeze in. It glides through the tangle of grape and woodbine to find other members of its kind, and still others of the serpent clan very different from itself. There are copperheads and rattlers on the shelf of the ledge, coiled tightly in precise circular fashion as is the way of these fanged species, each with a symmetrical, and lateral loop of the neck laid flat upon its coils ready for a lunge of the head. The blacksnake may glide directly over some of these forms, but there is never a move on the part of the poisonous members, seldom as much as a tongue flash.

The serpent clan is particularly tolerant or passive about the changing of position, arrival or departure of other members, unless such are of the attacking or cannibal types and in the northerly areas of the black-snake's range there are no such disturbing enemies. The blacksnake is alleged to attack the rattler, but he does nothing of the kind. He may eat an occasional young garter or ribbon snake, but he never battles with the rattler. He has no means of fighting such a powerful snake. Despite the scientific name constrictor, the blacksnake is not a con-strictor. The title was applied to him years past by Linnaeus, in times when the respective habits of serpents were but vaguely noted.

So the rattlers, copperheads, and blacksnakes go into the den to-gether in fine fraternity. I have seen bevies of heads of the three kinds peering from the crevices in spring when they had been lured by the warming ground to peek out, but were not inclined to venture forth as yet.

Such is the typical mountain den. Other kinds of serpents are not so keen about the higher ledges. The big mountain blacksnake, a slower and much heavier serpent than the racer, occasionally takes advantage of such dens, but prefers sheltering deep in some disinte-grating hollow of a big tree where the rotting debris is safe from freez-ing temperature. The striped snake and water snake prefer crevices in shaly banks close to streams.

During May the ledge-dens are populous with the emerged mem-bers—on certain days. These are times when the air is still and shade temperature along the ledge is close to seventy. As the ledge usually faces south and is in a great sheltered pocket of the mountain—for we have noted how particular the serpents are in selecting this spot—the ledge area is warmer than the outside open country.

May is the breeding season. It is the only breeding period through-out the warm months. During this time of the year occasional black-snakes of either sex may deliberately attack a human intruder upon the ledge. I have had them follow me twenty-five feet or more and make long sweeping strikes as high as my knees. Possibly one in twenty individuals will do this. The others skim over the rocks in flight with a grace and speed that invariably causes me to ponder just how they do it. I have never noted a rattler or copperhead indicate any hint of actually attacking a human, as does the harmless member of the ledge clan.

There is no thought of eating among any of the serpents on the ledge until the mating period is over. By the end of May the exodus into surrounding woods and meadows where food is numerous is well under way. There is an outward stop at the transient rocks, then the clan radiates out in all directions. A favorite path of exploration is, oddly enough, provided by their greatest enemy—man. This is the old stone wall with its sheltering labyrinth of passageways and offering good hunting for the smaller rodents.

By mid-June, if the season is normally warm the average den is deserted. Selected as it is to get every benefit of the spring sun, the rocks are too hot for the snakes. On mountains running to a flat top and with numerous shelving rocks sun-sheltered by brush, some of the rattlers may remain not far from the den if hunting is good and water is available. Around the greater number of dens, however, one may look for days during the summer and see not the sign of a snake. The clan is scouting far afield and some may be as much as two miles away.

In a way, such habits apply to all serpents. They are not aimless wanderers. They live in little worlds of their own. Even in the mild winters of southern Florida, where hibernation is short and there may be practically no frost, I have noted that the great diamond rattler, found singly, here and there the greater part of the year, has its favorite spots to congregate in moderate numbers during the cool season. There are no extensive dens, but every rattler has its homing spot and six or eight may gather here each fall. The favorite sheltering place is under the roots of a great pine, which, standing well out of the soil at the base of the tree, offer cave-like shelters beneath, these extensively hollowed out by some burrowing mammal, or possibly a big gopher tortoise. The tropical serpents have similar places. And with them the shelter may be utilized in avoiding undue heat instead of the benumbing touch of lowering temperature avoided by their northern allies. The roots of sage brush or fissured rocks form dens for the desert kinds. But all of them have specific places to which they regularly return, which places are the mating grounds. Summer wanderings are directly guided by two necessities—food and water.

SOUTH BEACH, STATEN ISLAND

by William T. Davis

William Thompson Davis was born October 12, 1862, on Staten Island, (New York), lived there all his life except for brief expeditions to "the mainland," and died there at the age of eighty-two on January 22, 1945. Small and thin, he was a little man with a lively mind and a great love of all outdoors. In particular he was a keen entomologist and such an expert in the study of one group of insects that he was often called "the cicada man." He named and described something over a hundred North American cicada species, which is more than half the total number found on this continent.

However, this was merely his specialty. He was interested in every phase of natural history, and he enjoyed every aspect of Nature. He was a parish scientist, like Gilbert White. He kept a journal and in it he wrote at an early age: "There is no need for a faraway fairyland, for earth is a mystery before us. The cowpaths lead to mysterious fields." He wrote many scientific papers but only one book, Days Afield on Staten Island, published privately in 1892 at a cost to the author of $152.75 for 310 copies, which he sold to those who wrote to him for it at 90 cents a copy. It was a delightful little book, highly prized by those who were lucky enough to own one, and in time it became something of a "collector's item." In fact, it was so much in demand that the Staten Island Historical Society sponsored a reprint of it in 1937.

Davis made himself the official historian of the different broods of seventeen-year locusts (which are cicadas, of course) in the New York City region, and on an expedition to Long Island to see "Brood No. 1" emerge from the shell in 1944 he was described by a field companion as follows: "Dr. Davis was by far the oldest, smallest, and liveliest person in the party. He wore a *business suit, and a stiff straw hat of the kind irreverently called a 'skimmer.' He peered through spectacles and he flourished a walking stick blithely as he sauntered along with a little knapsack on his back. We discovered that in the knapsack he carried many items that a naturalist might want in the field—knife, tweezers, three brassbound magnifying-glasses of different powers, an assortment of small boxes to contain any specimens that he collected, several packages of sweet crackers and two bars of chocolate. He was an old hand at the game and prepared for any emergency."*

That was his last expedition to "the mainland." The lively and delightful old gentleman slowed down to a walk a few months later, then took to his bed and slowly faded until he died the following January. A wildlife sanctuary named for him on his native heath will keep green the memory of William T. Davis on his beloved Staten Island. The following selection is one of the chapters in the one little book that he ever wrote.

THERE is but one short stretch of sandy beach on Staten Island from which the shore rambler may see the line where sky and ocean meet; in all other directions the view is bounded by New Jersey or Long Island, and the waves come more gently to the shore.

It was along this South Beach that in 1679 Jasper Dankers and Peter Sluyter wandered, the place being quite wilderness then, and their description of the herds of deer, the wild turkeys and geese, cause one to-day to read the account several times over, so interesting is the narrative. They visited the Oude Dorp and the Nieuwe Dorp; made leg-wearying journeys around the creeks that reach far inland, and found great difficulty in climbing the steep tree-covered bank where Fort Wadsworth now stands. No longer, indeed, do the mossbunkers lie dying by the thousands, as they described, "food for the eagles and other birds of prey," for though it might seem improbable to those not interested in the matter, yet it is true that not only do the land animals fall year by year before advancing civilization, but the life that ocean would seem to hold so securely, is also being gradually stolen away.

When Thoreau lived on Staten Island in 1843, residing with Mr.

William Emerson on the Richmond road, he rambled on this shore, and he tells us about the dogs that used to bark at him as he tramped along. He says: "I used to see packs of half-wild dogs haunting the lonely beach on the south shore of Staten Island, in New York Bay, for the sake of the carrion there cast up; and I remember that once, when for a long time I had heard a furious barking in the tall grass of the marsh, a pack of half a dozen large dogs burst forth on to the beach, pursuing a little one, which ran straight to me for protection, and I afforded it with some stones, though at some risk to myself; but the next day the little one was the first to bark at me."

Mr. Aug. R. Grote, the naturalist, and author of some pleasing poems, says in his "Check-List of North American Moths": "What a range of thought one can run over catching butterflies along the hedgerows. I come back to my first surprise, when, as a boy, I caught Cicindelas on the south beach of Staten Island. I saw that there were numerous questions hanging about unsolved as I was bottling my captures."

Though these tiger-beetles still fly on the South Beach, each July seeing their return, yet the scene has changed considerably. Indeed we cannot ramble along the same shore that Dankers and Sluyter and Thoreau did, for the beach of a hundred, or even of fifty, years ago is now far out under the waves. It has been estimated that each century brings with it several inches depression, and owing to the flat character of the country, many acres of woodlands and field have been washed away. History says the Elm Tree lighthouse received its name from a tree of this kind growing, in 1840, beyond the end of the present dock, which extends about four hundred feet into the water. On an old map, published in 1797, this tree is depicted as one of the landmarks, and before the days of the lighthouse it served to guide vessels into the harbor. On the map is written this inscription beside the figure of the tree: "Large Elm tree Standing by the Shore a Mark for Vessels leaving and going from New York to Amboy, Middletown and Brunswick." Further along the shore we have been shown two cedars in front of which the old men used to play ball when boys, but the trees now stand near the edge of the bank, which is crumbling away a little each year.

It was not long ago that the boulevard was built, a little up from the high-tide mark, and New Creek was bridged, but in many places only a trace of the road now remains.* New Creek is very erratic as

* This refers to the first boulevard.

regards at least a portion of its course, and previous to the Winter of 1883–84 emptied a quarter of a mile or more to the southwest of its present mouth. There was a great point formed by its winding course, on which the ribbed Pecten shells occurred in numbers. Each year this point grew longer, until at last the stream flowed so slowly that in the Winter mentioned it froze up, and the upland became flooded. When Spring came the water broke through straight to the ocean, and now another point is being slowly formed.

In 1797 the creek is portrayed as emptying straight to the ocean, without any accompanying point, but on the maps of 1850, 1859, and 1872, the point is shown. On the old map already referred to a line of trees is depicted near the mouth of the creek, and probably there was considerable wood there. Now there remains a clump of cedars, and the dead post oaks are ranged in rows, and branches that belonged to trees of the same kind may be pulled out of the peat, that in places forms little cliffs. This peat was originally formed when the present shore was a part of a salt meadow, and in its way is very interesting, for it offers a secure retreat to many a tender-shelled mollusk and timid crab. Pieces of it are constantly being broken off, and roll with ceaseless roll, until they mimic the most approved forms of the baker's loaves. Cedar trees may also be seen dead or dying, their trunks buried a foot or more in the sand, or the soil washed away from their roots, which sprawl in a ghastly fashion mid dead crabs and the wrecks of things that the ocean has thrown away. What a marvelous hoard of dead creatures the sea casts up to the land! Many poor mussels that seemed securely anchored in the morning, ere night are dying on the shore. It seems useless to throw them back, for the waves, with a roar, bring them again and cast them at your feet.

On Winter tramps I meet the crows looking for cast up treasures, and their success oftentimes is greater than my own; for many a fine "lady crab" or "decorator" have I mourned over—sighed for the lost leg or missing "apron." The gulls, too, rejoice at the death of the crab, and in Winter they frequent in numbers the sandy points, from which they rise with weird screams. They often sit motionless in rows at low-water line, apparently many of them asleep, and when the tide rises they float on the waves in nearly the same place where they were standing before. A few of their cries sound remarkably like some one hoisting a sail with the aid of a creaking pulley, and I have several times been deceived thereby, and have looked about expecting to find a mariner close in shore.

Of all the shells that line the shore, mid "jingle shells," that rattle
with a metallic sound, and "boat shells," whose inner coloring is equal
to anything in nature's art, there is one of curious shape and delicate
marking called the shell of Pandora. Three faint lines radiate from one
end of the hinge over the pearly surface, and the valves are generally
found together, resisting storm and waves. There is a little space between, for they are not usually tightly closed, but Hope being so great
a thing is still held as captive. Thus is this shell most aptly named, and
we peer within to see what may be hidden there, and in the grains
of sand are our hopes and our fortunes portrayed, for perhaps to the
world the one is as important as the other.

On cold Winter days, as well as in Summer, a blind man comes out,
and, with a long stick feels carefully for the drift-wood. Oftentimes
the small boys collect sticks, and placing them in his path, watch him
find them.

A hermit came to the shore a few years ago and built his house of
drift-wood on the sand near the bridge, covering it with old tin and
putting one small pane in the front for a window. With the fish he
catches, the gulls and ducks that he shoots, and what can be found on
the beach, he gets a living, and pays no taxes. "A fellow must do
something," says he, "and so I came here and built my house. I used
to live over on Long Island." In the morning the sun comes up from
the sea in front of his door, and at evening it sinks behind the western
hills; but no man comes to disturb the hermit. He is a stranger to the
rush and the set tasks of the world, and he is free, where many are
fettered.

Of drift-wood there is no end, neither is there of old shoes, mouse-
traps, brooms and all other household utensils. Even coal and metal
objects are washed ashore. I found a table one day, with a full
complement of legs, and a friend discovered a coffee pot, cover and all,
and with a blameless bottom. One might become quite a connoisseur
in bottles, for the Frenchman, the German, the Italian and the Irish-
man each throws his bottle overboard, and coming ashore they mix
with the American bottles on the beach. So various in shape and
general appearance are they that one readily falls to giving them supposed qualifications, such as phlegmatic, sanguine and bilious bottles.
I have seen those that looked ill though full of medicine, and they
are certainly often very blue. Some have contained "St. Jacob's Oil
for man and beast," and others of a very odd shape that appear to

have more difficulty in standing than most bottles, often protrude from the pockets of amateur fishermen.

There is nothing with which the waves seem to take more sport than with an empty barrel, and if the wind be high its bouncings and tossings are wild and fantastic. It rolls down the beach to meet the incoming wave, and then, mid the foam, is sent on its journey up the strand again. There is no scarcity of barrels on the beach, and on Crooke's Point, which might be called the Cape Cod of Staten Island, they form the sides of the well. Several have been placed one above the other in the sand, and fresh water accumulates at the bottom.

All fruits in their season find their way hither, and ocean lays things side by side in strangest contrast. A loaf of bread, some withered flowers, an old straw bed on which, perhaps, a sailor died, often lie close together. Maybe he took some of the nostrums contained in the bottles scattered about, and they introduced his spirit to the unknown shore.

Thus, when we wander along this sandy South Beach, and see our foot-prints and think of the strange vagaries that beset us, as Hawthorne did on his ramble along the shore, other things come crowding before us too, and we look at the houses, the bulkheads, the line of the proposed railway, and think of the deer and wild turkeys in the days of Dankers and his friend. Do we not then conclude that however desirable civilization and all that it brings may be, yet its presence in no way tends to beautify the scene.

And now the years have sped on, a great portion of the beach is changed, the long stretch of uninhabited strand has been curtailed. Pleasure seekers abound on the Summer days, and there is a laugh, a gayety, a gentle splashing in the water, and a rumbling of the railroad trains.

The unconscious sand is held at great price, and the tiger beetles have been banished to further along the shore. Waiters rush about with their trays, where once the crows devoured the lady crabs, and the crowd is as blithesome and gay as were the sand-fleas of old.

There are as many footsteps on the sand as on a city pavement, and it is plain that it is not the beach, but the people, that form the chief attraction—they come to see one another. A stretch of the strand is their meeting-place, while all beyond is vacant, where only a few fishermen or lone wanderers find enjoyment.

There is a particular type that discovers the beach most congenial.

Here his favorite beverage abounds, and he enjoys himself hugely all day long. He is possessed of much rotundity of person, his eyes are bulging, he is quite certain he knows all about the world. His philosophy is, that we live a little while, but are a long time dead. He bets that he can throw a ring over a cane, or can hit the bull's eye in the target, or one of the little tin birds that are ever going round. The publicity of the whole matter is what pleases him, and when he rides the deer or the polar bear, in the merry-go-round, he waves joyously to the crowd, and claps his hands to the music of the organ behind the screen.

That wonderful cow with a tin udder, that curiously enough fills her body to the exclusion of heart and lungs and other less important matters, is very attractive. He steps up and has some ice-cold milk, for this bovine is providently organized for Summer weather.

Someone bets him that he cannot send the weight in the sledge-machine up to the bell, and he bets he can. He grasps the heavy hammer confidently, and for once he is right; before his vigorous strokes the weight flies up and the bell rings. After all of that exercise he does not resort to the wonderful cow, but celebrates his success with lager beer.

At night he goes home supremely happy; he sings on the cars, and even dances a little. Maybe the conductor comes by and holds a quiet talk with the merrymaker, but the official produces only a momentary quiet.

The simple blithesomeness of such a soul—the boyish manhood—is not without its pleasing aspect, and sometimes it is accompanied by an entertaining personality of no mean order. Once, while the train lay in the station, the passengers crowding the smoker and the car adjoining, a jolly party sang their songs. One large man sang "Climbing up the Golden Stairs" in German, and with one accord two carloads of passengers ceased speaking, there was a perfect hush while he sang, such was the power and the charm.

In September, 1889, the swells of the sea visited the "hotels" in person, and few of the houses escaped without damage, some of them having their broad piazzas taken away, for such was the rollicking dance of Neptune's company. After nearly a week of dark and sullen skies, when the sun seemed to have forgotten the earth, it came at last, struggling through the clouds, and the workmen appeared in numbers on the beach, and engaged themselves in repairing the damage caused by the breakers. Among them was a young man with staring dark eyes, that protruded far from his head, and had hardly a human expression. There was more of the white visible than of the colored iris and the effect was ghastly—he looked to have the soul of a demon. He was in a hole, adjusting a post beneath a tottering bathing house, and I and another man approached—I from curiosity to see the wild eyes, which I had noticed on my way up the beach, and he to inspect the progress of the work. But those frightful eyes were truthful windows to a soul, and their possessor demanded, with an oath, what we had come to see.

Beyond New Creek much of the old time quietness still remains; we may ramble as of yore and sniff the salt breeze, and make a quiet loitering inspection of that wondrous hoard of wreck that ocean has flung to the land. The great value of these free gifts of the sea have always been taken account of, and in the days of the Revolution, in the announcement of the sale of the Seaman farm, the beach and its wealth are not forgotten. The property is described as "a valuable plantation that did belong to Mr. Jaquis Poilloin, deceased, containing 190 acres, exclusive of the beach and flats on the front of the said farm, which will be included in the purchase, on which comes great quantities of seaweed (a very valuable manure)."

Even in the days of Summer I have rambled for miles without meeting anyone—have gone in bathing and sat on a log and ate my lunch while I dried, the warm, gentle breezes blowing about me. One day as I came upon the beach from the meadows there were heavy black clouds in the south, and a distant sound of thunder. Soon the sun was hidden, and there were flashes of lightning. I hastened, and, getting a few boards together, made a little shed against a log, under which I placed my clothes—then I went into the water. Soon the waves rose white-capped, and I came ashore; a small boat in the distance drew down its sails and lowered its anchor. The sand was blown so swiftly before the gale that it stung my unprotected back; then there came a lull, and then the rain—a gentle summer shower. The drops pelting down on me seemed cold, and they dug little pits in the sand, striking it with much force. So long have we had umbrellas, coats or sheepskins, and dwelt in houses, that to stand thus unprotected in even a summer shower, is a memorable experience. Anon the sun burst forth, and quickly dried the sand and me; and to look over the placid scene one would have thought it unlikely that a few moments before the leaves had been wrenched from the trees. The black clouds went sailing off in the distance, the small boat drew up its anchor and spread its sails, and the grasshoppers sang again in the meadow.

The coming in and going out of the tide gives an extra interest to the shore, and he that lives by adjusts much of his daily employment to its rise and fall. He may go out in the morning and find a chair or a neat little boat cast up at his door, or maybe some poor fish that missed his reckoning, and was thrown on the sand in consequence. There is ever a newness, and you stand by expecting something, just as the fishermen do who look in the direction in which they cast their lines, though they can see nothing but the waves. I have noticed that when dogs are seated on the beach they generally look seaward, too, and will often sit watching the horizon for a long time.

About thirty species of mollusks may commonly be collected upon the beach, though many more have actually been found there. The large collections of shells and little stones, which are held together by the silken cords with which the edible mussel attaches itself to all objects within its reach, are fruitful places for research when cast upon the shore, and there may be found the greatest number of prizes. Also the large native sponges, that come rolling in with the waves, contain many shells and other animals that find in them protection and a home.

In a few days thousands of shells of one species will sometimes be cast ashore, and next week it may be a school of fish or a countless multitude of crabs. Thus have I seen the shore for long distances so covered with the recently cast up shells of the sea, or skimmer clam, that it was impossible to walk without crushing them. The mole-crab is also occasionally thrown ashore in great numbers, forming a definite line along the beach where they have been left by the highest wave.

It was the large shells of the skimmer clam that were tied to sticks by the Indians and used as hoes.

In September there are many kinds of fish in the creek—young bluefish, killifish, and pipefish—each kind in schools, and on the unprotected shore there is a certain little fish with a silvery band on its side that swims in the shallow water, going in and out with the waves. It comes so close to the dry beach that I have succeeded in capturing it with my insect net, which I slapped down upon it as if it had been a butterfly. Further out from the shore there are often large schools of fish, that make the water dark for a space, and which may be individually distinguished as they are momentarily raised in a swelling wave above the general level of the sea.

Many sandpipers run along the beach at certain seasons, just at the edge of the waves, and sometimes the zig-zag of their motions is remarkable. They look like little dancing-machines, their movements are so rapid, and they turn at such sharp angles in their pursuit of the sandhoppers. It is fatal for a sand-flea to have rheumatism. One stormy day I particularly observed four of these birds standing in shoal water, and occasionally running their bills into the sand. The tide was out, and they appeared to be less active than usual, but stood about, scratched their heads with their wet feet, preened their feathers, and looked like four old men in gray coats standing solemnly together, with their heads pulled down between their shoulders. One of the number had but a single leg, but he nevertheless got about quickly, and seemed well-grounded and sure-footed. He would stand where the incoming wave washed against him, and I could not detect that he even so much as rocked on his frail support. The surviving leg was slanted under his body from left to right, so as to make the center of gravity fall in the proper place. One often hears the reports of guns by the meadow-creeks and on the shore, and sees the little clouds of smoke curl upward. It was thus that the sandpiper lost his leg, but the rest of his body was fortunate enough to fly away. In these days of pensions, what is he to receive?

The fishermen stand in a line along the beach, or sit on empty barrels, or old baskets, or boxes, and often they support their poles in uprights, and anxiously watch for them to bend. They busy themselves about the fire, and while one watches the poles another collects drift-wood to feed it. Their lunch is spread out near by, and they dig a hole in the sand wherein to put the apples and tomatoes, thus keeping them from rolling down the beach. The fire, with its crackle and blue curling smoke, and the captured fish lying by, all remind you of a primitive simplicity, and indeed it is this desire to live close, at least for one day, to the essentials of a natural life that prompts many of the men to visit the sea-shore. When seen at a distance, the smoke from the fires tones admirably with the ocean tints, and gives a pleasing haziness to the surroundings. Occasionally the fires are made against a big beam, or a pile, that has broken loose and drifted ashore, and these immense pieces of wood becoming ignited, burn with a dull sullenness long after the rest of the fire has gone out. These are pleasant places to tarry on the cold days, when the wind blows across the meadows from the north, and you may even sit on the beam and hang your hands over, near the glowing embers. The fire imparts an indescribable character to the wood; the beam that smokes seems to be essentially different from the others along the shore, and you discover yourself regarding it as half alive. But be very circumspect as to the logs, the drift-wood, and pieces of old vessels, that you sit upon. On the warm days different substances—tar, pitch, resin, and their various combinations which give to a vessel a peculiar and not unpleasant odor—stew out of these logs that lie on the hot sand. Though it is very easy to sit down upon them, yet it is not so easy often to get away at the precise moment you desire, and for a time you are like Theseus or Pirithous on the wayside stone in the land of Shades.

When the tide is low, the peat-cliffs, that rise a yard or more above the sand below their perpendicular fronts, form convenient stations from whence the fishermen cast their lines. The placid and shallow pools that remain between the tides on the peat-beds are most transparent, and usually some living creature is entrapped in the larger of them, and has to await the return of the waves to regain his liberty. There are also many sea-weeds in the pools that deck them out in bright array, and while you peer in at the marvels that are hidden there, you may hear the water splashing in a miniature fall over the peat-cliff, as the pool is gradually drained away. The peat is not over a foot or two thick in most places, and under it is a layer of clay containing innumerable water-worn pebbles. Many of them are of brown sandstone, and it is from this source that the pebbles that line the immediate up-shore come, and from which much of the beach to the eastward is entirely free. There is also a great number of edible mussel shells at this part of the shore, and they crackle under your feet as you walk along, and here it is that the crows pay regular visits, for the mussels and soft-shell clams are favorites with them. Not only do the empty shells lie about the logs high on the beach, where the crows have taken them, but they are also found far inland, in the most central portions of the island. Sometimes in the midst of the ferns and woodland vegetation, when you least expect to find a denizen of the sea, you come upon the empty valves of a soft-shell clam. An interesting feature connected with the life-history of this clam is the effect which the character of the beach exerts upon the shells. In the sandy shore, where the resistance is not great and about equal in all directions, the shells are thin and evenly developed, and are often very beautiful in form and color; but on the rocky shores of the island, where the conditions are not so favorable, the shells are distorted to fit the apertures in which they have grown. On the peat they are even more deformed than on the stony shore, and there are also many of a rounded form, the peat acting as a hard-pan, preventing them from burying deeply, and the constant scraping along its surface of drift material breaks the upper ends of the shells. The ribbed mussel also abounds in places on the peat, and I have sometimes found it difficult to secure perfect specimens, owing to the shells being broken on the edges from the cause already mentioned.

In several places on the surface of the peat there are evidences of ditches having been dug in years agone; perhaps most of them were made when the shore was a portion of the meadow. In a few instances they may be property lines, and not originally constructed for the more ordinary purpose of drainage. Now they are washed by the waves, the "property" is gradually being devoured by the ocean, and they serve as channels wherein the sea may swash and swirl in that menacing playfulness that is often its mood.

Gradually the incoming tide forces the fishermen who are not protected by rubber boots, or who had not discarded artificial coverings to their feet, to seek the drier up-shore, and it is then, while the waves break in the cavernous recesses that they have worn in the face of the low cliffs, that the little fires of drift-wood are most welcome.

In certain localities wild beans grow in abundance on the up-shore, beyond the reach of the tide, and in September a great number may be gathered in a short time. The Indians picked them when they were here, and cooked them in their earthen vessels, and I, in these later days, have cooked them also. They have a curious tang—a concentrated bean flavor—but are not distasteful, and if it were not for Limas, the Valentines and the other cultivated varieties, we would be glad to get the wild Phaseolus.

At the commencement of the Point, and in places before you get so far along the beach, the shore is higher at the flood-tide mark than the contiguous meadows, and every now and then in the Spring and Fall, and occasionally during storms at other seasons, the waves wash entirely over the beach. There is in consequence a bank of sand—a sort of sandy wave that gradually rolls over the low-lying meadows, and you may see the cedar-trees standing dead, and, as it were, knee-deep in the sandy inundation.

In one place on the shore there stand a few cedar and cultivated cherry trees in a row, and they probably mark the site of an old fence, but all other evidences of the line are now obliterated by the sand. Where there is a growth of smilax, small cedars or any other thick and low vegetation, it will for a short time protect the meadow immediately behind it, and thus occasionally there is a low place on the upland side of one of these clumps, where the cattails still grow, while all about it will be sand.

The line is generally well defined between this barren waste and the fertile meadow, and close to its threatening edge grow the goldenrods and asters, whose roots by next year will probably be deeply buried. The purple and the green-stemmed stramoniums find the sandy wastes to their liking, and particularly just along its edge often grow luxuriantly. The beach-grass follows the sand, and the little tufts that spring from the subterranean rhizomes all stand in a row and look like some queer feathery little soldiers marching across a sandy desert. There are sometimes quite complete circles described about these clumps of grass that stand alone, for being buffeted about by the wind, marks are left in the sand of their furthest reach in every direction. Some days the wind roars across the beach, and if you have a companion you must needs put your head close to his and shout loudly in order to make him hear. Then the sand is lifted off the up-shore, where it is dry, and comes flying against your face, and it does not do to turn the eyes in the direction from whence it comes. If the wind is from the north or northwest the spray from the waves is blown seaward again in great clouds, the gulls clang their doleful cries, and there is a grim seriousness in the scene that lives long in the memory. The hills, viewed from the shore across the intervening lowland, give you the impression of life, as if somehow the ridge that you saw in the distance was the dorsal crest of some monstrous beast. It seems to be quietly slumbering there; to be dark and gray in Winter and in Spring to suddenly change its color, like a chameleon.

The wind also blows the sand off the deposits of black and slightly cemented iron-sand. These sheets are very thin and brittle, and it is seldom that one of any considerable size can be lifted by the hand from the place where it was formed.

On the Point there are many cedars, and near the house once stood a number of Lombardy poplars; but they have nearly all been cut down. It is said that the wind made too much noise "roaring in their branches"; they were so high and lithe that they responded to every breeze, and so ailanthus trees were planted near the house and the poplars felled. There are some very old bay bushes that have grown twelve feet high and proportionally robust in trunk, and under them the fowls congregate. The rooster may crow ever so lustily on the

Point, and only be answered by the dismal cry of a seagull, for all the tones of defiance from the mainland come attempered by the breeze, and the chanticleers themselves would not know what to think of the far-away sound. Even the European or English sparrows do not often make their way thither, but the native song sparrow is quite domestic, and hops about among the hen-coops or perches on their tops.

Years ago a few cultivated blackberry bushes grew near the house, and when in fruit they were tied with dangling shingles. Some poor catbird, in passing over the Point, always found these few bushes most tempting and tarried awhile—hence the shingles. Rabbits, too, frequent the vicinity, and in Winter, after the ground is covered with snow, their tracks are innumerable. But one rabbit is very industrious in track-making, and it is surprising how many places he has a mind to visit, thus leading you to believe that a great number have been about the hen-coops.

The dunes on the Point run parallel and near to the shore on the south side, and it is pleasing to walk through the little vales that separate them. Often the evening primroses are conspicuous there, and the lowly camphor weed, the prickly pear and the gray and sombre *hudsonia* find favored situation. But I should not call the *hudsonia* gray and sombre, for though it appears during eleven months of the year that the earth has brought forth a grizzly and shaggy coat that seems about to wither and die away, yet in June and the latter part of May it decks itself in yellow blossoms, and shows that latent vitality that is ever so surprising in nature. *Syneda graphica*, a pretty moth, with marbled wings of yellow, of gray and of brown, frequents these patches of *hudsonia* twice a year, for its caterpillars feed upon it, and *Utetheisa bella*, that orange and white moth, with showy pink hind wings, also flies in numbers in the vicinity.

The beach-plums are a great attraction to a shore rambler, and the bayberries to the white-breasted swallows that congregate on the Point in great flocks. It is believed to be a weather sign, this vast gathering of birds, for it is said that when the swallows visit the bayberry bushes a storm is near. The branches of the bay often bend under their united weight, and the dark glossy blue of their backs make the group resplendent in color. On other portions of the island they may, in the late Summer and Fall days, be seen winging their way shoreward in the morning, flying irregularly as if catching insects by the way, and at

evening the flocks return northward. It is nothing for a swallow to feed
on the bayberries by the sea shore and fly to a far away roost.

You would hardly suspect, in walking along the sand, that many of
the clumps of bay bushes were connected one with another by subterranean branches; but when this is once discovered it will also be observed how they, like the tufts of beach grass, often stand in line.
These rootstocks are most marvelously contorted and interlaced, and
it is no uncommon matter to find one that has doubled completely
on its course. They are covered with a silvery yellow bark, like that
at the base of the white birches, and many of them are over two
inches in diameter and extend a number of feet, giving rise, as has
already been said, to several clumps of upright, leaf-bearing branches.
Thus do the bay bushes stand together in the sandy waste, and as the
waves eat into the dunes, those that are furthest inland support for a
little while the outermost member of their group.

There is a very thin subsoil of a blacker hue than the sand, and it is
the highway to which many of the roots adhere. When the ocean
covers it with several feet of cast-up shells and sand, and a pit has
been dug into these several layers, then does the narrow black seam
and its accompanying roots show most plainly.

Hawks fly about slowly over the dunes, close to the tops of the
bushes. Mice are ever running in and out among the tussocks of grass,
and the silent winged hawk steals upon them unawares. Then, too, the
great blue herons visit the unfrequented meadows, and stand sentinel
there. The white herons used to come also, and the farmers and fishermen will tell you about them; but now they have ceased to visit the
shore, or, at most, are a great rarity. Though the herons are imposing,
and you feel that the earth still has a great bird when you see them fly,
yet those ever busy, cawing crows, that meddle with the meadow hen's
eggs, and incur the scoldings of the marsh wrens, are of more general
interest. It is said that they used to be seen in vast numbers flying to
their roost among the cedars on Sandy Hook. That in its day was one
of the great crow roosts of the vicinity.

There are several wrecks along the beach, not those of recent years,
but remains of old crafts that went to pieces long ago. What with the
gradual washing away of the shore and the ever-busy sandmen, who
land their schooners and sail away with portions of the Point, these
wrecks have been exposed. I have stood in wonderment on the old
water-worn sides of one of these hulks, whose iron bolts, eroded by
time, encrusted the planking for many inches about their heads with a

cement of iron, of pebbles and of sand; and the planking itself was eaten and worn and carved by the sea. Those feathery little sea plants that seem so incapable of withstanding the force of the waves, and yet are really so tough and strong, floated in the incoming tide; and the portholes, through which murderous cannon had once shown their iron faces, looked peaceful enough, manned by barnacles and fringed by the soft, waving green weeds.

Perhaps it was in the days of the Revolution when this cruiser went ashore, and HYLER, that tormentor of the British stationed on the island, was responsible for her destruction. But it is just as likely to have been the other way, for the old wreck and the waves can tell nothing of the fortunes of war.* No doubt they were rough, brawling men who manned this war vessel—men who lived to eat, to drink, to fight and to swear; but they were hardly tougher customers than those who sail the sand-boats of to-day. Great brawny fellows are many of these, that absorb nearly as much fresh oxygen and sunlight through their skins as a Hottentot, for they wear in Summer hardly more clothes than the African. A flannel shirt and drawers, that are often sieve-like in character, complete their apparel, and, bare-footed and bare-headed, they wheel the sand aboard the schooners, and for each voyage they receive five dollars. The captain, perhaps, is slightly fuller dressed and may own the boat; if not, he receives seven dollars per trip. At half-tide they get the schooner close into the shore, and place wooden horses from the vessel's side to the up-beach, and on these planks are laid. It is the custom for the captain, if he works, to walk off first, with his wheelbarrow, followed by the crew, and when the captain's barrow is full it is expected that each man will have his fully laden also, so that he may precede the captain up the plank. Thus, while the men dig, they keep an eye to the skipper, and lag or hasten as the exigencies of the situation seem to demand. It takes them commonly five or six hours, according to the number of the crew and the size of the vessel, to complete the cargo.

If they do not intend to pay for the sand, that is, have the amount collected from the vessel in New York, where she is usually registered, the crew is large, and they lay several planks from the schooner to the up-shore, and work with the greatest diligence. One day I came upon a crew of this description, and overheard their comments as I approached, one of them declaring that I looked remarkably like a mis-

---

* What remained of this wreck was broken up in the storm of October, 1890. At the same time great changes were wrought in the shifting sand of the beach.

sionary. A member of the group had a guilty conscience, and I heard the others rallying him that I had come to spy him out. As it was late in the Fall they had donned their coats, but that same party-colored, harlequin-like attire worn in Summer was still in vogue, and one long-legged, thin fellow, with vermilion drawers and black coat, was particularly conspicuous as he walked up the plank.

It is related that a German, who lived down the beach some years ago, seeing the sand-boatmen wheeling his property aboard, went to collect the dollars that he thought were due him. But the sand-men didn't view it in the same way, and, calling him a Dutchman, with flourishes, whacked him severely with their shovels, until he was glad to part with his sand and their blows.

While waiting for the tide, the crews that have finished loading walk about the beach, split wood or lie on the sand, and if another sloop is being laden nearby, as sometimes happens, they watch the proceedings with evident interest. Then do they talk of what pleases them in life and what they regard as its unpleasantries, the merits of the schooners, the captains and such matters. Above all do they discuss the purchasing power of the five dollars they are about to receive, when applied to the market value of beer and whiskey. A flaxen-haired giant of this description, who might have played with us as Otus or Ephialtes, for his muscles stood out large and strong, stood on the beach one day and lamented, in terms that would fill this page with dashes, the fact that he was minus all cash. A good specimen of anything—a resplendent flower, or even a big toad—is pleasant to gaze upon, and so this muscular youth, with his vivacious glances and rollicking ways, was a vigorous scion of the race, and admirable for his hardihood.

Such characters, no doubts, were the buccaneers of old days, who sailed the sea about the Point and landed on the shore, and who, it is said, buried money on the banks of Bass Creek. Perhaps even the burly, copper-nosed Yan Yost Vanderscamp and his roistering followers from the "Wild Goose," at Communipaw, landed on this strand.

About eighteen hundred and twenty or thirty, men came for several successive years at Christmas time, and taking sight from a rock exposed at low-water, dug a long trench, and it is believed that they finally found the treasure, for remnants of tarred canvas and pieces of an old box were discovered in the trench which they had dug.

Crooke's Point was formerly known as Brown's Point, and on the old map of the island, already referred to, it is denominated a "Beach of Sand." Bass Creek is laid down on this and subsequent maps as of considerable proportions, but now only vestiges of it remain, it being nearly obliterated by the sandy waves. This old map also makes the Point about three-eights of a mile at its greatest breadth; but it is much less than that now, and, ere long, it will be "Crooke's Island," instead of Point. The waves have left but a narrow neck of sand only two or three yards wide in one place, and over this they often wash to the reedy meadows that lie between the beach and the Great Kill.

There are several lanes that lead from the upland across the meadows to the shore, and muddy, swaley roads are they. The cattails grow high at their sides, and nearer to the shore the taller varieties of salt meadow grass. One of these long, straight lanes, ditched on either side, has always left a pleasing memory picture, with the several hummocks over which it passed, where stood the gnarled wind-torn appletrees, and where grew a few cabbages surrounded by a fence. I never saw anybody working there, and they might have been grown by the sea-gods or by some wild man of the moors, for all that appeared to the contrary. From my seat under the haystack I could see a lone tree in the distance that bore a crow's nest in its branches, and the occasional splashing of a musk-rat in the creek nearby, the chirp of a song sparrow or the squeak of a meadow mouse, indicated the life that was near. The shad-frogs are common on the meadows at times, and the easy-going toad also comes down to the sea.

Oft have I watched for a long time the soldier-crabs, or "fiddlers," that abound along the creek. I take it that life cannot be very dull to them mid so much sociability, they are so neighborly. In retreating to their holes they do not always leave the big claw outermost, but sometimes go in with that claw first. They feed themselves with the little claw, often picking the mud, etc., from off the big one and putting it into their mandibles. Those with small claws only, feed themselves with both, first with one and then with the other, and seem to get on much faster than the others. At some seasons there is no quarreling among them, though they will lock their large claws occasionally, but do not pinch. Again, in the Spring, I have seen the males quite belligerent, many of them with their large claws interlocked, and so enraged that I have picked them up without their loosening their hold. Often, too, have I put several individuals into one hole and had them retire, nor do they speedily show themselves again, though so strangely situated. It is comical to see them bring their long, stalked eyes to bear upon you. "We are looking at you," they seem to say.

It is best when you come to a wet place in the meadow to run through it as fast as you can—to jump with judgment, but rapidly—for if you stop to look after each step the water soaks into your shoes. The meadow-grass hides a deal of moisture, and you slump into a depression or a miniature creek before you are aware. Thus do I remember falling into a ditch, for being preoccupied, looking at the *Helenium* flowers, I did not observe what the rank vegetation concealed until I was knee-deep in water. How surprised we are at getting suddenly soused; one would think that water was a new element to us.

With an old piece of bamboo from the shore, or a tree-branch from the upland, to serve as a jumping-pole, you may often get over the wet places in the lane tolerably well; and if, mayhap, your shoes get wet, run in the grass awhile on some dry knoll or ridge, for the grass will dry your shoes quite speedily.

I remember one cold, bright, windy day, as I came along the beach, seeing one of the Hermit's dogs tugging at the remains of an old white horse that lay on the sand. The dog stood with his legs braced and pulled at the tough, hard skin with all of his strength, but when he saw me, he ran across the bridge, casting an occasional sullen look behind. Then there was a general barking, and the four or five dogs made a rush for me—came bounding up on the end of the bridge, but I greeted them as a friend, and they concluded to regard me in that light, though I do not think their first intention was so kindly. Soon I had them growling at one another as each tried to get a larger share of the caresses I so lavishly bestowed.

Near by there was a stack of hay, and I sat myself down on its sunny side to eat lunch while the north wind blew. At one end of the stack there was a second white horse, a forlorn, decrepit animal, and probably the survivor of some hackman's team, whose other member I had seen lying dead. As I ate my crackers and bread and orange I could hear the horse grinding his provender, and when I returned three hours later, he was still eating. There he stood, with his eyes half closed, and slowly munched the hay, while the north wind cast his shaggy coat into ridges.

It seems useless to describe natural scenery when every one may see it if they will, but the very color of the beach, swept smooth by the broom of the ocean every twelve hours, and the yellow-brown tints of the meadow-grass in Autumn, tempt you to stop and to gaze. When all of this is spread out into acres, and into miles, and you recline, half dreaming, on a dune, and the pleasant wonderment of the scene steals into your mind, mayhap the tears will stream down your face. Yet you know not why the common scene affects you so, and that you should feel that sadness that seems akin to heavenly joy.

"It is a view of delight," says Lucretius, "to stand or walk upon the shore-side, and to see a ship tossed with tempest upon the sea . . .";
so, likewise, it is pleasant on the hazy and foggy days to hear the horns of the unseen steamers far out over the water. The sound comes booming across the waves—like some giant cow mooing most obstreperously in the distance, having lost her way.

At night the beach is strange. I have been there on dark, cloudy evenings, such as follow the lowering days that come late in the Fall. All of the drift-timber seems then to entangle your feet, and you come suddenly face to face with ghastly pieces of wreck, that mimic in their strangeness the fantastic forms of the creatures that inhabit the sea. What can be a greater wonder than the phosphorescent glimmerings that bedeck the waves as they break on the shore? The jellyfish, that die at the end of Summer and disintegrate, make the sand luminous, and at every step you see your glowing tracks behind you; you make golden footprints in the sands, as if indeed some superhuman being had passed that way. The glowing embers of the fishermen's fires start and die with the breeze, and the lighthouse alternately opens and shuts its great red eye.

I have had one of the larger owls follow me at night for half a mile along the beach, flying in circles about my head, but keeping at a respectful distance, and retaining a sullen silence. When I have come to the bridge I have stolen across quietly, for the Hermit's dogs lay sleeping close by; and then gone along the shore as near to the waves and as far from the drift-wood as possible, as silently, as stealthily as the owl itself.

* * * *

There is no jesting in nature; she may seem glad or sad, but she is earnest. A trifling man in the field cannot fool the crickets; and yet there is much misrepresentation in nature. God's creatures often appear to one another what they are not—they are tricky. Harmless snakes mimic poisonous ones, the semblance of many moths to yellow leaves is striking; white spiders inhabit white flowers, and yellow spiders occur on yellow ones. Thus they escape their enemies, or prove the hidden enemies of others. When we walk in the woods we cannot be sure of what we see, so much is done for appearance sake alone, the truth is hidden mid a pageant of bright petals. Circe is ever abroad, and the milkweeds lure flies and bees and hold them captive till they die.

Any action that is possible is permissible in nature; she even tolerates murder. Let those who can, do, is the motto in the fields. The crimes that a lone man may commit in the woods, or on the sea shore know no law, and even seem without the pale of the conscience. If he crushes a snail, or barks a tree, nature does not revenge herself.

Yet the ants have a standard of justice among themselves, that is a conscience as far as their community and species go. Also there is a law among crows, they do not destroy each other's nests. Our own justice hardly steps outside of human affairs, but we owe something to animals. The cow in the field appreciates kindness, and we should strive to please the more helpless creatures, as well as our friend and our kindred.

Perhaps the chief value of going afield, is that we are judged by a true standard—a dollar isn't worth a cent there. Death is a great leveller it is said, and so is nature's influence. In the city a man is surrounded by artificial conditions and has the help of his fellows, but in the open country he comes more to the realization of himself. A lone journey in the meadows or a day spent silently in the woods, is sobering, and many suffer considerably when thus imprisoned with themselves. They cannot find anything of interest in the meadows, they complain of quiet in the midst of warfare, and are generally fretful.

A man who concerns himself principally with the artificial, and who thinks that the world is for stirring business alone, misses entirely that divine halo that rests about much in nature. To him all things are certain. He can have a particular tree cut down or an ox killed at command, and he is ever busy spinning a web of affairs. You see him hurrying across the street with rapid strides, for hasn't the Valley railroad declared a dividend! Such things must be, but they are not the safest springs of pleasure. We must not put by entirely the chippy singing in the apple tree, or the white clouds, for nature declares a dividend every hour—the dew drops always pay par to the summer leaves.

If we could constantly bear in mind many of our experiences, most of us would be quite content to remain in some sequestered nook for the length of our days, but the freshness of the smart wears off—we forget, and are burned again.

Those who are inconsolably miserable, and feel that they have all of the ills, should inspect the lilies of the field. There is hardly a perfect one among them, and no doubt they would often be glad to spin and reap, if they might thereby forget the gnawing caterpillars that devour their leaves. There should be many doctors among the plants. I meet with ailing individuals that would gladly consult specialists on stamens and pistils.

We sometimes get a wider view of our homes by going afield. Like Lynceus, we see well at a distance. The chief value of an excursion is often the last step across the threshold. We walk twenty miles in order to get acquainted with our family cat. We walk and walk, and think we are going to discover something of interest; we go a long way from home and find ourselves finally in some man's back yard, where he is already at home. Stanley in all his explorations always found some one at home. The black men fed him with vegetables from their kitchen gardens.

Our enjoyment of a place is often proportioned to the effort we have made to get there. The further it is away and the longer the tramp, the sharper our eyes become, and vivid is the mental picture we carry away. One of the chief advantages in visiting different meadows and pieces of woodland, is, that it whets our perception, we are more on the lookout. But probably there isn't a ten-acre woodlot even near home, that has been thoroughly explored. If you think there is, go through it again, and see if there isn't a nut tree, that you have before passed by without discovery.

It is often well to select some circumscribed piece of mother earth, and watch it particularly throughout the year; comparing it with the other fields to which occasional journeys are made. The rhythm of the warmer months is broken by scattering our observation too wide. There is a cadence of the year; one continuous song changing gradually and almost imperceptibly, and of which each musical creature sings in turn his part. The first outburst of melody of the song sparrow, the blackbirds in the swamp, the crickets, the katy-dids, the z-ing of the harvest flies, and the late fall notes of the birds going southward; these and many more, all come as signs of the seasons, and mark for each patch of mother earth, the progress of the year. They make a beautiful and pathetic march, and are best seen and most forcibly impressed, by looking steadily at the same acres. If we stand with open eyes, there is no pageant so varied as the march of the warmer days. But the rapid change that characterizes Summer is gone in Winter. There may be snow or there may be none, but we have generally to look close to note that a few more dead leaves have blown off an oak on the hill-side, or that the black haw berries are a little more shrivelled than they were a month ago. When the ban of Boreas is o'er the land, and the leaves huddle together in the depressions in the woods, as if they would keep one another warm, and the snow lies on the earth, then a view of one field, of one hill-side, is so similar to the view a month hence, that one falls back on the calendar, for the want of any change betokening the march of time out of doors.

Nature does indeed will us strange fortunes, but generally she is tolerably kind, and if we do not try to visit the North Pole, or spend a Summer in the Sahara, we may live along without any marked break in our mutual, friendly relations. We may go musing calmly in the meadows, in the woodland, and along the country lanes, and hark to those inward murmurings of fancy that cause a strange array of natural and human transactions, to move in turn over old Staten Island, that seems to sleep so peacefully to-day beneath the Autumn sun. The patroons and their Bouweries, the Peach war, the British troops quartered on the Island, and the domestic scenes in the Dutch and Huguenot families, wear to us a garment of quiet and pleasing interest, though its seams chafed harshly enough many of those who wore it of old. No doubt the present is quite as unquiet and wrangling as many a bygone year, but over the past there always rests a halo, and time, like a kind critic, idealizes for us the jumbled maze, and only gives forth a poetic tincture of the whole.

AN ORNITHOLOGIST IN CUBA

by Frank M. Chapman

Before the sovereign State of New York, the Commonwealth of Massachusetts, and other such segments of the United States produced bird guides of their separate regions, Chapman's Handbook of Birds of Eastern North America *was the bible and pocket companion of all the bird-watchers of the country east of the Mississippi. Roger Tory Peterson has gone the past grand master one or two better by doing the colored plates as well as the text for his field guides and by turning out a handy book on Western as well as Eastern birds of this country, but Frank M. Chapman ruled supreme for many years.*

Born in Englewood, New Jersey, June 12, 1864, he took a lively interest in birds as a boy. Those were the days of collecting and mounting specimens, and it wasn't long before young Chapman was taking instructions in taxidermy. However, his ornithological career was postponed or held in abeyance by his acceptance of a position as a bank clerk in New York City after his graduation from Englewood Academy in 1880. He spent six years with the bank, but before and after banking hours he watched birds, collected birds, read about birds, talked about birds, and wrote to men who knew about birds. He read Wake-Robin *by John Burroughs and wrote to the author. He kept records of warblers on migration and reported them to the scientific authorities. He joined the Linnaean Society of New York. He quit the bank. He attended a meeting of the American Ornithological Union in Washington. He became a part-time assistant at the American Museum of Natural History, and finally he took a full-time job there in the bird department on March 1, 1888, at a salary of fifty dollars per month. In time, of course, he rose to be head of the department, a leader of many expeditions to foreign countries, the writer of numerous articles and books on birds, a*

*leader in bird protection, founder of the biological station on
Barro Colorado Island in Gatun Lake of the Panama Canal Zone,
and altogether the ranking ornithological authority in North
America.*

*He was a brisk, stocky figure in action. In his autobiography—
from which the following account of a Cuban adventure is taken
—he wrote that he "never had rugged health or great staying
power," but his long and energetic career disproved that modest
statement. He traveled through jungles and over mountains. He
studied hard. He spoke forcefully. He even wrote with vigor. And
he was fast man in a give-and-take argument over the walnuts
and the wine. He died in New York City, November 15, 1945, in
his eighty-second year.*

C HARLES CORY'S publications on West Indian birds had
aroused my interest, not only in the birds themselves but in
the problem of insular distribution. In 1892, therefore, I went
to Cuba to meet in life birds which had been only names or
dried skins and to see the conditions under which they lived. Moreover, Cuba was in the tropics. Circumstances prevented me from going to South America, but in Cuba I should see Parrots and Trogons
and Jaçanas and other species about which hung the lure of low latitudes. My course was also in a measure determined by the fact that it
led through Florida, so after a few days in Gainesville I sailed from
Port Tampa, February 18th, on the steamer *Olivette* bound for
Havana.

Today one crosses from Florida to Cuba as one crosses the street.
Forty years ago it was a journey; at least so it seemed to me. I had
never been outside the United States before, I was going to a Spanish-
speaking country and planned to reach its wilder portions where
English would be a wholly unknown tongue. My Spanish had been acquired from Meisterschaft booklets under my own tuition; but I was
a willing, responsive pupil and felt that with a little practice my vocabulary would answer my needs. One of my early attempts at using it met
with a somewhat unappreciative response. My first purchase, after
reaching Havana, was a straw hat. I selected one in the window of a
shop on Obispo Street, I think No. 93, rehearsed my little sentence
several times, then entered the door and addressed a salesman with

"Yo quisiera comprar un sombrero, Señor." Whereupon he replied, with a strong Teutonic accent, "Oh, you vant to buy a had?"

On the same day I had a convincing demonstration of the Latin's use of the word *mañana*. I had gone by preference to a Spanish hotel —El Telegrapho. The light in my room was supplied by an L gas fixture, but the burner was clogged. I called the chamber-boy, he mounted a chair and with a pin remedied the difficulty, lighted the gas and left. Then I discovered that the cock would not turn, recalled the boy and further explained the situation, upon which he took the soiled towel (badge of office) hanging on his left arm, with a flick extinguished the gas and turned to go. Meisterschaft had not provided a phrase suitable for the occasion, but with the aid of gestures in which the nose was not omitted I succeeded in conveying the information that this procedure would not do at all; but the boy assured me that it was all right and would be repaired to-morrow! Needless to say it was repaired at once.

After breakfast at eleven o'clock on the following morning, the 20th, I called on Cuba's famous naturalist, Juan Gundlach, at the Instituto de 2 *a* Enseñanza, Calle Obispo, No. 8. My journal reads: "I found him at his post studying land-shells. He is, I think, about eighty years old, and his life is a finc example of the inborn enthusiasm that never dies. His collections of birds, mammals, reptiles and insects are owned by the Institute, and we went over them. Dr. Gundlach speaks very broken English and our conversation was carricd on principally in that language with a mixture of Spanish, French, Latin and German. His birds are all mounted, an adult pair, with sometimes young or immature, of each species and the collection contains a Cuban example of every species that has been recorded from the island with the exception of the Scarlet Ibis, which is represented by a Nicaraguan example. It is the result of fifty-four years' work, chiefly in the eastern end of the island." He said, "You get some birds new to Cuba? Yes, perhaps; but new Cuban birds? No!" I wonder what he would say, if he were alive to-day, to the recent discovery of three new *genera* of birds within seventy miles of Havana, through the initiative of Dr. Thomas Barbour.

It was agreed by the gentlemen to whom I presented letters of introduction that the presence of bandits on the north shore of Cuba made this side of the island undesirable ground for an unprotected American. Finally, I decided to make my base at the old city of Trinidad on the southern side of the island some sixty miles east of Cienfuegos.

Leaving Havana on the morning of the 24th by train for Batabanó I embarked there on a coasting steamer and reached Casilda, the port of Trinidad, at 3 o'clock the afternoon of the following day. The journey to Trinidad, three miles up the coastal slopes, was made in a *volante*, a two-wheeled, springless buggy-topped vehicle, rare or unknown in the Cuba of to-day. It served to emphasize the feeling that I was a long way from home, and this sensation increased when my *cochero* deposited me at the entrance to a structure which might have been a jail, where I was shown to a bare room behind bars that looked out upon the street.

Before I had learned whether I was a guest or a prisoner, the American Vice-Consul, Daniel Quayle, a native, born of English and Spanish parents, appeared and informed me in what, at the moment, seemed the most perfect English I had ever heard, that I was in the Hotel Aseo. He was one of those "friends in need" that, be it said to the credit of the race, one finds the world over.*

Thanks to his assistance, four days later I found myself established in the mountains eight miles from Trinidad at El Nacimiento del San Juan de Letran. My journal, which may be pardoned for somewhat overstating the case, reads: "I feel like a Wallace or any real exploring naturalist you may name, for if my surroundings are not strange now, they never will be. I am in a mud hut in the mountains about eight miles from Trinidad. It has two rooms, each about 15 feet square, one window (no glass), two doors, and is thatched with palm. My man of all work, Martin Lopez, a handsome young Cuban, makes up in willingness and intelligence what he lacks in English, but with my growing knowledge of Spanish we get on very well. We arrived at sunset to-night and got our supper by candlelight—tea, boiled eggs, bread and guava paste. The journey from Trinidad was a difficult one. After much trouble Mr. Quayle got two horses and a burro to carry me and my outfit. I sent Martin ahead and after two hours followed him, joining three mountaineers (charcoal burners) who were coming this way. One of my companions had three burros, two of which he drove on before him, while, seated cross-legged like a tailor, he rode the third.

"Halfway up the mountain we overtook Martin. His horse refused to go and we transferred its pack to one of the burros. Our party now numbered four men, four burros and four horses and a very Andean-like looking group we made winding up the side of the mountains or passing down into the tropical valleys. The scenery is grand beyond my powers of description. The ascent is made over outlying spurs between which and the succeeding crest are valleys watered by clear streams, with cascades and pools and ideal tropical vegetation.

"Looking back, one sees the beautiful valley of Trinidad, about three miles wide and I know not how long. It is enclosed on the south by the coast range and on the north by the mountains we are ascending. Bisected by the Trinidad River, dotted with thousands of stately royal palms, mangoes and many other tropical trees, with cane fields and white *Ingenios* and with a background of sea and mountain, it forms as grand a picture as often meets mortal eye."

Then followed two joyous weeks in which every day brought important additions to my collection and to my knowledge of a fauna almost wholly new to me. Trogons, Paroquets, Hummingbirds and Tanagers, the quaint little Todies (*Todus*), strange green Woodpeckers (*Xiphidiopicus*), great lizard-eating Cuckoos (*Saurothera*) and many other species became actual personalities in my growing list of bird acquaintances. I was at sufficient altitude to find a delightful climate. The average temperatures at 7 A.M., 2 P.M., and 9 P.M. were, respectively, 66°, 74° and 65°. Occasionally, at night, it went below 60°; 57° was the lowest, and in spite of much clothing and three blankets, I still recall how, on my canvas cot, I suffered with the cold.

After the rattlers of Texas it was a relief to be in a country where there were no venomous snakes. Without thought of danger I explored the region far and wide, discovering fresh beauties and birds new to me almost daily. One morning, my journal reads, I followed the course of "a dry, summer stream through the forest, up, up, over huge bowlders tossed about in chaotic masses, until I saw a light ahead and, strange to say, banana leaves growing here in the woods. The course of my stream led through a narrow cañon whose precipitous walls were densely grown with climbing trees, plants and vines. The way was very rough, and I had to crawl over the rocks on all fours, but when I reached the spot whence the light came, behold! here was a beautiful little garden. The walls of the cañon expanded and formed a circle 100 feet or more in diameter. The floor was perfectly smooth and covered with rich soil, and here were growing luxuriantly palms, coffee and the tallest, most perfect bananas I have seen. Some were

20 feet in height and, protected from the wind, most of the leaves were without a rent, a condition impossible in the mature leaf when exposed to the wind. Some bore bunches of fruit, green and red. I shot one stem off, the bananas rolling at my feet.

"Half expecting to see some one I looked about me for the inhabitant of this ideal retreat and found her. Placed on the swaying branch of a coffee tree was a gem of a nest and on it nestled a Hummingbird.* This was her garden and here was her home."

My only visible neighbor was Mariano Reyes, a charcoal burner, his wife Lucia and many children. I found later that it was currently believed I was a doctor and that my collections were in some way connected with my profession, as remedies. Hence, the morning after my arrival, Mariano sent one of his children to say that he was ill and would I not come to see him. When I awoke, Martin was in his hammock with a slight fever and headache for which I prescribed and, still in the rôle of doctor, armed with clinical thermometer and various drugs, I called professionally on Mariano. I found him with a temperature of 105°, apparently suffering from what was then called grippe. This disease was epidemic in the region and there were said to be 2,000 cases of it in Trinidad, a town of 10,000 people.

Having myself just recovered from an attack of this malady before leaving New York, I was familiar with current methods of treatment and administered them to Mariano and an increasing number of patients with most satisfactory results. Mariano, however, had a relapse and one night I had a hurry call to go to him. He was gasping for breath and apparently dying. Eight persons had crowded into his room, barely twice the size of his cot and lighted only by a wick flickering feebly. They retreated at the "doctor's" command and under the influx of fresh air, a series of mustard poultices, and the mental effect of treatment, Mariano recovered.

It was doubtless the first time these people had received anything like medical attention, and their gratitude for what little I could do was pathetic. Mariano brought me gifts of eggs, bananas, corn and whatever their simple fare afforded. Lucia sent me especially prepared dishes some of which I could eat and some of which I could not. Mariano, who brought them, always sat down to chat and share my enjoyment of these dainties while I performed feats of legerdemain by depositing in my pockets things that started for my mouth. As a final favor Mariano loaned me a horse and two burros and was indignant

* *Sporadinus ricordi.*

when I offered to pay for them. Cordial, kindly, hospitable people
were these mountaineers.

One morning, in a tree at the entrance to the cave of San Juan,
I discovered a pair of *hutia congas* (*Capromys pilorides*), the largest
of the three species of this peculiar West Indian mammal then known
from Cuba. In general appearance they suggest a woodchuck and
reach a size of slightly over two and a half feet, of which the tail
measures one fourth.

A nocturnal animal, passing the day hidden in the rocks, the hutia
had thus far been looked for in vain and I considered myself more
than fortunate to find this pair in a guasima tree on the nuts of which
they had been feeding. Mariano and his family also rejoiced in my
good luck for, when the demands of science had been met, the remainder of the two animals supplied them with a savory and substan-
tial meal.

Returning to Trinidad for supplies and to store my collections, I
passed a morning in the maze of caves and passages in the limestone
rock beneath that city. I was looking for bats but incidentally collected a few bones from the floor of the caverns. Would that I had
gathered more for among these fragments there was a portion of a
skull of a new species of hutia.

These creatures were the first mammals mentioned from the New
World by Columbus. Being the only edible quadruped (except the
rare solenodont) they formed an important part of the natives' fare.
On the southern shores of Cuba, in the province of Ornofai, perhaps
within sight of the hills of Trinidad, Columbus landed with his crew
and was feasted by the natives on hutias, "huties," he called them.
It seemed fitting, therefore, to associate his name with this animal and
I named my new hutia *Capromys columbianus*.

I now transferred my headquarters to the eastern end of the Trinidad Valley, distant about twenty miles. Here I lived in the ruins of a
sugar-cane mill on what had once been the prosperous estate of San
Pablo. But Spanish misrule and the futile revolt against it, high taxa-
tion with absolutely no compensating returns, and the comparatively
low price of sugar incident to the development of the beet-sugar industry had brought financial disaster to the once thriving Trinidad
Valley. A planter, with whom I was trying to converse with the aid of a
dictionary, pointed to the word *remolacha* (beet) and drew his finger
across his throat.

But the fallow lands grown to guava scrub and forests bordering the streams flowing toward the Caribbean made fertile fields for me and I added many species of birds to my collection. Jaçanas, Limpkins, Caracaras, Quail-doves, White-headed Parrots, Cuban Crows, Honeycreepers were all new and striking forms to me and my journal abounds in observations concerning them.

A favorite collecting place was a large cupey tree, on the fruit of which many kinds of birds were feeding. My journal of March 18th reads: "It is a beautiful place at the edge of the forest, tall palms and other trees surround it, and a palm-bordered brook flows below. The air was filled with the calls of birds and there was a constant rustling and fluttering as they entered and flitted about the tree. The strange squawk of the Crows, the squeak of passing Paroquets, the grating note of Parrots, the odd whistles and hissing of Blackbirds, the chattering of Pitanga Flycatchers, the roll of Trogons all combined to make the scene appear truly tropical." Then followed a list of eighteen species seen or heard within a period of ten minutes.

This is a limestone country and in the hills are many caves, the homes of countless bats. I describe a "room" in one of these caves as "dark and about 75 feet in diameter with the roof 20 feet above. . . . The moment we entered there was a rush of wings like the wind through distant trees and we could catch glimpses of many forms, while from the openings poured a steady stream of bats. Bringing dead palm branches, we made torches of them and in their light I saw a wonderful sight. The roof of the cave, in places, was literally black with solid masses of bats while the air was filled with a storm of them. Not one but many thousands of bats were here; their number was incalculable." This was but one of many similar caves from which I soon secured all the specimens needed. All were of one species, *Artibeus perspicillatus,* and over half the females contained a single embryo each.

I had been at San Pablo only a few days when I discovered that my fame as a "physician" had preceded me. Patients with wounds from the last revolution or current encounters with machetes, and disorders beyond my power in diagnosis applied for treatment and were pathetically grateful for any attention I gave them. "A man to whom I gave a little vaseline," I wrote, "now brings me milk each morning, and his small son brought in a large piece of sugar cane. Another brings bananas, and a coolie always shares his catch of fish from the river. They all come into my room to see me work and take the liveliest interest in everything. 'Muchos pájaros' is my standing reply to their remarks, while Martin appears with the dignity befitting a naturalist's assistant."

It was my friendly relations with these people which doubtless lessened my surprise when, as I came in after dark one evening and cautiously picked my way over bits of broken machinery and other parts of the wrecked mill, a lantern was suddenly flashed, and I found myself face to face with a half-naked man armed with a machete. To my relief he explained that he was waiting for a *maja* (boa constrictor) that had been eating his chickens.

As an indication of an already existing interest in the problems of altitudinal distribution, later to form so important a part of my work, my journal at San Pablo compares its bird-life with that of San Juan, the preceding camp, and adds: "But these differences are due to purely local conditions, and I cannot see that altitude plays any part in the distribution of birds here. On the summits of the mountains the growth is scattered scrub palms, and of course few birds occur there, but this is a question of earth and water and not of altitude and temperature."

From San Pablo I went to a post of the Guardia Civil on the road between Trinidad and Cienfuegos. It was manned by three soldiers under command of Sargento Prats. All, of course, were Spaniards, for at this period no Cuban was permitted to have part in his own government.

It was Sargento Prats's ambition to attend the World's Fair to be held the following year in Chicago and, with a hope that he might acquire from "El Americano" enough English for the journey, he had invited me to be his guest. "To study," therefore, was the order of each evening, and when our books were laid aside the Sergeant doubly rewarded his teacher by playing tuneful Spanish melodies on his flute.

My object in going to Guanayara was to find shore and water birds on the nearby coast, but the waves of the Caribbean broke on a wall of limestone. There was neither beach nor marsh and after a short stay I moved to an American schooner which was anchored in the bay of Casilda while loading sugar from lighters.

The bay was surrounded by vast areas of mangroves, the home of a Clapper Rail of which I, knowing its pronounced tendency to vary in color with locality, was exceedingly anxious to secure specimens. Always elusive, in these great mangrove forests, this Rail was "but a wandering voice." To flush it was impossible and I had no traps. But luck was with me. Landing one Thursday morning at the little town of Casilda, I found that a combination of high tide and high wind had driven the Clapper Rails out of the neighboring mangroves on to the dryer ground at the edge of the town. I had just retrieved my third specimen when I saw a Civil Guard coming toward me. Armed with a rifle, girthed with a belt full of cartridges, he presented a formidable and martial aspect. As I stepped from the schooner's boat at the pier I had heard a ragged bystander say, "I should like to have a photograph of him." A covering of mud to the knees had not improved my appearance which, compared with that of the neatly uniformed soldier, was not designed to create a favorable impression. Nevertheless, hastily shoving my specimens into the pocket of my shooting coat, I advanced to present to him the official *cédula* that authorized me to carry a gun. Of the fact that it did not give me permission to fire it he made no mention, but, as he returned the document to me he said, "This, Señor, says nothing about shooting on Holy Thursday." I had broken, then, not a law of the state but of the church. My confession of ignorance and promise not to offend again were evidently so genuine that I was released with a reprimand, and with the Rails still in my possession I returned to the schooner. As I had hoped, they proved to be a new race which I described as *Rallus longirostris cubanus*. Three days later, as the straw effigy of Judas Iscariot was burning, and the town was rejoicing in the freedom of an Easter morning, I sailed from Casilda on the first stage of my journey home.

HOME-THOUGHTS, FROM ABROAD

I

Oh, to be in England
Now that April's there,
And whoever wakes in England
Sees, some morning, unaware,
That the lowest boughs and the brushwood sheaf
Round the elm-tree bole are in tiny leaf,
While the chaffinch sings on the orchard bough
In England—now!

II

And after April, when May follows,
And the whitethroat builds, and all the swallows!
Hark, where my blossomed pear-tree in the hedge
Leans to the field and scatters on the clover
Blossoms and dewdrops—at the bent spray's edge—
That's the wise thrush; he sings each song twice over,
Lest you should think he never could recapture
The first fine careless rapture!
And though the fields look rough with hoary dew,
All will be gay when noontide wakes anew
The buttercups, the little children's dower
—Far brighter than this gaudy melon-flower!

ROBERT BROWNING

THE HEADLONG WAVE

by Henry Beston

Henry Beston was born in Quincy, Massachusetts, June 1, 1888. Perhaps it was the pent-up feeling he must have experienced in the submarine division of the United States Navy in World War I that has made him shun crowded ways ever since. After the war he retreated to Cape Cod and spent some time there writing The Outermost House, *from which the offering below is taken. Possibly because even Cape Cod was becoming too crowded for him, he abandoned that area and moved up to the Maine coast, keeping out of sight as much as possible and enjoying the lonelier places as much as ever. He was on the staff of the* Atlantic Monthly *but gave that up to concentrate on books. In the series of books on the rivers of North America he wrote* The St. Lawrence, *and his* Northern Farm *is one of the fruits of his residence in Maine.*

THIS morning I am going to try my hand at something that I do not recall ever having encountered either in a periodical or in a book, namely, a chapter on the ways, the forms, and the sounds of ocean near a beach. Friends are forever asking me about the surf on the great beach and if I am not sometimes troubled or haunted by its sound. To this I reply that I have grown unconscious of the roar, and though it sounds all day long in my waking ears, and all night long in my sleeping ones, my ears seldom send on the long tumult to the mind. I hear the roar the instant I wake in the morning and return to consciousness, I listen to it a while consciously, and then accept and forget it; I hear it during the day only when I stop again to listen, or when some change in the nature of the sound breaks through my acceptance of it to my curiosity.

They say here that great waves reach this coast in threes. Three great waves, then an indeterminate run of lesser rhythms, then three great waves again. On Celtic coasts it is the seventh wave that is seen coming like a king out of the grey, cold sea. The Cape tradition, however, is no half-real, half-mystical fancy, but the truth itself. Great waves do indeed approach this beach by threes. Again and again have I watched three giants roll in one after the other out of the Atlantic, cross the outer bar, break, form again, and follow each other in to fulfilment and destruction on this solitary beach. Coast guard crews are all well aware of this triple rhythm and take advantage of the lull that follows the last wave to launch their boats.

It is true that there are single giants as well. I have been roused by them in the night. Waked by their tremendous and unexpected crash, I have sometimes heard the last of the heavy overspill, sometimes only the loud, withdrawing roar. After the roar came a briefest pause, and after the pause the return of ocean to the night's long cadences. Such solitary titans, flinging their green tons down upon a quiet world, shake beach and dune. Late one September night, as I sat reading, the very father of all waves must have flung himself down before the house, for the quiet of the night was suddenly overturned by a gigantic, tumbling crash and an earthquake rumbling; the beach trembled beneath the avalanche, the dune shook, and my house so shook in its dune that the flame of a lamp quivered and pictures jarred on the wall.

The three great elemental sounds in nature are the sound of rain, the sound of wind in a primeval wood, and the sound of outer ocean on a beach. I have heard them all, and of the three elemental voices, that of ocean is the most awesome, beautiful, and varied. For it is a mistake to talk of the monotone of ocean or of the monotonous nature of its sound. The sea has many voices. Listen to the surf, really lend it your ears, and you will hear in it a world of sounds: hollow boomings and heavy roarings, great watery tumblings and tramplings, long hissing seethes, sharp, rifle-shot reports, splashes, whispers, the grinding undertone of stones, and sometimes vocal sounds that might be the half-heard talk of people of the sea. And not only is the great sound varied in the manner of its making, it is also constantly changing its tempo, its pitch, its accent, and its rhythm, being now loud and thundering, now almost placid, now furious, now grave and solemn-slow, now a simple measure, now a rhythm monstrous with a sense of purpose and elemental will.

Every mood of the wind, every change in the day's weather, every phase of the tide—all these have subtle sea musics all their own. Surf of the ebb, for instance, is one music, surf of the flood another, the change in the two musics being most clearly marked during the first hour of a rising tide. With the renewal of the tidal energy, the sound of the surf grows louder, the fury of battle returns to it as it turns again on the land, and beat and sound change with the renewal of the war.

Sound of surf in these autumnal dunes—the continuousness of it, sound of endless charging, endless incoming and gathering, endless fulfilment and dissolution, endless fecundity, and endless death. I have been trying to study out the mechanics of that mighty resonance. The dominant note is the great spilling crash made by each arriving wave. It may be hollow and booming, it may be heavy and churning, it may be a tumbling roar. The second fundamental sound is the wild seething cataract roar of the wave's dissolution and the rush of its foaming waters up the beach—this second sound *diminuendo*. The third fundamental sound is the endless dissolving hiss of the inmost slides of foam. The first two sounds reach the ear as a unisonance— the booming impact of the tons of water and the wild roar of the up- rush blending—and this mingled sound dissolves into the foam-bubble hissing of the third. Above the tumult, like birds, fly wisps of watery noise, splashes and counter splashes, whispers, seethings, slaps, and chucklings. An overtone sound of other breakers, mingled with a gen- eral rumbling, fills earth and sea and air.

Here do I pause to warn my reader that although I have recounted the history of a breaker—an ideal breaker—the surf process must be understood as mingled and continuous, waves hurrying after waves, interrupting waves, washing back on waves, overwhelming waves. Moreover, I have described the sound of a high surf in fair weather. A storm surf is mechanically the same thing, but it *grinds*, and this same long, sepulchral grinding—sound of utter terror to all mariners— is a development of the second fundamental sound; it is the cry of the breaker water roaring its way ashore and dragging at the sand. A strange underbody of sound when heard through the high, wild screaming of a gale.

Breaking waves that have to run up a steep tilt of the beach are often followed by a dragging, grinding sound—the note of the baffled water running downhill again to the sea. It is loudest when the tide is low and breakers are rolling beach stones up and down a slope of the lower beach.

I am, perhaps, most conscious of the sound of surf just after I have gone to bed. Even here I read myself to drowsiness, and, reading, I hear the cadenced trampling roar filling all the dark. So close is the Fo'castle to the ocean's edge that the rhythm of sound I hear oftenest in fair weather is not so much a general tumult as an endless arrival, overspill, and dissolution of separate great seas. Through the dark, mathematic square of the screened half window, I listen to the rushes and the bursts, the tramplings, and the long, intermingled thunderings, never wearying of the sonorous and universal sound.

Away from the beach, the various sounds of the surf melt into one great thundering symphonic roar. Autumnal nights in Eastham village are full of this ocean sound. The "summer people" have gone, the village rests and prepares for winter, lamps shine from kitchen windows, and from across the moors, the great levels of the marsh, and the bulwark of the dunes resounds the long wintry roaring of the sea. Listen to it a while, and it will seem but one remote and formidable sound; listen still longer and you will discern in it a symphony of breaker thunderings, an endless, distant, elemental cannonade. There is beauty in it, and ancient terror. I heard it last as I walked through the village on a starry October night; there was no wind, the leafless trees were still, all the village was abed, and the whole sombre world was awesome with the sound.

II

The seas are the heart's blood of the earth. Plucked up and kneaded by the sun and the moon, the tides are systole and diastole of earth's veins.

The rhythm of waves beats in the sea like a pulse in living flesh. It is pure force, forever embodying itself in a succession of watery shapes which vanish on its passing.

I stand on my dune top watching a great wave coursing in from sea, and know that I am watching an illusion, that the distant water has not left its place in ocean to advance upon me, but only a force shaped in water, a bodiless pulse beat, a vibration.

Consider the marvel of what we see. Somewhere in ocean, perhaps a thousand miles and more from this beach, the pulse beat of earth liberates a vibration, an ocean wave. Is the original force circular, I wonder, and do ocean waves ring out from the creative beat as they do on a quiet surface broken by a stone? Are there, perhaps, ocean circles so great and so intricate that they are unperceived? Once created, the wave or the arc of a wave begins its journey through the sea. Countless vibrations precede it, countless vibrations follow after. It approaches the continent, swings into the coast line, courses ashore, breaks, dissolves, is gone. The innermost waters it last inhabited flow back in marbly foam to become a body to another beat, and to be again flung down. So it goes night and day, and will go till the secret heart of earth strikes out its last slow beat and the last wave dissolves upon the last forsaken shore.

As I stand on my dune top, however, I do not think of the illusion and the beat of earth, for I watch the waves with my outer rather than my inner eye. After all, the illusion is set off by an extraordinary, an almost miraculous thing—the embodiment of the wave beat in an almost constant shape. We see a wave a quarter of a mile off, then a few hundred yards nearer in, then just offshore; we seem to have been watching the same travelling mass of water—there has been no appreciable change in mass or in shape—yet all the while the original beat has taken on a flowing series of liquid bodies, bodies so alike, so much the same, that our eye will individualize them and follow them in—the third wave, we say, or the second wave behind the great wave. How strange it is that this beat of earth, this mysterious undulation of the seas, moving through and among the other forces stirring the waters close off the continent, should thus keep its constancy of form and mass, and how odd a blend of illusion and reality it all is! On the whole, the outer eye has the best of it.

Blowing all day long, a northwest wind yesterday swept the sky clear of every tatter and wisp of cloud. Clear it still is, though the wind has shifted to the east. The sky this afternoon is a harmony of universal blue, bordered with a surf rim of snowiest blue-white. Far out at sea, in the northeast and near the horizon, is a pool of the loveliest blue I have ever seen here—a light blue, a petal blue, blue of the emperor's gown in a Chinese fairy tale. If you would see waves at their best, come on such a day, when the ocean reflects a lovely sky, and the wind is light and onshore; plan to arrive in the afternoon so that you will have the sun facing the breakers. Come early, for the glints on the waves are most beautiful and interesting when the light is oblique and high. And come with a rising tide.

The surf is high, and on the far side of it, a wave greater than its fellows is shouldering out of the blue, glinting immensity of sea.

Friends tell me that there are certain tropic beaches where waves miles long break all at once in one cannonading crash: a little of this, I imagine, would be magnificent; a constancy of it, unbearable. The surf here is broken; it approaches the beach in long intercurrent parallels, some a few hundred feet long, some an eighth of a mile long, some, and the longest, attaining the quarter-mile length and perhaps just over. Thus, at all times and instants of the day, along the five miles of beach visible from the Fo'castle deck, waves are to be seen breaking, coursing in to break, seething up and sliding back.

But to return to the blue wave rolling in out of the blue spaciousness of sea. On the other side of the world, just opposite the Cape, lies the ancient Spanish province of Galicia, and the town of Pontevedra and St. James Compostella, renowned of pilgrims. (When I was there they offered me a silver cockle shell, but I would have none of it, and got myself a sea shell from some Galician fisherfolk.) Somewhere between this Spanish land and Cape Cod the pulse of earth has engendered this wave and sent it coursing westward through the seas. Far off the coast, the spray of its passing has, perhaps, risen on the windward bow of some rusty freighter and fallen in rainbow drops upon her plates; the great liners have felt it course beneath their keels.

A continent rises in the west, and the pulse beat approaches this bulwark of Cape Cod. Two-thirds of a mile out, the wave is still a sea vibration, a billow. Slice it across, and its outline will be that of a slightly flattened semicircle; the pulse is shaped in a long, advancing mound. I watch it approach the beach. Closer and closer in, it is rising with the rise of the beach and the shoaling of the water; closer still, it is changing from a mound to a pyramid, a pyramid which swiftly distorts, the seaward side lengthening, the landward side incurving— the wave is now a breaker. Along the ridge of blue forms a rippling crest of clear, bright water; a little spray flies off. Under the racing foam churned up by the dissolution of other breakers the beach now catches at the last shape of sea inhabited by the pulse—the wave is *tripped* by the shoaling sand—the giant stumbles, crashes, and is pushed over and ahead by the sloping line of force behind. The fall of a breaker is never the work of gravity alone.

It is the last line of the wave that has captured the decorative imagination of the world—the long seaward slope, the curling crest, the incurved volute ahead.

Toppling over and hurled ahead, the wave crashes, its mass of glinting blue falling down in a confusion of seething, splendid white, the tumbling water rebounding from the sand to a height almost always a little above that of the original crest. Out of the wild, crumbling confusion born of the dissolution of the force and the last great shape, foamy fountains spurt, and ringlets of spray. The mass of water, still all furiously a-churn and seething white, now rushes for the rim of the beach as it might for an inconceivable cataract. Within thirty-five feet the water shoals from two feet to dry land. The edge of the rush thins, and the last impulse disappears in inch-deep slides of foam which reflect the sky in one last moment of energy and beauty and then vanish all at once into the sands.

Another thundering, and the water that has escaped and withdrawn is gathered up and swept forward again by another breaking wave. Night and day, age after age, so works the sea, with infinite variation obeying an unalterable rhythm moving through an intricacy of chance and law.

I can watch a fine surf for hours, taking pleasure in all its wild plays and variations. I like to stand on my beach, watching a long wave start breaking in many places, and see the curling water run north and south from the several beginnings, and collide in furious white pyramids built of the opposing energies. Splendid fountains often delight the eye. A towering and deep-bellied wave, toppling, encloses in its volute a quantity of air, and a few seconds after the spill this prisoned and compressed vapour bursts up through the boiling rush in feathery, foamy jets and geyser plumes. I have seen fountains here, on a September day, twenty and twenty-five and even thirty feet high. Sometimes a curious thing happens. Instead of escaping vertically, the rolled-up air escapes horizontally, and the breaker suddenly blows, as from a dragon's mouth, a great lateral puff of steamy spray. On sunny days, the toppling crest is often mirrored in the glassy volute as the wave is breaking. One lovely autumn afternoon, I saw a beautiful white gull sailing along the volute of a breaker accompanied by his reflection in the wave.

I add one curious effect of the wind. When the wind is directly offshore or well offshore, the waves approach fighting it; when the wind is offshore but so little off that its angle with the coast line is oblique—say an angle never greater than twenty-two degrees and never less than about twelve—the waves that approach the coast do not give battle, but run in with their long axis parallel to the wind. Sitting in the Fo'castle, I can often tell the exact quarter of an offshore wind simply by looking at this oblique alignment of the waves.

The long miles of beach are never more beautiful than when waves are rolling in fighting a strong breeze. Then do the breakers actually seem to charge the coast. As they approach, the wind meets them in a shock of war, the chargers rear but go on, and the wind blows back their manes. North and south, I watch them coursing in, the manes of white, sun-brilliant spray streaming behind them for thirty and even forty feet. Sea horses do men call such waves on every coast of the world. If you would see them at their best, come to this beach on a bright October day when a northwest wind is billowing off to sea across the moors.

III

I will close my chapter with a few paragraphs about heavy surf.

It is best to be seen, I think, when the wind is not too high. A gale blows up a surf, but it also flattens out the incoming rollers, making monstrous, foamy travelling mounds of them much like those visible from a ship at sea. Not until the wind has dropped do the breakers gather form. The finest surf I have ever seen here—it was a Northern recoil of the great Florida hurricane—broke on three pleasant and almost windless autumn days. The storm itself had passed us, but our seas had been stirred to their deeps. Returning to the Cape at night from a trip to town, I heard the roar of the ocean in Orleans, and on arriving at Nauset, found the beach flooded to the dunes, and covered with a churn of surf and moonlight. Dragging a heavy suitcase and clad in my go-to-town clothes, I had an evil time getting to the Fo'castle over the dune tops and along the flooded marsh.

Many forces mingle in the surf of a storm—the great earth rhythm of the waves, the violence of wind, the struggle of water to obey its own elemental law. Out of the storm at sea come the giants and, being giants, trip far out, spilling first on the outer bar. Shoreward then they rush, breaking all the way. Touching the beach, they tumble in a roar lost in a general noise of storm. Trampled by the wind and everlastingly moved and lifted up and flung down by the incoming seas, the water offshore becomes a furious glassiness of marbly foam; wild, rushing sheets of seethe fifty feet wide border it; the water streams with sand.

Under all this move furious tidal currents, the longshore undertow of outer Cape Cod. Shore currents here move in a southerly direction; old wreckage and driftwood is forever being carried down here from the north. Coast guard friends often look at a box or stick I have retrieved, and say, "Saw that two weeks ago up by the light."

After an easterly, I find things on the beach which have been blown down from the Gulf of Maine—young, uprooted spruce trees, lobster buoys from Matinicus, and, after one storm, a great strewing of empty sea-urchin shells. Another easterly washed up a strewing of curious wooden pebbles shaped by the sea out of the ancient submerged forests which lie just off the present coast. They were brown-black, shaped like beach stones, and as smooth as such stones.

The last creature I found in the surf was a huge horseshoe crab, the only one I have ever chanced to find on the outside. Poor *Limulus polyphemus!* The surf having turned him upside down, he had as usual doubled up, and the surf had then filled with sand the angle of his doubling. When I discovered him, he was being bullied by a foam slide, and altogether in a desperate way. So I picked him up, rinsed the sand out of his waving gills, held him up all dripping by the tail, and flung him as far as I could to seaward of the breakers. A tiny splash, and I had seen the last of him, a moment more, and the surf had filled the hollow in which he had lain.

Autumnal easterlies and November tides having scoured from the beach its summer deeps of sand, the high seasonal tides now run clear across to the very foot of the dunes. Under this daily overflow of cold, the last of the tide-rim hoppers and foragers vanish from the beach. An icy wind blusters; I heard a dry tinkle of sand against my western wall; December nears, and winter closes in upon the coast.

THE GUANAY
"The Most Valuable Bird in the World"

by Robert Cushman Murphy

One of the great ornithologists of the world, Dr. Robert Cushman Murphy is also one of the best writers on that subject. He is a linguist and classical scholar as well as a distinguished scientist. Everything that he writes turns out to be delightful literature in the guise of accurate ornithology—or perhaps it should be put the other way around. His Oceanic Birds of South America, *in two hefty volumes, is the standard work on the subject and at the same time a treasure house of adventure stories, "of moving accidents by flood and field, of hairbreadth 'scapes i' the imminent deadly breach." His* Logbook for Grace *is a touching human document as well as a vivid account of a two-year whaling expedition to South Georgia.*

Born in Brooklyn, New York, April 29, 1887, Robert Cushman Murphy was graduated from Brown University in 1911 and immediately took up science as a career, going directly from the campus at Providence, Rhode Island, to the deck of the ship that was to take him to the little island of South Georgia in the South Atlantic. Eventually he became the head of the Department of Birds of the American Museum of Natural History, an authority on the birds of many lands and all the oceans of the world. He has lived in South America. He was twice to New Zealand. He has visited Europe many times. He is tall and handsome and a delightful lecturer, always salting his wisdom with wit. He has indeed "all the good gifts of Nature," and, in addition, an honorary degree from the oldest university in the western hemisphere, the University of San Marcos in Lima, Peru. This chapter on the guanay is from his Bird Islands of Peru.

PICTURE to yourself the shining, rainless coast of Peru, washed by ocean waters to which storms are unknown, where the swells surge northward, from month to month and year to year, before winds that blow regularly from a southerly quarter. On such an ocean dark flocks of guanayes form rafts which can be spied miles away. Slowly the dense masses of birds press along the sea, gobbling up fish in their path, the hinder margins of the rafts continually rising into the air and pouring over the van in some such manner as the great flocks of passenger pigeons are said to have once rolled through open North American forests in which oak or beech mast lay thick upon the leafy floor.

At other times, when the guanayes are moving toward distant feeding grounds, they travel not in broad flocks but rather as a solid river of birds, which streams in a sharply-marked, unbroken column, close above the waves, until an amazed observer is actually wearied as a single formation takes four or five hours to pass a given point.

Equally impressive are the homeward flights of these cormorants, after a day of gorging upon anchovies, when in late afternoon slender ribbons, wedges, and whiplashes of guanayes in single file twist and flutter, high in air, toward the rounded plateaus of white islands which gradually turn black as the packed areas of birds swell out from clustered nuclei toward the borders of the available standing room.

Whence came this astounding sea bird, which has made the Peruvian coast its own?

In the northward extension of this representative of an antarctic group to a point within six degrees of the equator, we recognize one of the profound effects of the Humboldt Current. The cool stream, lying between a tropical continent on the one hand and the heated surface waters of the open South Pacific on the other, forms, as it were, a tongue of littoral ocean in which the environment, and consequently the marine flora and fauna, is such as ordinarily holds for the subantarctic zone rather than for equatorial or even temperate seas.

Given, therefore, a belt of cool ocean waters replete with small organisms of more or less polar type, together with nesting sites upon islands which for climatic reasons could never become encumbered with vegetation, and the geographic stage was set for the northward emigration of the ancestors of the guanay. Furthermore, because of the normal superabundance of food, conditions seem to have been prearranged for the increase of the birds to numbers limited only by competition with other animals and by the amount of safe, insular space for reproduction. Although suitable islets are very numerous, the enormous food supply in the Humboldt Current is still out of all proportion to the area of the breeding places. This doubtless explains the excessively colonial nesting habit of the guanay, in which it surpasses all other birds, even the penguins, for in the middle of a bounteous sea there would be a constant tendency for the cormorant population to become more and more congested upon the islets. The doctrine of Malthus applies to birds as well as to men.

The guanay, unlike any other cormorant, "hawks" its food, that is, it hunts exclusively by sight and from the air, locating the fishes which it seeks before descending to the water to catch them. Most cormorants search for their prey individually, swimming alone or in loose groups at the surface, then plunging in what seem to be favorable places and conducting the hunt as well as the capture while they are submerged. For the most part, moreover, they subsist upon bottom-living species of fish, often diving down many fathoms in pursuit of single victims. But the guanay feeds altogether upon surface-swimming fishes, such as anchovies, young herrings, and the toothsome silversides which the Peruvians call *pejerreyes* ("kingfish"). Such forms travel in tremendous schools which are assailed en masse by proportionately large flocks of birds.

The correlation between the numbers of the fishes and the extreme gregariousness of the cormorants results among the latter in a system of efficient cooperation which almost suggests certain customs of ants or other social insects. The vast flocks of guanayes which spend their nights upon the islands do not start hunting in a body when morning breaks. On the contrary, the birds first sally forth only in small scouting parties, which can be seen flying erratically above the ocean, usually keeping well in air, and frequently "back pedalling" or hovering when they see the silvery glint of schooling fish or the ruffled appearance of the sea which indicates the presence of fish below. The dropping of the scouts to the surface, and the shallow dives which mark the beginning of an orgy, are the signals that cause the approach of such rivers of birds as have been described above. The cohort of guanayes then spreads out as a great fan over the unfortunate anchovies, which are likely to be no less harried from beneath by bonitos and sea-lions. Small wonder that the Peruvian fishermen, who are familiar with such sights, believe that the guanayes and the seals have a working understanding! However this may be, the gorging proceeds until both sea-lions and birds must cease long enough to allow their rapid digestions to fit them for another meal. From the crop and gullet of a dead guanay the remains of no less than seventy-six anchovies, four or five inches in length, have been taken.

Sometimes the guanayes pursue the fishes to the very beaches, so that a rare view of a one-sided fray may be enjoyed by a landsman. One morning during my sojourn at Independencia Bay shoals of silversides were packed in deep, glittering ranks close to the quiet shore, when a raft of guanayes, accompanied by a few pelicans and a horde of screaming gulls, drove the fishes before them against the shelving sand. Soon the water gleamed like flashing quicksilver, and in wild rioting the birds jammed and crowded each other until hundreds of them were pushed clear beyond the tideline by the scrambling mob behind.

The guanay stands and walks erect, somewhat after the manner of a penguin. Its height is in the neighborhood of twenty inches and the weight of a full-grown bird about four and a half pounds. It has a glossy green and blue-black neck and back, a white throat-patch which is a conspicuous mark in flight, a white under surface, and pinkish feet. During the courtship season a crest of plumes develops at the back of the head. The guanay's iris is brown, but an area of green, naked skin surrounding the orbit makes it look at close range like a veritable personification of envy. A second ring of turgid red skin, outside the staring "green eye," heightens its extraordinary expression.

Since the fame of the guanay proceeds chiefly from sheer numbers, it is not unnatural that observers have made extremely high estimates or guesses concerning the population of its colonies. The birds breed upon the plateaus and windward hillsides of the Peruvian islands in concentrated communities, the nests averaging three to each square yard of ground. Dr. Coker's measurements show that not fewer than a million adult birds dwelt within the limits of a single homogeneous colony on South Chincha Island during one of his visits. Another naturalist has written that these cormorants "congregate to the number of ten millions."

The breeding season, like that of many tropical ocean birds, is practically continuous, but it reaches a climax during the southern summer months of December and January. Individual pairs of guanayes are believed commonly to rear two broods during a single year. The flight of the last families of the young of one season, in May or June, is at any rate followed hard by the courting and love-making of adults in preparation for the breeding season of the second spring.

At South Chincha Island in mid-October the breeding grounds were covered with just one year's accumulation of sun-baked guano, and the cormorants were getting ready to nest again. They stood in compact bodies, each comprising thousands of birds, on the flat top of the island, and, when a human being approached, all those on the nearer side began to stir—not *en bloc*, nor yet individually but in groups of a few hundred, each of which for the time constituted a unit. One group would move rapidly away, the birds carrying themselves bolt upright. Another group would advance toward the observer, so that this section of the army would gleam with white breasts instead of shiny, dark backs. Still another unit would rush to the right or to the left, so that both the dark backs and the white breasts showed at once, and the long bills and red nasal warts became conspicuous. Such closely huddled companies soon collided with others moving in different directions, producing much confusion about the margins. A few of the birds showed no fear at all, stolidly permitting a man to approach within a few feet. The greater proportion, however, frantically took to flight, rushing helter-skelter down the slope, and raising a cloud of dust with their whistling wings. The air became bewilderingly thick with birds as they circled overhead, but within a few moments the number returning to earth once more exceeded the number taking wing.

When an observer makes his way slowly and very quietly into the heart of a colony in which nesting has definitely begun, the guanayes gradually retreat, and one may sit down in a clear circle which is at first fifty or more feet in diameter. But almost imperceptibly the birds will edge in again, until the bare circle narrows to but three or four paces. From such a point of view it seems as though the ground were covered with as many pairs of sprawling webbed feet as there is room for, and yet new arrivals plump down by scores or hundreds every minute. Over the ocean, moreover, to the north, south, east, and west, one may commonly see endless black files still pouring in toward the island. The hum of wings is like the effect of an overdose of quinine upon the ears, and the combined voices seem like mutterings of the twelve tribes of Israel. It reminds me of all sorts of strange, oppressive roarings, such as the noise of railroad trains in river tunnels. The near-by voices, which can be distinguished individually, are merely sonorous bass grunts and screepy calls. It is the multiplication of such

sounds by numbers almost too large to imagine that makes the outlandish and never-to-be-forgotten babel.

Toward evening of such October days, most of the guanayes would
be courting, after strenuous hours at sea during which all their energies had doubtless been devoted to winning the sustenance of life.
Privacy does not enter into their notion of fitness, and while six or
seven birds occupy each square yard of ground, the love-making antics
are often in full progress. These are in general not unlike the courtship habits of the closely related antarctic cormorants. Two guanayes
stand side by side, or breast to breast, and ludicrously wave their heads
back and forth or gently caress each other's necks. The crests upon
their crowns are frequently erected, and the feathers of the nape puff
out so that the velvety necks appear twice their normal thickness.
Cheeks and chin-pouches continually tremble, and chattering bills are
held wide open. Now and again one will bend its body forward and
at the same time extend the head upside down along the spine and
toward the tail, holding their curious, paralyzed attitude for several
seconds. Sometimes the birds of a pair snap so much at one another
that it is hard to judge whether they are making love or quarreling.

Indubitable quarrels between birds of different pairs also go on
without cessation, and occasionally many join together in a mêlée.
Every now and then, for example, some unfortunate guanay, which
seems to be the butt of all bystanders, will go dashing through the
throng, holding its head as high as possible in order to avoid the jabs
and bites which all others direct at it. If the victim would but stop
fleeing, perhaps the blows would cease, but it keeps more and more
desperately running the gantlet, flapping its wings, bumping into innumerable neighbors, until eventually it bursts from the vicious crowd
into a clear space, shakes itself with an abused air, and opens and shuts
its mouth many times with an expression of having just swallowed an
unpleasant dose.

In the early stages of courtship it often happens that several cocks
select the same female for their addresses. In one instance, five as-
siduous suitors, all with necks expanded, were observed bowing around
a single hen which crouched in their midst. But by no means all the
birds are engaged in love-making at every moment, for they spend
much time preening their feathers, frequently raising the coverts of
the tail and thrusting the bill toward the oil gland. Then, after combing their heads and necks thoroughly with their claws—a real feat in
balancing—they promenade in small troupes along the outer edge of
the colony.

Visible actions, rather than unusual sounds, alarm the courting birds. A quick motion of the hand will start sudden pandemonium. Even when an observer rises to leave them as slowly, silently, and unostentatiously as possible, a small panic inevitably results, many of the near birds beginning to scamper about or to take flight. On the other hand, the firing of a gun straight into the air produces scarcely a stir provided the weapon is not brandished. The effect of human conversation is, however, most amusing. Whenever a man, sitting perfectly still, begins to talk to the guanayes in a loud voice, a silence falls over all the audience within hearing. Their mumbles and grunts die away, and they listen for a while as if in amazement.

During the course of a few hours' resting on any island, the birds get much befouled with fresh guano, which hardens upon their plumage. They periodically rid themselves of this by flying some distance off the lee side of the island where they plunge and violently beat the water with their wings. Sometimes most of the inhabitants of a colony will make their toilet in this way at one time, producing a thunderous roar which can be heard from afar. It is often audible during morning fogs, when the flocks are invisible, and as a boat draws near such a gathering it is easy to mistake the sound for the dreaded crashing of waves upon unseen rocky shores.

The grandest sight of the day, when the homeward flight is at its maximum, usually comes during the hour before sunset. From some point far away the birds make a bee line for the center of their island, but, as they near their destination, they invariably skirt the shores so as to come down across the wind. The instinct of following a leader is evidently strong; if, for any reason, a file is broken, and the rear birds turn toward the left coast instead of the right, those behind will obey the signal and all swing into the new course. Close over gulches and ridges of their home island the oncoming streams of birds flow, the separate "rivulets" cutting across each other like the blades of scissors. At the same time these files also rise and fall in beautiful undulations which can best be seen from the crest of a hill above them. Sometimes three or more such lines will flow along for a while ten or fifteen yards apart, but sooner or later one of them will make leeway until two files interweave. Then the soft, humming swish of wings is interjected with sharp clicks as the quills of two guanayes strike together in air. When one beholds the endless mingling, the crossing and recrossing and tangling of the lines, it seems incredible that more birds do not clash.

THE GLORY HOLE

by Thomas Barbour

To those who love Nature, a good natural history museum is an enchanted palace full of the most fascinating sights. What the great art galleries of the world are to art lovers, the natural history museums are to the Nature lovers. There never was a good museum that didn't have a good story of its own; who started it, how it grew, who staffed it, what it holds, and who goes next to some distant part of the world to bring back either something new or something long wanted to round out a collection.

Thomas Barbour, a huge, genial man, born to wealth, endowed with a love of learning and a special enthusiasm for natural history, was eminently fitted to write about museums. He had visited museums around the world. He had contributed generously to many in funds and collected material. He was closely associated with three in Boston, Cambridge, and Salem, and for many years was Director of the Agassiz Museum at Harvard. Thomas Barbour could and did write of his many field trips to all parts of the world, and of the plant experiments he supported in Florida and elsewhere, but museums need somebody to speak and write for them, and nobody could be better qualified than the author of the following selection taken from his Naturalist at Large, published in 1943.

THE man in the street has always been inclined to look down his nose at museum curators, and for as long as I have been one of them I have been pondering the reason. I think I have it. The average man doesn't like a miser and, one way or another, the curator cannot help appearing miserly. When I first took charge of the Agassiz Museum, I found one big glass jar filled with chicken heads, another with burned matches, another with old rubbers. The chicken heads were potential material for dissection, and the fact that a dollar's worth of heads filled a twenty-dollar jar never occurred to the man who ate those chickens, who was no other than Louis Agassiz himself.

The Museum at one time housed an unbelievable number of strange odds and ends accumulated through the years and saved because the old-time museum man thought it was a sin to throw anything out. I have been accused of erring in this manner myself. It is true that if you look at a thing long enough you lose perspective. Any object, no matter how revolting and loathsome, seen sufficiently often, blunts the senses, and one becomes disinclined to the effort necessary to destroy it or get rid of it.

Pride of possession is a curious attribute of mankind. This was brought sharply to my mind recently when it occurred to me to ask myself, "Why didn't Mrs. Chase *give* the Peabody Museum her gallstones?" Many other people had, for there were a pint or more of miscellaneous gallstones in the Peabody Museum in Salem, curiously enough in the case with an old reindeer. But these were donated gallstones; it was only Mrs. Chase's that were on loan. The answer is, Mrs. Chase's gallstones were larger than any others in the whole place and she obviously just couldn't bear to part with them permanently. I bethought me, Has this situation ever occurred before? And then I remembered that not long ago I was reading the last Annual Report of the Curator of the Museum of the Royal College of Surgeons in London. This venerable institution, containing much material that was priceless indeed, suffered a direct hit from a German bomb. It was almost completely destroyed, and the story of the catastrophe was told, sadly and meticulously, by its distinguished curator. But if our friend in the street were to read this report he might be inclined to laugh heretically at the cool and unemotional statement that along with the many terrific losses suffered by that venerable institution were listed the facts that the jar containing Napoleon's bowels was cracked and that the rib of Robert the Bruce was broken.

I have found myself justifying the preservation of objects which were inherently unpleasing to the eye by saying, "That illustrates the taxidermy of a hundred years ago." Or the preservation of a codfish pickled in alcohol by saying, "Someone may want to dissect that fish sometime," forgetting that fresh cod, infinitely preferable for dissection, are plentiful in the Boston area. And so it goes. The more I think of it, the more I believe that the average man is entirely entitled to his opinion and the average curator is a queer fish.

Now granted that the curator is a queer fish, is he a rare fish? I fear me the answer today is nay. My friend Alexander Wetmore, Director of the United States National Museum, in an address at the opening of the Dyche Museum at the University of Kansas, remarked, "There are today throughout the world more than seven thousand museums, of which more than a thousand are in the United States." Every museum has at least one curator, and the breed came into being, no doubt, back in the days when the "Repositerry of Curiosity," the *Anlage* of our University Museum here at Harvard, was visited by Francis Goelet on the twenty-fifth of October 1750. Unfortunately, Mr. Goelet does not tell us how old the museum was at that date. He does, however, tell us that its treasures included "horns and bones, fishes' skins and other objects, and a piece of tanned Negro hide."

Professor John Winthrop, Hollis Professor of Mathematics and Natural Philosophy, evidently had started even at this early date to make what we call a "Glory Hole." I have had some interesting experiences cleaning out "Glory Holes" in Cambridge, Boston, and Salem. Only a few months ago I opened a parcel in Salem, the wrapping paper of which was superscribed, "Please do not disturb these shells. Caleb Cooke, February 1857." This behest had been scrupulously obeyed for eighty-five years and six months. The parcel proved to be pure gold, for the shells were collected from one of our New England rivers in which today it would be impossible to collect a single living thing, so polluted have its waters become. I hold in my hand a little vial in which is a label saying, "This vial contains two feathers of a large penguin." One wonders why these two feathers out of the tens of thousands which that penguin carried were singled out for preservation.

The only old museum I ever saw where, so far as I could see, there was no Glory Hole was the museum in Charleston, South Carolina. This venerable institution, founded in 1773, has had plenty of time to accumulate one, but the gay and carefree cavaliers of the South were willing to throw things away even when they became museum curators, while the penny-pinching men of the New England states fairly reveled in the making of Glory Holes. Certainly nothing equaling the collections of zoological atrocities once preserved in Boston, Salem, and Cambridge has ever been known in America, and probably but seldom in Europe. I remember one of my colleagues, now passed to his reward, pointing regularly to a certain cask and saying, "That's filled with the pickled heads of Chinese." Well, it was. They were garnered on the beach at San Francisco years ago after a battle, by Thomas G. Carey, no less. Now after some seventy years these heads, boiled out and the skulls bleached and cleaned, serve a useful purpose: Hooton of Harvard uses them in teaching physical anthropology.

Alexander Agassiz collected but one living spirula, a little squidlike mollusk whose dried shells may be found along the beaches of the tropics in countless thousands. The living spirula carried an important message, for its shell was like certain fossil shells of ages ago and gave us a clew to what the soft parts of those fossil animals were like. That spirula disappeared about forty-five years ago from the very desk at which I now sit writing these lines and it has never been seen from that day to this.

Mr. Alexander Agassiz always said that Professor E. D. Cope was the greatest thief in the world, for the reason that he stole the largest object ever stolen. The story ran something like this: Captain Atwood of Provincetown, who did the Museum many good turns, once notified Mr. Agassiz that a strange whale had drifted ashore on the Outer Cape. Mr. Agassiz asked J. A. Allen and some students to go down and rough out the skeleton. This they did, and laid out the partially cleaned bones on a flatcar. They little dreamed that Dr. Cope from Philadelphia also had a scout on the Outer Cape, and Cope was a canny man. He went to Provincetown, hired a room in a farmhouse, where he could watch proceedings, and waited until the Cambridge crew went home. Then he greased the palm of the station agent to the end that a Philadelphia waybill instead of a Cambridge waybill was affixed to the flatcar and the whale ended up as the type of a new species which Mr. Cope described, its skeleton still being preserved at the Academy of Natural Sciences in Philadelphia. So the story runs, and I have often heard it told in the past.

I can hear the reader mildly say, "Why on earth does anyone want to be a museum curator?" This question, however, I can answer bravely and with positive assurance. To one who has by inheritance or training acquired the pack-rat instinct it is the most exciting calling in the whole world. For who, having a spark of imagination, could fail to be thrilled to hold in his hand our specimen of *Drepanis pacifica?*

This was the bird from which the feathers were taken to make the royal robe of Kamehameha the Great. The bird is extinct and our specimen was collected by Bloxam, who sailed on the *Blond*. It is, moreover, the cotype of a species. Any naturalist will know what I mean.

Edward S. Morse wrote an article for the *Atlantic Monthly* in July 1893, entitled "If Public Libraries Why Not Public Museums." I think Morse was entirely wrong in the type of museum which he outlined as being instructive to the public. Morse's all-consuming intellectual curiosity led him to believe that all of us were similarly endowed, as of course we are not. Bits of desiccated slime in a row of bottles carefully labeled captured Morse's interest just as rows of rock samples, all looking more or less alike, enabled him to point with pride to the fact that this exhibit included a piece of every sort of rock found in Essex County. This sort of material has no value for purposes of public instruction; nothing has except that which is inherently attractive.

The Mineralogical Hall in the University Museum in Cambridge contains a vast number of objects of the most extreme beauty and rarity, yet not one person in a thousand who comes to see the glass flowers in an adjoining hall steps across the threshold to look at the minerals. This was even more conspicuously the case in the museum in Salem, where the minerals were relatively inaccessible and really only displayed for the instruction of public-school classes, and the number of visits made by such classes had dwindled to one a year and that class only looked at about half a dozen minerals. The glass models of plants in Cambridge and the equally beautiful botanical models in the Field Museum in Chicago interest and attract the public. Samples of wood and dried foliage have absolutely no value for exhibition.

This is how I came to think up a new kind of museum. The trustees of the Peabody Museum in Salem voted to restore East India Hall to its original monumental simplicity and to display here figureheads of ships and other objects that are best seen from a distance. The Hall for years had been filled with a jittery miscellany of zoological objects. There was a good representation of the fauna of Essex County, specimens excellently prepared. All else was a miscellaneous accumulation, acquired through the years from sea captains and others, of specimens which varied in quality from the utterly revolting to a few really fine things. It was easy to dispose of the repulsive material. Some of it had scientific value and the rest of it, when tossed out of a second-story

window into the back yard on Charter Street in Salem, was fought
for by a swarm of urchins, who carried the critters off in triumph. The
police, at first unbelieving and suspecting theft, soon became ac-
quiescent.

The question was what to do with the few good things which did
not illustrate the zoology of Essex County. These naturally presented
a dilemma. I proposed discarding them all. Then one day I chanced
to lunch with Gus Loring and Stephen W. Phillips, men of original
mind and deep learning, who had an honest sentimental feeling for
some of the objects I proposed to discard. It was quite obvious that
I could not proceed without seriously wounding feelings. I suddenly
thought, "See if we can't make a human-interest story out of each one;
display the object with its relation to man." A sort of rough classification gradually grew on me. There was a good skylark, and a good
wandering albatross. Get a nightingale and set up a display. Label it
"These birds have inspired great poetry." Use pictures of the poets,
facsimiles of the poems, and some of the most superb verses in boldly
typed labels.

What do domesticated animals teach us beside carving at table? Domestic fowl and the pigeon have been extraordinarily plastic in man's
hands. Think of the contrast between a Shanghai rooster and a Sea-
bright bantam. The Shanghai and the Langshan are the largest of the
so-called Asiatic breeds of fowl, enormous creatures standing over two
feet high. The breeds are now out of fashion and almost extinct.
Luckily the Museum had some really historic fowls. Here was the
rooster brought back over a hundred years ago, the progenitor of the
stock which gave rise to the Rhode Island Red. And I found a wild
jungle fowl which could be spared from the collections in Cambridge.
With the help of my neighbor Harry McKean, I soon had plans for
this exhibit well under way.

Various species of jungle fowl, which look exactly like small game
chickens, are found all over southeastern Asia. When you are living
in the country where they occur, you seldom see them, but their crow-
ing at morning and evening sometimes becomes a positive nuisance.
Now, conversely, although there is no reason to believe that the Aztecs
did not hold the turkey in domestication for as long a time as any
of the peoples of Asia had the fowl, the turkey has not proved plastic
at all. Cortez sent domesticated birds which he found in Mexico back
to Europe. From there they spread all over the world. They came to

New England, and to this day domesticated turkeys, most of them, are hard to tell from wild birds. A few varieties have been produced, but only by the chance dropping out of elements of the normal pigmentation of the bird's plumage. In the reddish-colored turkeys, the black or the dilute black pigment—the gray—has gone and the red element alone remains. In the white turkeys all pigmentation has disappeared; albino races are always easy to produce in domestication. White rats and mice and guinea pigs come to mind, as well as leghorn fowl and fantail pigeons.

I visualized an exhibit around William Endicott's magnificent bull bison, not using the animal as a zoological object, a member of the Bovidae, but as a creature which provided food, shelter, sport, and even an object of worship to many tribes of Indians. And here illustrative material is abundant and spectacular.

The Museum had a first-class ostrich, given it some years ago by Mrs. Stephen Phillips—an ostrich far too good to throw away. By good fortune, I had a sample of dried ostrich meat, one of the various kinds of "biltong" carried by the Boers as rations when at war or on trek. An ostrich feather fan, an old-time bonnet, and headdresses of the Nandi Masai all proved obtainable.

Think what a story you can build about the giant tortoise of the Galápagos. The old whalers called them turpin. For generations all of the ships that chanced to be near the Galápagos Islands, about six hundred miles southwestward of Panama, went ashore turtling. The crews carried the beasts down to the beach, boated them to the ships, and piled them up in their empty holds. Here, being the strange creatures that they are, they survived for months without food or water. When scurvy appeared, the turtles were butchered. The flesh was savory even when poorly prepared. There was enough fat in each one to shorten a mess of "duff," and the water in their bladders was cool and clear. I have seen a compilation made from about thirty whalers' logs which shows that they carried off more than eleven thousand of these animals. Once they occurred in countless multitudes on no fewer than nine of the islands. Seventeen zoological species of turtles have been described. But this is not the point which we want the magnificent specimen at Salem to illustrate—rather, what turtles like this meant to seamen from the time of Dampier down to about 1867, when petroleum knocked out whale oil. Probably no less than half a million turpin were carried away, and now all the races of the creatures are rare or extinct.

Captain Phillips brought back from Fiji an enormous giant clam. The superb pair of matched valves are at least three feet long and weigh over a hundred pounds each. But I don't want this to be a malacological specimen—rather, the terror of the pearl diver. For if a diver inadvertently thrust a hand or a foot into one of these gaping shells as it yawned open, the instant reaction was for the animal to close up, like any other clam, and the death of the diver ensued.

These giant clams were undoubtedly eaten, the meat being chopped fine and stewed. No doubt it was as good as conch, most delectable of all sea viands, unfortunately unprocurable in New England. What a dramatic underwater scene could be depicted with modern methods of creating illusions! Mold a lovely Polynesian maiden vested only with a net reticule of pearl shells tied to her waist and struggling for release from the clutch of this giant mollusk. I fear, however, such pageantry is beyond our means—and might shock Salem, anyhow.

It is probable that all of the various races of domestic duck are derived from the wild mallard, and where man first began to breed ducks for food is doubtful. It was probably in China. Anyone who has traveled into the interior of China, say up the Si-kiang River from Canton to Wuchow, will recall the floating duck farms. These great arks built on rafts move about from place to place, a gangplank is let down, and the ducks scuttle overboard and dip and dive and feed. At evening the proprietor of the establishment stands by with a bamboo wand and beats a gong and the ducks rush up the gangway, for they know from bitter experience that the last few ducks will be assiduously whacked with the bamboo just for being last.

The people in Bali have had the duck for years. The characteristic race is a white one with a large fluffy top-knot, and the Balinese positively assure us that unless a bunch of cotton wool on top of a twig is put before the setting duck where she must observe it constantly, the young will not be bedecked with the much admired pompon of feathers on their heads. And though unquestionably man has played with the duck for a long time, no such enormous variety of named races has been produced as in the case of the fowl. The Muscovy duck is far distantly related to all the rest of its kin. This bird is found in a wild state through the tropical lowlands of Central and South America. By this I mean, of course, the forested areas. It was domesticated in Mexico, and possibly by other Indian tribes than the Aztecs. When it was brought to Europe, the tradition of its origin was apparently lost, but just why it should have been considered to be of Muscovite origin I can't remember, although I have been told. Except for albino and pied individuals, most of the Muscovy ducks are essentially the same as their wild ancestors. This is also true of the guinea hens which came to America on the slave ships from West Africa. As everybody knows, these can hardly be called domesticated. They have a tendency to run wild, and indeed in many localities in Haiti and Cuba they afford good sport with a shotgun, being strong, fast flyers.

Look at the pigeons on Boston Common and you will be struck by the fact that the vast majority of them are essentially like the blue rock dove, which is their wild ancestor. Man has produced an extraordinary number of bizarre and curious types of pigeon, but let them become feral, as they have in Boston or Venice, and they revert to the ancestral type, at least in a vast majority of cases. And the accidental additions which come from escaped fancy pigeons are soon bred out and absorbed into the essentially blue rock mass of the population. But I don't want to crowd our museum at Salem to where it appears to overstress the exhibition of domesticated animals. This aspect has been treated elsewhere. There is a wonderful collection of all sorts of domesticated types at the British Museum of Natural History in London, of dogs at Yale, and a fair synoptic collection in Cambridge.

A good many dyed plumes of birds of paradise seized in the Customhouse and turned over to the Peabody Museum for exhibition recalls the trade in birds of paradise. When the Dutch and Portuguese first arrived in the Moluccas, they found some of the Malay sultans receiving dried skins of birds of paradise as tribute from Papuan tribes of savages who owed them suzerainty. These skins were legless, and the notion grew that the birds spent their lives flying in the air and admiring the sun. During the last years of the last century and the first decade of this, the number of birds of paradise which were garnered from the western part of New Guinea and the Aru Islands was stupendous. Queen Wilhelmina stopped the slaughter some years ago. But birds of paradise were still abundant, even considering the enormous numbers killed for trade, because the females were so inconspicuous and so utterly unlike the males that they were never disturbed and all the species are highly polygamous.

And so, to my great surprise, I find myself at last engaged in building up an entirely new type of museum. There will be many objects displayed beside the ones which I have indicated. I believe that with thoughtful labeling, some zoology, some history, some folklore, and some poetry may be taught in a very attractive way. And I wish we could find a good name for our innovation. I can think only of "Museum of Ethnozoology," which sounds utterly loathsome.

> So work the honey-bees,
> Creatures that by a rule in nature teach
> The act of order to a peopled kingdom.
> They have a king and officers of sorts;
> Where some, like magistrates, correct at home,
> Others, like merchants, venture trade abroad,
> Others, like soldiers, armed in their stings,
> Make boot upon the summer's velvet buds:
> Which pillage they with merry march bring home
> To the tent-royal of their emperor:
> Who, busied in his majesty, surveys
> The singing masons building roofs of gold,
> The civil citizens kneading up the honey,
> The poor mechanic porters crowding in
> Their heavy burdens at his narrow gate.
> The sad-ey'd justice, with his surly hum,
> Delivering o'er to executors pale
> The lazy yawning drone.
>
> SHAKESPEARE, *Henry V*

WINGED BULLETS

by Edwin Way Teale

Insects lead remarkable lives, and so do some of the men who study them and write about them. Not that Edwin Way Teale confines himself to the field of entomology, but as an author-naturalist he first rose to fame through his intimate knowledge of (and photographs of) those "armored exoskeletons" that, according to some gloomy prophets, in the long run will defeat the human race and inherit the earth.

Born in Joliet, Illinois, June 2, 1899, Edwin Way Teale was graduated from Earlham College at Richmond, Indiana, in 1922. He taught for a couple of years and then came to New York in 1924 to try to earn a living by writing. As he tells the story, he almost starved to death in the process, but happily he shows no sign of it now. When last encountered in the field he was a husky six-footer packing about two hundred pounds of bone and muscle over Long Island sand dunes in energetic fashion. He gradually forced himself on the attentions of magazine editors with remarkable photographs of insects and fascinating text to go with the pictures. His Grassroot Jungles, *made up of such material and published in 1937, was an immediate success and gave him the opportunity to go on to greater heights over a much wider range in the field of natural history. He went ahead to write* The Golden Throng, Near Horizons, Dune Boy, The Lost Woods, Days Without Time, North With The Spring, *and* Autumn Across America.

To catalogue all his accomplishments and the many distinctions that have been conferred upon him is impossible here. His books have been printed in Swedish, Finnish, French, Spanish, and Braille. His accomplishments give evidence of his physical energy, his intellectual integrity, and his never-failing enthusiasm in the pursuit and enjoyment of knowledge of Nature. As a field

*companion he tops it all off with a rollicking sense of humor that
not even the worst weather or the worst luck can keep in sub-
jection. The selection that follows is a chapter from* Grassroot
Jungles.

ONE winter, years ago, I lived in a house on the road to
Santa Monica. Less than a mile away, in an open California field, lay the tar pits of Rancho La Brea, the so-
called Death Trap of the Ages. The great beasts of the
earth—the saber-toothed tiger, the Dire wolf, the imperial elephant—
had been caught there like insects on flypaper.

Even now, tar, heavy and glistening, oozes from the ground and
creeps away down the slope into great pools where bubbles rise, expand, and burst in rainbow hues. Here, one day when the air was
filled with the stillness which precedes a downpour, I encountered a
fleeting moment of drama. Time slipped backward a hundred million
years and I watched an event occurring before the initial word of written history.

A dragonfly, slanting over the pool on glittering wings, had swooped
too low. Writhing and twisting, it lay gripped by the black glue of
the tar pit, its long segmented body straining first to one side, then
to the other. Finally its struggles ceased. Quiescent, it sank deeper
and deeper into the tar just as, long ago, so many of its ancestors had
done at this identical spot on the changing, eroding face of the earth.

For the dragonflies, with the silverfish and the cockroaches, were
insect pioneers, one of the earliest forms to appear. In the prehistoric
jungles of the Carboniferous Age dragonflies as big as hawks soared
through the steaming air. Their fossil remains have been discovered
in the Permian rocks of Kansas, in the Jurassic formations of Siberia,
in the Miocene beds of Colorado, and in the coal deposits of Belgium.
Possessed of wings that measured nearly thirty inches from tip to tip,
they were the largest insects that ever lived.

The towering trees of that day have been dwarfed to the club moss
and the ground pines of the present. And the dragonfly has shrunk
with them. The largest of the 2,000 and more species known has a
wingspread of approximately seven and a half inches.

In their long existence on earth many have been the changes seen
by these familiar "snake feeders," "devil's darning needles," "mosquito

hawks," "gauze flies," "virgins of the water"—to give but a few of the many names by which the dragonfly is known. It has lived on while the dinosaurs passed from the earth; while cave-men, mound builders, and cliff dwellers evolved into modern man. Yet, in many of its habits and characteristics, the dragonfly is still a creature from the distant past.

Often it rushes through the air, scooping up its victims in a basket formed of spine-fringed legs, sucking their bodies dry and letting the carcasses fall to the ground, all without slackening its headlong pace. Its great compound organs of sight may contain as many lenses as the eyes of 15,000 men. Its head, resembling half of a hollowed-out marble, is attached to the slender body by a sort of ball-and-socket joint that enables the dragonfly to turn its head almost completely around and see below as well as above. Its veined and transparent wings, moving on the average twenty-eight times a second, can carry it through the air at speeds approaching sixty miles an hour.

Probably no other insect is so much a creature of the air. It has legs but it never walks. Its jointed and spine-bordered limbs, bunched far forward, enable it to cling and climb. When it leaves the earth, its awkwardness falls away; it becomes the acme of grace, swooping, turning, zooming at will. It can dive like a pursuit plane or hover like an autogiro. As soon as the sun lifts above the horizon, the dragonflies are a-wing. Only one Oriental species hunts at night. Most other members of the family are children of the sun.

So true is this that certain species alight if the sun even goes under a cloud. I remember one sultry morning when I was working my way slowly through a dense stand of flags bordering a swamp pond. With beads of moisture clinging to the vegetation at the base of the tangle, the flags rose like a thick head of hair on a perspiring scalp. I had paused motionless to watch a small gray insect which had fallen into the pond. Its feeble struggle sent tiny ripples running across the surface. Then all was still.

Over the spot swept the shadow of a dragonfly, zigzagging back and forth above the stagnant water. A cloud passed before the sun. Instantly the dragonfly, a shining little fellow with delicate, red-spotted wings, swept toward me, seemed to halt in amazement with wings aquiver, and then dropped lightly to the tip of a flag almost within reach of my hand. Without difficulty I caught it and, after a momentary struggle, it clung to my finger and even rode along as I moved slowly through the flags. The cloud passed by, the brilliance of the sunshine struck us once more and, as though actuated by a spring, my little passenger leaped into the air and darted away.

So completely is the dragonfly a creature of the air that the female often remains upon the wing when laying her eggs. Unlike the gangling crane fly, which soars aloft scattering its eggs through the air, she usually bumps along the surface of a pond, dipping the tip of her abdomen in the water at intervals, leaving behind clumps of tiny eggs. During the hottest days of summer I have seen dragonflies in the heart of New York City making their characteristic bumping flights amid the fumes and noise of traffic on Fifth Avenue, as though laying eggs on a smooth black river of asphalt. Sometimes the female dives completely under the surface to attach her eggs to the leaves or stems of plants. She is incased in a film of air which enables her to remain submerged long enough to complete the work.

A small relative of the dragonfly, the frail and gauzy damselfly, follows an even stranger procedure in depositing her eggs beneath the surface of a pond. Because the female, alone, would have difficulty breaking through the surface film on returning to the air, the male accompanies her, flying ahead and gripping her with the "pincers" at the tip of his abdomen, pulling like a locomotive attached to a train. Flying tandem in this way, they dive into the water and, when the eggs have been deposited, break through the surface, the male gaining his freedom first and using his wings to drag the female after him.

The shape of the dragonfly's egg varies. Some are stubby, like roundish grains of wheat; others are elongated, like kernels of rice. The latter are always deposited in slits in the stems or leaves of underwater plants. Nobody knows how many eggs a dragonfly is capable of laying. Dr. Leland O. Howard tells of finding 110,000 separate eggs in a single clump.

What would happen if all these eggs hatched out and reached maturity is indicated by the "dragonfly year" of 1839. Over a large part of the continent of Europe, and especially in Germany, France, and the Netherlands, immense swarms of the insects followed the rivers and darkened the sky. The superstitious believed them harbingers of famine and war. But scientists pointed out that preceding springs had been unusually rainy. Rivers and lakes had overflowed, providing wide areas of shallow water where the dragonfly nymphs were relatively safe from the fish that usually attacked them. As a consequence, increased numbers had become winged adults and hunger drove millions to seek new feeding grounds.

Occasionally dragonflies migrate in great numbers, especially when droughts dry up ponds and swamps. One of the biggest of these migrations occurred in 1881. Over southern Illinois the air was reported "literally alive with dragonflies," all streaming southwest, some flying only a foot from the ground, others soaring almost out of sight. Drought was thought to have caused the mass movement of the insects. Off the coast of Europe, vessels have sometimes sighted small swarms far out at sea.

Under normal conditions the many enemies of the dragonfly keep down the number of these insects. Even before the eggs hatch, one curious foe, a certain hymenopterous parasite, begins its work, laying its eggs in those of the dragonfly. To reach the ones hidden away in slits in underwater plants, the almost microscopic fly descends far beneath the surface. It uses its wings as oars and carries with it tiny bubbles of air that keep it alive until it reaches the surface again.

If the eggs survive the dangers that beset them, they hatch into insect ogres, the underwater nymphs of the dragonfly. With dirty gray-green bodies making them inconspicuous, they lie in the mud or lurk among the pond weeds. The thin walls of the lower intestines are formed into gills which absorb oxygen from the water. Curiously, the nymph breathes and swims in the same manner. When it expels water forcibly from the lower end of the food canal, after absorbing the oxygen, the recoil drives it ahead. Thus, like a tiny submarine rocket, the nymph progresses across the mud bottom of the pond.

Almost as strange as its method of locomotion is its manner of catching prey. Unlike the adult dragonfly, the nymph is sluggish and captures its living food by stealth. It lies in wait until some mayfly or mosquito larva, some caddis worm or water bug swims too close. Then an underlip, so long it folds down under the body and between the nymph's front legs when not in use, shoots out. At its end are sharp pincers which grip the victim and pull it into the wide mouth of the insect goblin. Then the underlip folds down again and the mouth disappears behind a chitinous mask which gives the creature the appearance of wearing a frozen, perpetual smile.

The nymphs are insatiable cannibals, devouring each other and even catching and destroying newly emerged adults before their wings have a chance to harden. As they grow older, the nymphs are able to overpower tadpoles and small fish. Larger fish, in turn, hunt them down and they form an important item in the diet of trout and other game fish.

Most smaller dragonflies pass a year in the water as nymphs. Larger species are often two or even three years old before they are "born" as aerial insects. During this long wait they may molt from ten to fifteen times. The transformation from the underwater nymph to the aerial dragonfly is almost as amazing as though a trout should suddenly shed its skin and become a robin.

Usually this miracle occurs during the heat of the day, although a few dragonflies emerge at night. In either case they climb from the water and cling to the bank, a stick or weed, while the suit of chitin armor splits down the back and the wings, damp and crumpled, unfold. Then, when the glistening coat has hardened, the insect darts into the sunshine. It leaves behind the ghost of its other self, a brown, translucent shell which continues to cling to the spot of transformation, a chitinous monument to Nature's miracle.

The shining wings, on which the dragonfly rides, are supported by a vast network of veins. In a single wing there may be as many as 3,000 separate cells between the veins. The insect skims through the air with one goal in sight, appeasing an insatiable appetite for living food. This appetite is approached by only two other insects I know: the praying mantis and the robber fly.

The most surprising experience I ever had with a dragonfly occurred one day when I was holding one of the insects by its tough, parchmentlike wings. I was watching the metallic segments of the abdomen moving in and out in rhythm with the insect's breathing. Suddenly the body curled upward, the tip reached the dragonfly's mouth, and the insect calmly began eating off its own tail! I was almost as astonished as if I had seen a man crunching off his fingers or making a meal of his arm. Since then I have read that hungry dragonflies will consume parts of their own bodies to appease the craving for food.

Many other instances attest to the abnormal appetite of these insects. Dr. Howard tells of one specimen which had been chloroformed and mounted. Evidently the anesthetic was insufficiently strong, for the insect revived after it had been secured to a board by a large pin thrust through the thorax. In spite of this terrible injury it ate ravenously when flies were placed within reach of its jaws. The pleasure of swallowing food seemed to make it forget the pin thrust completely through its body. As long as the feeding continued, it made no effort to escape.

In a space of two hours one dragonfly was seen to devour more than its weight in horseflies. Sometimes these predatory creatures will swoop down and pick small moths from twigs and leaves. With their needle-sharp teeth, they attack bees and wasps without hesitation. Frequently larger dragonflies will catch and consume smaller species and, on at least one occasion, a dragonfly was seen with a large swallowtail butterfly in its grasp. However, mosquitoes and gnats form the bulk of its diet, thus making it an invaluable ally of man. At dusk some species of these winged hunters cruise back and forth in squadrons, looking for swarms of gnats and mosquitoes.

When aquatic insects become scarce, the larger dragonflies will sometimes travel miles inland from the nearest water in their search for food. The larger the dragonfly, the higher it hunts in the air. The smaller species skim so low above the water that trout and other game fish sometimes leap into the air and catch them on the wing. Bullfrogs also snap them up when they come too close and the webs of spiders snare the smaller dragonflies. The larger ones, however, break through and escape. In the words of an old Japanese poem: "Through even the spider's fence, it has force to burst its way."

Like all other insects, dragonflies have their individual traits. Some are wild and shy; others are sociable and inquisitive. I remember one in particular, a big fellow with blue metallic body, which hovered near a raft on which I was fishing in a lonely little lake far back in the woods of Maine. The bottom of the lake was strewn with rotting logs and among these skeletons of trees swam great black leeches, undulating like ribbons. Gaunt pine stubs, killed by some fire of long ago, lined the shore. Clinging to them were scores of nymph skins, some new, some old, some light tan, some weathered to a chocolate brown. All around us, on these dead pines, creatures of the mud had been transformed into creatures of the air.

This particular dragonfly of which I speak would perch on the raft beside me, circle around and around my rod, make passes at the line as I reeled it in. Several times it dashed at flies buzzing about my head, picking them out of the air and then stopping in front of me like a matador who had killed a bull and was taking his applause. Fishing became dull in comparison to watching this neighborly insect, and, much to the disgust of my guide, I reeled in my line and turned to tossing bits of wood into the air for the dragonfly to swoop upon.

How a similar ruse is used to capture elusive dragonflies is told in Lafcadio Hearn's A Japanese Miscellany. Children attach tiny pebbles to the ends of long hairs and throw these miniature bolas into the air where dragonflies are circling. When one of the insects pounces upon the passing object, the hair twists about its body and the weight of the pebbles brings it to earth.

After more than a hundred million years on earth the dragonfly asks no more of life today than it did in the age of the dinosaurs. Sunshine and living insects are the twin needs of its existence. In a world of infinite change its wants have remained the same.

During the evenings of one whole week, years ago when I was a boy on an Indiana farm, I pored over the pages of a mail-order catalogue, making a list of everything in the world I wanted. The total cost, as I remember it, was only $392.80. Today how strangely small is the satisfaction of knowing that, if I wished, I could buy the list complete. Successive years have brought new wants; desire is fleeter of foot than any gain. "Man," says Henry George, "is the only animal whose desires increase as they are fed; the only animal that is never satisfied."

But the dragonfly, so perfectly fitted for its small and transitory existence, desires no other food or home than its ancestors have had through the ages. For it, life is simple and direct.

In Northern states the first cold of fall kills off these children of the sun. Only the nymphs remain in their underwater home to carry on the chain of life. Lingering old age is virtually unknown in the world of insects. There is no wasting decrepitude; no long deterioration of powers. For the dragonfly there is only the swoop of an enemy or the numbing anesthetic of autumn cold. Death, for it, is also simple and direct.

THE LASSOING SPIDER

by Willis J. Gertsch

Spiders constitute an odd lot in the animal world. Most men, women, and children think of them as "insects" if they give the matter any thought at all, but insects have six legs and spiders have eight. They are in a class by themselves in that respect. Most grown men ignore spiders. Most small boys step on them if they can. Let a housewife catch sight of a spider indoors and she takes after it brandishing a broom. An oppressed or neglected class, whichever way you look at it. For all that, there are many spiders with remarkable talents as weavers, spinners, hunters, and animal engineers, and the lassoing spider described by the author of the following selection is one of the many. When Willis J. Gertsch writes of spiders he does so with the authority of a Curator of Insects and Spiders (and particularly a specialist in arachnids) at the American Museum of Natural History. The following article is from Natural History magazine, published by the museum.

I N all societies, you are apt to find some nonconformists who persist in a determination not to follow the communal line of least resistance. Usually such heresy is productive of nothing that can survive, but also from such heretics may come the geniuses who originate new methods and establish new lines. Among the orbweaver spiders, we find a group that has broken so completely with the past that its members do not spin orbwebs at all but have substituted an entirely different method of capturing insects. Instead of relying on the static but dependable round web, they spin a line, weight it with a sticky drop of liquid silk, and hurl it at their prey, much as the gaucho throws his bolas or the angler casts his line.

No pounding hoofs or shrill cries attend the throwing of the viscid ball by *Mastophora*, the Bolas Spider, whose successful effort is marked at most by a frenzied beating of soft wings. Very quickly the fluttering ceases, and no record of the means of capture is evident when we see the spider with her bulky prey. Long before the South American Indian learned to throw his bolas of round stones tied to ropes of braided rawhide, the Bolas Spider was an accomplished boleadora. But she has kept her secret so well that few Americans know of her existence. With the license of an inventor, she keeps her line attached to the single bola and hurls it as a sort of lasso. The viscid ball is the noose that holds the unwilling prey until she enswathes it in bonds of silk.

Spiders have devised many ingenious methods for stopping and ensnaring flying insects. Most of these are based on a copious production of silk and the use of this strong, elastic material for expansive webs. Perhaps the one best known and most pleasing to the eye is the round web or orbweb, composed mostly of radiating and spiral threads. *Mastophora* belies her true heritage as an orbweaver and gains a livelihood by a parsimonious use of silk.

Such amazing creatures must come from far-off places, perhaps from the depths of tropical jungles or from little-known areas where few men live. Not so! These exotic spiders are found over most of the United States and are within reach of anyone with the inclination to find them and the time to observe their activities. Indeed, some of them seem to prefer the formal vegetation of our city parks and live in the shrubs and trees along the walks and riding lanes. Close relatives of the Bolas Spiders live in Australia, where their incredible habit of angling for prey has gained them the name of Angler Spiders. One of these heretics from Africa, *Cladomelea*, varies the fishing procedure by spinning its line around like a whirligig.

All are fat spiders of above average size, whose bodies are ornamented in a most grotesque manner. The carapace is bedecked with sharp, branched crests or horns and set with many small, rounded projections, whereas the voluminous abdomen is lined and wrinkled and surmounted with rounded humps. These bizarre specializations, reminiscent of such ornamentation in the dinosaurs and many other groups of animals, are not known to play an important part in the life of the spiders. Indeed, there is little indication from the general appearance of these creatures that they do anything exciting. The spinelessness of the first pair of legs, and their greater length as compared with the other pairs, probably contribute to a better handling of the pendulum fishing line and thus may be said to be specialized for that purpose.

Fall is the best time to search for the Bolas Spiders, which, though not uncommon throughout their range, rarely come to our notice. Their failure to spin an expansive web, as do most of their relatives, increases the difficulty of discovering them. One factor that also contributes to their apparent rareness is their habit of living in bushes and trees, often at considerable heights. Usually we are attracted first to the conspicuous egg sacs and see near them one of these curious spiders. Once we have her, we can carry her home and install her in a convenient spot; or, better still, watch her in her own hunting grounds.

The site is usually an outer branch several feet above the ground in plain sight, and the spider may be exposed or only partially hidden from view during the day. Mementos of her previous activities are numerous silken lines, which soon form a thin coating over the twig and the leaves. Hanging to the lines or hidden among the nearby leaves may be one or more egg sacs, beautifully and durably made, and representing many hours of tireless spinning.

During the daylight hours, *Mastophora* clings to the twig or leaf, completely immobile, perhaps deriving some sort of protection from this simulation of an inanimate object. A confirmed introvert, she can be said to resemble a bud, a nut, a snail, or, with considerable faithfulness, a bit of bird dung. Indeed, her resemblance to bird lime makes one of her common names, the bird-dropping spider, quite appropriate. If we take her in our fingers, she shows only a momentary evidence of life and then quickly resumes her inanimate role. We roll her around in our cupped hands like a nut or marble, and she does not even respond when we accidentally drop her to the ground. Finally, we place her back on her perch and find, an hour or more later, that she has seemingly not moved an inch during our absence. Few spiders are so completely inscrutable.

But *Mastophora* is a creature of evening and night, and as we watch her later in the performance of her marvelous routine, we forgive the early listlessness she showed. The disappearance of the last rays of twilight is her signal for action, for soon after that she takes up her position for the evening's sport.

With her plump body swinging from the ends of numerous legs, she moves to one end of the branch and affixes her thread to the lower side by pressing her spinnerets against the bark. Grasping this thread with one of her hind legs and holding it away from the branch, she crawls along for several inches and finally pastes the line firmly at the other end. The result is a loosely hung line. She often moves about on it and strengthens it with an additional dragline thread. This strong trapeze line is strung far enough below the branch to allow a clear space for her fishing.

Moving to the center of the trapeze line, *Mastophora* now touches her spinnerets and pulls out a new thread, which lies clear of the other and is drawn out to a length of about two inches. Still keeping it attached to her spinnerets and held taut, she now combs out on the line quantities of viscid silk by means of her hind legs. Each leg alternates in combing out the liquid until a shining globule as large as a seed pearl is formed.

The spider now pulls out a greater length of line, allowing the weighted portion to drop part of the distance to its natural point of equilibrium, and then turns and severs the line just below the globule with the claws of one of her hind legs. The freed line swings back and forth like a pendulum, but the spider turns quickly and approaches it, searching and groping with a front leg until she is able to grasp it. Quickly she swings her massive body and grasps the trapeze line by the hind legs of one side and adjusts the fishing line between her palpi and one of her long front legs. Poised and ready now is the boleadora, and she waits for the approach of any suitable victim, with the patience that characterizes this spider.

Also roused to activity at this time of night are many nocturnal insects, which soon fly along their accustomed lanes, dipping down close to the foliage and fluttering in and out among the branches. A large-bodied moth, with wings spreading nearly two inches and with great eyes shining red in the last rays of reflected light, dips down toward the hunting grounds of the waiting spider. As the insect approaches, *Mastophora* gives every evidence of knowing of the nearness of a prospective victim. She moves her body and adjusts her line as if in tense expectancy. At just the right moment, when the moth comes within the reach of the line, the spider swings it rapidly forward in the direction of the flyer. The viscid ball strikes on the underside of a forewing and brings the winged creature to an abrupt stop, its tether an unyielding line that will stretch half its length before it will part.

Fluttering furiously at the end of the lasso, the moth makes every effort to free itself from the sticky globule, but the spider is quickly on hand to deal out the final coup by biting the victim on some part of its body. Resistance ends quickly with the venomous bite, and the paralyzed moth is rotated and trussed up like a mummy with sheets of silk. To the victor belong the spoils, and *Mastophora* now sets to work feeding on the body juices of her catch. This bountiful food supply will keep the spider busy for some time. After having satiated her appetite, she cuts loose the shrunken remnant from the trapeze line and drops it to the ground below. Later in the night a second capture may be made, but *Mastophora's* needs for food are usually well met by a single sizable victim.

It must not be concluded that the life of this spider is quite as simple as the incident portrayed might indicate. *Mastophora* may wait in vain for a flying creature to come near enough for capture. In many instances, her aim may not be as accurate as pictured, or the prospective victim may be too large to be held even by the strong band of silk. But patience is one thing at which spiders excell, and *Mastophora* is no exception. Should no victim reward her after half an hour of sitting with her line ready for casting, she winds the globule and line into a ball and eats it. Quickly she spins another line, prepares another sticky bead, and resumes her vigil.

How wonderfully complex is the pattern of instinctive activities that makes up the fishing habit of *Mastophora!* Although endowed with glands that produce silk in copious quantities, the spider now bases her whole economy on a blob of sticky silk dangling at the end of a short line. And still not content with a niggardly use of this vital material, she eats the viscid globule if it is not put to use against her prey. One would like to think that the stickiness of the viscid globule is impaired by exposure to the air, and that a wise spider is renewing it, but we know this is not the case. This action is often seen with great surprise by casual observers, but it is characteristic of the orb-weavers as a group. Perhaps it is inspired by the fact that they must so often roll up the lines of their tattered webs and build them up again.

Mastophora's lifeline is a silken dragline thread of great elasticity and of a tensile strength said to be second only to fused quartz fibers. The trapeze line, the pendulum thread, the viscid globule, and the instincts of the hungry spider combine to give us one of the most sensational of all devices for the capture of prey.

In September, 1903, there appeared in the *Scientific American* an article entitled "A Bolas-Throwing Spider," in which were given full details of the angling habit as practiced by *Mastophora cornigera,* one of the Bolas Spiders. We owe the first description of this moving drama to the patience and keen observation of Mr. Charles E. Hutchinson of Glendale, California. Nearly twenty years later, in 1922, the similar habits of the Australian Angler Spider, *Dicrostichus magnificus,* were described by Mr. Heber A. Longman, who knew nothing of Hutchinson's early paper. American spider specialists have likewise either forgotten or were completely unaware of the existence of this fine description of one of our most interesting spiders.

The Australian spiders of this group have been studied rather carefully by various workers, but the fundamental investigations are to be credited to Mr. Heber A. Longman of Brisbane. He noted the complete absence of a web of viscid silk and watched the remarkable method by which the Magnificent Angler Spider, *Dicrostichus magnificus,* caught one of the common Noctuid moths. His description deviates little from what we know of *Mastophora.* "From its slender bridge it would spin a filament, usually about one and a half inches in length, which was suspended downwards; on the end of this was a globule of very viscid matter, a little larger than the head of an ordinary pin, occasionally with several smaller globules above. This filament was held out by one of the front legs, the miniature apparatus bearing a quaint resemblance to a fisherman's rod and line. On the approach of a moth, the spider whirls the filament and globule with surprising speed, and this is undoubtedly the way in which it secures its prey. The moths are unquestionably attracted to an effective extent by the spider, whether by scent or by its color we cannot say. We certainly could not distinguish the slightest odor. But the fact remains that night after night one or two moths would flutter up and be caught. Other moths nearby seemed to be indifferent, but two were often secured in the space of an hour, one of which would be packed away on the line to be sucked later. The spectacle of the moth fluttering up to the spider, sometimes two or even three times before it was caught, is one of the most interesting little processes which the writer has ever witnessed in natural history. The supposed desire of the moth for the star is a poet's fancy, but the attraction of the moth to the *Dicrostichus,* although mysterious, can be seen by any patient watcher."

We have saved mention of the *Cladomelea* from Africa until the end of this section, because the habits of this species are a further innovation. *Cladomelea* spins the same horizontal threads as do the other species and attaches the usual perpendicular line with a viscid globule at its end. Instead of holding the weighted line with the long front legs as do her cousins, *Cladomelea* grasps it by the third or shortest leg and uses her other legs to secure herself to the trapeze lines. Mr. Conrad Akerman of Pietermaritzburg, South Africa, tells us that "This spider does not wait for the appearance of her prey and then hurl the droplet at it as with *Dicrostichus magnificus,* but whirls it rapidly on the end of its thread with a rotary motion in a horizontal plane. She keeps up this movement for about fifteen minutes without a pause, then draws up the thread and swallows the viscid droplet. After resting a few minutes she repeats the performance, spinning another line with a terminal globule and rotating it again for about fifteen minutes. Should any insect come within the radius of the circling droplet it would be struck with considerable force, and so, I imagine, would be captured by sticking to the viscid matter; the spider could then seize it or enshroud it in silk. The droplet is always rotated in a clear place and never struck any of the stationary objects in its vicinity."

Thus we note that already *Cladomelea* has introduced a refinement to the fishing line in the design of a whirligig. Or perhaps the converse is true—the measured, less wasteful practice of *Mastophora* may represent the real advancement in technique.

The habit of angling for prey must be a very old one, inasmuch as it is shared by spiders in such widely separated areas as Africa, Australia, and America. Just when it arose and what inspired it belong at present only within the realm of speculation; the solution must await fuller data on this group and on related spiders. The place of origin of this new method is tied up with the origin of the group itself, and of that we know nothing. Nor are enough of the spiders known to give us some clue, in their structure or in the instincts of the young, to the probable beginnings of the group.

We are inclined to be dogmatic in our belief that these spiders were once nearly typical orbweavers, but just how long ago this was, we can only surmise. It seems reasonable to suppose that the angling habit arose within the web itself and that the orbweb was discarded only after the habit was perfected. The repudiation of the orbweb must have occurred some time after the new process was devised, for dependence on the orb must have been fairly complete at the time the new habit was forming. We can visualize the parent spider of the group on her orb in the process of subduing a fluttering insect and see her force out great sheets or drops of viscid silk to entangle it.

We have only to place one of these globules on the end of a short line to have the fishing line of *Mastophora*. The instinctive actions that gradually refined the technique and guided the spider to the normal position for holding the line must have been acquired very slowly, perhaps only after long periods of time. Once the new method proved a success, the orbweb became superfluous and was finally lost altogether in its normal form. Perhaps in the trapeze lines of the Bolas Spider we have a vestige of the once mighty orbweb.

In a recent letter, Mr. Hutchinson informed me that the angling habit is fully developed in young females one-fourth grown. However, the activities of young spiderlings just beginning to capture their prey still remain a mystery. We know that young spiderlings have little need for food soon after emerging, but efforts to maintain and study them have so far been unsuccessful. Perhaps in the early habits of some of the other species or some other orbweaver heretic we may discover a hint or definite recapitulation of the ancient practices of these atypical round-web spinners.

In all of the descriptions of the angling habit there have been speculations as to the role of the moth in the drama. Some principle of attraction seems to impel the victim to fly toward the spider, indeed to return repeatedly if it does not become entangled the first time. Hutchinson, who studied *Mastophora* very thoroughly and has continued his interest in the spider to the present time, found the method of capture a most successful one and was inclined to believe that an agreeable odor was emitted either by the spider or the silken line. The dearth of suitable moth prey in the vicinity and the consistent success of the spider contributed to this inference. Longman's conclusions were similar, and they are largely contained in our quotation from his splendid paper. It seems reasonable to suppose that the attraction must be the chemical one of odor or a visual one. The moth is probably well supplied with receptors for space perception, for we know that many moths are attracted to baits and other odoriferous objects.

On the other hand, it is more probable that visual stimuli could be responsible for sending the moth into the jaws of the spider. The compound eye of the moth is a wonderful organ, specialized for nocturnal use and no doubt responsive to even small quantities of light stimulus. The glistening globule of viscid silk or, perhaps, the pale body of the spider itself, might be sufficiently illuminated by light rays, either not evident to man's diurnal eye or outside his visual range, to cross the responsive threshold in the eye of the moth.

However, there is no real evidence that either of the above alternatives even approximates the truth. The true explanation may well be that the whole business is only a fortuitous one, largely dependent on the random flying activities of the moth. Mere chance would bring one or more within the reach of the spider almost every night, and if not, the creature could go without food for days or weeks without being profoundly affected. Although this solution would be at variance with the reasonable impressions of two eminent investigators, its simplicity has much in its favor.

But let us return to Mastophora, who hangs on her trapeze line and awaits the approach of her prey. With what senses does she detect the presence of the flying insect and know just when to hurl the viscid globule? Her eight small eyes are of little use to her, and at night they probably convey no visual impressions at all. At the expense of better eyesight, her progenitors developed an expansive web and substituted touch-vision to keep them informed of activity in any part of it. Her relatives respond to the presence of prey by rushing to the spot and are informed of its nature by the vibratory disturbance. Although reduced in size, the web on which Mastophora hangs in midair is still adequate as a sounding board. She feels the vibrations heralding the arrival of the moth and orients herself accordingly.

The egg sacs of the Bolas Spiders are hardly less spectacular than the spiders themselves. As is the case with many spiders, the process of laying the eggs and encasing them in a distinctive sac is a long and exhausting ritual. Even so, several egg sacs may be spun by the same female at intervals of about a week apart. In Mastophora the sacs are essentially equal in size to the spider herself and are hung near the site of the angling grounds, sometimes in the sun but more often partly protected by leaves. The sacs are hard objects that resemble nuts or other plant fruits. The distinctive feature of the sacs is the long stem, which is drawn off the rounded base and attached to twigs or leaves, and the globular base, which is variegated with light and dark kinds of silk. In one of our species the base is broadly attached to a twig, and the stem is free. In another the sac is somewhat bell-shaped and embellished with lateral extensions, the whole resembling a small, dried apple.

The female usually dies in the late fall and rarely lives to see her progeny emerge from the egg sac, an event that ordinarily occurs in the spring. The emergence of the spiderlings from the cocoon is an occasion of great moment in the life of the species and a thrilling sight to one who is lucky enough to be on hand to watch it. A small opening near the base of the stem, perhaps the result of concerted action on the part of the creatures inside, is barely large enough to allow each tiny spiderling to wriggle through. As soon as one has emerged, another appears at the small opening, and then another, until they are out in considerable numbers and beginning to string their silken lines on neighboring objects. The instinct to move upward asserts itself strongly, and soon many of the spiderlings are scattered far from the egg sac and many of them are being wafted into the air on their silken lines. Within a few hours, the whole family of perhaps 150 spiderlings may be far dispersed from the site of the empty egg sac. Inasmuch as some female bolas spin as many as five egg sacs, the possible progeny from a single spider may be as many as 700 spiderlings. The rarity of adult spiders of this group indicates that the mortality must be exceedingly high among their newly emerged spiderlings.

Up to now, all of our attention has been focused upon the female Bolas Spider and her egg sacs. What about her mate? The answer is found in a closer perusal of the spiderlings wriggling out of the small aperture in the cocoon before us. Some of the creatures are much redder than the others and have the tiny palpi armed with bulbous enlargements, which signalize the male spider. Closer inspection shows that these palpi are fully developed and indicates that these pygmies, averaging about one-sixteenth inch in length, are the mates of the Bolas Spider, which herself frequently attains a body length ten times as great. These adult males crawl out of the sac in company with baby sisters of equal size, which will not become full-grown and sexually mature for several months.

After studying the contents of various egg sacs in different stages of development, we are able to reconstruct the probable happenings within the egg sac. Several days or weeks after the eggs are laid, their pearly white shells break and allow the still embryonic spiders greater freedom for further development. The first true molt brings to light the creature we know so well as a spiderling, a small replica of the adult, which is able to spin and to eat. The males at this stage are precocious and have the palpi enlarged, but they are still not fully developed, being comparable in appearance to the penultimate stage of most male spiders. Following the first true molt, most spiders break out of the egg sac, and no doubt that happens often with *Mastophora*. However, very frequently another molt is undergone within the egg sac before the males walk out of the sac—perfect adults as far as we are able to judge on the basis of external appearance. Naturally, we have no way of knowing without resorting to histological means whether a corresponding maturity is present within the creature, but from analogy with most other spiders, we can predict that this is probably so.

From an egg sac of *Mastophora cornigera*, sent to me from California through the generosity of Mr. Hutchinson, there issued on September 1, 147 spiderlings, of which 72 were baby females and 75 mature males. The young sisters that desert the egg sac in company with their tiny brothers must undergo several molts before they attain maturity. The question that immediately arises is whether there are in the vicinity contemporary, mature females to be matched with the precocious males. If emergence occurs in the fall, which in California may be a more frequent occurrence than is generally supposed, many females may still be available, and perhaps even the parent female may be visited by one of her precocious sons. On the other hand, it is probable that the new generation emerges oftener in the spring, and that the tiny males must then live through the long months until the female spiderlings attain adulthood.

Rarely within the limits of one small group of creatures do we find such an array of startling peculiarities and amazing habits. Such sensational performers deserve fuller study from biologists lucky enough to come in contact with them.

> I strove with none; for none was worth my strife;
>   Nature I loved, and next to Nature, Art;
> I warmed both hands before the fire of life;
>   It sinks, and I am ready to depart.

WALTER SAVAGE LANDOR (On his 75th birthday)

THE SNAKES ARE ABOUT

by T. H. White

This business of linking T. H. White with snakes is a bit mis-leading. Anyone who inquires for this English author now may get the answer that Sir John Falstaff received when he asked Mistress Ford—one of the Merry Wives of Windsor—the where-abouts of her husband: "He's a-birding, sweet Sir John." T. H. White has, indeed, gone in for falconry with enthusiasm in recent years, and his book The Goshawk, *published in this country in 1951, is something of a modern literary classic on the care and training of hunting hawks. To be sure, a goshawk is an accipiter and not a falcon, but the term falconry is extended to cover eagles and accipiters as well as falcons in the art of training raptorial birds to hunt at the command and under the control of human masters.*

Terence Hanbury White was born in Bombay, India, May 29, 1906, and was educated at Cambridge University. He was a teacher at Stowe for some nine or ten years after graduation, and, when not in the schoolroom or sleeping, he spent his time either roaming the countryside or writing. He gave up teaching in 1936 to concentrate on writing and has turned out a baker's dozen of books on an astonishing variety of subjects—modern love, Arthurian legend, Shakespearian England, field sports, and social satire, all with a deft touch and deep insight approaching genius. He paints too, wears a beard, and goes fly-fishing in sea-son. He has woven a considerable amount of natural history into the otherwise pure reading matter of half a dozen of his books. The selection that follows is taken from one such book, England Have My Bones, *published in 1936. From what edition of Shake-speare the author borrowed this title is a minor mystery. The first folio has the hapless Prince Arthur saying: "Heaven take my soule and England keep my bones." Most editions stick to the*

*same wording. It could be that the author quoted from memory
or from some* King John *he found on a library shelf at the British
Falconers' Club in London. Or perhaps it's that* T. H. White, *a
brilliant individualist, prefers to wear his rue with a difference.*

THE snakes are about again. Last year I used to go out with
Hughesdon to catch them, and then turn them loose in the
sitting-room. At one time I had about a dozen. There are
four in the room just now.

Grass snakes are fascinating pets. It is impossible to impose upon
them, or to steal their affections, or to degrade either party in any
way. They are always inevitably themselves, and with a separate
silurian beauty. The plates of the jaw are fixed in an antediluvian
irony. They move with silence, unless in crackling grass or with a scaly
rustle over a wooden floor, pouring themselves over obstacles and
round them. They are inquisitive. They live loose in the room, except
that I lock them up at nights so that the maids can clean in the mornings without being frightened. The big open fireplace is full of moss
and ferns, and there is an aquarium full of water in which they can
soak themselves if they wish. But mostly they prefer to lie under the
hot pipes of the radiator, or to burrow inside the sofa. We had to
perform a Caesarian operation on the sofa last year, to get out a big
male.

It is nice to come into the room and look quickly round it, to see
what they are doing. Perhaps there is one behind Aldous Huxley on
the book-shelves, and it is always worth moving the left-hand settle
away from the wall. One of them has a passion for this place and
generally falls out. Another meditates all day in the aquarium, and
the fourth lives in the moss.

Or it is nice to be working in the arm-chair, and to look up suddenly at an imagined sound. A female is pouring from behind the sofa.
As the floor is of polished wood she gets a poor grip on it (she prefers
the sheepskin hearth-rug) and elects to decant herself along the angle
between wall and floor. Here she can press sideways as well as downwards, and gets a better grip.

She saw our movement as we looked up, and now stops dead, her
head raised in curiosity. Her perfect forked tongue flickers blackly
out of its specially armoured hole (like the hole for the starting handle

in a motor, but constructed so as to close itself when not in use) and waves itself like lightning in our direction. It is what she feels with in front of her, her testing antennae, and this is her mark of interrogation. An empathic movement: she can't reach us, but she is thinking Who or What? And so the tongue comes out. We sit quite still.

The tongue comes out two or three times (its touch on the hand is as delicate as the touch of a butterfly) and flickers in the air. It is a beautiful movement, with more down in it than up. It can be faintly reproduced by waggling the bent forefinger quickly in a vertical plane. Then she goes on with her pour, satisfied, towards her objective in the moss. We sit as still as a mouse.

I try to handle these creatures as little as possible. I do not want to steal them from themselves by making them pets. The exchange of hearts would degrade both of us. It is only that they are nice. Nice to see the strange wild things loose, living their ancient unpredictable lives with such grace. They are more ancient than the mammoth, and infinitely more beautiful. They are dry, cool and strong. The fitting and variation of the plates, the lovely colouring, the movement, their few thoughts: one could meditate upon them like a jeweller for months.

It is exciting to catch them. You go to a good wood, and look for snaky places in it. It is difficult to define these. There has to be undergrowth, but not overgrowth: a sunny patch, a glade or tiny clearing in the trees: perhaps long grass and a bit of moss, but not too wet. You go into it and there is a rustle. You can see nothing, but dive straight at the sound. You see just a few inches of the back, deceptively fluid for catching hold of, as it flashes from side to side. You must pounce on it at once, for there is no time to think, holding it down or grabbing it by head or tail or anywhere. There is no time to select. This is always exciting to me, because I frighten myself by thinking that it might be an adder. As a matter of fact, there are very few adders in the Shire, and in any case they move differently. An adder would strike back at you, I suppose, but a grass snake does not. It pretends to strike, with mouth wide open and the most formidable-looking fangs; but it stops its head within a millimetre of the threatened spot, a piece of bluff merely.

When you have grabbed your snake, you pick it up. Instantly it curls round your hand and arm, hissing and lunging at you with the almost obtuse angle of its jaw; exuding a white fluid from its vent, which has a metallic stink like acetylene. Take no notice of it at all.

Like an efficient governess with a refractory child, you speak sharply
to the smelly creature and hold it firmly. You take hold of its tail,
unwind it, roll it in a ball (it is wriggling so much that it generally
helps in this), tie it up in your handkerchief, put it in your trouser
pocket and look for another.

When you loose it in your sitting-room it rushes off along the floor,
swishing frantically but making little progress on the polished wood,
and conceals itself in the darkest corner. At night, when you come to
lock it up, it makes a fuss. It produces the smell again, and the hiss.
In the morning it is the same. Next night perhaps the smell is omitted,
or fainter. In a few days there is only a dim hiss, a kind of grumble.
This goes as well, until there is only a gentle protesting undulation
as it is lifted off the ground.

I remember particularly two of last year's snakes. One was a baby
male (the yellow markings are brighter in the male) only about eight
inches long. He was a confiding snake, and I once took him to church
in my pocket, to make him a Christian and to comfort me during the
sermon. I hope it was not an undue interference with his life: I never
carried him about like that again, he seemed to like the warmth of my
pocket, and I believe he did not change his creed.

Talking of Christians, I never christened the snakes. To have called
them names would have been ridiculous, as it is with cars. A snake
cannot have a name. If it had to be addressed I suppose it would be
addressed by its generic title: Snake.

The other one, I regret to say, was nearly a pet. She was a well-
grown female with a scar on her neck. I suppose this had been done
to her by man. It was the scar that first attracted me to her, or rather
made me take special notice of her, because she was easy to distinguish. I soon found that when the time came for putting her to bed
she did not undulate. She never troubled to conceal herself at bedtime, nor to slide away from me when I approached. She would crawl
right up to me, and pour over my feet while I was working. There
was no horrible affection or prostration; only she was not afraid of me.
She went over my feet because they were in a direct line with the
place she was making for. She trusted, or at least was indifferent.

It was a temptation. One coldish afternoon she was sitting in my
chair when I wanted to read. I picked her up and put her in my lap.
She was not particularly comfortable, and began to go away. I held her
gently by the tail. She decided that it was not worth a scene, and
stayed. I put my free hand over her, and she curled up beneath it, the

head sticking out between two fingers and the tongue flickering every now and then, when a thought of curiosity entered her slow, free mind.

After that I used sometimes to sit with my two hands cupped, and she would curl between them on cold days. My hands were warm, that was all.

It was not quite all. I am afraid a hideous tinge of possession is creeping into this account. When other people came into the room she used to hiss. I would be dozing with her tight, dry coils between my palms, and there would be a hiss. The door would have opened and somebody would have come in. Or again, if I showed her to people she would hiss at them. If they tried to catch her, she would pour away. But when I gave her to them she was quiet.

I think I succeeded in keeping my distance. At any rate, she had a love affair with one of the males. I remember finding them coiled together on the corner table: a double rope-coil of snake which looked like a single one, except that it had two heads. I did not realise that this was an affair of the heart, at the time.

Later on she began to look ill. She was lumpy and flaccid. I became worried about the commissariat. Snakes rarely eat—seldom more than once a fortnight—but when they do eat they are particular. The staple food is a live frog, swallowed alive and whole. Anybody who has ever kept snakes will know how difficult it is to find a frog. The whole of the Shire seems to be populated by toads: one can scarcely move without treading on a toad: but toads disagree with snakes. They exude something from the skin.

I had been short of frogs lately, and (as I merely kept them loose in the aquarium so that the snakes could help themselves when they wanted) did not know when she had last had a meal. I thought I was starving her and became agitated. I spent hours looking for frogs, and found one eventually, but she wouldn't touch it. I tried a gold-fish, but that was no good either. She got worse. I was afraid she was poisoned, or melancholic from her unnatural surroundings.

Then came the proud day. I got back at half-past twelve, and looked for her on the hearth-rug, but she was not there. She was in the aquarium, sunlit from the french windows. Not only she. I went closer and looked. There were twenty-eight eggs.

Poor old lady, she was in a dreadful state. Quite apathetic and powerless, she could scarcely lift her head. Her body had fallen in on itself, leaving two ridges, as if she were quite a slim snake dressed in clothes too big for her. When I picked her up she hung limp, as if she were actually dead; but her tongue flickered. I didn't know what to do.

I got a gold-fish bowl and half-filled it with fresh grass clippings. I put her in it, with the frog, and tied paper over the top as if it were a jam jar. I made holes in the paper and took it out on to the lawn, in the full glare of the summer sun. Snakes are woken up by heat, and the bowl would concentrate the sun's beams. It was all I could think of or do, before I went in to lunch.

I came back in half an hour. The bowl was warm with moisture, the grass clippings were browning, the frog was gone; and inside was Matilda (she positively deserved a name) as fit as a flea and twice as frisky.

The scarred snake may have been a good mistress, but she was a bad mother. If she had known anything about maternity, she would not have laid her eggs in the aquarium. It seems that water is one of the things that is fatal to the eggs of grass snakes. I picked them out, and put them in another gold-fish bowl, this time full of grass clippings that were already rotten. Then I left them in the sun. They only went mouldy.

She was completely tame, and the inevitable happened. The time came for me to go away for two months, so I gave her her liberty. I took her out into the fountain court (next time it shall be into the deepest and most unpopulated forest) and put her on the ground in the strong July sunlight. She was delighted by it, and pleased to go. I watched her to-froing away, till she slipped into the angle of a flower-bed, and then went resolutely indoors. There were plenty of other things in the future besides grass snakes.

That night I went down to the lake to bathe, and stepped over a dead snake in the moonlight. I guessed before I looked for the scar. I had kept my distance successfully, so that there were no regrets at parting, but I had destroyed a natural balance. She had lost her bitter fear of man: a thing which it is not wise to lose.

I feel some difficulty in putting this properly. Some bloody-minded human being had come across her on a path and gone for her with a stick. She was harmless, useless dead, very beautiful, easy prey. He slaughtered her with a stick, and grass snakes are not easy to kill. It is easy to maim them, to bash them on the head until the bones are pulp. The lower jaw no longer articulates with the upper one, but lies sideways under the crushed skull, shewing the beautiful colours of its unprotected inner side. The whole reserved face suddenly looks pitiful, because it has been spoilt and ravaged. The black tongue makes a feeble flicker still.

These things had been done, to a creature which was offering confidence, with wanton savagery. Why? Why the waste of beauty and the degradation to the murderer himself? He was not creating a beauty by destroying this one. He cannot even have considered himself clever.

When well-appareled April on the heel
Of limping winter treads.

SHAKESPEARE, *Romeo and Juliet*

Night's candles are burnt out, and jocund day
Stands tiptoe on the misty mountain-tops.

SHAKESPEARE, *Romeo and Juliet*

I know a bank whereon the wild thyme blows,
Where ox-lips and the nodding violet grows;
Quite over-canopied with lush woodbine,
With sweet musk-roses and with eglantine.

SHAKESPEARE, *Midsummer Night's Dream*

THE GHOST CRAB

by Howard J. Shannon

Half a century ago Howard J. Shannon was sketching and painting on the dunes and along the great beaches on the south shore of Long Island. It wasn't long before the artist discovered that there was more offshore, on the beach, and among the dunes than met the eye. He began to fish the waters, dig in the sand, and explore the dunes. Of his findings by the seaside the late Roy Waldo Miner, former Curator of Marine Zoology at the American Museum of Natural History wrote: "He has discovered new species and new facts of life history." In short, the artist became a fine naturalist and the ultimate result was The Book of the Seashore, *admirably written and beautifully illustrated by Howard J. Shannon. The account of the ghost crab and its mysterious ways is taken from that book of which a first edition is a treasured volume in the compiler's library, treasured not only for its contents but for an inscription on the flyleaf: "To John Kieran, with a Merry Christmas, 1935. Theodore Roosevelt Jr." Author and naturalist like his famous father, it will be remembered that Brigadier General Theodore Roosevelt, Jr., died of exhaustion in battle in Normandy with the Fourth Infantry Division in July, 1944.*

NEVER will I forget my startling introduction to this ghostly creature. It stood, white as the sand, poised on the crest of a dune; then, swift as a hare, it dashed sidewise away upon its eight flashing feet—for it was a ghost crab. After a time, when again I idly glanced in that direction, *there it was once more*, fixed, immobile, and apparently studying me with a steady implacable stare. Certainly it is a disturbing creature, so white as hardly to be distinguished from the sand upon which it moves—hence the ghostly name—and the only large crustacean along our north Atlantic shores which has deserted its native water element to live on the precarious land.

In fact, in the eccentricity of its every act, one doubts the wisdom of that hazardous experiment. A fearful caution veils all its elusive goings to and fro, with sudden disappearances from one area to be followed, very soon after, by equally mysterious reappearances in another, and often so close at hand as to seem truly uncanny. These secretive and almost unreal maneuvers seem like confessions of a profound uneasiness experienced by a marine animal while attempting a partial adjustment to that dangerous and foreign realm—the land.

That peering gaze, too, with which it scrutinizes a chance intruder, and that frenzied combative pose which it strikes when apprehended—both seem the result of a confused uncertainty. It also possesses an even more disquieting trait. I refer to its actual advance upon an accidental human visitor. Yet such hidden deviltries seem to inspire that steady approach, such a calculating threat seems to emanate from its prolonged and resentful scrutiny, that one instinctively perceives in this crab an alien being. An emergent apparition from the marine stands before us, foreign and untransmogrified from its elder past when more bestial struggles for existence prevailed in the depths of the sea.

Its curious and ghostly elusiveness had attracted me from the very first. Even now, after twelve years of absence from its habitat, that quality impresses me again, as well as its curious intentness of scrutiny, its sidling advance upon an intruder, and its swifter flight. For again I am on this southern New Jersey shore, near Longport, where *Ocypoda arenaria* lives.

Their burrows are all about me. Some, situated along high-tide line, are almost within reach of the water. But most of them are well above the tidal zone or along the base of the dunes—a congregation of circular openings each accompanied by its mound of cast-up sand. Yet it seems a dead city, a windswept reach of shore punctured with many idle doorways about which small mussel shells or other marine debris are strewn. But they seem bereft of life. Do the crabs often emerge in daylight? Do they feed at night—or when? How did they come to desert their home in the sea for the precarious land? Little is told in the books—and not all of that is reliable.

Let us station ourselves, on this September afternoon, beside a dune slope—and wait. For a long time there is no sign of life. The settlement of the ghost crabs seems as deserted as Pompeii; a relic, like that tragic city, of a once populous past. My eyes continually glance from one burrow to another seeking *some* sign of stirring life. Still no object moves. Wait! What is that whitish buff object lying low along the edge of a distant burrow? It wasn't there a few moments ago. See! A pair of alert, black-tipped eye-stalks is lifted, periscope-like, above the sand. The creature, crouching low, scrutinizes its surroundings. So persistently does it remain so, motionless, apparently inert, that my eye strays farther up the shore.

Look! There comes a fleet ghost. It's fully exposed—and running! Now it pauses, moves slowly along in a sidling zigzag manner, stops again, lifts itself, with legs a-tiptoe, watches—and how steadily and persistently! Suddenly alarmed, it crouches low with body close-pressed against the sand. Again it stands erect and cleans a dimmed eye by clasping that stalked organ in its upper, hair-fringed mouth parts, slipping it through the cleansing hairs and then releasing it until the eye once more springs aloft, erect and watchful. Now, sidling along, the crab occasionally hastens its progress by short running starts which bring it farther and farther down the shore. See! It is actually approaching me! Nearer and nearer it comes, until it faces me squarely. More hesitant now, it advances within a dozen feet—then halts as if puzzled by this large dark object reposing within its own domains. Again it moves restlessly about. Quite evidently, the creature is disturbed, uncertain, not at all assured as to what course to pursue. After a moment, it creeps slowly away, crouches for a brief time in a chosen depression for another scrutiny; then rises and slowly disappears far down the shore.

That cautious appraisal and reappraisal of its surroundings interrupts its every activity. Witness, for example, this other crab about to dig out its burrow.

Suddenly two legs emerge along one side of the burrow entrance. Then an eye, supported on its long stalk, appears and studiously scans the neighborhood. This watching phase of the procedure is prolonged sometimes for two minutes, by actual count. But my patience is greater than the crab's. See! Fully reassured at last, the ghostly creature suddenly walks out upon the exposed beach, hugging a mass of damp sand against its left side by means of one claw and two forelegs which are clasped about it. Quickly it throws its burden outward over the terrain with a sharp fillip of these carrying parts, then immediately darts back into the burrow—but only part way. It remains half in and half out, studiously regarding the neighborhood again with the same untiring scrutiny. Finally it becomes fully satisfied and darts out of sight.

Sometimes its cautious study takes on an amusing repetitiousness. For it may start to retreat, then pause, *only to emerge again* part way, and repeat that steady stare, as if some object in the neighborhood had aroused a deeper suspicion. After a final retreat, often a lengthy one, the series of movements is repeated: first, a cautious eyeing of the surroundings; second, the sudden emergence; third, the casting away of the dug material, and then the retreat again.

Its immense trepidation, indeed, is often manifested in other and most curious ways. A fly buzzing overhead will cause its sudden disappearance. So also will a sudden uprushing lip of foam sent far toward its domicile by the incoming tide. Obviously, the crab is beset on every hand by forces not understood and perhaps only dimly seen.

But see! The burrow digger we have been watching now executes a most curious maneuver. It walks slowly out over the lumps of sand so recently cast out, bestrides one, and then, by steadily tramping and pressing it, gradually crumbles it to fragments. We afterward discover that this is not, by any means, a rare procedure. The outer and under surfaces of the claws are employed much as we might use the knuckles and backs of our hands and fingers to pulverize some coherent substance. Meanwhile the animal has been watching me; and now, strange to say, it walks in my direction, slowly, steadily, with an immense deliberation. The creature *is* certainly spookish. It halts, and again moves restlessly about. Evidently the crab is suspicious of the large dark object lying so silently there. Was that breaking up of the sand fragments, then, a procedure designed to clear away the obstructed view?

True, they are occasionally picked over after pulverization, and the creature may be seen daintily carrying small particles to its mouth. So this maneuver may be designed, in part, to uncover small food elements, such as minute crustaceans, which form no inconsiderable part of the crab's food. Often, however, no such feeding transpires. The breaking up and tamping down of the sand lumps seem independent of any such after-act. Perhaps an endeavor to clear the view *is* the true explanation.

Immense trepidation is, undoubtedly, the price this creature has paid for its rash desertion of its native water element. Such an expression seems almost present amid that curious agglomeration of features which is not a face and yet masks an alert and unsleeping intelligence. See! Its suspicions *are* deeply aroused. It retires within the burrow and becomes engaged at some new-found task at the very entrance. (Subsequent observations have shown that the crab first brings up rounded bunches of sand from below and packs them about the immediate entrance, where they form a shelf-like support.) Now the crab's right legs reach far out over the beach surface, grasp a generous armful of loose material, and then drag it inward. The crab is sealing the entrance. Now it turns as if on a pivot, to repeat the procedure on the opposite side, and totally disappears. An examination shows that the burrow is completely closed.

Foraging operations, too, are not without interest. Look! Two crabs are now sallying forth to search for desirable food along the tide-swept area. An interruption occurs. A peacock butterfly, fluttering along, flies so low as to pass only a foot above one crab's shell. Instantly, it leaps aloft like a cat, to catch it. The leap falls short; the butterfly sails away. Evidently, the crabs must content themselves with less fancy food today. So a tangled mass of weeds and mussels is found in the tidal zone. One crab grasps this firmly and, by toilfully tugging away, is able to drag it to its burrow. There it is roughly adjusted upon the nearby mound of cast-up sand, when the hungry creature squats upon it, complacently reposes there, and daintily begins to pick apart and carry to its mouth the disengaged fragments. Truly, it's a picture of contentment and sufficiency.

Farther up the beach, a disturbance occurs. Two other foragers have fallen afoul of each other. Rising on tiptoe, they sidle about, looking for an opening; then, clashing their claws, fall to in desperate struggle. However, the encounter is brief. Soon separating, they draw entirely apart and sidle away.

Young crabs, too, little fellows, only an inch wide, that flit like fragments of wind-blown foam over the sand, are also "watchers," although their field of vision is more restricted. Often their burrows are dug only a few feet from those of the adults, thus creating a real community scene. Their movements, too, are possessed of such an instantaneous celerity that the small pepper-and-salt bodies, so closely resembling the sand, can hardly be seen at all. On the open beach, they move by sudden running starts that are interrupted by equally sudden halts, quite in the manner of the beach spiders, which, in fact, they almost resemble. So, even more than the parents, they are really "ghost crabs," cloaked, as they are, by protective coloration.

Drive a youngster from its burrow or block its return and watch the result. The small creature immediately flattens itself, and, by grasping the loose sand in its outreaching legs, is able to draw it inward and over itself like a garment. Then the legs also sink and bury themselves quite out of sight. Only the rim or forward part of the shell or carapace is now visible—and one alert eye erect on its stalk. Soon, as a reconnoitering measure, the other stalked eye also uprears itself. Now both are shining brightly aloft and surveying the dubious situation. A sudden gesture of my hand—and both eyes snap down into their sockets. Soon, however, the right eye once more lifts itself erect, periscoping to its hidden owner below the sand authentic news of the hazardous conditions above. Again my hand waves. Once more both eye-stalks snap down! After a long interval of quiescence upon my part, however, while I am engaged in sketching, once more both eyes cautiously lift themselves until the little crab is in possession of its full visual capacity. I wave my hand again, and, most amusingly, the left eye alone snaps down. The other, remaining brightly aloft, seems to say, "I am not as frightened as I was." Then, as I move quietly away, the impish creature disengages itself from its blanket of sand and skitters off.

This crab's ancient home in the sea has been forsworn so long that it is adapted for life no longer in that element. So, when danger threatens, it seeks safety in self-burial, as we have seen. Yet, under exceptional circumstances, as when cornered, these "ghosts" will retreat into their former native element, the sea.

One day as I approached the familiar colony from the south side of a breakwater that parallels the ocean, a large ghost crab was seen moving along between wall and sea. Disturbed by my approach, he retreated behind some spiles and remained there. So I quietly seated myself until he should emerge. This soon happened, when he quietly continued his progress up the shore. To test his fleetness, and also to discover what the crab would do when caught between ocean and wall, I suddenly rushed forward and touched him. Immediately, he was off! As quickly, I followed.

Now, fully alarmed, he dashed down into the swirling waters that were rushing, in foam-covered sheets, far up the strand. This ancient home was his no longer, yet he fled to it for immediate protection. As I continued to advance, he retreated farther and farther into the sucking swirl of the on-rushing waters, even to the extent of almost completely and irrevocably entering the crashing turmoil of the surf itself. Clutching the wet sand with grasping claws, he held his uncertain foothold. Then, as I mercifully withdrew, he permitted the impulse of the oncoming wave rushes to carry him farther and farther toward his known and habitual home of dry land. At my second approach, he again retreated, and even into greater danger than before. Upon my subsequent withdrawal, however, he slowly and laboriously emerged, with many a setback as the spent waves swept outward over him, and appeared once more upon the sands. Then he moved away toward the farther shore.

Upon second thought, we see there is little mystery in this adoption of a land habit by certain crabs. For the oscillating shore levels of prehistoric time might easily have forced certain creatures to a terrestrial mode of life. Even today, some marine species temporarily seek the land of their own volition. Sometimes at sunrise, when a still sea sends hardly a creaming ripple up the strand, blue crabs will emerge and walk along the immediate waterline searching for food. An accidental blocking of a much-used channel may force these crabs to travel over the new-made land in order to reach the sea. Such an occasion has been described by Willard Nye, Jr., who saw a migration of this kind over the blocked entrance of Quick Sands Pond in Rhode Island. Owing to the blocking of their usual autumn channel down to the sea by reason of this drifted bar, many blue crabs, to the number of scores and hundreds, steadily emerged upon the land and "trekked" over into the deeper water beyond rather than endure the winter freezing in the shallows of the pond.

So the transition from a watery habitat to one of a terrestrial nature is not as remarkable and inexplicable as it might appear at first sight. A wholesale elevation of the early continental shores, known to have occurred more than once during our local prehistoric past, might have readily immured many crabs in landlocked bays far removed from the sea. Later, these areas could have become wholly dry. Thus, perhaps, certain adaptive types were persuaded to habituate themselves to an existence on the land and to forget entirely, during the long ages of a gradual habit modification, their former marine home.

THE AIR BLADDER IN FISHES

by Brian Curtis

Who cares about the air bladder in fishes? Well, sir—or madam, as the case may be—it's wonderful what a writer or lecturer can do with any topic when he knows his field and has enthusiasm for his work. This selection is offered as a sample of that combination. Brian Curtis, who at one time was in charge of biological investigations on fresh-water fish for the State of California, is not only an ichthyologist of high repute and wide experience but a witty writer to boot, as the reader will see. In addition to which, fishes are important creatures from many standpoints, and we should never miss a chance to learn more about them. They pro-vide a goodly portion of the food supply of the world. They are of ancient and honorable lineage. Even the humble anchovy is touched with greatness in direct line of descent. Its ancestors, like those of all fishes, were the first creatures with real back-bones, a feature that made them the aristocrats of the Paleozoic Era and the forerunners of all the vertebrates on the face of the globe. The following selection is a chapter extracted from The Life Story of the Fish, *written by Brian Curtis and published in* 1949.

ONCE upon a time, all the bony fishes breathed air. This was many, many million years ago, long before there were any human beings. The bony fishes were then living in streams, lakes, pools, and swamps, where they at first breathed only water. When, in the Devonian era, the climate changed, the inland waters began to dry up and stagnate. They no longer contained enough oxygen to sustain animal life. By processes which we still do not entirely understand but which we name evolution, the fish acquired a pouch, opening out of the throat, into which air could be taken to provide the oxygen which the water no longer held.

By the time the climate changed again and the waters increased once more, some of the fishes, armed with the new pouch which made them free of water, had gone out on land and become amphibians and reptiles. A few remained in the water but kept on breathing air, like the present African lung-fish. The majority ceased to breathe air and went back to complete water-dwelling, but they retained, and still carry, the remains of that pouch without which they would have perished. It is now called the air-bladder. And so both the human lungs and the fish's air-bladder derive from the same primitive respiratory sac.

The sharks and rays lack all trace of an air-bladder. All the bony fishes alive today either have an air-bladder, or show that they once had it. The sharks and rays must have left the fresh water and gone out to sea before the great Devonian drought set in. They must have branched off from the other fishes before the fish which gave rise to both humans and present fishes developed. We do not descend from sharks.

And this is a scientific fairy story which many scientists believe.

The air-bladder is, as its name indicates, a bladder. It lies between the stomach and the backbone. In the trouts it is a fragile organ, noticeable only in the inflated condition it assumes when the fish has been dwelling in deep water. In shallow-living individuals, it appears to be nothing more than a space inclosed at the top and sides by the inner body wall, at the bottom by a thin shining membrane which the angler's thumb-nail punctures when it pokes in to remove the blood from under the backbone in cleaning fish. In other species, like the Lower California "sea-bass" (*Totuava*) whose air-bladder the Chinese esteem highly as a soup-base, it is a conspicuous sac with thick walls which shut it off from the other organs. In all the soft-rayed fishes—the salmon, trout, tarpon, herring, pike, pickerel—a tube leads from the air-bladder to the gullet. This is the tube through which their ancestors breathed air, and because they still retain it they are called primitive—near to the first fishes. In the other fishes the tube no longer exists, and they are called advanced.

What the air-bladder used to do is pretty well known. It saved the fish from perishing by acting as an auxiliary air-breathing organ. What it does now is not altogether certain. In some fish it serves as an auxiliary sense organ, in others it is purely part of the internal workings. This is why we have given it a chapter to itself between the two.

The scientists of the old guesswork school had a theory which seemed to solve the problem. They believed that the purpose of the air-bladder was to act as a hydrostatic stabilizer—an organ which would permit the fish to change depth without trouble, and to remain at any level without exertion. If the fish is to be at rest in the water, its weight must be the same as that of the volume of water it occupies. Technically speaking, it must have the same specific gravity, the same weight-to-volume ratio, as the surrounding water. It will then neither rise nor sink. Suppose that a fish is so adjusted that this condition is met at a depth of, let us say, twenty feet. If the fish rises ten feet, the pressure of water on its exterior will decrease, and its body will, according to their theory, expand. It will take up more space. The volume of water it occupies increases. Since its weight is unchanged, it will now weigh less than that water, and it will be unable to stop rising until it floats at the surface. To avert this danger, the fish decreases the size of its air-bladder as it rises, and thus keeps its volume constant in spite of the diminishing pressure. The ratio of its weight to its volume remains unchanged, and it is still stable at ten feet depth.

When it descends to thirty feet, the reverse takes place. The pressure of the water on its exterior increases as it goes down, crushes it into a smaller space, diminishes its volume. It takes up less space, but its weight is unchanged. It therefore weighs more than the volume of water it occupies, and it would sink down and down with ever-increasing speed until it struck bottom, if it did not inflate its air-bladder sufficiently to keep its volume constant and thus maintain itself in equilibrium with the water. Some scientists even went further, and asserted that the fish could make active use of the air-bladder to raise or lower itself. If it wanted to rise, it pumped up its air-bladder, and up it popped. If it wanted to sink, it deflated its air-bladder, and down it went.

This theory is engaging, and has the merit of harboring some truth. Certainly in fish in which there is an air-bladder it must have a hydrostatic effect. In some this effect is far from beneficent. Most widely publicized is the "explosion" of fish from abyssal depths when brought to the surface by scientists. This is, of course, caused by the expansion of the air-bladder when released from pressure. Its occurrence is much rarer than is popularly supposed because many deep-sea fish do not have air-bladders, and their tissues, composed largely of water, are so incompressible that they do not expand. Less spectacular is the Great

Lakes fish known as the pike-perch. When brought up in a net from a depth of one hundred feet, it swells so that it floats helplessly at the surface. If a hollow needle is inserted through the flesh into the air-bladder, the hiss of escaping gas can be heard, and the fish is able to resume normal swimming. The pike-perch is obviously supersensitive in this respect, for we all know of other fish which can come up from greater depths with no such alarming manifestations. The swordfish is a famous diver, but when we get it to the top it is by no means a helpless floater.

So far our glimpses of the air-bladder have been far from reassuring. To the fish which we have mentioned, it seems to be about as pleasant a possession as we should find a hand-grenade which we had to carry around in our pockets, equipped with a barometric fuse which would set it off and blow us to pieces if we climbed a high hill or went up in an express elevator. However, we have been considering artificial conditions—abrupt, man-made changes. On the Pacific Coast the rock cod lives at a depth of 100 feet. Bring him to the top, and he is helplessly bloated, but let him spend a week in an aquarium, and he can reduce himself to normal. Another set of Pacific Coast residents, the lantern-fishes, have a family habit of spending the night at the surface of the sea but going down to depths of 600 feet for the day. Now, the pressure at 600 feet is nearly twenty atmospheres. If you bring them suddenly up from that depth, they are in a highly explosive state, and yet they make the round trip every day of their own volition —two changes of twenty atmospheres every twenty-four hours. The conclusion is that each of these two species can adjust the air-bladder to the conditions, but that it must be done gradually. The lantern-fish is quicker at it than the rock cod, but each has the capacity to accomplish it. The old theory is to some extent borne out, but appears in a new light. The air-bladder, instead of being something which helps the fish to change levels, is something which the fish has to guard against, to keep under control.

How does the fish make these adjustments? If he is one of the species which retain that tube leading from the gullet to the air-bladder, through which his ancestors used to take in air, it might be assumed that he uses this. It may be that in some cases he does, although at the time that he needs air most, to expand his bladder against increasing pressure as he descends, there is no air to be had, for he is under water; and further, it has been found that in some species the tube is so grown together, or so clogged with mucus, that there is little possibility of anything passing through it in either direction. Such fish, and the many species which lack the tube entirely, must have other methods. Principally, they depend on secretion of gas into, or absorption of gas out of, the air-bladder by the blood. This may seem like a mysterious and unnatural kind of operation, but it is a kind very commonly used in the life processes, both animal and vegetable. The fish's air-bladder has walls rich with thin-skinned blood-vessels, and these vessels have the ability to put forth gas into the interior of the bladder, thus pumping it up against external pressure, or to absorb gas from the interior of the bladder, thus preventing it from overexpanding when the external pressure is released. But the process is not, in most cases, a rapid one, and so the fish must have time to make the adjustment gradually.

At this point in their reasoning, a great light dawned on certain scientists, and they brought forth the theory that it was the duty of the air-bladder to keep the fish within certain depth limits, or to prevent it from making depth changes too suddenly. This is at first sight a tempting idea. Rapid changes of altitude bring about undesirable disturbances in our internal workings. And yet for us to go up to ten thousand feet from sea-level is no more, so far as change in pressure is concerned, than for a fish to come up from a ten-foot bottom to the surface, an act which he can accomplish in a few seconds. The air-bladder is there to prevent him from over-indulging this ability and thus unknowingly injuring himself. If he comes up too far or too fast, the air-bladder expands and pokes him in the stomach. If he goes down too far or too fast, his stomach pokes him in the air-bladder. In either case, he has an ache in his insides which warns him that something is wrong, and that he had better go back where he came from.

There is no question that something of this kind does happen. An Italian experimenter found that if he increased the pressure in the air-bladder by injecting sterile, air-free water, the fish tried to swim up, and if he reduced it the fish tried to swim down. In other words, increased pressure gave the fish the sensation that he was too far down and had better come up, and *vice versa*. This proves that an air-bladder out of adjustment with the depth does warn the fish to seek a different level, but it does not prove that the same fish, if it had no air-bladder, would have any disturbance in its other organs at that depth. The whole theory of the air-bladder serving as a warning pressure gauge is wrecked by the number of fish which have no air-bladder at all, and which safely make great changes in their level just the same. The halibut sometimes lies on bottom at a thousand feet, sometimes feeds at the surface. It has no air-bladder. The chub mackerel has an air-bladder, the common mackerel has not. They are not only almost indistinguishable in appearance, but they frequently live side by side and school together. It is difficult to believe in the indispensability of an instrument which one of them gets along perfectly without.

At this point we have to stop and consider the connection which the air-bladder makes with the ear in some fishes. Controversy has gone on for years about this apparatus, one school of thought holding that it serves to keep the fish more completely informed as to the state of its air-bladder, the other, that it is a hearing mechanism.

In the cod and some other fishes, the connection takes place merely through forked lobes of the forward end of the air-bladder which rest against the auditory capsules. Much more complicated is the system found in a great group of fresh-water fishes which includes not only such familiar forms as the catfish, the carp, and the sucker, but also the characins so abundant in South America and in fish-fanciers' aquaria. Here there are four small bones linked together with movable hinges. These are called, after their discoverer, the Weberian ossicles, but they are not to be confused with the ossicles in our ears, the hammer, anvil, and stirrup. The latter derive, as we have seen, from three bones in the fish's jaw, and the carp is still using them to eat with, whereas his Weberian ossicles he has improvised out of the forward end of his backbone. But, however different their origin, there is a similarity in their present action, for our ossicles form a bony linkage between our membranous ear-drum and our auditory capsule, and the carp's Weberian ossicles form a bony linkage between the membrane of his air-bladder and his auditory capsule. It is this similarity which first suggested that the Weberian ossicles might be used in hearing: the tense air-bladder would be well adapted to receive vibrations coming through water, and would use the ossicles to transmit them to the ear.

The opponents were quick to point out that while this might be all very well when the air-bladder was fully expanded, it would not work at all when the air-bladder, in the course of its hydrostatic duties, reached the shrunken state. In that state, not only would the membrane of the bladder be so relaxed as to be no use in receiving sound-waves, but the ossicles would cease to press against the ear, and would be unable to transmit them. To these people it was evident that the system was a device to keep the fish informed as to its relative depth by the increase or decrease of the pressure transmitted by the ossicles from the air-bladder to the ear; and since the ears were known to have the equilibrating sense in the semicircular canals and their auxiliaries, it was thought not unreasonable to assume that they have this depth sense also.

The proponents of the hearing-mechanism theory offered two points in rebuttal. First, even if the air-bladder in these fish does change size with change in depth and pressure, which has never been proved, does it ever become slack? For as long as the fish remains under water there will be pressure on the bladder, and as long as there is pressure on it, its walls will remain tense and will be capable of receiving and transmitting sound-waves. Second, of what use would such an elaborate depth-measuring or pressure-registering device be to these fishes? The great majority of them live in comparatively shallow waters, and their opportunity to change levels is thereby very much limited. For that same reason—because for a great many of them the bottom is so near the top—they might find a device which strengthened their hearing very useful, especially if it enabled them to detect enemies above the surface.

It remained for the German physiologist whose experiments were described in the section on "Hearing" to settle the matter in a scientific manner. It will be recalled that he worked with a minnow, a member of the carp family, which is equipped with the Weberian ossicle connection between the ear and the air-bladder. He had found that his minnow had such an acute sense of hearing that it would show response to a tuning fork at a distance of 200 feet sounded so softly that a man under water (in the form of one of his students who volunteered to occupy the same tank with the fish) could hardly hear it. However, when he operated on the minnow and removed its air-bladder, its hearing became much poorer. It could still be trained to sounds, but they had to be a great deal louder. He found that the characins showed a well-developed sense of hearing; and that the mormyrids, Egyptian fish from the Nile in which the air-bladder makes a direct connection with the membranes in the cranium, hear as well as the minnow. Other species which lack the ear-air-bladder connection heard much less acutely; they could be trained to sounds, but the sounds had to be much louder. From this the trout and black bass anglers may take comfort, for absence of the connection in these fishes may be taken to indicate poor perception of sounds made in the air.

So the controversy has been settled, and it is accepted that in many fishes the Weberian ossicles are a part of the hearing apparatus which serve to transmit vibrations to the ear from the air-bladder, which acts as a resonant sounding-board. And to complete the argument, it is now known that, at least in many of these fishes, the forward compartment of the air-bladder can be closed off by a sphincter muscle, so that it can be kept taut no matter what the condition of the rest of this organ.

Thus, while there are still things about the air-bladder that we do not understand, there are many things which we actually do know. In the first place we definitely know that it still retains to some extent its original respiratory function. This, its primordial duty, is still one of its most widespread and most important ones. In the lung-fishes, those five species of living fossils scattered through Africa, South America, and Australia, this is true to such an extent that *Protopterus*, the African form called by the natives *Kamongo*, can no longer breathe water through his gills. If caught in a net so that he cannot reach the surface, he soon drowns; and he can live literally for years in the cocoon of dried mud which he makes for himself when the waters of his swamp disappear, in Devonian style, during times of drought.

The tarpon has perfectly good gills, but it also has a fine large open tube leading from the upper side of its gullet to its air-bladder, and the inside of the air-bladder is well supplied with blood-vessels. Young tarpon are frequently found in lagoons which have been cut off from the sea by sand-bars for so long that their water is stagnant, brackish, even sulphurous, and the tarpon's ability to survive there seems with little doubt to be due to its ability to come to the surface and take atmospheric air into its air-bladder.

But aside from the fish which actually "breathe" air in this way, a great many others use the air-bladder as a sort of respiratory reservoir. Deep-sea fishes have an unusually high percentage of oxygen in the air-bladder, and in some species, the deeper the fish the more oxygen. The oxygen content of the water is low at these depths, and the fish extracts from the water more than its current requirements and stores it up in the air-bladder against emergencies. Further, when fish are experimentally suffocated, the oxygen in the air-bladder is greatly reduced, showing that fish do fall back on this reserve when the normal oxygen supply is cut off.

In the second place we definitely know that, in those fish which have it, the air-bladder plays a part in the permanent equilibrium between the fish and the water. This is self-evident, and has nothing to do with adjustment of pressure to changing levels. It has to do with density. If a fish has an air-bladder, that air-bladder must be of such a size that the total volume of water occupied by the fish will weigh just about what the fish weighs, if he is not to be in constant struggle with his environment. The actual tissue of which most fishes are made is denser than water, and all fish would weigh more than water and tend to sink if they did not have some way of buoying themselves up. The air-bladder supplies this need, but paradoxically, all fishes do not have to have air-bladders to keep them from sinking. The shark lives in the open sea, and rarely sinks to bottom. He has no air-bladder, but instead he has an enormous liver full of oil which keeps him afloat. The flounder, on the other hand, is a very solid fish. It has no air-bladder, and you can almost feel the thud with which it lands when it settles on the bottom. It is heavier even than salt water.

In the much lighter, less buoyant fresh water, it is impossible for any fish to carry enough fat or oil to keep afloat. Without exception, the fresh-water species which lack the air-bladder are bottom dwellers. To those which wish to carry on their lives on a higher plane, it is indispensable as a float. Without it the pickerel and the muskellunge could not hang motionless in the water, waiting for their prey; without it, the black bass could not hover over its nest, guarding its offspring against marauders; and without it the trout and its relatives could not lie for hours just below the surface, rising to take in the food drifting down the stream. Further, to those fish which go from fresh to salt water, or the reverse, the ability to *adjust* the air-bladder is indispensable. For a fish in proper adjustment in fresh water will find itself too light when it goes into the heavier salt water, and it will tend to float at the surface unless it can reduce its air-bladder, thus reduce its total volume, and increase its weight-to-volume ratio, its specific gravity, to that of salt water. In the same way, when a fish adjusted to salt water goes into fresh water it will tend to sink unless it can increase its volume. This does not mean that the former fish will be unable to get below the surface, as you are when you bathe in the Great Salt Lake. It does not mean that the latter will be unable to get off the bottom, as even the best human swimmer is if he falls into an oil-tank. The difference between natural fresh and natural salt water are not so great. What it does mean is that a fish in equilibrium in one will, if he goes to the other, have to work to keep below the surface or to stay off bottom unless he can make an appropriate change in his volume. Experiments with killifish, some of which are able to stand abrupt change from fresh to salt water or the reverse, show that when first placed in salt water they have to swim constantly downward to overcome their buoyancy, and when first placed in fresh water, constantly upwards to overcome their weight, but that in fifteen minutes they adjust themselves sufficiently to the changed density to maneuver without any perceptible difficulty.

In the third place we definitely know that the air-bladder has been turned into an efficient hearing aid in one way or another by many species of fish, including the predominating group, both in number of species and number of individuals, in all the fresh waters of the world.

In the fourth place we definitely know that some fish use the air-bladder to make noises. Best known is the weakfish and its allies. It has a peculiar muscle by which it can set the air-bladder into vibration and produce sounds. The male only possesses this muscle, and the male only can make the sound, from which we judge that it has something to do with mating; and so loud is this sound that it has been heard six feet above water when the fish is fifty feet under water.

So much for the positive side—for the things which we know that the air-bladder does do. As for the things which we know that the air-bladder does not do, while at first thought a summary of the negatives may seem of little value, it is undertaken here to dispel the many misconceptions which have been held in the past and which are to some extent still held.

We know that the air-bladder is not an active instrument for changing levels—that fish do not raise or lower themselves by increasing or decreasing their size. For this reason it seems to me that the name "swim-bladder," which is sometimes given it, is misleading. With locomotion in any direction it has nothing to do. True, the mixture of gases which it contains is not air, and it should really be called "gas-bladder," but at least the name "air-bladder" is more indicative of its true nature than "swim-bladder."

We know that it is not even a passive help to the fish in making depth changes, as the first theory held. Fish without the air-bladder are almost incompressible, and therefore have an almost constant volume at all depths. If they are in equilibrium with the water at one level, they are in equilibrium at all levels. They change from one depth to another without disturbance. Fish with air-bladders are compressible. In order to maintain their constancy of *volume* they have therefore to increase or decrease the *pressure* in their air-bladders. The air-bladder has to work to overcome the weakness which it itself has introduced. It is in no way a help; it merely succeeds in overcoming the obstacle of its own presence. It is probably just as much of a nuisance to the fish, in so far as depth changes are concerned, as our lungs would be to us if we suddenly acquired gills and took to living under the water.

And we know that it is not an indispensable device to keep the fish from too rapid or too great changes of level. If such a pressure register were necessary to keep the fish within safe limits, the halibut with its great changes of depth would long since have perished.

And it may be that some day exceptions will be found to every one of the statements we have just made; but they will still remain, in general, true.

There is one more point about the air-bladder which is of interest to human beings. In most present-day fish the tube which connects the air-bladder to the throat opens into the upper side of the gullet; but this was not always so. In the Devonian fishes it opened into the lower side, for the air-bladder or "lung" lay below the digestive organs. This seems mechanically unsound, since the bladder, being light, should naturally be above the stomach, and it is possible that the tendency of the bladder to rise is responsible for the present position of the opening. Anyway, whatever the reason, in the early fishes the opening was on the lower side of the throat. The nostrils, however, were on the top of the head, and when they succeeded in acquiring a passage through the skull into the mouth cavity for the fish to breathe through, the path of the air came to cross the path of the food. For the air came in at the top and went out at the bottom, whereas the food came in at the bottom and went out at the top.

If the fish had moved that air-bladder connection around to the top of the throat before the land animals branched off from it, it would have been much more convenient for us. We might then have succeeded in working out two separate passages, one leading from the nose directly to the lungs, one from the mouth directly to the stomach, with no trouble-breeding interconnections. But it did not. The result is that the land animals carried on that crisscross arrangement and never modified it, and handed it on to us. Our food and our air have to cross over, and sometimes the food gets into the passage leading to the lungs. It "goes down the wrong way."

And so, when you choke over a piece of bread, it may, or it may not, be some consolation to you to realize that that particular bit of discomfort had its origin in the Devonian drought some three hundred million years ago.

Now, my co-mates, and brothers in exile,
Hath not old custom made this life more sweet
Than that of painted pomp? Are not these woods
More free from peril than the envious court?
Here feel we but the penalty of Adam,
The seasons' difference; as the icy fang
And churlish chiding of the winter's wind;
Which when it bites and blows upon my body
Even till I shrink with cold, I smile and say—
This is no flattery; these are counselors
That feelingly persuade me what I am.
Sweet are the uses of adversity,
Which, like the toad, ugly and venomous,
Wears yet a precious jewel in his head;
And this our life, exempt from public haunt,
Finds tongues in trees, books in the running brooks,
Sermons in stones, and good in every thing.

SHAKESPEARE, *As You Like It*

When daffodils begin to peer,—
With, heigh! the doxy over the dale,—
Why, then comes in the sweet o' the year;
For the red blood reigns in the winter's pale.

SHAKESPEARE, *The Winter's Tale*

FORTUNE OF FORESTS

by Lewis Ketcham Sillcox

The author of this treatise on trees and their worth to humanity is not a naturalist or a professional conservationist but a mechanical engineer and, in fact, a past president of the American Society of Mechanical Engineers. Lewis Ketcham Sillcox was born in Germantown, Pennsylvania, April 30, 1886. He was educated in Belgium, receiving his engineering training at L'Ecole Polytechnique in Brussels in 1903. He is an expert on railroads and other forms of transportation and has delivered lectures on mechanical matters at most of the engineering schools of the great universities in this country. He received the honorary degree of Doctor of Science from Clarkson College in 1932 and Doctor of Laws from Syracuse University in 1948. This report on forests was delivered as a lecture to engineering students at Massachusetts Institute of Technology February 7, 1956. It was rescued for inclusion here in the hope that students of Nature and conservation might profit from it, too.

TO begin with it is well to recall that three centuries ago the whole of our North American continent was six thousand years behind European civilization. It was inhabited by not to exceed one million Indians, while long stretches of wild prairie and primeval forest, extending to the farthest distance, had no human dwellers at all. Since then that wonderful and vastly fertile continent has been Europeanized—only rather more so—and covered with scattered cities, towns and villages and coupled together by a network of roads and railways traversed by millions of powerful machines. In the meantime the population has increased to the point of becoming a primary problem. The red man never dammed a stream,

never drained a swamp, never exterminated an animal. What ground
he cleared for his primitive agriculture was negligible. Believing that
every natural object possessed a divinity, he attached special importance to the shades of trees and approached the cottonwoods as if
they were beings of higher intelligence than himself, and believed that
misfortune would overtake and would follow were one to fail in showing due respect to the spirit of the tree.

When the early settlers had got rid of the natives it only remained
to take over the territory. A new, immense, uninhabited country lay
open before them. Endless forests and long fertile valleys such as had
never before and would never again confront the eye of man, were
theirs for the taking. This was the last unspoiled wilderness of the
temperate zone, teeming and complete with all that the builders of a
new world might require. The empire of virgin forest occupied an
area more extensive than any European state save Russia. The more
than 800-million acres of forest held the continent in a grip which
neither water nor wind could possibly disturb. Nor was there any danger of losing the more than 400-million acres of open woodland. The
desert-scope which amounted to 50-million acres, was held at a minimum by the play of forces in the natural equilibrium. The rainfall,
whether gentle or torrential, was committed to pass through a system
of perfect natural drainage which assured that its distribution was expansive, its flow orderly, its storage adequate and its composition clean
and clear. The forest contained a mighty host before the new settlers,
erect and menacing. But it was unarmed and could not defend itself.
It could not even retreat like the Indian host before, since it was rooted
to the ground. The forest was an enemy that could be destroyed and
they set to work to destroy it. Three immediate objectives were to be
gained: first, room in which to grow crops, and second, the necessary
supply of timber with which to construct homes, workshops, mills and
all other necessary facilities for the new civilization, and third, to maintain it initially with fuel. It was a big task, this subduing of the wilderness. It took toughness and time before the first 100-million acres of
trees had been brought down.

There have been many civilizations but there had never been anything like this before in the history of man and Nature. Men had
grown up with Nature in this place and that place. They had seldom
been wise or good in their relations with the earth. They had made
many mistakes, huge blunders had been committed in tree-killing, soil-
injury, and water-wastage for which they had been repaid with dust,

sand, famine and destitution. When we watch the modern spectacle of the wholesale ripping up of grasses in every direction, of the crashing down of entire forests under machine methods and where this fails, resorting to careless ways in setting fires, is it any wonder that we create a problem of puzzling human perplexity? We are forced to look back and turn our minds in the direction of contemplating man when he was unclouded by his comforts and uncorrupted by his engines. We seem to have no time, for we must keep pace with our machines, we go forward as if we owe debts to no one and have nothing to fear. For the people of the world America has symbolized plenty. This profusion of resources, this practically free and truly accessible abundance of goods, has borne a significance that transcends the field of economics.

Our way of life on this continent has, in the broad sense, been made possible by a condition of economic abundance, and the constant incidence of this degree of plenty has differentiated our way of life from all others less richly endowed. Abundance, then, must be dealt with as a major force in our history. The western wilds, from the Alleghenies to the Pacific, constituted the richest free gift that was ever spread out before civilized man. Never again can such an opportunity come to mankind. Through most of its course our growth presents a series of recurring social evolutions in diverse geographical areas as our people advanced to colonize a continent. The chief characteristic was expansion; the chief peculiarity of institutions, constant readjustment. Into raw and differing areas men and institutions and ideas poured from older regions, there to return to a more or less simple primitive pioneering state and then rise slowly back toward complexity. The process was similar in every instance, with some common results but always with differences peculiar to time and place. With more land than it could use and fewer people than it needed this continent presented a fundamental economic difference to that experienced in Europe and elsewhere; but it was a condition which had more influence than any other in shaping the course of our progress. Today we have, perhaps, as large an industrial capacity as the rest of the world, and yet, it is clearly not merely the greater endowment of land which made our growth a compelling factor. It was the greater supply, also, of timber, of iron, of copper, of petroleum, of coal, of water. It then becomes more nearly the equivalent of physical abundance rather than mere soil or land area alone. A green girdle of protection had also been thrown over the whole continent by virtue of forests and

grass which furnished us our initial supply of water power. Then came
the time when our forests were cut down. This was followed by the
plough which knifed its way through the prairies, and thus the skin
was torn off the land in enormous sectors. The offensive of deforesta-
tion and ploughing-up of the prairies did not exhaust the campaign
against the green girdle. Cattle and sheep were brought in to eat it
and tread it under foot in order to provide meat, wool and leather.

The criticism not only of man's achievement but of natural insuffi-
ciency has been a topic of constant serious study because neither is felt
any longer to be final if properly approached. It has long been known
that the vegetation of the earth, on which the volume and vigor of
life depend, is a function of moisture and sunlight. The enrichment
of vegetation which is now accepted practice and the cultivation of
forests will in the future cause our present attempts to appear barren
and its method laborious and poor. Those to come will look down
with understanding on areas of marsh and scrub, bare wilderness of
rock, rainless regions, marginal land areas and avalanche slopes with
a world of promise still to be fulfilled. Nitrogen is yielded up by the
inorganic world to the uses of life with extreme reluctance and the
fundamental poverty of terrestrial existence can be traced through
most of the geological record. Until science had arisen no individual
intelligence could ever penetrate the hidden hoard of plenty which we
now foresee.

At first the lumber trade was of less importance than the actual
business of clearing the ground for crops. But the steady growth of
millpower at length made of the lumber merchant an important and
powerful institution. When we realize that the first water-power mill
in 1631 could only cut one thousand board feet a day; that in 1767 the
gangsaw cut five times this much; that in 1820 the circular saw cut
eight times more again; that in 1830 the steam saw handled one hundred and twenty-five thousand board feet a day; and that the figure
at this time stands at one million board feet a day, we may understand what the lumber industry has grown to mean. Forests once covered six-sevenths of the State of Wisconsin with hemlock and pine,
and by 1899 the lumbermen who had moved from Maine and Michigan, employing one thousand and thirty-three saws, were cutting
thirty-four billion board feet a year, until in 1932 there was nothing
left. The trees were not trees but dollars in terms of timber to be
translated by the expert hand of man into all things, the endless things,
specified by civilization. Wood is the most versatile and the most in-

dispensable of materials. The industrial civilization that is forever inventing substitutes for it is also constantly developing ways of treating, manipulating, or transforming it that make it in effect a substitute for the substitutes—and so place a further strain on the supply. There is an ethyl alcohol made from wood—which is not wood alcohol by any means and may serve most importantly in our future supply of liquid fuel. We can, therefore, never have enough research on wood no matter who does it. A dollar spent in funding is invested toward the next decade's dividends and the next century's population—it is as simple in a financial sense as spending a dollar on treating a tree right. There are species covering millions of acres which, if given the right initial treatment in the earliest years of their growth, will increase in value seven per cent a year for over a century.

Wood, contrary to the impression of many, is not a dwindling enterprise but is today more important than ever before in history. Metals and plastics have hardly dented the area of the wood processing industries. Of its many uses, one of the most important in our modern world is the manufacture of paper. The fabrication of paper from fibrous matter was first practiced by the Chinese in the second century B.C. It spread to Persia and Arabia in the next ten centuries. The Moors carried the art to Spain in the twelfth century. The first paper mill in this country was established in Germantown, Pa. in 1690. There are at present three hundred wood pulp mills in the United States employing some 8 per cent of the Nation's industrial workers and paying more than 9 per cent of its industrial wages. Although only about 5 per cent of all wood used commercially is made into paper, approximately 20 million tons of wood pulp were so used in the United States in 1953. An added 8 million tons of wood fiber was consumed in the form of reprocessed waste paper. The rest of the lumber cut annually is employed in construction ranging from toothpicks to telegraph poles; for new synthetics and for fuel. Despite constant depletion of the forests since the early 16th century, and the continual loss due to fire, one third of the total land area of the United States is still wooded today. And through tree farms and conservation reserves, steps are being taken to assure timber harvests for the future.

When you open a highway through a hardwood forest, along its sides the birches begin to die—they are now getting too much sun. If you log a mountainside too heavily or with improper methods, the spring runoff will gouge out the creek-bottom, destroy the plant life, and kill the trout. The soil chemistry on the mountainside will be

changed (much more radically than a fire would change it) and therefore the association of grasses and shrubs and trees that will grow later.
Denude a sufficient number of mountainsides or hillsides in a water-
shed by overlogging, or overgrazing which works in the same way to
the same outcome, and you are in for major trouble. There are, of
course, many ways in which to damage land. But it is of particular
interest to here note that the combination of overcutting and overgrazing has been, historically, the deadliest of all ways, destroying
some civilizations, reducing many to permanent poverty—the Tigris-
Euphrates valley, the land of Canaan that is now a desert though once
filled with abundance, the cities of North Africa that were obliterated
by these twin evils quite as effectively as Carthage was by the Roman
armies. For three centuries Spain has been plagued with poverty, starvation, and by repeated civil wars because of the privileges granted its
national wool-growers' association and the executive stupidity with
which they were administered. As a result, Spain's agricultural and
forest land slowly contracted and more rapidly deteriorated. At least
ten per cent of the country became a desert and perhaps thirty per
cent more of it was permanently impaired. Any conservationist can
name many areas on our continent where similar deterioration result-
ing from the same causes is under way.

Forest fires so alter soil chemistry and other factors that condition
growth as to permanently change the plant associations and the character of the stand. For this and related reasons there may be areas,
though if so they must be comparatively small, where it is misleading
to speak of climax types or a climax association. No species except
man could so alter the working of ecology relationships that nature
could not restore them. In a multitude of places over the centuries
man has so altered them that nature's readjustment has been infinitely
the worse for him; and sometimes it will require not centuries but
geological epochs to restore them to the equivalent of what they were.
It may turn out that nuclear fission has enabled him to alter them to
the point where no one will have any further interest in the matter.

IN DEFENSE OF OCTOPUSES

by Gilbert C. Klingel

This is what comes of being shipwrecked. Gilbert C. Klingel is a man who made enough money to allow him to indulge in a hobby or two, and one of his hobbies was doing volunteer research for the American Museum of Natural History. On such a mission he sailed a thirty-eight-footer for the Bahamas with a friend aboard as his crew. They planned to stay on the island of Inagua and do research on tropical life by land and sea. Skipper Klingel's navigation was perfect; he hit the little island right on an offshore reef! He lost his boat and much of his equipment, and a little later he lost his friend, who had to return to the United States. Our author stayed and gathered enough material to fill a good book, Inagua, *published in 1940. The following selection is a chapter from that book.*

I FEEL about octopuses—as Mark Twain did about the devil—that someone should undertake their rehabilitation. All writers about the sea, from Victor Hugo down to the present, have published volumes against them; they have been the unknowing and unwitting victims of a large and very unfair amount of propaganda, and have long suffered under the stigma of being considered horrible and exceedingly repulsive. No one has ever told the octopuses' side of the story; nor has anyone ever defended them against the mass of calumnies which have been heaped on their peculiar and marvelously shaped heads. We have convicted them without benefit of a hearing, which is a most partial and unjust proceeding. I propose that the octopuses, and their near relatives the squids, are among the most wonderful of all earth's creatures, and as such are deserving of our respect, if not our admiration.

My personal interest in octopi dates back to the moment when I turned to climb out of the drowned ravine at the base of the Inaguan barrier reef. I had reached the lower portion of the final slope and was about to seize on a piece of yellow rock to steady myself when I noticed that from the top of the boulder was peering a cold dark eye that neither blinked nor stirred. In vain I looked for eyelids; the orb apparently belonged to the rock itself.

Then suddenly, I felt a chill wave creep up my spine. Before my gaze the rock started to melt, began to ooze at the sides like a candle that had become too hot. There is no other way to describe the action. I was so startled at the phenomenon that it was a full second or two before I was conscious of what I was watching.

It was my first acquaintance with a live, full-grown octopus. The beast flowed down the remainder of the boulder, so closely did its flesh adhere to the stone, and then slowly, with tentacles spread slightly apart, slithered into a crevasse nearby. The head of the octopus was about as big as a football, but as it reached the fissure, which was not more than four inches in width, it flattened out and wedged itself into the opening. It seemed somewhat irritated at my disturbing it, for it rapidly flushed from pebbled yellow to mottled brown and then back to a livid white. It remained white for about twenty seconds and then altered slowly to a dark gray edged with maroon. I stood stock-still but it made no overt motions and I slowly edged away. Quite possibly it might have been a nasty customer, for the tentacles were about five feet from tip to tip.

This last statement may seem a contradiction to my opening paragraph; and, I must admit, that is the way I felt about the octopus at the time. However, since that hour I have collected and observed a number of these creatures, including the squids. I have found them animals of unusual attainments and they should be ranked among the most remarkable denizens of the sea. They are endowed with considerable intelligence and they have reached a system of living all their own which they have maintained for approximately 500,000,000 years. As far back as the Ordovician period of geology we find their ancestors, and there is good evidence that at one time the forefathers of the present octopi very nearly ruled the world. Had they been able to pass the barrier of the edge of the ocean as the early fish-derived amphibians did, there might have been no limit to the amazing forms which would have peopled the earth.

Within the bounds of pure speculation, however, the fact remains that the cephalopods, as the entire octopi-like group of animals is termed, have missed the status of brainy intelligence, of which man is the highest criterion, only by a very narrow margin. There is reason to believe that they are the most keen-witted creatures in the ocean and had they developed an opposable thumb and fingers instead of suckers with which to manipulate various objects, the entire course of the earth's existence might have been altered.

There are some very curious similarities between the development of intelligence in man and in the modern cephalopod. Both acquired brains after their individual fashions because the course of organic evolution left them without adequate physical protection against the vicissitudes of nature. Man, the weak and the puny, without claws and rending fangs to battle the beasts and without long legs with which to flee, had to acquire cunning or perish. That marvelous addition, the opposable thumb, made possible holding and using tools and gave a stimulus to cunning that nothing else in the mechanics of evolution could have provided. The thumb is by far the most remarkable portion of man's anatomy. Literature, music, art, philosophy, religion, civilization itself are directly the result of man's possession of this digit.

Like man, the modern cephalopods have been thrown upon the world naked and without the armor protection of their ancestors. For cephalopods are shellfish, blood brothers to the oyster, the clam and the conch; they are mollusks which have been deprived of their shells. The only present day cephalopods which still retain their shells are the Nautiloids which are direct descendants of the ancient types whose fossils are found in the tightly compressed rocks of the Upper Cambrian. Over three thousand fossil Nautiloids have been named, an imposing group ranging in size from a tiny seven-millimeter creature called *Cyrtoceras* to the immense 14-foot cone of *Endoceras!* Only four closely related species of this mighty shelled host remain, all occurring in the South Pacific.

To compensate for the loss of their shells, which were their bulwarks against fate, these unclothed cephalopods have developed, like man, cunning and intelligence. Alone among the mollusks they have acquired by concentration of their chief nerve ganglia what may be truly considered a brain. With the casting aside of the shell they have also gained their freedom, speed and mobility.

Safety often goes hand in hand with degeneration. It is a curious circumstance that those creatures which live completely guarded lives also have a very dull existence. What, for example, could be safer and more stupid and sedentary than an oyster, clad in its house of lime? The loss of a shell not only rescued the cephalopods from dullness but it probably also saved them from extinction. The most highly ornate shelled cephalopods of all time, the gracefully coiled Ammonoids, which are so named because of their resemblance to the ram-like horns of the deity Jupiter Ammon, and which developed during the Upper Silurian and lasted until the close of the Age of Reptiles, went out of existence because the extent of their external sculpture and complexity of septation rendered them so specialized that they failed to respond to change. Some of these fantastic Ammonoids, of which six thousand species are known, possessed coiled shells more than six feet in diameter!

"Cephalopods," the scientific name of the octopi and squids, immediately characterizes them as something unusual, for it signifies that they walk on their heads. This is precisely what they do, for their tentacles or "feet" are located between their eyes and mouths. No other animals on earth utilize this position or method of progression.

However, it is in their mode of swimming that the motion of these weird beings is most amazing. They are beautifully streamlined when in action, and can dart about at remarkable speed. I recall once being out to sea in a fishing trawler off the Virginia Capes. I was sitting in the dark on deck watching the stars and swaying to the slight roll of the boat when suddenly I heard a rapidly reiterated splashing in the sea. The sound was slightly reminiscent of the pattering noise of flying fish. I knew that I was too far north for any quantity of these volant creatures. I went below and returned on deck with a flashlight. Its beam pierced the dark and glowed on the wave tops. The ship was passing through a school of small surface fish. They were being preyed upon by hundreds of *Loligo* squid. The squid were shuttling back and forth through the water at incredible speed. Most wonderful was the organization with which they seemed to operate. Entire masses of these cephalopods, all swimming in the same direction, would dart at the mass of fish, quickly seize and bite at them, then abruptly wheel as a unit and sweep through the panic-stricken victims which scurried everywhere. Some of these squid were traveling so rapidly that when they approached the top of the water they burst through and went skimming through the air for several yards, falling back with light splashes. In the morning I found several on the deck of the trawler where they had jumped, a vertical distance of at least six feet! There is another record made near the coast of Brazil of a swarm of squids flying out of the water on the deck of a ship which was twelve feet above the surface and which was further protected by a high bulwark, making a minimum jump of fifteen feet! Several score were shoveled off the ship when daylight came.

The cephalopods and particularly the squids might be compared to living fountain pens or animated syringes, for they accomplish their flight-like swimming by pulling liquid into their body cavities and squirting it out again. Their likeness to a living fountain pen is even further heightened when one considers that some of the cephalopods contain ink and a quill. Nor is this all, for nature, not content to offer all these wonders in one creature, has ordained that they may swim, not only forward like all other creatures of the sea, but backward! They can swim forward and sideways, too, but the normal mode is stern foremost.

The quill of these mobile fountain pens is the remnant of the shells of their prehistoric ancestors, and it persists, like our vermiform appendix, as a useless but telltale evidence of former usage. The quill, reduced in the octopi to two chitinous rods, and in the squid to a long narrow fluted pen, remarkably resembling an old fashioned quill, is buried deep within the tissue. In a sense, the octopi and squids are shellfish which have surrounded their shells.

It is in the ink of these cephalopods that we are confronted with a true paradox. This ink, basis of the familiar India ink, is utilized for two diametrically opposite purposes. It is intended to provide concealment and, diversely, to enable the animal to keep in touch with its fellows. When there is fear of an attack by enemies, the ink is expelled into the water to form a "smoke screen" behind which the cephalopod flees to shelter. Thus the modern military technique of employing the smoke screen to conceal retreating movements was conceived by the cephalopods as early as the Jurassic, as is proved by a beautifully preserved fossil of that period which shows the ink bag prominently limned in the highly compressed tissue impression of a squid. However, when night closes down on the water shrouding the blue vastness of the deeps in impenetrable gloom, it is by means of this same ink that the members of a school of squids are able to keep in contact with one another. It is believed that the ink is extruded in very small quantities and is picked up by unusually sensitive olfactory organs. The more solitary octopi use it in much the same manner to locate their mates.

I had no idea of the efficiency of this inky fluid until my third or
fourth meeting with the octopus of the valley. I had been going down
for a half hour or so each day near the same spot in the reef and almost
always finished the day's dive with a final excursion to the limit of
the hose on the base of the ravine. In these trips I saw a number of
octopuses, mostly much smaller than the first. These seemed to live
in the crevasses near the base of the reef, and often all that I saw of
them was a tentacle or two twitching or writhing languidly from a
fissure. Some I discovered by the neat piles of mussel shells and other
mollusks near the entrances to their hiding places. Some of these shells
were, surprisingly, unopened and, it can be assumed, were being stored
against an hour of larger appetite. Also, most interesting, the only
locality on Inagua where the mussels were to be found in any abundance was in the area of the surf, a living habit that might be attributed to the ceaseless raids of octopi on colonies in more peaceful
localities. The mussels, in self-defense as it were, had established
themselves in the only place where they might live undisturbed,
which was, in contradiction, the most violent area of all the world of
underwater. They were, so to speak, between the devil and the deep
blue sea, or to be more exact, between the devil and the hot dry air.

Most of these octopi were exceedingly shy, fleeing into their shelters
at my approach, and drawing far back out of reach, a reaction quite
at variance with the accepted theories of ferocity and malignancy. I
tried to capture some of the smaller ones, but they were too fast for
me. The big fellow on the slope of the ravine, however, while it did
not seem quite so timid, always gave me a wide berth and invariably,
the few times I encountered it, withdrew to its fissure where it was
never quite hidden, but was revealed by a portion of the body and the
restless arms. At first I left it strictly alone, but curiosity about its
peculiar color changes prompted me to come closer.

It always seemed irritated at my presence. Its nervousness may have
been caused by fear, for it certainly made no pretense of belligerency,
and it constantly underwent a series of pigment alterations that were
little short of marvelous. Blushing was its specialty. No schoolgirl with
her first love was ever subjected to a more rapid or recurring course of
excited flushes than this particular octopus. The most common colors
were creamy white, mottled Van Dyke brown, maroon, bluish gray,
and finally light ultramarine nearly the color of the water. When most
agitated it turned livid white, which is, I believe, the reaction of fear.
During some of the changes it became streaked, at times in wide bands

of maroon and cream, and once or twice in wavy lines of lavender and deep rose. Even red spots and irregular purplish polka dots were included in its repertoire, though these gaudy variations seldom lasted for long.

I had heard that a light touch on the skin would leave a vivid impression of color and I was anxious to see if this were the case. From the boatman I borrowed a long stick and dropped down to the sea floor again. The octopus was still in place and I walked over to it with the pole in my hand. At first I was hesitant about the experiment. The creature had behaved so nicely that I almost decided to give it up. But the old curiosity prevailed and with my pole I slowly reached out and stroked it along the side of its body.

Then things began to happen. The stick was snatched from my fingers and went floating to the surface. The octopus flashed out of the fissure and ejected an immense cloud of purplish ink. For a brief moment I saw it swimming away, long and sleek in shape, and then I was surrounded by the haze. The fog was not opaque but imparted much the same quality of nonvision as thick smoke in dry air, except that I did not notice much in the way of wreaths. In fact I was so confused and startled, that my only thought was to get away. From underneath the helmet there arose a faint odor quite unlike anything else. Fishy musk is the nearest description I can think of. The color was most interesting, as I had always been under the impression that cephalopod ink was black. Rather, it appeared dark purple which later faded to a somber shade of azure. I can also remember, when it thinned considerably, seeing vague shafts of reddish when the rays of sunlight far above caught the substance at oblique angles. The ink spread out in a cloud extending over several yards and in the still depths of the ravine took quite a time to dissipate. Actually it floated away as a hazy smudge before it evaporated.

I was not able to continue my observations on color changes until several days later when I netted a baby octopus from some turtleweed growing a few yards from shore near the place where the reef reached its final termination in a mass of sandy shoals. I transferred the mite, a youngster of seven or eight inches spread, to the tidepool near my old house where I kept it for several days. It took to its new surroundings very gracefully and made no attempt to escape but made life miserable for the numerous small crabs and fishes that shared the pond. The crabs were its principal prey which it captured by stealth and by lying patiently in wait. Patience was its most evident virtue, and much to my disgust it would sit for hours in one spot without moving, staring endlessly at the moving forms in the water. It used a great deal of intelligence in securing the crabs and selected a spot to lurk where it had ready command of an entire corner of the pond.

The rocks of its dwelling were creamy brown, and this was the exact hue it assumed while waiting to make a capture. It had perfect control of its pigmentation. In comparison the renowned chameleons are but rank amateurs. The mechanics of this alteration of hue are very complex but are controlled by the expansion and contraction of a group of cells attached to pigmented sacks, known as chromatophores, residing in the outer layers of skin over the entire surface of the body. In addition there is scattered over the body another great series of cells capable of reflecting light. These are yellow and impart a strange iridescent shimmer, slightly suggestive of the glow of pearls. The chromatophores, which are of a variety of colors, are opened and shut at will, producing any or all colors of the rainbow.

These color cells are manipulated by highly sensitive nerves communicating with the brain and with the eye. The eye principally dictates the choice of color although emotion also seems to have a definite influence. When frightened, the octopi usually blanch to a whitish or light tone; irritation will cause them to break out in dark pigments. No other creatures in the world can alter their color as quickly and completely. Emotion will cause a human being to flush with anger or become pale with pain or anxiety; but no one can hold his hand and will it to be green with yellow stripes, or even yellow or plain brown, let alone lavender or ultramarine. An artist may paint a picture; only an octopus can color its skin with the portrait of its emotions, or duplicate exactly the pattern of the soil on which it rests. Only a very highly-organized creature, one with a brain and an unusually well co-ordinated nervous system could accomplish the mechanical marvel of operating several thousands of cells at once, rapidly opening and closing them in proper order.

The cephalopods are not limited to color change but are also credited with being able to produce the most brilliant light known in the realm of animals. While this luminescence is limited to a very few deep-sea species of decapods, which are the ten-armed squids, their light is so vivid that they outshine the fireflies. These light organs may be found on any portion of the body, including the eyeball itself, and oddly enough, even in the interior of the animal! In these last forms the body tissues are quite transparent, so the light is not necessarily concealed. These light organs are quite varied, some being but mounds of glowing fluid, others complex and carefully constructed lenses with mirrors of reflecting tissue. As yet very little is known of these abyssal octopi and squid, though a few captured specimens have been observed burning with a strong light for several hours. Some day when the means of exploring the vast deeps of the ocean comfortably and safely has been devised, we will learn more of these unbelievable cephalopods.

Quite unseen, my octopus would wait until a crab ventured near. Then it would either swoop quickly over the victim, smothering it in its diminutive tentacles or suddenly dart out an arm and seize its meal before it had time to flee. It seldom missed, but when it did it usually retrieved its dinner by a quick pursuit before it had gone far. Before twenty-four hours were up, the entire bottom of the pool was littered with the hollow carapaces of crabs. Peculiarly, the animal almost always devoured its victim bottom side up, biting through the softer lower shell with its small parrot-like beak and rasping out the contents with its filed tongue before casting the empty shell away. The legs and feet were seldom eaten and were usually torn off and discarded. Little of this feeding was done during the day. At high noon I even saw a crab crawl over the relaxed tentacles without being molested or becoming aware of the danger it was courting. In the evening, however, particularly just before sunset, the octopus seized everything within reach.

The capture of fish was not nearly so easy, and although I saw it make a number of attempts, its only successful capture was a small goby that very injudiciously decided to rest a few inches below the octopus' chosen corner. As in the case of several of the crabs, it was blanketed by a mass of writhing tentacles. Once the fish was grasped by the vacuum cups of these tentacles it was finished, for in their method of attacking, the octopi utilize one of the most efficient systems devised, a principle more certain than curving claws or the sharpness of teeth. Only the hand of man with its opposable thumb is superior.

The feel of these vacuum cups on the bare flesh is most unusual. It is not unpleasant, and in a small specimen, gives the sensation of hundreds of tiny wet clammy hands pulling at the skin. The strength of the suckers is amazing. When I tried to lift the youngster off my wrist it clung tenaciously and, even when I had dislodged all the tentacles except one, I still had to give a strong pull in proportion to its size to release the suckers. There have been cases in which the tentacles have been torn apart before the suckers released their grip. These suckers, which operate on much the same principle as the little rubber cups with which we attach objects to automobile windshields, are actuated by a muscular piston. The rim of the cup is fastened to an object, then the floor of the center is raised and retracted to form a vacuum. The cups, I found, would slip easily from side to side but, when pulled directly, exercised considerable power. In the octopods the suckers are sessile, or are mounted on low mounds; the squids carry the mechanism a bit further and produce them on stalks. In the giant squid the rims of the suckers are even equipped with fine teeth to render them more efficient. Whalers have recorded capturing whales with dozens of circular scars on their heads, inflicted in gargantuan battles with these monsters of the open ocean. Some of these scars have measured over two inches in diameter, so the creatures that possessed them must have been huge.

How large do the squid and octopi grow? There is an authentic record of a North Atlantic squid which measured fifty-two feet over all! Its tentacles had an abnormal reach of thirty-five feet and the remaining seventeen feet was taken up by the cylindrical body which had a circumference of twelve feet. The eye of this fabulous animal was seven by nine inches, the largest visual organ in the world. The suckers had a diameter of two and a quarter inches, and as some of the scars on captured whales have exceeded this measurement, it is not unreasonable to assume that there may exist somewhere in the abyssal depths of the North Atlantic, still larger squid of perhaps sixty or seventy feet. Even these amazing squid, however, are preyed upon by the great sperm whales which tear them apart with their long shearing teeth. In that old classic and favorite *The Cruise of the Cachalot*, the author, Mr. Frank Bullen, gives a vivid description of a battle between a large sperm whale and one of these squid.

"At about eleven p.m.," he writes, "I was leaning over the rail, gazing steadily at the bright surface of the sea, when there was a violent commotion in the sea right where the moon's rays were concentrated, so great that, remembering our position, I was at first inclined to alarm all hands, for I had often heard of volcanic islands suddenly lifting their heads from the depths below, or disappearing in a moment, and . . . I felt doubtful indeed of what was now happening. Getting the night glasses out of the cabin scuttle where they were always hung in readiness, I focused them on the troubled spot, perfectly satisfied by

a short examination that neither volcano nor earthquake had anything to do with what was going on; yet so vast were the forces engaged that I might well have been excused for my first supposition.
A very large whale was locked in deadly conflict with a cuttlefish or
squid almost as large as himself, whose interminable tentacles seemed
to enclose the whole of his great body. The head of the whole especially seemed a perfect network of writhing arms, naturally, I suppose, for it appeared as if the whale had the tail part of the mollusk
in his jaws, and, in a business-like methodical way was sawing through
it. By the side of the black columnar head of the whale appeared the
head of a great squid, as awful an object as one could well imagine,
even in a fevered dream. Judging as carefully as possible, I estimated
it to be at least as large as one of our pipes, which contained three
hundred and fifty gallons; but it may have been, and probably was,
a good deal larger. The eyes were very remarkable for their size and
blackness, which, contrasted with the livid whiteness of the head,
made their appearance all the more striking. They were at least a foot
in diameter, and seen under such conditions looked decidedly eerie
and hobgoblin-like. All around the combatants were numerous sharks,
like jackals around a lion, ready to share the feast, and apparently
assisting in the destruction of the large Cephalopod."

Unfortunately Bullen does not tell the result of the combat but one
might assume that the whale was the victor, for the food of sperm
whales consists almost exclusively of squid.

If the squid and octopi are accused of being fearsome and savage,
it might be argued that they live in an underwater world in which
savagery and primitive instincts are the most common passions, and
the only way to exist is to conform to the mode. There is no doubt
that an enraged large cephalopod could be a formidable antagonist.
The authentic instances of octopi or squid attacking human beings
or divers, however, are so rare as to be considered non-existent in spite
of a large literature to the contrary. Most of their savagery is confined
to securing their food, which is a normal and reasonable function.

The tentacles serve still another and more wonderful purpose, for
it is by means of their arms that these unorthodox creatures are able
to perpetuate their race. The arms that serve in this function are
known as hectocotylized arms and this name was derived from an honest and understandable mistake by Cuvier. The name also signifies
the arm of a hundred cells, and the mistake was made when the detached portion of one of these many-celled arms was found clinging

in the mantle cavity of a female paper nautilus where it was erroneously thought to be some new sort of parasitic worm. The strange
worm was named hectocotylus and the error was not discovered until
further researches had been undertaken in regard to the animal's
breeding habits. It appears that the arm of the male paper nautilus is
extended during breeding time until it looks like a long worm-like
lash. This lash is charged with the fertilizing spermatophores. When
the male and female meet they intertwine their tentacles in a medusa-
like embrace, and when they disengage from their fantastic lovemak-
ing, the end of the lash is deposited under the mantle of the female,
where it is held for a time, for the female is not yet ready to spawn.
When her eggs are eventually extruded, they are fertilized by the waiting sperm. The broken arm is not completely lost, for the male can
grow another and still another.

The cephalopods are so delightfully versatile that they have still
other systems of reproducing. In some forms the hectocotylized arm
is not detached but is specially modified so that it can develop and
transfer spermatophores to the females' mantle cavity near the oviduct. The spermatophore is itself the most remarkable creation of all
this complex mating. It is a long tubular structure loaded with sperm,
an apparatus for extruding it, and, most wonderful, a cement gland for
attaching it to the female. It can be utilized at will; a thoughtful provision considering that the female may then take her good time in
depositing her eggs under favorable circumstances. In other species the
spermatophore is grasped by the male as it passes from his mantle and
is placed in her mantle cavity or attached to the membrane around
her mouth where the eggs are sometimes fertilized.

Some of the cephalopods show an amazing amount of mother-love
and parental care. The common octopus *vulgaris* has been observed
in aquaria guarding its eggs which were attached to the stone walls.
It fiercely resented any interference and kept a constant circulation of
water flowing over them to insure that no parasites would take hold
and that proper oxygenation would occur. The eggs were not even
left long enough for the mother to secure food, even though the period of incubation lasted for a considerable time. So intense was this
guardianship that another octopus in the same tank which ventured
close too frequently was set upon and slain. Mother-love in an octopus
seems a strange and outlandish emotion, but no doubt it is actuated
by the same flame that causes human parents to sacrifice their pleas-

ures and desires that Junior, or his sister, for example, might go to college.

Cephalopodian care of the egg is responsible for another of the truly paradoxical things about these creatures. In the genus *Argonauta* the female carries about with her a beautifully coiled and graceful shell. This seems a contradiction to an earlier statement that the modern cephalopods are creatures which have cast aside their shells. Actually the shell of the Argonauts is not a true shell but is an egg case formed on the spiral shell pattern, which is mechanically a very strong and structurally efficient shape. The Argonaut is not bound to the shell in any way, for it may leave it whenever it desires, which it has been reported to do under certain conditions. No other mollusk is so equipped. Imagine an oyster, for example, opening its valves and stepping out for an airing! The shell is held in position by two arms which are specially formed for the purpose. Only the female possesses this protection, and she forms the shell, not with the mantle as do all other mollusks, but with her two modified arms with their expanded membranous disks. When the Argonauts are first born they have no shells and they do not begin its construction until they are a week or two old. Unfortunately for the natural history of Aristotle, they do not sail over the surface of the sea like miniature ships with the arms held as sails as that ancient and inquiring naturalist so quaintly believed, but creep and crawl along the bottom or swim by means of their siphons like any other cephalopod. While the eggs of the Argonauts are well protected and carefully mothered, the adult has paid a reverse penalty for its acquisition of a shell, even though that shell is not a true one. The Argonauts have lost some of the intelligence and freedom of other octopods, for they appear to be the most sluggish and stupid of their class.

Inagua from above the sea gives no hint of the host of octopods that must harbor in its reefs, or of the tiny frond-colored squids that shelter in the growths of sargassum weed that float ceaselessly by on the currents, or of the larger and more appalling-looking decapods that move about in small groups in the open water. Nor is there much indication even to the diver of their presence. Unlike the reef fishes, they are mostly nocturnal. During the bright hours they lie quiescent, curled up in the crevasses of their coral homes or float suspended and still, in the magic manner of underwater between top and bottom, waiting patiently with staring round eyes for the sun to drop and extend vague shadows over the blue depths. Then they creep from their dens and go slithering over the coral boulders or swim like living arrows through the green waters, pouncing on their prey and doing whatever amazing things fall to the lot of cephalopods.

Whenever I think of the great barrier reef of Inagua I think always of two things: first, of the fairyland of the coral itself and the pastel colors, and second, of the octopus of the drowned ravine with its weird eye and rubbery body. More than any other creature, the octopus is the spirit of the reef; unreal themselves, completely fantastic, unbelievable, weird, they are fitting residents of a world in which all the accepted routines are nullified, in which animals play at being vegetables, where worms are beautiful, where the trees are made of brittle stone, where crabs pretend to be things they are not, where flowers devour fishes, where fishes imitate sand and rocks and where danger lurks in innocent color or harmless shape. That they should, also, be inhabitants of the shadowy night places is the final touch on their characters. The octopi fill a niche of creation claimed by no others and a niche which they occupy to perfection.

The glow-worm shows the matin to be near,
And 'gins to pale his uneffectual fire.

SHAKESPEARE, *Hamlet*

O Proserpina,
For the flowers now that, frighted, thou let'st fall
From Dis's waggon! Daffodils,
That come before the swallow dares, and take
The winds of March with beauty.

SHAKESPEARE, *The Winter's Tale*

WHAT MAKES THE WEATHER

by Wolfgang Langewiesche

For centuries the "weather prophets" who held honored sway around the world were seamen and tillers of the soil. In their professions it was important for them to know about coming changes in the weather, and they were respected as men with trade secrets to divulge to favored friends. The sailor and the farmer were supposed to be able to cast a knowing eye aloft and foretell rain or shine, hard frost or long thaw, and when the wind would haul around to the southwest. When they didn't know, they guessed. Peace be with them. As weather prophets they are dead and buried. The esteemed weather prophets of today are the meteorological experts of the commercial air lines and the armed air forces of the world. They have to know, and they must not guess.

Wolfgang Langewiesche has become weather-wise as a result of his enthusiasm for flying. He learned to fly as soon as he could earn enough money to pay for flying lessons. As a college student he studied aviation, and as a college instructor he wrote several books and many magazine articles on the subject. As a pilot he soon discovered how important a knowledge of the weather was to an airman. He studied the matter at some length, and the result was this selection, originally published in Harper's Magazine in 1943. Incidentally, he is still studying and writing in the meteorological field, and it's an ill wind that doesn't blow some of his pages your way.

Y OU wake up one morning and you are surprised: the weather, which had been gray and dreary for days and seemed as if it were going to stay that way forever, with no breaks in the clouds and no indication of a gradual clearing, is now all of a sudden clear and sunny and crisp, with a strong northwest wind blowing, and the whole world looks newly washed and newly painted.

"It" has become "fine." Why? How?

"Something" has cleared the air, you might say. But what? You might study out the weather news in the back of your newspaper, and you would get it explained to you in terms of barometric highs and lows; but just why a rise of barometric pressure should clear the air would still leave you puzzled. The honest truth is that the weather has never been explained. In school they told you about steam engines or electricity or even about really mysterious things, such as gravitation, and they could do it so that it made sense to a boy. They told you also about the weather, but their explanations failed to explain, and you knew it even then. The lows and highs, cyclones and anti-cyclones, the winds that blew around in circles—all these things were much more puzzling than the weather itself. That is why weather has always made only the dullest conversation: there simply was no rhyme nor reason to it.

But now there is. A revolutionary fresh view has uncovered the rhyme and reason in the weather. Applied to your particular surprise of that morning, it has this to say:

The air which was warm, moist, and gray last night is still warm, moist, and gray this morning; but it has been pushed fifty or one hundred miles to the south and east of where you live, and has been replaced by a mass of cold, clear, dry air coming from the north or west. It is as simple as that; there is no mysterious "It" in it; just plain physical sense. It is called Air Mass Analysis.

It is based upon the researches and experiments of a physicist named Vilhelm Bjerknes, of Norway, and though in this particular case it seems almost childishly simple, it is Norway's greatest contribution to world culture since Ibsen. Or perhaps because it is simple—the rare example of a science which, in becoming more sophisticated, also becomes more common sense and easier to understand. It is so new that it hasn't yet reached the newspapers, nor the high school curricula, much less the common knowledge of the public in general. But the weather bureaus of the airlines have worked by it for years, and pilots have to learn it. It is indispensable both in commercial flying and in air war; we could fly without gasoline, without aluminum, perhaps without radio, but we could never do without Bjerknes's Air Mass Analysis.

You might inquire next where that morning's new air came from, and just how it got to be cold, dry, and clear. And there you get close to the heart of the new weather science, where meteorology turns into honest, common-sense geography.

That air has come from Canada, where it has been quite literally air-conditioned. Not all parts of the world have the power to condition air, but Canada has. Especially in the fall and winter and early spring, the northern part of this continent becomes an almost perfectly designed mechanical refrigerator. The Rocky Mountains in the west keep currents of new air from flowing into the region. And for weeks the air lies still. The cool ground, much of it snow-covered; the ice of the frozen lakes; plus the perennial stored-up coldness of Hudson's Bay— all cool the layer of air immediately above them. This means a stabilizing and calming of the whole atmosphere all the way up; for cool air is heavy, and with a heavy layer bottommost, there is none of that upflowing of air, that upwelling of moisture-laden heat into the cooler, high altitude which is the mechanism that makes clouds. Thus there may be some low ground fogs there, but above them the long nights of those northern latitudes are clear and starry, wide open toward the black infinite spaces of the universe; and into that black infinity the air gradually radiates whatever warmth it may contain from its previous sojourns over other parts of the world. The result, after weeks of stagnation, is a huge mass of air that is uniformly ice-cold, dry, and clear. It stretches from the Rocky Mountains in the west to Labrador in the east, from the ice wastes of the Arctic to the prairies of Minnesota and North Dakota; and—the third dimension is the most important—it is ice-cold from the ground all the way up to the stratosphere. It is, in short, a veritable glacier of air.

That is an air mass. In the jargon of air-faring men, a mass of Polar Canadian air.

When a wave of good, fresh Polar Canadian air sweeps southward into the United States—it happens almost rhythmically every few days —you don't need a barometer to tell you so. There is nothing subtle, theoretical, or scientific about it. You can see and feel the air itself and even hear it. It comes surging out of a blue-green sky across the

Dakotas, shaking the hangar doors, whistling in the grass, putting those red-checkered thick woolen jackets on the men, and lighting the stoves in the houses. It flows southward down the Mississippi Valley as a cold wave in winter, or as relief from a heat wave in summer, blowing as a northwest wind with small white hurrying clouds in it. In winter it may sweep southward as far as Tennessee and the Carolinas, bringing frosts with brilliantly clear skies, making the darkies shiver in their drafty cabins, and producing a wave of deaths by pneumonia. Sometimes it even reaches the Texas Gulf Coast; then it is locally called a norther, and the cows at night crowd for warmth around the gas flares in the oil fields. A duck hunter dies of exposure in the coastal swamps. A lively outbreak of Polar Canadian air may reach down into Florida, damage the orange crops, and embarrass local Chambers of Commerce. And deep outbreaks have been observed to drive all the way down to Central America, where they are feared as a fierce wind called the Tehuantepecer.

Polar Canadian is only one of many sorts of air. To put it in the unprecise language of the layman, the great Norwegian discovery is that air must always be of some distinct type: that it is never simply air but always conditioned and flavored. What we call weather is caused by gigantic waves in the air ocean which flood whole countries and continents for days at a stretch with one sort of air or another. And there is nothing theoretical about any of these various sorts of air.

Each kind is easily seen and felt and sniffed, and is, in fact, fairly familiar even to the city dweller, although he may not realize it. Each has its own peculiar characteristics, its own warmth or coolness, dampness or dryness, milkiness or clearness. Each has its own quality of light. In each, smoke behaves differently as it pours from the chimneys: in some kinds of air it creeps lazily, in some it bubbles away, in some it floats in layers. That is largely why the connoisseur can distinguish different types of air by smell.

Each type of air combines those qualities into an "atmosphere" of its own. Each makes an entirely different sort of day. In fact, what sort of day it is—raw, oppressive, balmy, dull, a "spring" day—depends almost entirely upon the sort of air that lies over your particular section of the country at that particular time.

And if you tried to describe the day in the old-fashioned terms—wind direction and velocity, humidity, state of the sky—you could never quite express its particular weather; but you can by naming the sort of air. An airplane pilot, once he is trained in the new weather thinking, can get quite impatient with the attempts of novelists, for instance, to describe weather. "Why don't you *say* it was Polar Canadian air and get on with your story?"

And if you are a connoisseur of airs just about the first thing you will note every morning is something like, "Ah, Caribbean air to-day"; or if you are really a judge you can make statements as detailed as "Saskatchewan air, slightly flavored by the Great Lakes."

For just as wines do, the airs take their names and their flavors from the regions where they have matured. Of the seven airs that make up the American weather, one is quite rare and somewhat mysterious. It is known by the peculiarly wine-like name of Sec Superieur. It is believed to be of tropical origin, but it comes to this continent after spending weeks in the stratosphere somewhere above the Galápagos Islands. It is usually found only high aloft, and interests pilots more than farmers. But once in a while a tongue of it reaches the ground as hot, extremely dry, very clear weather; and wherever it licks there is a drought.

The other six airs all come from perfectly earthly places, though faraway ones. The easiest to recognize, the liveliest, is Polar Canadian. Its opposite number in the American sky is Tropical Gulf or Tropical Atlantic air—the steamy, warm air of the Eastern and Midwestern summer, the kind that comes as a southwest wind and starts people to talking about heat and humidity, the kind that is sometimes so steamy that it leaves you in doubt as to whether the sky means to be blue or overcast. This air is brewed of hot sun and warm sea water in the Caribbean region. The mechanism that does the air conditioning in this case is mostly the daily afternoon thunderstorm which carries moisture and heat high aloft in it.

Not quite so obvious is the origin of the moist, silvery, cool-in-summer, cool-in-winter air that dominates the weather of Seattle. It is called Polar Pacific, and it is a trick product. Its basic characteristics have been acquired over Siberia and it is cold and dry; but on its way across the Pacific its lower five to ten thousand feet have been warmed up and moistened. Sometimes such air comes straight across, reaching land in a couple of days. Sometimes it hangs over the water for a week, and it takes a good weatherman to predict just what sort of weather it will produce.

Its counterpart is a flavor known as Tropical Pacific. That is the air they sell to tourists in Southern California. It is really just plain South

Seas air, though the story here, too, is not as clear-cut as it might be.

A clear-cut type is Polar Atlantic air. It sometimes blows down the New England coast as a nor'easter, cold, rainy, with low clouds. It is simply a chunk of the Grand Banks off Newfoundland gone traveling, and you can almost smell the sea.

And one air that every tourist notices in the Southwest is Tropical Continental. Its source region is the deserts of Arizona and Mexico. It is dry and hot and licks up moisture so greedily that it makes water feel on your skin as chilly as if it were gasoline. It is not an important one for America, though its European counterpart, Saharan air, is important for Europe. Oklahoma, Colorado, and Kansas are as far as it ever gets; but even so, a few extra outbreaks of it per year, and we have a dust bowl.

II

The air mass idea is simple. As great ideas often do, the air mass idea makes you feel that you have known it right along. And in a vague way, you have. Take, for example, that half-brag, half-complaint of the Texans that there is nothing between Texas and the North Pole to keep out those northers but a barbed wire fence: it contains the kernel of the whole idea—the invading air mass—but only in a fooling way. Or take the manner in which the Mediterranean people have always given definite names to certain winds (boreas, sirocco, mistral) that blow hot or cold, dry or moist, across their roofs. They are names, however, without the larger view. In creative literature such things as a cold front passage—the sudden arrival of a cold air mass—have been described several times quite accurately, but always as a local spectacle, with the key thought missing.

Actually it took genius to see it. For air is a mercurial fluid, bubbly, changeable; it is as full of hidden energies as dynamite; it can assume the most unexpected appearances. There are days, to be sure, when the air virtually advertises its origin. Offhand, you might say that on perhaps half the days of the year it does. But there are also days when its appearance is altogether misleading.

Take, for example, the amazing metamorphosis that happens to Tropical Gulf air when it flows northward across the United States in winter. It starts out from among the Islands looking blue and sunny and like an everlasting summer afternoon. When it arrives over the northern United States that same air appears as a dark-gray, shapeless, drizzling overcast, and in the office buildings of New York and Chicago the electric lights are on throughout what is considered a shivery winter day. It *is* still the same air; if we could mix a pink dye into the air, as geographers sometimes mix dyes into rivers to trace the flow of water, a cloud of pink air would have traveled from Trinidad to New York. It has hardly changed at all its actual contents of heat and water; but as far as its appearance and its feel are concerned—its "weather" value—a few days of northward traveling have reversed it almost into a photographic negative of itself.

What happens in this particular case—and it accounts for half our winter days—is simply that the cool ground of the wintry continent chills this moist, warm air mass—chills it just a little, not enough to change its fundamental character, and not all the way up into its upper levels, but in its bottommost layer and that only just enough to make it condense out some of its abundant moisture in the form of visible clouds; it is quite similar to the effect of a cold windowpane on the air of a well-heated, comfortable room—there is wetness and cooling right at the window, but the bulk of the room's air is not affected.

Perhaps the oddest example of this is the trick by which Polar Pacific air, striking the United States at Seattle, cool and moist, arrives in eastern Montana and the Dakotas as a chinook, a hot, dry, snow-melting wind.

As Polar Pacific air flows up the slopes of the Sierras and the Cascades it is lifted ten thousand feet into the thinner air of higher altitude. By one law of physics the lifting should chill the air through release of pressure. If you have ever bled excess pressure out of your tires you know this cooling by release of pressure—you know how ice-cold the air comes hissing out. But in this case, by a different law of physics, Polar Pacific reacts by cooling only moderately; then it starts condensing out its moisture and thereby protecting its warmth; hence the tremendous snowfalls of the Sierras, the giant redwoods, the streams that irrigate California ranches.

Once across the Cascades and the Sierras, the air flows down the eastern slopes. In descending it comes under pressure and therefore heats up, just as air heats up a tire pump. Warmed, the air increases its capacity to hold moisture; it becomes relatively drier—thus this air sucks back its own clouds into invisible form. When it arrives over the Columbia Basin, or the country around Reno, or Owens Valley, it is regular desert air—warm, very clear, and very dry. That is why the western deserts are where they are. Flowing on eastward, it comes against another hump, the Continental Divide and the Rockies. Here the whole process repeats itself. Again the air is lifted and *should* become ice-cold; again it merely cools moderately, clouds up, and drops its remaining moisture to protect its warmth; hence the lush greenery of Coeur d'Alene, the pine forest of New Mexico. Finally, as the air flows down the eastern slope of the Rockies, compression heats it once more, as in the bicycle pump. Twice on the way up it has dropped moisture and thus failed to cool; twice on the way down it has been heated: it is now extremely dry, and twenty degrees warmer than it was at Seattle. *That* is the chinook, a wind manufactured of exactly the sort of principles that work in air-conditioning machinery, and a good example of the trickery of air masses. But it is *still* a simple thing; it is still one actual physically identical mass of air that you are following. If you had put pink smoke into it at Seattle, pink smoke would have arrived in South Dakota.

That is how the air mass concept explains all sorts of weather detail: the various kinds of rain—showery or steady; the many types of cloud —low or high, solid or broken, layered or towering; thunderstorms; fog. An air mass, thus-and-thus conditioned, will react differently as it flows over the dry plains, the freshly plowed cotton fields, the cool lakes, the hot pavements, the Rocky Mountains of the United States.

An airplane pilot's weather sense consists largely of guessing the exact manner in which a given sort of air will behave along his route. Tropical Gulf in summer over Alabama? Better not get caught in the middle afternoon with a low fuel reserve. We shall have to detour around many thunderstorms. The details are as multifarious as geography itself, but much of it has by now been put into the manuals, and the pilot memorizes such items as these:

Canadian air that passes over the Great Lakes in winter is moistened and warmed in its lower layers and becomes highly unstable. When such air hits the rolling country of Western Pennsylvania and New York and the ridges of the Appalachians, the hills have a sort of "trigger action" and cause snow flurries or rain squalls with very low ceilings and visibility.

In summer, Canadian air that flows into New England, dried, without passing over the Great Lakes, will be extremely clear and extremely bumpy.

Tropical Gulf over the South forms patchy ground fog just before sunrise that will persist for two or three hours.

As Polar Pacific air moves southward along the Pacific Coast it forms a layer of "high fog."

In Colorado and Nebraska fresh arriving Canadian air frequently shows as a dust storm.

Given two types of country underneath, one kind of air can produce two sorts of weather only a few miles apart. Tropical Atlantic air, for instance, appears over the hills of New England as hot and summery weather, slightly hazy, inclined toward afternoon thunderstorms. A few miles off the coast the same air appears as low banks of fog. That is because the granite and the woods are warmed all through, and actually a little warmer than Tropical Gulf air itself, at least during the day; while the ocean is much colder than the air, and cools it.

Again, one kind of country can have opposite effects on two different types of air. For example, the farms of the Middle West in the spring when the frost is just out of the ground: that sort of country feels cool to Tropical Gulf air that has flowed up the Mississippi Valley. The bottom layers of that warm moist air are chilled and thus the whole air mass is stabilized. It will stay nicely in layers; the clouds will form a flat, level overcast; smoke will spread and hover as a pall. But to a mass of freshly broken-out Canadian air that sort of country feels warm. The air in immediate contact with the ground is warmed, and the whole mass becomes bottom-light and unstable.

And that means action: a commotion much like the boiling of water on a huge scale and in slow motion. The warmed air floats away upward to the colder air aloft, forming bubbles of rising air, hundreds of feet in diameter, that are really hot-air balloons without a skin.

Those rising chunks of air are felt by fliers as bumps. When the ship flies into one it gets an upward jolt; when it flies out again it gets a downward jolt. They are what makes it possible to fly a glider, even over flat country; all you have to do is to find one of those bubbles, stay in it by circling in a tight turn, and let it carry you aloft.

The clear air, the tremendous visibility of such a day is itself the result of instability: the rising bubbles carry away the dust, the haze, the industrial smoke. The air is always roughest on one of those crisp, clear, newly washed days. If the rising air gets high enough it makes cumulus clouds, those characteristic, towering, puffy good-weather clouds. That sort of cloud is nothing but a puff of upward wind become visible. The rise has cooled the air and made its water vapor visible. Soaring pilots seek to get underneath a cumulus cloud—there is sure to be a lively upflow there. Sometimes, in really unstable air, the rising of the air reaches hurricane velocities. We call that a thunderstorm, but the lightning and thunder are only by-products of the thing. The thing itself is simply a vicious, explosive upsurging of air: the wind in thunderstorms blows sixty to one hundred miles per hour —straight up! The most daring of soaring pilots have flown into thunderstorms and have been sucked up almost to the stratosphere.

The weatherman, unlike the pilot, need not guess. He has got a slide rule; he has got the laws of gases, Charles's Law, Boyle's Law, Buys Ballot's Law at his fingertips. He has studied thermodynamics, and he has got a new device that is the biggest thing in weather science since Torricelli invented the barometer—the radio sonde with which he can take soundings of the upper air, find out just how moisture and temperature conditions are aloft, just how stable or unstable the air will be, at what level the clouds will form, and of what type they will be.

Radio sondes go up in the dead of night from a dozen airports all over the continent. The radio sonde looks like a box of candy, being a small carton wrapped in tinfoil; but it is actually a radio transmitter coupled to a thermometer and a moisture-meter. It is hung on a small parachute which is hitched to a balloon. It takes perhaps an hour for the balloon to reach the stratosphere, and all the time it signals its own readings in a strange, quacky voice, half Donald Duck, half voice from the beyond. Then it stops. You know that the balloon has burst, the parachute is letting the instrument down gently.

The next morning some farm boy finds the shiny thing in a field, with a notice attached offering a reward for mailing it back to the weather bureau.

Also the next morning a man in Los Angeles paces up and down his office, scanning the wall where last night's upper-air soundings are tacked up. Emitting heavy cigar smoke and not even looking out of the window, he dictates a weather forecast for the transcontinental airway as far east as Salt Lake City, a forecast that goes into such detail that you sometimes think he is trying to show off.

III

With the air mass idea as a key, you can make more sense out of the weather than the professional weatherman could before Bjerknes; and even if you don't understand Boyle's Law and all the intricate physics of the atmosphere, you can do a quite respectable job of forecasting.

It goes like this: suppose you are deep in Caribbean air. You will have "air mass weather": a whole series of days of the typical sort that goes with that particular type of air when it overlies your particular section of the country in that particular season. There will be all sorts of minor changes; there will be a daily cycle of weather, clouds, perhaps thunderstorms, or showers; but essentially the weather will be the same day after day. Any *real* change in weather can come only as an incursion of a new air mass—probably Polar Canadian.

And when that air mass comes you will know it. New air rarely comes gently, gradually, by imperceptible degrees; almost always the new air mass advances into the old one with a clear-cut, sharply defined forward front. Where two air masses adjoin each other you may in half an hour's driving—in five minutes' flying—change your entire weather, travel from moist, muggy, cloudy weather into clear, cool, sunny weather. That clear-cut boundary is exactly what makes an air mass a distinct entity which you can plot on a map and say, "Here it begins; here it ends"; these sharp boundaries of the air masses are called "fronts" and are a discovery as important as the air mass itself.

You are watching, then, for a "cold front," the forward edge of an advancing mass of cold air. You will get almost no advance warning. You will see the cold air mass only when it is practically upon you. But you know that sooner or later it must come, and that it will come from the northwest. Thus, an occasional long-distance call will be enough. Suppose you are in Pittsburgh, with a moist, warm southwest wind: the bare news that Chicago has a northerly wind might be enough of a clue. If you knew also that Chicago was twenty degrees cooler you would be certain that a cold air mass had swamped Chicago and was now presumably on its way to Pittsburgh, traveling presumably at something like 30 m.p.h. You could guess the time of arrival of its forward front within a few hours. That is why the most innocent weather reports are now so secret; why the British censor suppresses snow flurries in Scotland; why a submarine in the Atlantic would love to know merely the wind direction and temperature at, say, Columbus, Ohio; why the Gestapo had that weather station in Greenland.

Knowing that a cold front is coming, you know what kind of weather to expect; though some cold fronts are extremely fierce, and others quite gentle (noticeable only if you watch for them), the type is always the same. It is all in the book—Bjerknes described it and even drew pictures of it. It was the advance of such a cold front which occurred while you slept that night before you awoke to find the world fresh and newly painted.

Cold air is heavy; as polar air plows into a region occupied by tropical air it underruns; it gets underneath the warm air and lifts it up even as it pushes it back. A cold front acts physically like a cowcatcher.

Seen from the ground, the sequence of events is this: an hour or two before the cold front arrives the clouds in the sky become confused, somewhat like a herd of cattle that smells the coyotes; but you observe that by intuition rather than by measurable signs. Apart from that, there are no advance signs. The wind will be southerly to the last, and the air warm and moist.

Big cumulus clouds build up all around, some of them with dark bases, showers, and in summer thunder and lightning—that is the warm moist air going aloft. A dark bank of solid cloud appears in the northwest, and though the wind is still southerly, this bank keeps building up and coming nearer: it is the actual forward edge of the advancing cold air. When it arrives there is a cloudburst. Then the cold air comes sweeping in from the northwest with vicious gusts. This is the squall that capsizes sailboats and uproots trees, flattens forests and unroofs houses.

The whole commotion probably is over in half an hour. The wind eases up, though it is still cool and northwesterly, the rain ceases, the clouds break and new sky shows: the front has passed, the cold air mass has arrived.

The weatherman can calculate these things too. He has watched and sounded out each of the two air masses for days or even weeks, ever since it moved into his ken somewhere on the outskirts of the American world. Thus an airline weatherman may look at a temperature-moisture graph and say, "This is dynamite. This air will be stable enough as long as it isn't disturbed. But wait till some cold air gets underneath this and starts lifting it. This stuff is going to go crazy."

In making your own guess you would take the same chance that the weatherman takes every morning—that you might be right and yet get an error chalked up against you. Suppose the Chicago weatherman, seeing a cold front approach, forecasts thunderstorms. One thunderstorm passes north of the city, disturbing the 30,000 inhabitants of Waukegan. Another big one passes south of Chicago, across farms just south of Hammond, Ind., affecting another 30,000 people. None happens to hit Chicago itself, with its 3 million people. On a per capita basis, the weatherman was 98 per cent wrong! Actually he was right.

Now you are in the cold air mass, and you can reasonably expect "air mass weather" for a while rather than "frontal" weather, i.e., a whole series of whatever sort of day goes with Canadian air in your particular section of the country at that particular season.

Any real change in the weather *now* can again come only with an incursion of a new and different air mass—and now that will probably mean tropical maritime air of the Gulf kind. To forecast that invasion is no trick at all: you can see the forward front of the warm air mass in the sky several days before it sweeps in on the ground. Warm air is light. As Caribbean air advances into a region occupied by Canadian air it produces a pattern that is the exact opposite of the cold front. The warm front overhangs forward, overruns the cold air; the warm air mass may appear high above Boston when at ground level it is just invading Richmond, Va.

Again the sequence of events is predictable—Bjerknes drew the picture. It is the approaching warm front that makes for "bad" weather, for rain of the steady, rather than the showery kind, for low ceilings.

Consider a warm front on the morning when its foot is near Richmond and its top over Boston. Boston that morning sees streaks of cirrus in its sky—"mares' tails," the white, feathery, diaphonous cloud arranged in filaments and bands, that is so unsubstantial that the sun shines clear through it and you are hardly conscious of it as a cloud— and actually it doesn't consist of water droplets, as do most clouds, but of ice crystals. New Haven the same mornings has the same kind of cloud, but slightly thicker, more nearly as a solid, milky layer. New York that same morning sees the warm air as a gray solid overcast at 8,000 feet. Philadelphia has the same sort of cloud at 5,000 with steady rain. Washington has 1,500 feet, rain. Quantico and Richmond report fog, and all airplanes are grounded. Raleigh, N.C., has clearing weather, the wind has shifted that morning to the southwest, and it is getting hot and humid there. Raleigh would be definitely behind the front, well in the warm air mass itself.

By nightfall Boston has the weather that was New Haven's in the morning. The moon, seen through a milky sheet of cirrus clouds, has a halo: "There is going to be rain." New Haven that night has New York's weather of that morning; New York has Philadelphia's; and so on down the line—the whole front has advanced one hundred miles. In forecasting the weather for Boston it is safe to guess that Boston will get in succession New Haven weather, New York weather, Philadelphia, Washington, Richmond weather—and finally Raleigh weather—in a sequence that should take two or three days: steady lowering clouds, rainy periods, some fog—followed finally by a wind shift to the southwest, and rapid breaking of clouds, and much warmer, very humid weather.

And then the cycle begins all over. You are then deep in Caribbean air again. You will have Caribbean air mass weather, and your weather eye had better be cocked northwest to watch for the first signs of polar air.

IV

There *is* a rhythm, then, in the weather, or at least a sort of rhyme, a repetitive sequence. All those folk rules that attribute weather changes to the phases of the moon, or to some other simple periodicity ("If the weather is O.K. on Friday, it is sure to rain over the week-end") are not so far from the mark after all. The rhythm does not work in terms of rain or shine; but it does work in terms of air masses; and thus, indirectly and loosely, through the tricky physics of the air, it governs also the actual weather.

What makes the air masses move, and what makes them move rhythmically—that is the crowning one of the great Norwegian discoveries. Some of it had long been known. It was understood that the motive power is the sun. By heating the tropics and leaving the polar region cold, it sets up a worldwide circulation of air, poleward at high altitude, equatorward at lower levels. It was understood that this simple circulation is complicated by many other factors such as the monsoon effect: continents heat up in summer and draw air in from over the ocean, in winter they cool and air flows out over the ocean; there was the baffling Coriolis Force that makes all moving things (on the Northern Hemisphere) curve to the right. In everyday life we don't notice it, but some geographers hold that it affects the flow of rivers, and artillerymen make allowance for it; a long-range gun is always aimed at a spot hundreds of yards to the left of the target. The monsoons and the Coriolis Force between them break up the simple pole-to-equator-to-pole flow of the air into a worldwide complicated system of interlocking "wheels"—huge eddies that show variously as trade winds, calm belts, prevailing westerlies. Charts have been drawn of the air ocean's currents showing how air is piled up over some parts of the world, rushed away from others.

But it remained for the Norwegians to discover the polar front— perhaps the last-discovered geographical thing on this earth. Bjerknes himself first saw it—that the worldwide air circulation keeps piling up new masses of polar air in the north and pressing them southward; it keeps piling up new masses of tropical air in the south, pressing them northward; and thus forever keeps forcing tropical and polar air masses against each other along a front; that the demarcation line between tropical air masses, pressing northward, and polar air masses, pressing southward, runs clear around the world: through North America and across the Atlantic, through Europe and across Siberia, through Japan and across the Pacific. The polar front is clear-cut in some places, tends to wash out in others; but it always reestablishes itself.

In summer, the polar front runs across North America north of the Great Lakes; in winter, it takes up a position across the United States. Wherever it is, it keeps advancing southward, retreating northward, much like a battlefront. And all the cold fronts and warm fronts are but sections of this greater front.

The rhythmical flowing of the air masses, the Norwegians discovered, is simply this wave action along the polar front. Like all the rest of the modern weather concepts, this one becomes common sense, almost self-evident—the moment you realize that air is stuff, a real fluid that has density and weight. Except that it occurs on a scale of unhuman magnitude, wave action along the polar front is almost exactly the same thing as waves on a lake.

In a lake, a dense, heavy fluid—the water—lies underneath a thin, light fluid—the air—and the result is that rhythmical welling up and down of the lake-surface that we call waves. Along the polar front, a dense, heavy fluid, the polar air, lies to the north of a thin, lighter fluid, the tropical air; the result is a rhythmical welling southward and northward of the two kinds of air. When a water wave rolls across a lake its first manifestation is a downward bulging of the water, then an upward surging. When a wave occurs in the polar front it appears first as a northward surging of warm air, and that means all the phenomena of a warm front. Then, in the rhythmical backswing, comes the southward surging of cold air, and that means all the phenomena of a cold front.

These waves are bigger than the imagination can easily encompass. They measure 500 to 1,000 miles from crest to crest. When tropical air surges northward it will wash to the edge of the Arctic; when polar air surges southward it reaches down into the tropics. Such a wave will travel along the polar front all the way from somewhere out in the Pacific, across the United States and out to the Atlantic; that is the

meteorological action which underlies the recent novel *Storm* by
George Stewart: the progress of a wave along the polar front.

So similar are these air waves to the air-water waves of a lake that
there are even whitecaps and breakers. What we call a whitecap or a
breaker is a whirling together of air and water into a white foam. In
the great waves along the polar front the same toppling-over can occur:
warm and cold air sometimes wheel around each other, underrun and
overrun each other, in a complicated, spiral pattern.

And that is where the old papery weather science of the schoolbooks
merges with the realistic observations of the Norwegians. You remember about those Lows that were traveling across the weather map and
brought with them bad weather. You know how a dropping barometer
has always indicated the coming of bad weather—though we have
never quite known why.

Now it turns out that the barometric low is nothing but one of those
toppling-over waves in the polar front—or rather, it is the way in which
the spiral surging of the air masses affects the barometers. Look at
the Middle West when it is being swept by one of those waves, take
a reading of everybody's barometer, and you get the typical low. Look
at it when a low is centered, watch the kinds of air that are flowing
there, the wind directions, the temperatures and humidities and you
find that a low has a definite internal structure: the typical wave pattern, with a warm air mass going north and a cold air mass going
south, both phases of the same wave.

Barometric pressures turn out to be not the cause of the weather,
but simply a result, a rather unimportant secondary symptom of it.
What weather actually is the Norwegians have made clear. It is the
wave action of the air ocean.

> As it fell upon a day
> In the merry month of May,
> Sitting in a pleasant shade
> Which a grove of myrtles made,
> Beasts did leap and birds did sing,
> Trees did grow and plants did spring;
> Every thing did banish moan
> Save the Nightingale alone.
> She, poor bird, as all forlorn,

Lean'd her breast up-till a thorn,
And there sung the dolefull'st ditty
That to hear it was great pity.
"Fie, fie, fie," now would she cry;
"Teru, teru," by and by:
That to hear her so complain
Scarce I could from tears refrain,
For her griefs so lively shown
Made me think upon mine own.
—Ah, thought I, thou mourn'st in vain,
None takes pity on thy pain:
Senseless trees, they cannot hear thee,
Ruthless beasts, they will not cheer thee;
King Pandion, he is dead,
All thy friends are lapp'd in lead:
All thy fellow birds do sing
Careless of thy sorrowing.

RICHARD BARNFIELD

TOO DEEP TO BE SEEN

by William Beebe

There is no way of deciding who is the best known and the most widely read author-scientist in the world today, but William Beebe must be in the running. He has been almost everywhere on the surface of the globe and has turned out articles on almost every phase of natural history. He has been on more than half a hundred expeditions and has written a dozen popular books on scientific subjects. He has done more than scratch the surface of the earth, too. He has been 3000 feet under water in his famous bathysphere and 30,000 feet above ground on some of his plane flights. He made two voyages to the Galápagos Islands and from the results of each voyage he minted a best-selling book. The first was Galápagos—World's End. *The second was* The Arcturus Adventure. *He conducted two expeditions to the wilds of India—fifty years apart! He was born in Brooklyn, New York, July 29, 1877, received a B.S. degree from Columbia University in 1898, did a year of postgraduate work under the great Henry Fairfield Osborn, and then joined the staff of the New York Zoological Society at the Bronx Zoo as Curator of Ornithology. Later he widened his interests to take in most of the other "ologies" in the field of natural history. He has collected in many lands and on many seas. He has done a vast amount of research in his laboratory and his library. He is an expert photographer and a delightful lecturer. And in his eightieth year he is still cheerfully at work. The selection that follows is a chapter from one of his later books,* Unseen Life of New York, *published in 1953.*

THE best-known Hudson Terminal is a tunnel in lower New York built a few decades ago. The original Hudson Terminal is a canyon, one hundred miles southeast of New York City, lying one mile below the surface, and excavated sometime around a million years ago. This canyon is a crack in the doorstep of the city, and lies on the continental shelf, bordering the Atlantic coast, and extending far out beyond Sandy Hook.

The exact method of formation of this mighty Hudson River Gorge is still uncertain, but we know that the area which lies deep beneath the turbulent waters was once part of a great river system that drained not only the Hudson Valley, but the valleys of the Great Lakes, and the present Connecticut, Housatonic, Passaic and Hackensack rivers.

When our own Hudson was in its glory the great glaciers of the ice age had not yet filled its bed with boulders and gravel as it is today. In that past time the Palisades rose four times as high above the water as they do today. The river flowed seaward 45 miles beyond the present coastline, then dropped first over an 1800 foot waterfall, then three others, until the canyon lost itself in the level bed of the uttermost depths.

A matter of about twenty thousand years ago we might have walked far out, along the river of the gorge, for the last advancing glacier had locked up so much water in its icy embrace that the level of the entire ocean was lowered several hundred feet. Thus, because of the erosion of past ages, the creatures living at a mile depth are today brought within the limits of our New York circle.

A few years ago I made a small expedition to investigate these primitive New Yorkers, and we must not forget, as I have said before, that far, far back in the dim mists of early evolution, we and they were one—so we may think of them as ancestral neighbors.

At present, visitors are taken daily on a sight-seeing yacht which steams around Manhattan Island and shows the city from a new point of view. The time will come when tourists, as well as native New Yorkers, will be able to board a ship, head seaward to the hundred-mile line, and in the course of a few hours watch "monsters of the deep" brought to the surface before their eyes, fresh from the black, icy depths. Meanwhile, a brief account of my own expedition will anticipate and envisage such a tour.

Late on a July evening, on the seagoing tug *Wheeler*, we backed slowly out from a Brooklyn slip. Our first attempts at sleep were in-

terrupted by a magnificent, unseasonable display of northern lights—
flashes and ribbons and radiating spokes of yellow and rose and green.
At eight o'clock the following morning the little tug was rolling gently
on the threshold of New York's abyssal world, something more than
one hundred miles out at sea, with the ultramarine of open ocean
stretching all around to the rim of the world. The only life on the
planet seemed to be our tugful of selves and a quartet of Mother
Cary's Chickens.

The small *Arcturus* winch was uncovered, given a breath of steam,
and the wire began to uncoil. To it a series of great silken nets was
attached, and they went billowing back in the wake of the tug, settling slowly out of sight. A mile and a half of wire was run out and
for several hours we crawled along at a speed of barely two knots.
I put my hand on the taut, vibrating spider web of steel; my eye followed it down into invisibility into the liquid blue, and the underworld of the deep sea became very real. I have walked in comfort, in a
metal helmet, ten fathoms deep; once I exceeded a half mile straight
down in the Bathysphere, but in general, the North Pole is far more
accessible than where the nets were being drawn. At the surface of the
water, temperature is 68 degrees; five hundred fathoms down it is 40
degrees, and at the bottom of the Hudson Gorge the thermometer
would read 31 degrees. In this unbelievable world, not only does bitter
cold prevail, but complete and eternal darkness, and the pressure, at
a mile depth, of a ton to each square inch.

Finally I waved my hand, the bell in the engine room clanged, the
idling propeller rested and the sturdy bulk of the tug began to roll,
swinging to the wind. Slowly the wire reeled in, and after a long time
the great nets, at their apex, came dripping and cold to the surface and
were drawn on board. Our final count showed fifty-five species of
deep-sea fish, of which five were new to science.

Into big jars and aquariums were poured the pink treasure, glittering
and gleaming, trembling with strange vitality, every spoonful a cosmos
of hundreds of living creatures. There loomed through the translucent
mass a long black and bronze eel, or, as it finally proved, a nine-inch
scimitar-fanged sea dragon. I picked it up and at the first touch felt
almost pain from the bitter cold. In the heat of a still July day, my
hands became numb as I dipped them into the glistening gelatin, and
the strange character of this deep world began to shape itself in my
mind.

As I picked up the dragonfish, the mouth opened unbelievably wide, as wide as would be the gape of a saber-toothed tiger, and the long needle-sharp fangs came together with a snap. I had wondered how the teeth could be managed, and I now saw that the two longest went straight through concealed grooves in the head and appeared above the skin near the eyes. A long tentacle thread from the dorsal fin drooped forward in advance of the head. Later by accident the fish bit upon my fingers, but so weak had exposure to these surface pressures rendered the creature, that the tips of the needle fangs did not even pierce my skin.

Several large shrimps caught my eye, for they were of the most intense flaming scarlet. I put one into a small glass, ran down to a dark cabin, shut the door and watched magic. Little by little, from out of several pores there flowed a fluid within fluid—a foggy mist sifting and billowing through the water, a mist which suddenly took fire and in the darkness I saw I was holding a glowing glass—the water alight with soft radiance. As a squid escapes through his own sepia smoke screen, so this deep-sea shrimp was covering his being with a dazzling cloud of fire. A second realization came to me—the utter darkness along the path of the net. Sixty feet below the surface I have watched fish swim in what seemed tropical moonlight. Even at this slight depth the red end of the spectrum goes first. So at his infinitely greater depth, the scarlet shrimp would be black as night, or his surroundings, there being no reflected red rays. Until I brought him to the surface he was not and had *never* been red.

We think of the darkness and we see the great fangs and we see a relation between the two. Plants cannot grow without sunlight, so, far beneath the surface, every creature is carnivorous. We know that some are cannibals, and others have a stomach so elastic that they can swallow a fish several times their own length.

If absolute and perpetual midnight should suddenly envelop our city, only those of us could survive who had access to adequate illumination, or who by blind skill could manage to avoid danger and find food. As we study our deep-sea creatures we learn that the same thing holds good in the gorge of the Hudson. Many of the fishes, shrimps and squids are covered with powerful searchlights, or dotted with lesser beacons, and their eyes are large and far-seeing. In other creatures we find long feelers reaching out in all directions and associated with blind or nearly blind eyes. As a blind man hangs a lettered sign about his neck—a sign he himself can never read—and sits patiently waiting for it to attract pennies, so occasionally we find a

blind fish with the sockets of its eyes turned into glowing headlights.
We can explain this only as a lure to draw small victims close enough
for some other sense to detect them.

In every net there are many unsolved problems. A tiny white thread
of a fish, which we scoop into a glass of sea water, has perfectly good
eyes far out on the ends of slender stalks, each half as long as the
body. The life history of these stalk-eyed dragonfish would be considered sheer fantasy were it not scientifically factual. If the fish were
shaped like a human being the length of the stalks would locate the
eyes on the tips of the fingers, most efficient for watching a passing
parade, but of no use to the fish that we know of. These are very
young, but as the fish grows older the eye-stalks begin to shorten and
draw the eye nearer the head. The cartilage skeleton is absorbed, the
nerve crumples and twists and finally, is actually crowded down into
vacant eye sockets, ready for it. The eye follows, is drawn close, and
takes root.

From now on the eyes of the stalk-eyed dragonfish are just where
we find them in all normal fish. Another phase of the strange life
begins. The sexes commence to diverge, the female increasing rapidly
in size, until she measures almost a foot in length, turning black, developing a row of shining portholes along her sides, and a large brilliant
beacon near the tail, all luminous pink. She also grows an elaborate,
leaflike, chin barbel and a terrifying set of fangs.

The male remains dwarfed, two inches over-all, and is almost transparent. His mouth is toothless and he can neither ingest nor digest
food. A great light appears on each side of his head with an efficient
reflector and he barges slowly along through life, hoping against hope
that a mate will find him before he dies of starvation. That all this
is a very real handicap is shown by there being many more males than
females. What a life! Shining forth his twin lamps, he watches always
for the thousand and one chance that a form, approaching through
the utter darkness, is not an implacable enemy but one of his own
kind.

In spite of all these obstacles the species seems to prosper. They
have been found in almost every sea, and in two seasons of deep-sea
trawling in Bermuda we took more than a hundred, most of them a
full mile down. Off New York, on the present trip, two stalk-eyed
dragonfish found their way into the nets.

In the depths of the sea hundreds of little fish are swimming, all
exactly alike, less than two inches long, tail fins wagging furiously,

eyes striving to glimpse some friendly spark of light in all the eternal darkness. Their nostrils are very large, ready to detect the faintest hint of an odor. The jaws are produced into a sort of snout like a pair of pincers, each armed with a cluster of toothlike spines. In addition to complete external identity, every one is a male. In the Hudson Gorge, in one of the deepest nets, we found two of these dwarf males. So we can recount their known story as concerning our abyssal New York neighbors.

Thousands upon thousands of these small fish hatch, pursue their frantic search and perish. Or, through sight of a flaming globe, or the diffusion of a subtle odor, one, more fortunate, detects and approaches a great creature one hundred times as large as itself—an unlovely, awkward, black fish, flaunting a yellow lantern on a long tentacle. Her eyes are minute, almost useless, and every inch of skin is covered with large, ivory-hard, sharp spines. Even among the dragons and gargoyles of deep-sea fishes, this abyssal fishing frog must be accounted ugly.

With a single gulp she could swallow a dozen of the little black fish if they clustered around her beacon. But for the one following close upon her scent the shining globe has no attraction. Like an iron filing drawn to a magnet, he rushes headlong upon her. He may strike upon her sides or back or even on her head. Wherever it may be, he seizes hold with his clusters of bristles, finding a tiny area of soft skin somewhere among the spines. Holding fast—like a burr to wool—he begins to gnaw with his teeth until he exposes a bit of raw flesh. In some manner, as yet unknown, the capillaries of the giant fish merge with those in his mouth, and a perfect union is formed of flesh and blood. Such is the marriage of the little bristle-snouted male with this huge, black, female lantern bearer.

Marvels only begin at this moment, for after the fusion is complete there sets in an appalling degeneration in the body of the small parasite. He loses eyes, nostrils, brain, bones, stomach. He is nourished by the life-giving blood of his strange mate; he is carried wherever she wishes to go; he is protected from harm by his smallness and his flabbiness, half-hidden among the horny, mountainous spines of his consort's skin. His only remaining destiny is to fertilize the eggs which in course of time stream out into the water. After this he may perish, or else, preserving whatever individuality is left, he may exist until his hostess succumbs, when, automatically, death comes to him.

Another fish is round and of glowing silver, and has all its batteries of green and violet lights directed downward, while its eyes forever stare immovably upward. A fourth fish has series of great curved teeth along the jaws, but outside, at various angles on the skin, where they seem utterly useless.

Now and then we see something which needs no explanation, but demands only appreciation and wonder; a curious, pale violet, hump-backed shrimp with a brood of tiny humpbacked offspring. All are gathered on the inside of a transparent, fluted barrel which the mother has taken from its original owner, and, like a more unselfish Diogenes, used it for a nursery. With her swimmerets she is able to kick her house along so that a stream of water and food pours through. Though hosts of hungry dragons may nose about the sides, yet the shrimp and her brood are safe. The courtships and battles, the comedies and tragedies of family life in this underworld seem to our over-imaginative minds to be tales of ingenuity, horror and devotion.

With all this strangeness there is also beauty. In and out through the mass of life swim active opals—gleaming and scintillating as they twist and turn—tiny, oval, living tissues of flame and ash, which glow as brightly after death, for their colors are due not to pigment but, like a hummingbird's throat, to a myriad prisms.

With our present meager facilities we can best revive the glories of the sea depths by taking the newly caught beings into a darkened room, and watch the shift and play of colored lights, the lines upon lines of glowing portholes, each beacon as complex as an eye, with lens and reflector; other lights arranged in certain patterns along the sides are for recognition by members of the same school, and finally, we watch the penetrating flashes which, as they are different in the two sexes, may be of use in finding and securing a mate.

With body cramped from a day of long and intensive inactivity, I am roused by a steady throbbing, and look up to see that the tug is heading homewards. Far off on the horizon is a tiny black smudge in the sky, and I realize that there is another world than this of the ocean deeps—that on the great liner on the horizon people are playing bridge, gossiping, looking at the water with unseeing eyes, while in the dimming light of day the sea dragons beneath their keel are swimming along on their tigerish quests in this Unseen World.

CONCLUSION

We are now in the fourth interglacial period of warmth, and it seems absolutely certain that in the course of the usual thousands of years to come, the fifth glacier will begin its swing southward.

I remember, when a child in the year 1888, being drawn upon the top of the snow on a sled over the tips of the city's street lamps, and wondering if I should ever again see the streets or the ground. Sometimes at night when I look out upon a world of swirling snowflakes and listen to the howl of the bitter winter gale, it seems as if Labrador had already liberated glacier number five.

If we keep to the cosmic schedule, the inception and development of our present city occupy only a fleeting second of geological time, conservatively one forty-millionth. What of the future? As I write, let us suppose hundreds of thousands of years have already passed. It is in the dim, distant future, and my faltering human mind can be certain of only one ultimate happening.

Let us visualize it. I came to the zoo a few weeks ago in a driving snowstorm. The Rocking Stone was capped with white, and, all around, the ground was a foot deep in millions of snow crystals. My imagination can conceive the next day and the next and the next as of continued storm; frantic messages come from Canada of a slow-moving continent of ice, coming nearer and nearer, of never-ending snow. From along all ocean shores come reports of the slow sinking of the sea itself, leaving the beaches bare and frozen.

All animals and human beings flee southward or perish. No man-made explosives or heating plants can do anything to stop the cataclysm for a moment. Soon come the last living creatures, polar bears whimpering with fear, snowy owls, musk oxen searching for a final bit of moss, walruses swimming down the coast. At last the enormous pale green ice front of cliff, a half or a full mile in height, crunches and grinds its way to the zoo, just as it has done twice before. The houses, everything, crumble like clusters of twigs and pebbles. Last of all, if there could be any human eye to see, the age-old Rocking Stone itself is stirred, pushed from its bed, and like a great snowball rolls slowly southward in the forefront of the glacier.

Another ice age is on its way!

ARMIES OF ANTS

by William M. Mann

Widely known as the Director of the National Zoological Park in Washington, D.C., for many years, William Madison Mann was born in Helena, Montana, July 1, 1886, attended Staunton Military Academy in Virginia, was graduated with an A.B. degree from Stanford in 1911, and immediately thereafter took off on the trip to Brazil described in this selection. On his return from Brazil he went to Harvard to work and study, the result of which was the degree of D.Sc. in 1915 from Harvard and a traveling fellowship for a year that carried him to the Near East on a collecting trip.

As an adventurous boy on a Montana ranch he had generously taken all Nature for his province. He studied birds. He trapped and skinned mammals. He frightened neighbors by pulling snakes out of his pockets. But he found he could make money collecting insects for specialists in that field—and he needed the money to finance his college career. For that reason he concentrated on insects, and, when he returned from the Near East in 1916, he joined the United States Bureau of Entomology and remained with it until he accepted the position of Director of the National Zoological Park in 1925. This, of course, widened his field again, and he derived much enjoyment from his daily work with lions, tigers, elephants, giraffes, and other zoo occupants much larger than the Diptera, Coleoptera and Hymenoptera with which he had been chiefly concerned. But even as a zoo director he continued to be a specialist in insects and famous as an "ant man" who had collected and studied the Formicidae of six continents on their home grounds on repeated expeditions.

The selection that follows, taken from his Ant Hill Odyssey published in 1948, will give the reader not only a vivid impression of the author's personality and cheerful enthusiasm in pur-

*suit of his prey but also a good picture of the conditions that a
scientist may encounter on expeditions to wild places.*

THE members of the Stanford Expedition to Brazil came east
by various routes and assembled in New York two days before sailing time. In addition to Dr. Branner, Dr. Fred Baker,
Starks, Heath, and myself, there were three students, all ma-
jors in geology—Dr. Branner's son; Olaf Jenkins, and Earl Lieb. We
met in a New York hotel, and sailed out of Brooklyn on the *Minas
Geraes*, a three-thousand-ton Brazilian steamer, neat and well run. Until we got used to it, the manner of serving meals seemed queer. All
the plates to be used in numerous courses were piled one on top of
another, and as you finished one course that plate was removed, leaving a clean one underneath. On the plate next to the bottom was
served a rich omelet that had been covered with sugar and then baked
in the oven, and the final course was always cheese and guava paste.

There is no finer feeling then moving into a steamship stateroom
and knowing that it is going to be your home for a long time. Dr.
Branner had been making trips to Brazil since 1874 and the Brazilians would not believe that he was a real North American: few could
speak such perfect Portuguese. He had written a grammar of the
language, which we attempted to absorb on the way down, and we
learned a little, with his help and that of some of our fellow passengers. There was a Peruvian school official from Iquitos, returning to
his home by way of the Amazon rather than by crossing the Andes
from the West Coast. It was he who passed me a dish of dried prunes,
explaining: "Rare tropical fruit." There was also a Chilean family of
two sisters and three children, one a baby in arms, going to join the
husband of one of them, an English mining engineer named Innis.

At the end of twelve days we saw ahead of us the sharp line of
demarcation between the clear, blue Atlantic and the muddy water
of the Amazon. As the boat entered the river, dark brown water and
spray dashed up the sides and my Peruvian friend said to me, "Just
like New York coffee." The river is four hundred miles wide at the
mouth, so we sailed in it till dark, and woke up in the morning off
Brangança, where I heard, for the first time, parrots and macaws
screaming in the wild.

In Pará, Heath and I went to the Museo Goeldi by streetcar, or *bonde.* When streetcars were first built in Brazil, bonds were sold to cover the cost, and since then the cars themselves have been known as *bondes.* Two cars together formed first and second class accommodations, and ignorant of the conventions of Brazil I stepped aboard the first one, clad in white duck trousers and a shirt; but that was not proper. Coats were absolutely *de rigeur* first class, and the conductor explained that I would have to ride second class. As the cars were tied together and exactly the same, it made little difference. The next time I rode I was properly coated, and after handing the conductor my ticket, lit my pipe, to be informed, courteously though firmly, that pipes were not permitted first class, only cigars and cigarettes.

The beautiful zoological and botanical gardens of Pará contained also the museum of natural history and archaeology, with a large collection of pottery from the island of Marajó, representing a civilization completely gone and forgotten.

The zoo cages contained numbers of things I had never seen alive before: delicate monkeys from the Upper Amazon which ordinarily will not survive in other areas, and a manatee swimming in its cement pool, coming to the surface from time to time, and opening its nostrils to inhale. It was easy, there, to give it its natural food of water weed. There was one in the Amsterdam zoo twenty years later that had been in captivity more than a year—a record for this animal. The director of the zoo told me that it consumed 1700 guilders' (about seven hundred dollars') worth of lettuce a year. More recently, a couple of manatees were exhibited at a pier in Atlantic City. They had learned to eat boiled potatoes. They were also exhibited in the Aquarium in Chicago; but they died after a few months.

In a tank in a small aquarium was a specimen of the *piraracu,* giant catfish of the Amazon. I remembered this from a picture in my first geography book, where it was labeled "Giant Arapaima of the Amazon," and shown with an Indian holding a spear and sitting on the fish. It attains a length of eighteen feet and the meat, dried and smoked, is a common food on the Amazon. The *piraracu* scales can be more than an inch long and wide and are used by Brazilian women to file their fingernails. A ten-foot boa constrictor, instead of lying lethargically in its cage as in American zoos, here, in its native climate, charged visitors when they approached. The only non-Brazilian animal in the collection was a large chimpanzee which had been used by the English Dr. Thomas at Manaos in his studies on yellow fever.

More impressive than anything in the zoo were the ants stalking around—ones that had hitherto been wondrous rarities, things that I had only seen glued on tiny strips of cardboard on insect pins. There was a large one, half an inch long, slender and heavily armored with spines, walking slowly along the fences (*Cryptocerus atratus*). There were others smaller and even spinier (*Dolichoderus bispinosus*) that had made great carton nests three feet in length, and when these were prodded with my forceps the ants emerged in thousands and fell like rain to the ground, scattering in all directions, but chiefly in mine. They did not sting, but bit ferociously. Another ant, a yellow one with spines (*Daceton armigerum*), with a large heart-shaped head that at first glance looked as though it had been put on upside down, was just standing around on tree trunks. Before the day was over there were some dozens of different kinds of ants in my preserving bottles.

The museum and gardens were in charge of a German woman scientist, Dr. Amelia Schnetlage, an ardent collector and student of birds, specializing at that time on ant-thrushes, a group of small birds that follow the legionary ant to feed on the insects that they scare up, and sometimes on the ants themselves.

Heath and I could hardly wait for night and the wonderful collecting at the electric street lights. But it was an off night for insects. We saw a few cockroaches, and nothing more, and dejectedly returned to the ship.

We landed at Ceará May 6th and moved into a hotel where we waited twelve days for a smaller steamer to take us down to Natal. The first evening a young Brazilian doctor came in, asking for Dr. Branner, who was not there at the time. He had come to tell our party that two Italians had died twelve days before of yellow fever in an adjoining hotel, separated from us by a small garden with a cement pool in it. Heath and I looked into the pool and noticed quantities of unmistakable Aëdes larvae, the little mosquitoes that carry this disease. In the morning, in my mosquito net were six adults, all so fat there was no doubt I had been exposed at least six times. I hurried excitedly into the dining-room to tell Dr. Branner, who was breakfasting, but Lieb had got there first and was saying, "Eight mosquitoes in my net, all full of blood." The doctor was so sarcastic to him that I never mentioned the paltry six that I had found. Twelve days is the period of incubation of this fever and I admit that we did some thinking about it, and afterwards laughed it off because none of us had anything the matter with us. It was not a laughing matter, though; the Innis family, our Chilean friends of the steamer, moved into a mining camp and both women and two children died of yellow fever within a month of landing, leaving the father and the baby. We saw him later at Pará, on his way to take the baby back to England.

Ceará was an attractive town and nearby were woods and a small river with numerous pools, where Starks hired all the youngsters of the village to collect fish. Part of the area was well-cultivated, with fields of cane and cotton. One man was building a fence, digging holes and putting in branches of trees, which often took root and grew, making a permanent fence. In digging these holes he found a couple of rare caecilians, burrowing wormlike batrachians, anomalous in being the only batrachians that have scales on them. These delighted Heath's heart.

The coast regions of Ceará are exceedingly arid. A breeze from the ocean tempered the heat, but when one got inland, out of this breeze, it was oppressive. We were there in the dry season. My first collecting was disappointing, a few beetles and little else during the heat of the day, but toward evening Heath and I strolled out to the vicinity of a stream and found some insect or other sitting on almost every leaf. They had known enough to avoid the midday heat, as we had not.

In New York we had purchased some ex-United States Army helmets, designed for the Philippines and then condemned by the army. They were so constructed that when we threw our heads back to look up, the back would hit us in the neck, and the helmet would fall off. At the end of the second day, five little native neighbors of ours were wearing white helmets and calling each other *ingenieros*, a name applied to foreigners because so many of them were engineers.

Mr. Williams, director of the railway, took us by train to the Baturité Mountains, where long ago a Father Schmitt had collected and sent specimens to Europe, so it was the type locality of a number of species. Lieb and I made a trip to the Maranguape Mountains, where the humid hillsides furnished a different variety of species. Naturally each of us collected as he could for the others, so I picked up some snakes for Heath. There was a black one that I picked up by the neck, and not having a bag to put it in, I asked Lieb to disrobe and lend me his BVD's to tie it in. He demurred at first, but as the alternative was to hold the snake while I took off my underwear, he loaned me his.

In the evening we walked some miles to the railroad that took us back to Ceará, and part of the road was through a swamp where a chorus of giant toads (*Bufo marinus*) bleated "ha-ha" and "ho-ho" at each other and at us. This is one of the largest of the toads, occurs widely in tropical America, and has been distributed to other parts of the world, to destroy cane-boring beetles.

At Natal the governor had provided for us a house, thick-walled and high-ceilinged. The massive furniture was of Indian teak inlaid with ivory, teak being one of the few woods that is resistant to termites, the curse of all tropics. But in true Brazilian style there were hammock hooks in the bedrooms and we slept in hammocks alongside the elegant beds.

The town was mostly of mud houses, with a great deal of poverty, though I have no memory of anyone begging. A group of mixed Europeans, Spanish, Portuguese, and a few English, were drilling for oil. I said to Dr. Branner one day that the town would boom when they struck oil; but he replied, geologically and laconically, "No oil here" —and he was right.

Food was brought to us and here we became acquainted with *carne seca*, the dried meat of southern Brazil and the Argentine, a staple food on the East Coast, though supplemented with fish. The demand for fish was much greater than the supply and Starks would have to be up early on the beach where the fishing boats came in, to get a few specimens for his collection. So great was the demand for fish that a Grimsby trawler had actually been imported from England to help supply the local market. The boat was equipped with an otter trawl, and Starks made a couple of trips on it, but there was so much seaweed to wreck the net that very few fish were obtained. He fished in the tidal pools, and later in ponds and creeks in the interior.

At Lake Papary, about twenty-four miles south of Natal, the use of gill nets was prohibited, as that method of fishing was so destructive. However, the enthusiastic colonel in charge of enforcement suspended the law for a day, and a gill net was set out, enclosing a large area of water with many fish in it, which were then caught with cast nets or in the gill net itself. Starks returned elated with an enviable and interesting collection.

Heath and I collected in the nearby countryside the "large terrible ant" (*Dinoponera grandis*) known to the Brazilians as "*tocandero*" and, according to them, having a sting which brings on fever. I can well believe it, having been stung by one of its smaller relatives. It is a heavy-set creature an inch in length, one of the very largest of the ants. Heath and I often observed it walking about, usually singly, in the evenings or on cloudy days. Following one that was carrying an insect, we found its nest in a thicket. I dug out the nest, which extended along the under side of roots that formed protective roofs. The ants move slowly—which was lucky for us, because the colony was much more populous than I had imagined it would be, and my available vials of alcohol were soon filled. The ants kept coming and coming, in no haste, but with evident intent, and the two of us, who had been squatting among a tangle of branches and vines, got out with little dignity, but without being stung.

The railroad company gave us an excursion to Baixa Verde at the terminus of the little railway that ran out from Natal in a northwesterly direction. After a banquet in the railroad station, we had time for a short stroll nearby. The country was arid, with much scrub and cacti, but little life in evidence. On the return trip there was an unfortunate accident. Our special train was running at an odd time, so a man asleep on the track did not expect it till it was on him. He was hurled through the air and instantly killed. All of us were sickened by the sight. Lieb shrieked out something in the direction of Dr. Branner, who told us most sternly that we had seen nothing at all. He wished to avoid having us taken as witnesses, who in those days were sometimes locked in the local jail till the trial was over.

What we had seen of Baixa Verde so interested Lieb and me that we returned a couple of days later. Lieb was especially anxious to look at some cuts in the rock along the railroad track. This time there was no table in the station, laden with food, nor were any of the officials there to welcome us. The village was tiny, and there was no hotel. The owner of a nearby house saw us as we stood on the station platform, remembered us as having been guests at the recent function, and took us into his home. We worked out from there for several days. On one hillside we found a number of hollow stumps of small trees that had been cut down. I hacked one open with my machete (known as *espada* in Brazil) and found a handful of the brilliantly colored beetles that are used so much as jewelry. These jewel beetles feed on morning-glories, and were estivating in the log during the dry season waiting for the vines to put out leaves again. They were in nearly every stump that I cut open, but where they did not occur, a wasps' nest did, adding to the interest of collecting. Under stones, with which the ground was strewn, were beetles, centipedes, and scorpions. I found no centipede as large as the one I had found in my shoe the morning after arriving at Natal. That one had taught us all the good tropical habit of thumping the heel of your shoe in the palm of your hand every morning to see what has taken refuge there during the night—a habit I am still apt to follow in Washington after returning from a trip to the tropics.

While I collected insects, a few lizards and land snails, Lieb made geological drawings of a cut near the railway. Our host was a prominent man locally, and one evening some cowboys, wearing broad-brimmed leather hats and leather trousers, came to visit him. Naturally, I exhibited my catch of small fry, and Lieb exhibited the drawings he had made. Later on, I heard loud and angry conversation outside, and though my knowledge of Portuguese was limited, I could make out the theme, "He is making maps. This is *our* country." Then I heard an itinerant jewelry salesman, also visiting the house that night, say something about "these North Americans" and calling our host's attention to the fact that he had a very beautiful daughter. To make it more melodramatic, the beautiful daughter came to me and told me in a low voice that an engine and a car were leaving the station in about half an hour. However, we decided to stay, and spent another night there, returning to Natal the following day.

From Natal, a group of us were guests of the railway that runs south. We were entertained at Itamatahy, near the village of Independencia in the state of Parahyba. This was the headquarters of two engineers on the railroad, Nye, an American, and Tessire, an Englishman. The country was hilly, with enough moisture to make abundant vegetation with numerous bamboo brakes; and collecting was so good, at least for Heath and me, that we wanted to stay longer, but naturally our large group could not impose on our hosts, whose house was small. Then came one of those breaks that one gets sometimes in travel: Heath and Nye got talking, uttered a few esoteric words, shook each other's hands, and disappeared into an adjoining room. Heath emerged with a broad grin and said, "He says the two of us can stay." They had discovered that they were fraternity brothers, so we stayed a week.

One night, awakened in my hammock by a prodigious itching, I turned on my light and found I was completely covered with bumps. As I wondered what tropical disorder I had picked up, I heard Heath mutter from his hammock, "Oh my, oh my!" We compared notes, and decided that we both had a particularly severe case of hives. Most of the night we spent passing back and forth a small tube of analgesic balm, a little bit of which I would put on the bump that seemed to be itching most at the time and then wishing I had put it on the adjacent bump. We assumed that we had hives from the rich food

we had been eating, but I have since thought that it might have been a
case of "chiggers."

Back in Natal, I had my first case of malaria, shivering and quaking
in my hammock, and obediently taking the three grains of quinine
that Dr. Baker prescribed. A kindly, tall, bearded man in his sixties,
he was a doctor of the old school and had had little experience with
tropical medicine. Later on, upriver, when I got fever, a doctor accustomed to South American malaria made me take thirty grains instead of three.

After three months, Dr. Branner was taking his group back to Stanford, but Dr. Baker and I were in no hurry to return. There was a
little money left in the expedition funds and I had read a book entitled An Ill-fated Expedition to the Madeira-Mamoré. This was an
account of a former expedition to build a railroad around the great
falls of the Madeira River. The attempt had been a complete failure
but the book had described the magnificent forest. Knowing nothing
except what I remembered of the book, I talked so hard to Dr. Baker,
explaining that no one had ever collected in that region, and that
most of his land snails would undoubtedly be new species, that he
was persuaded. An American contracting firm was working again on
the railroad project, which meant a place for us to stay and facilities
for going about.

Dr. Branner turned over to us what funds were left. I was to take
over the fish and reptile collecting in place of Starks and Heath.

Our week in Pará (now officially Belém) was not time wasted, because we collected every day and all day. First thing in the morning
it was my duty to go to the market, where fishermen and country
people would come from the Tapajós, the Tocantino, and other
tributaries of the Amazon, beaching their boats at low tide on a muddy
bank near the market and bringing their produce in for sale. This
municipal market was in itself a museum of fish and other animal life,
as well as of fruits and vegetables. I would go from stall to stall, selecting fish here and there for preservation, refreshing myself with
great slices of ripe, juicy pineapple. Then we would go into the nearby
suburb of Souza, where Alfred Russel Wallace had collected years before. Pará is said to have two seasons, six months of rain and six months
of heavy rain. This was still the dry season, and we got only one shower
a day, usually at two o'clock, so shortly before that we would stroll
into the shelter of a cement strip that covered some water tanks, and
there assort specimens till the rain was over, when a few moments of

hot sunshine steamed up the entire world and insects became active again.

Our boat, the *Rhaetia* of the Hamburg-South American Line, arrived on its way from Germany to Manáos. It was a 6000-ton steamer, nearly twice as large as the one on which we had traveled from New York to Brazil, and exceedingly elegant.

We had been told to get up early the next morning to enjoy the voyage through the Narrows, where the steamer winds in narrow channels between islands. The branches of trees on the adjoining islands were almost close enough to scrape the boat as it stayed near shore to avoid the current at midstream. We saw a harpy eagle over the treetops, in quest of sloth or monkey, but little else in the forest except egrets and other birds.

Among the magazines in the ship's library was one that had a chapter of Conan Doyle's *Lost World*. Later I read the entire book, which impressed me as a delightful, imaginative tale, but on the river itself, looking out at the passing forest, it did not seem so improbable.

Four and a half days brought us to Manáos, and we put up at a comfortable hotel. We went in search of the United States Consul, who, we hoped, would introduce us to the railroad construction company, and help us get up the river. His office was in a large building and when we entered we met a dark-complexioned, heavy-set man and asked where the American Consul's office was. He indicated a room up the stairs, and then when I asked, diffidently, "Do you suppose he's busy?" he replied, "I hope so. He's working for me."

He was at that time merely a Vice Consul, and was employed by the railroad construction company, to the head of which, Mr. May, we had been speaking.

We heard a great deal about yellow fever in Manáos, but the Vice Consul, who was keeping statistics, cheered us by telling us that in the previous year there had been quite as many deaths from tuberculosis as from yellow fever.

The next day we boarded a two-decker river steamer, the *Madeira-Mamoré* (known as the *Mad Mary* to railroad employees), as guests of the construction company, and headed for Porto Velho, head of navigation on the Madeira, some eight hundred miles away and headquarters of the company.

Each night we anchored and Captain Miranda would take some of his crew and a net about a hundred feet long and seine for fish off the shore. This was jam for me, because he let me accompany the

party, and I had the fun of fishing as well as the pick of the catch
for our collection. Once a six-or-seven-foot cayman was caught. In the
excitement of having a big alligator-like creature thrashing around in
the net, somebody kicked over the lantern, and the cayman had to be
dispatched by the light of matches and the captain's revolver.

One evening we were fishing on a beach where a lot of logs and
branches interfered with the seine. When we had come to anchor I
had noticed a nice beach with no obstructions on the other side of
the river, so I asked the captain why we did not fish over there. He
replied, "Parantintin." I thought that was a Portuguese expression I
did not understand, but next morning fellow passengers told me it was
the name of a tribe of exceedingly dangerous Indians who had a habit
of killing small groups of Europeans and dissolving into the forest
when large ones came. The construction company had recruited engineers, draftsmen and laborers from every part of the world, including
eight German storekeepers who got tired of the railroad, made a raft,
broke their contract and floated down the river toward its mouth. Ig-
norantly they camped on a beach in Parantintin country and the next
time the river boat passed, the passengers saw eight heads impaled on
sticks on the beach.

Porto Velho was situated below the last falls of the Madeira near
the native town of Candelaria, and contained a series of well-constructed screened houses for the staff. The railroad crowd was as
heterogeneous as one could find: native Brazilians, Barbadians, and
Jamaicans ("I's a British object, sir"). Some of them, when offered a
tobacco pouch, would scoop most of the tobacco out, instead of just
a pipeful, beam and exclaim, "God will bless you for that."

The medical department took care of us, and Baker and I moved
into a house with Dr. Laidlaw, an English physician. Despite the fact
that medical men had been recruited from the Panama Canal Zone
and from various schools of tropical medicine, death from malaria and
the concomitant black-water fever continued at a fearful rate. We were
told that four thousand employees were already buried in the cemetery at Candelaria. Dr. Laidlaw immediately instilled such a respect
for fever in me that I took ten grains of quinine a day and twenty on
Sunday. The typical set-up on the dining table consisted of a bottle
of Worcestershire sauce, a jar of pickled onions, and a large bottle of
quinine in five-grain capsules, two of which were supposed to be taken
with your first sip of coffee in the morning.

One doctor, a young graduate of Tufts Medical School, made his home in a heavily screened box car, and was almost unique in that he did not take quinine. Neither did he catch malaria, for he stayed protected when the mosquitoes were about. He believed, he said, in turning off the tap when it leaked instead of mopping water from the kitchen floor.

Food was good and abundant; medical care was the best that could be obtained, but still there was much sickness, including a number of cases of beriberi. It was not generally known in those days that this was a dietary disease, and as many who were sent downriver recovered when they reached the Amazon, they thought that the fresh breeze on the river had cured them.

The road was being built on a cost-plus basis, and nothing was spared for the comfort and well-being of the employees. We had an icebox in our quarters and Dr. Laidlaw's unfailing greeting to me when I came in was, "There is a bottle for you cooling on a cake of ice." It was English ginger ale.

The railroad was built to connect the upper reaches of the Amazon tributaries with Porto Velho, head of navigation on the Madeira River, and to avoid shooting the tremendous rapids which each year took toll of many lives and many tons of rubber. It was built by American contract for the Brazilian government. The 266–kilometer railroad is said to have cost a life for each tie.

Brazil has been described as "one great ant nest" and observers have stated that there is not an inch in the forest that is not visited by ants in the course of a day. One of the most common was the kelep (*Ectatomma tuberculatum*), at one time introduced unsuccessfully into Texas to prey on the cotton boll weevil. Large and powerful as it is, it could not withstand attack by the smaller, local ants, and did not persist. There had been some exciting controversy on the subject of these ants by Dr. Cook of the United States Department of Agriculture, who advocated importing them, and Dr. Wheeler, who thought that they would be a failure, and each of them had indulged in print in some delightful acrimony against the other. We would see the keleps everywhere in the forest, on tree trunks or shrubs, moving slowly, and often carrying dead insects back to their nests.

In the evening would come columns of army ants, sometimes into the houses, to be fled from by the human inhabitants till they had completed exploring the quarters and marched away, carrying cockroaches and other insects. They would do a thorough job of housecleaning, though we did not appreciate it when we had to sit outside in the rain for half the night. They sting as well as bite, and travel in such tremendous hordes that they can be dangerous to large animals, including humans. In all, I found fifteen kinds of these army ants, from tiny species, some of which lived entirely underground, up to large ones nearly an inch in length, though in each colony there was much variation in size.

Eciton hamatum, one of the species, ranges from Mexico through Central America and over all of tropical America, and was abundant along the upper Rio Madeira. Armies, found in the woods almost every day, contained enormous numbers of individuals. The big-headed soldiers marched at intervals of from ten to twenty feet in the procession, conspicuous because of their large, light-colored heads and their mandibles, which, looking like old-fashioned ice tongs, were so long that the heads had to be held high to keep them off the ground.

The march of the army is rapid, and at times very definite in direction. Often it divides and sends some of its members up into the tallest trees, while others cross and recross the trails. If a grub, lizard or small snake is tossed near the column, it is instantly covered with the workers and stung to death.

Unlike some of the other species, *E. hamatum* marches in the daytime, especially on cloudy days, and the column travels beneath or over the leaves, over logs, and along the trails. Trunks of fallen trees are a favorite runway. Other species of ants seem to be the usual prey, for larvae and pupae of these made up the greater part of the booty carried by the workers. Several times I saw columns descending trees bringing larvae, pupae and even adults of an ant (*Dolichoderus lugens*) which secretes from the anal glands a large drop of yellow liquid to repel enemies.

In spite of its large size, and the number of individuals in a column, *E. hamatum* is timid in comparison with some of the others. When the column was disturbed by my picking up some of its individuals, those nearest would turn and run back, zigzagging from one ant to another, apparently missing none. An instantaneous antennal communication took place, the warned ant turned also, and instantly the whole army was retracing its steps as rapidly as it had come. In a few minutes, some would return, then more, and presently the army would resume its march. At other times, it followed a new path.

These columns were accompanied by guests or parasitic insects, some tubby Histerid beetles that looked ludicrous as they ran along in the file. Other beetles, a half-dozen species, resembled the ants in form and coloration. They had long legs, and moved so much in the same way as their hosts that it was difficult to make them out until my eyes became accustomed to discerning the differences.

There were long-legged wasps, wingless ones, the size of the smaller ants. These wasps are undoubtedly parasitic on the young of the ants and no one knows the reason they are permitted to live with them. Once I noticed one of these parasites stop running for a moment, whereupon one of the ants picked it up, held it underneath its abdomen in the same manner that it would carry one of its own young, and resumed the march.

Some of the Ecitons are subterranean and I found a colony of them that had come up to rest for the day under the carcass of a sheep. The gases engendered by the decomposition of the meat had evidently asphyxiated the entire colony, for there were piles and piles of dead ants.

The forest teemed with life, but during the heat of the day it was quiescent except in the deep shade. I used to sit on a log at the edge of a trail and look at things. Among the ants there would be hunting Ponerines, wandering about singly on the ground. Columns of the leaf-gathering, fungus-growing, big-headed ants of the genus Atta looked like a flowing line of leaves along the ground, as each ant carried its piece of leaf or flower to the deep, subterranean nest. Sometimes so many of these ants passed that they actually wore a path in the forest. When carrying brightly-colored petals of flowers, they looked like some miniature holiday procession. But however romantic they appear to the observer, they are a pest to the planter, and there are instances in which they have defoliated and ruined overnight entire citrus orchards.

By digging out their nests I found large masses of the mycelium (fungus) on which they feed, attended by the very smallest of the ants that function as gardeners. Running in and out among these food masses was a tiny cockroach, Attaphila, a parasite which lives in the nests and shares the food. Pulling some loose bark from the log on which I was sitting, I found the nest of another species of a different mushroom-growing genus (Apterostigma). Tiny patches of fungus had been planted on a little pile of caterpillar droppings.

One of the most curious insects I have ever seen appeared on a low bush in a clearing near the camp. This membracid (*Combophora beski*), popularly known as "leaf-hopper," had, attached to the pronotum (the first section of the thorax), a large, thin, shell-like structure,

armed with spines, mottled in color, and actually larger than the rest
of the insect. Among the Membracidae the pronotum varies a great
deal in structure. It may resemble in miniature a Roman helmet, an
anchor, or a pawnbroker's sign, and is often so large and awkward-
looking that one would think it an actual hindrance to the insect. On
the food plant it is not particularly noticeable, and may even be a
good imitation of galls, seeds, fruit, and other things of a vegetable
nature, and so be considered a protective adaptation. Numbers of
them were on the leaves from which I was collecting ants, and, apparently disturbed by my forceps, they began to buzz and fly away.

I took two before they all disappeared, and then found that those
I had picked up had flown also, after detaching themselves from the
conspicuous pronotal development, and leaving only this for me to
put in the collecting vial. Sometimes when a lizard is attacked it drops
its tail off, and itself scurries to safety, the attacker grabbing the tail
and the lizard eventually growing another one. But in the case of this
leaf-hopper the attacker gets nothing more than a hollow shell.
Whether or not its owner reproduces another is not known.

Higher up on a branch was a stalactite-like paper nest of triangular-
headed Aztecas. Disturbing the nest caused them to drop by the thousands, scurry around, run up blades of grass from the tips of which
they could be lifted off in clusters and dropped into the collecting
vial.

In the fork of a tree I found an ant garden, earth brought from the
ground and held together in a ball by the roots of growing plants. As
far as I know no entomologist has ever actually seen the ants (Dolichoderus) start one of these gardens, but we assume that the queen
begins it with a small particle of earth, in which she plants a seed, and
the colony, as it develops, builds up the nest gradually into the form
in which we know it. These arboreal nests of fiber or carton or earth,
each one with its own distinct form, were a source of never-ending
wonder. One particularly interesting nest was in the fork of a recently
felled tree at a height of what had been approximately forty feet. The
nest was ovate in form, made of earth and about a foot in length and
eight inches in diameter, held firmly together by the fine roots of a
plant that ramified through it in all directions. When I dug into it,
numbers of a tiny red ant emerged. While I was collecting some of
these, I had a momentary glimpse of another ant, colored similarly
but much larger and with longer legs. It came out of one chamber
and immediately disappeared into another. Hoping to collect all

phases of the ant, I brought a large empty quinine can containing a piece of cotton soaked in chloroform, broke the nest apart, and threw it into the tin. Numbers of the larger ant rushed out and my hand was severely stung before I realized that colonies of two different kinds of ant occupied the same nest. The large ones belonged to the genus Odontomachus, the "tick-ant" genus of the tropics. As they run along they hold their long mandibles spread apart at right angles to the head; these mandibles are provided with long tactile hairs and when they come in contact with anything the ant violently snaps them together, making a ticking sound, and sometimes throws itself backward.

There were all phases of both species of ant in my nest, so it was evident that the two were living together. The tick-ant feeds chiefly on other insects, and it seemed strange to have it living with the smaller, more delicate ant. I returned on several occasions to what was left of the nest, and they had not moved out. A gentle tap on the surface with my forceps would bring out the little fellows. At a more serious blow the big ones would emerge.

This phenomenon of two species of ants living amicably together had been described before by Forel, the Swiss ant student, who had given it the name of "parabiosis." Odontomachus is normally a ground-inhabiting species, but here, high in the air, it had found the equivalent—that is, earth brought up by Dolichoderus. Both the ants were new to science, and the larger, more belligerent one, I named after Mr. May, the head of the railroad company.

Baker elected to stay at Porto Velho, but I traveled around to a number of work camps. As guest of the railroad I was given letters of introduction and could travel on work trains and stay at the various construction camps. Some of these were only small clearings with the immense forest adjacent. Life at the camps was always comfortable, people were hospitable, and the continual felling of trees along the right-of-way made it possible for me to spend two months collecting in actual treetops, where live a large percentage of the forest creatures. I carried letters of introduction, but only once did I have to show them. One evening at Camp 28, Mr. Fry, the engineer in charge, appeared a bit disturbed and offish, and asked me to repeat my name. I did; he said, "Oh, you're the bug hunter!" and everything was all right. It appeared that somebody on his way to Bolivia had had a ruction with some of the railroad officials and word had gone ahead for none of the camps to show him any courtesy.

Fry and I became close friends and I spent a great deal of time at

Camp 28. He was interested in insects, and was my companion on many forest jaunts. Sometimes the hospitality shown me became embarrassing. Once, toward evening, I stopped collecting near a train that was being loaded with dirt. When it was ready to go I hopped aboard, expecting to be taken to Camp 28, but the train started the other way. The conductor climbed aboard the car in which I was standing and I asked, "Aren't you going to 28?" He made a grimace; signaled to the engineer; the train stopped, and then began backing. The conductor told me it would have been better if I had told him where I wanted to go before they had her all loaded. I have had railroad passes since then, but never again has a loaded train backed two miles through the jungle to take me where I wanted to go.

The railroad employed native hunters to shoot for the camp messes, and with two of these, Antonio and Sebastiano, and a borrowed rifle, I crossed the river into Bolivia and camped in the forest. My hammock was hung between two trees, and a mosquito net placed over it. Night in the tropics comes in a hurry, and here it was announced by a wave of noise in the jungle. One insect would commence with a loud, piercing shriek (the men called it the "six o'clock bug"). Then other creatures that had been sleeping during the day would wake up and go noisily about their business. Noisiest of all were the howling monkeys, and for a short time there was bedlam in the air. Then it would all die out as quickly as it had started. When things were quiet I went to sleep, but was wakened by the crashing of an animal, or animals, through nearby treetops. I got out of the mosquito net, and sat on the edge of the hammock with my rifle in my hands. This annoyed Sebastiano, who was sleeping on the ground, and he said sleepily: "As jupuras no faz mal." It was a troop of kinkajous that passed almost directly overhead—heavy-set, tawny-haired little animals that prowl around at night and jump from one tree to another. They are called "night monkeys" in Brazil, but are not monkeys at all. I have had several as pets—gentle, quiet, sleeping all day and coming out in the evening—the ideal businessman's pet; but when full-grown they can be vicious.

In the morning the three of us separated. Game was abundant, but to get it required a knowledge of the forest such as only forest-bred people like Antonio possess. He and Sebastiano hunted day after day in the forest and returned usually with something—deer, occasionally tapir, many curassows (a game bird the size of a large rooster), and even macaws, which made a palatable soup though they were too tough to eat otherwise. Tinamou, on the other hand, was excellent. It looks, acts and tastes like quail but is actually related to the ostrich. The tamandua, the middle-sized anteater, we sometimes stewed and ate. When well-seasoned, it was good food, but tough.

Another time Antonio and I sat silently in sight of what he called a game trail, although I could distinguish nothing that looked remotely like a path through the jungle. I watched him think, apparently with the aid of his forefinger, which he would raise slowly in the air to indicate that perhaps something was coming. Finally it did. I had heard or seen nothing. He fired, and the first glimpse I got of the deer that he had shot was when it leaped and fell.

When the hunters went off looking for game, I stayed in sight of my hammock, for I had had one experience of being in the forest without a path. A five- or six-foot boa constrictor was crawling along a log. Wanting its skull for my collection I hurried after it with *espada* in hand. It outdistanced me into a thicket of spiny plants and disappeared, and then I spent the better part of an afternoon finding the trail I had just left. A Greek cook in one of the camps had seen a curassow fly over the clearing into the forest. Grabbing a shotgun he went after it, and was never seen again.

Most of the time at Camp 28 a mule carried me along the trails into the forest and gave me a sense of security, it being brighter at finding the way home than I was. Once in a little clearing that was swarming with gaudy specimens, I tied the mule to a cecropia tree. I untied it immediately, for flowing from the tree down the reins toward the mule was a stream of elongated yellow ants (*Pseudomyrma arbores-sancti*). My hands were covered with stings, which was not nearly so bad as if the ants had reached the mule who, I am sure, would not have waited for me. The tree is Triplaris, called *palosanto*, the "sacred tree," because the hollow stems and branches are always inhabited by active, stinging hordes of ants which keep away all who know. Dead Triplaris never contain ant colonies, but all live ones, even the smallest, do.

There were other things in the forest besides ants—big, metallically-brilliant beetles, bees even more metallic and brilliant, wasps with dainty paper nests, each species with its own design; wasp-nests of mud and some that were simply holes in the ground; giant tree snails as big as a man's fist that made Dr. Baker's eyes bug out when I brought them back to him in Porto Velho; an occasional snake in or under a rotten log.

One evening in camp with the engineers we were having our usual after-dinner conversation when a native dashed in, shouting *"Jacare."* Two of the engineers and I followed him to the riverbank, and there saw, floating in the water, a cayman perhaps ten feet long, clearly distinguishable in the bright moonlight. They agreed in a low tone to shoot together, when suddenly a cloud momentarily cut off the light. One of them said, "When the cloud passes I will count three, and we will shoot together to be sure of getting him." The cloud passed and the cayman again made a beautiful target. The engineer counted, "One, two ——" but instead of "three" and a shot he swore in a loud voice and started slapping his ankles and stamping his feet. Hunter number two imitated him very well. What had happened was that while they were waiting for the proper time to fire, little black army ants in whose path they had stood, had had time to go above their shoetops and start stinging. Many ants were killed by whacking but, as far as we know, the cayman is still there.

Burton, who was in charge of the warehouse at Porto Velho, was also interested in natural history, and spent many hours at night with me at the strong lights at the warehouse, picking up whatever was attracted there. Among the thousands of insects that came were huge scarab beetles, sometimes as large as one's fist, and with long horns on their heads, known locally to the railroad crew as "flying mud turtles." There were moths galore, and curiously, numbers of wasps, differing from most wasps in being nocturnal in habit. One of these made a nest about the size and shape of a pie plate. A large brightly-colored tiger beetle that I had obtained earlier only by digging it out of holes it had made in the riverbank, came by the dozens.

After two months along the river, reveling in life that swarmed on every tree and branch, even on every leaf, on the ground, and under logs and stones, it was time to return. The "Mad Mary" took us to Manáos in four days instead of the eight it had taken to come up-river. We lazed on the upper deck, playing cards and caring for the young howling monkey that Burton had given me to take to the zoo in New York. We named it Guariba, the native name for this animal, and found it good company but tiresome because it wanted to spend most of its time clinging to us, not even getting off when it should have done so. One time Dr. Baker, in a clean white duck coat, had cajoled the little monkey into sitting on his shoulder. Monkeys cannot be housebroken, and I noticed an expression on its face that indicated something was going to happen. It did, and Baker beseeched me to take Guariba off his shoulder, because he had been bitten once before; when I recovered from my laughter I held out a hand, and the relieved baby climbed to my shoulder. If I left it tethered, it would raise a discord inconceivably loud for an animal of its size. Like most monkeys, it preferred to handle us, rather than to be handled, and was apt to bite if lifted up, though it would rapidly climb onto my hand and then onto my shoulder.

There was a delay of a week in Manáos till we could make arrangements to go downriver, and we were invited to a country place, called Ketepurangi, a short distance up the Rio Negro, the home of Don Antonio Autrun, a Cuban who years before had been cured of yellow fever by an American Army doctor. He had vowed to devote a certain part of his time in the future to nursing yellow fever patients, and had done so most successfully—and also profitably, we were told. He took us into his home. From the house a trail led to an open meadow covered with a cloverlike plant and teeming with bumblebees, carpenter bees, and the stingless bees that so abound in parts of tropical America. Some of these made a honey that was poisonous.

Across the meadow the trail entered the forest for about a quarter of a mile, and then suddenly stopped. I used to enjoy thinking that there was probably not another trail, except in the vicinity of Indian villages, between me and Venezuela. One day I heard something coming noisily in my direction through the dried leaves, and I stood silently to see what it was. A brilliant orange and black snake about six feet long crossed the trail a few feet away, and it dawned on me that I was seeing my first bushmaster, the largest poisonous snake in South America, attaining a length of eight feet or more. It is considered to be one of the few snakes that will attack man, but this one went into the woods and I went after it with my *espada*. It probably becomes aggressive only when man or another animal comes between it and its nest and frightens it; at any rate, although I stepped into a tangle of roots that trapped me for a minute, the snake did not come back, nor did I want it to as I struggled to free myself.

Don Antonio kept chickens, and he also had a pet peccary, a playful little pig that would nudge me gently while I was eating lunch, and when I did not immediately share with him would root in a determined manner. Dr. Branner had told me that one did not know what a domestic animal really was until one had lived in Brazil. One day at lunch we saw one of the hens fluttering along the ground as though badly wounded. Her chickens disappeared in the undergrowth as a large tegu lizard came on the scene. This habit of a mother feigning helplessness to attract a marauder away from her young is common among many wild birds, but this is the only time I ever saw it among domestic fowl.

We heard that a raft was being towed down the river from Itacoatiara to Santarém on the Tapajós to bring back railroad ties that were being cut for the company. To float down the Amazon on a raft sounded pleasant, so we left Manáos and got to Itacoatiara on a launch, and moved onto a steamship hulk anchored there that served as office and storehouse of one of the railroad's commissaries. The wife of the manager had secured piles of branches on which were growing a collection of exquisite orchids. These attracted so many brilliant, metallic-green bees with extremely long tongues (*Euglossa cordata*) that I made a good entomological collection even on a steamship.

In the village lived old man Stone, an American who had gone to California in the gold rush of '49, but in 1852 had come down the West Coast, crossed the Andes, gone down the Amazon and settled there. He had married a Brazilian woman and, with his sons, made the firm of Stone y Filhos, which produced cigarette tobacco, shredded and intensely strong. I spent hours with the old gentleman on the veranda of his house, drinking coffee to which had been added the beaten white of an egg, which was, he said, "much better than the canned milk you get." He kept in touch with the United States by subscribing to a couple of magazines. He had gone back once, and had been much impressed with the progress the country had made. This had been in 1876, to the Philadelphia Exposition. When I left he gave me a package of tobacco with instructions, "When you are up north and the snow is flying, and you are lonesome for Amazonas, just smoke this and think of old man Stone at Itacoatiara." The following year in Boston, on an unusually bleak and snowy day, I thought of this and put some in my pipe. It had become very dry and powdery, and after two puffs I saw black specks in the air and broke out in a cold perspiration.

The raft on which we traveled had a small cabin on it. We stayed in midstream to avail ourselves of the current, and the following morning were at Santarém. Looking overside we could see the bottom of the river, through the first clear water we had seen for months. Ashore in the village we met another American, David Riker. He was an old-timer there, his family having left the south after the American Civil War, so they would not have to live under Yankee domination.

They had established the first rubber plantation, long before plants were taken to the Far East.

The river steamer took us on to Pará, where we waited a week for the ship that was to take us back to the States. To my menagerie of one howling monkey, Dr. Schnetlage added a four-foot boa constrictor and a kinkajou, the latter elegantly housed in a hardwood cage with neatly turned bars imbedded in the front footboard, which had taken the zoo carpenter three days to make. Dr. Schnetlage had told me to be on the lookout for a certain large scaly-tailed rat up the river. She thought there might be a new variety on the other side of the Madeira. A native had brought me a specimen one evening, which was duly skinned and dried flat. I turned it over to her, and she sent it to Dr. Oldfield Thomas of the British Museum. He verified her suspicion and described it as a new subspecies.

At the Consulate was a stack of letters, and among them one from the Bursar at Harvard University, informing me that at the request of Professor William Morton Wheeler I had been appointed research assistant at a salary of thirty dollars a month. Naturally I was elated and bragged about it to Pickering, our good United States Consul there, who celebrated by giving me a pair of white duck trousers which covered more of me than the pair I had been wearing.

In New York I delivered the howling monkey to Ditmars at the Bronx Zoo, said good-by to Baker, and started off for Boston with the kinkajou and the boa, and a suitcase containing all the vials I had labeled with an X on the cork, indicating something rare or unusual. The bulk of the collection was shipped by express. I had with me also a long black-palm bow and a bunch of arrows obtained from the Carapuna Indians, which prompted a fellow tenant of the smoking car to ask me where I had been fishing.

ABOVE POLITICS

by Louis J. Halle, Jr.

*To orient the reader properly this selection should be date-lined
Washington, D.C., where its author has spent a number of years
as a member of the staff of our State Department. Born in New
York City in 1910, Louis J. Halle, Jr., was graduated from Harvard
in 1932, went to Guatemala to work for a railway system, learned
much about Central America, and was launched as an author
when his first book,* Transcaribbean, *was published in 1936. He
returned to Harvard for postgraduate work in anthropology, wrote
articles for magazines, won the John Burroughs medal with his*
Birds Against Men, *and settled down in Washington to work in
the State Department and turn out books about Nature on the
side. He took time out from his departmental tasks to serve in
the Coast Guard during World War II. In State Department circles he is looked upon as an expert on inter-American affairs,
but his office work does not concern us here. We share only in
his extracurricular activities as chronicled in his delightful observations on Nature in this selection taken from his* Spring in Washington, *published in 1947.*

I WOULD not willingly give up our four seasons for a Kingdom
of Heaven in which the sun shone eternally with equal warmth
and light, in which the grass was forever green and the birds
sang constantly. I would have no unchanging splendor. Though
the violin stopped at the most musical note in the sonata and sustained it indefinitely, I could not sustain it in myself. Let the violin
go on and return to that note at judicious intervals, so that I may
always hear it afresh. Nothing is precious without a degree of rarity.

Be warned that in the land of eternal spring you will find the inhabitants blind and deaf.

This is not to say that we must go through pain in order to enjoy any particular pleasure, though there is undoubtedly truth in this as the world goes. In my Kingdom of Heaven, as I choose to conceive it, enjoyment of life is sustained by the variety and contrast among its pleasures. The Kingdom has, I think, four revolving seasons, each with its own inspiration and delight. They bear a particular resemblance to the seasons in the northeastern United States; for the abundant variety and contrast of climates within this one area in the course of a year is its most notable feature. Where else are the summers so hot and the winters so cold, the springs so fresh and the autumns so mellow? Its separate seasons have so much to offer that the year is hardly long enough to contain them. I have lived in lands that boast an equable climate and found the year wearisome in its length, but here it moves and passes before your senses almost too quickly. In Washington, except for a month or a month and a half in winter, you can see changes in the season from week to week the year around. Often these changes are dramatic in their suddenness, taking place overnight. A wave of migrants, arriving while I slept, have transformed the scene for me since yesterday, and may be gone tomorrow; in two or three days of March the flowering trees have burst into bloom; in a few days of October the foliage has turned yellow and orange, purple and scarlet. I have read accounts of the subdued and gradually changing seasons in England, and I have seen something of the seasons in our own West, and in neither place is there anything as dramatic as this. We have tropical summers and arctic winters; our spring and fall are like nothing else on earth.

The night of April 17 the wind blew from the south. In the crepuscular daybreak of April 18 I awoke to the voice of a whippoorwill across the street: that rapid, vibrant, steady pulsation of sound, like something organic in the earth itself, like the beating of one's own heart. It invested the whole atmosphere, pausing occasionally, then resuming. The robins were already caroling, the cardinals contributing their beads of song to the chorus, which was constantly being swelled by additional voices. Suddenly a new voice came in, and for me a new season, a new life long awaited, had at last begun. It was a wood thrush, uttering the bell-like phrases, the trills and grace notes, that I recalled from other springs. Steadily, steadily it sang, with leisure and confident ease, as if knowing that for all its long absence it belonged on the scene as rightfully as anything else, more rightfully than much else. I had been expecting it and here it was, like the unfailing voice of truth in a world of rumor and delusion.

Whippoorwill and wood thrush had been borne up on the south wind of overnight—and what else? One gets dressed hurriedly, on tiptoe, straining one's ears for every sound from the woods across the street. I am out of doors while there is still a dawnlight and the freshness of dawn in the atmosphere, though the sun has risen clear of the horizon and bathes the earth in brilliant illumination. At the foot of the street, in some garden shrubbery, a catbird is chattering softly and continuously, with whistles and squeaks, recalling all the catbirds of yesteryear, of my almost forgotten life. In the deep woods of Massachusetts Park, where the road winds through them, in the same hollow under the slope where I had heard him each spring, the same individual every year by the cadence of his voice, I hear again the ovenbird, periodically asserting himself, dominating the atmosphere with the crescendo of his song. Other wood thrushes have taken up their stations here and there in the city overnight. There has been a clandestine invasion and occupation while we slept. More parula warblers and black-and-white warblers have arrived, and this morning you hear them everywhere, the wisps of song, the vocal signatures uttered at regular intervals from the trees. This is the news of the day.

*   *   *   *

Wherever you are in the city now, and at any time of day, you may look up from the streets, like a mouse peering up from its runways in the tall grass, and see the chimney swifts passing overhead. Here is the great world itself within the bounds of my nutshell, and suddenly I "count myself a king of infinite space." That very swift, now veering over the housetops, was lately careening in that same fashion over the forested expanses of the Amazon Basin, sweeping that other sky as now it sweeps this. It is as if I had the power to revolve this globe under my feet like a plaything. All movement is relative, so why may I not say that this very scene, this Washington, is like a ship crowded with humanity that cruises south into the tropics at this time of year, rather than that the warm weather and the luxuriance of flower and foliage and the multitude of summer birds come here to visit? Indeed, these swifts remain fixed with reference to the sun, and it is the world that tilts beneath them. I cannot complain at the sessile existence I am constrained to lead these days, since this continuous change of seasons is travel. Knowing the four seasons, here in Washington, I am more traveled than the swifts, which know hardly more than one.

It is the evening of April 19, the approaching end of a cloudless day. Og and I are free this evening, and there are any number of things we might do: go to the movies, or a concert at Constitution Hall, or whatever is playing at the National Theater. The newspapers list a number of spectacles for which we might buy tickets. They do not list the spectacle we choose, for which no tickets are asked. It takes place toward dusk at the garage behind the Wardman Park Hotel, on Calvert Street. As the hour approaches, you may see the swifts in twos or threes or dozens making for this roosting place across the housetops from all points of the compass. A small, irregular band of them is already wandering about the sky in the vicinity of the garage chimney when we arrive. You can hear their chippering above the noise of traffic in the streets. The band is constantly augmented by new arrivals until it is a mass of little birds streaming overhead, wandering out over the Shoreham Hotel and back again, here and there, growing constantly as the new arrivals join it until you see the full spectacle in its wonder and impressiveness, all the swifts for miles around gathered into a cloud that now begins to take shape. The shape is that of a great wheel revolving above the chimney. As the light fades from the sky, the revolving wheel is tilted obliquely, its lower side just clearing the chimney. Watch as you may, however, you will see no birds enter it yet. Some hesitate briefly as they pass, but are carried on in the stream. I do not know how the signal is finally given, but it is as if a sergeant among them had blown a whistle and cried "Fall in!" Instantly the wheel is broken, one end of it turning straight down into the opening of the chimney. The myriad birds in their formation now resemble a whirlpool of water being sucked into a drain. Within a minute the sky is utterly drained of swifts, and the chorus of chippering has ceased. Good night!

THE WORLD'S GREATEST WATERWORKS

by Rutherford Platt

The case of Rutherford Platt is possibly unique in the realm of Nature writing. The brisk and capable head of a successful advertising firm in New York City, he was lured into the field of Nature photography by a beguiling friend and soon was such an expert with the camera that his color and black-and-white photographs were eagerly sought for publication. The more he worked outdoors, the more interested he became in all kinds of plant and animal life. He stared, studied, collected, examined, and did research work to such good effect that in 1945 his book, This Green World, *a happy combination of clear, accurate text and superb photographs, won the John Burroughs medal. In* Our Flowering World, *published in 1947, he traced with text, charts and photographs the development of plant life from the Paleozoic Era down to the present time. A strange activity for an advertising mogul, but decidedly a turn to the right and a victory for our side.*

The selection that follows is a chapter from This Green World. *Where the author, toward the end, breaks out in fractions and describes the "dynamic symmetry" of plant growth, he is touching on a matter that students of mathematics call "the Fibonacci series," students of design refer to as "the logarithmic spiral," and students of geometry know as the "golden mean" or "divine section" of ancient Greek scholars.*

FROM one point of view, the drama of a tree may be described by calling it the "world's greatest waterworks." Actually all plants are waterworks. Their capacity to lift water depends on the size of their leaf area, which is like saying the size of the nozzle. As the capacity of the stem or trunk is much greater than needed the leaves are the "bottleneck."

In proportion to size the grasses can be said to be the greatest of the water raisers because they have a relatively large leaf area. In fact, most of the visible plant body in the grasses is leaf. Corn is a grass, and one stalk will lift 440 pounds of water during its brief growing season. A farmer across the road from my house has a rich cornfield. If all the water which his corn collected under ground and raised up and expelled into the air stayed on top of the field where you could see it, the farmer would have a lake of water five feet deep by the end of August.

An acre of grass in a lush meadow will lift six and a half tons of water per day at the height of its power in late June. The amount lifted by one plant may be only a few drops, but the number of grass plants in an acre is legion.

Of course, trees operate on a grander scale. A well-spaced apple orchard will have forty trees to the acre. If they're healthy and mature they will be equipped with about a hundred thousand leaves each, and those forty trees will lift sixteen tons of water a day. That's at the rate of four gallons per tree per hour. And as trees go, apple trees are comparatively small!

It takes a good deal of imagination to think of water traveling up the long tapering cylinder of a tall tree and spraying out through the perforations of the leaves as from a fine nozzle. Yet every leaf of the several million of the great elm, or the hundred thousand of a squat apple tree, and every blade of grass of the myriads in an acre of pasture is, as we have seen, constantly performing like a nozzle. The spray is so fine that it is invisible, so that we say the water is evaporating out of the leaf as water vapor.

In this way a tree serves as a vital link in the rotation of water. In all the world 340 cubic miles of water fall every day. This averages about sixteen million tons of rain per second! In a world-wide sense there is no such thing, therefore, as a drought. It's only a question of *where* the water falls. When the reservoirs of New England are low, heavy rain is reported from the Libyan desert. When the Atlantic seaboard is parched, the prairie states are fighting floods. The total volume of water throughout the world is constant, never less, nor more. It is present in three forms: water in seas, lakes, streams; water in vapor form in the air and clouds; water in the earth and inside of trees and leaves. Between these three forms water revolves restlessly. Although evaporation from seas, lakes and streams is a tremendous agency for getting water into the air, the world's greatest waterworks (the trees as well as all vegetation) taps the vast invisible reservoirs in the ground and keeps the water moving up and out. Locally this may have an even greater effect than evaporation from exposed water surfaces in determining rainfall.

Obviously with all this lifting, an enormous force is somehow exerted. Yet a tree is not equipped with a pump. It is essentially solid and stationary in all its parts.

One might suppose the tree could pull up water like a suction pump. If you create a vacuum in a vertical tube that has its lower end in water, the water will rise in the tube. It is drawn up by the suction. This sounds plausible for a tree. If water evaporates at the top, a vacuum could be formed somewhere lower down inside the porous tube system of the trunk. But this won't work, for two reasons. First, suction is due to air pressure and some free surface of water must be exposed for gravity to push down on it. But the roots of a tree are in the soil and not in a well of water, so that there is no water for gravity to push on. Another objection is even more final. The weight of a column of water balances air pressure at 33 feet. If a man wants to raise water with a suction pump, he can lift it 33 feet at sea level, even less on the mountains, and not an inch higher. That height would serve for small trees but not for tall trees. Water goes up to the top of trees a hundred feet or more without the slightest difficulty, even up to 300 feet in the sequoias of California. A redwood called "Founder's Tree," considered the tallest tree in the United States, lifts water 364 feet with the same efficiency as a strawberry plant a couple of inches tall.

Another theory is that roots exert pressure. Root pressure is the accumulated force of absorption. Liquids will travel up fine tubes. They call it capillary attraction. It's the principle of oil running up the wick in an old-fashioned oil lamp. The same force makes blotting paper work. The inside of a tree with its innumerable little empty spaces arranged into series of tubes is ideal for capillary attraction to go into action.

However, this theory only explains how water gets into the bole of the tree in the first place. The minute threads and tubes of the roots absorb the water and push it along into other minute tubes in the lower part of the tree trunk. This is an explanation of why sap flows in a tree trunk in later winter. When the snow is still on the ground and the buds have not yet loosened their scales, the Vermont farmer can tap his trees for maple syrup. The clear sap, ninety-five per cent or more water, drips into his bucket possibly as fast as 100 drops per minute. This means that root pressure is working down where the water is loosening up in the frozen ground! If he tapped his trees higher up, he wouldn't get more sap, he would get none at all.

Atmospheric pressure is fifteen pounds to the square inch at sea level. The maximum force of root pressure measured is two atmospheres. This gives 30 pounds to the square inch. But it would take 300 pounds to the square inch to lift sap to the top of the tallest trees.

The most plausible explanation of the mighty lifting force possessed by trees is something entirely different.

It appears that the world's greatest waterworks relies on cohesion in a column of water. From roots to tiptops runs an unbroken "rope" of water, woven out of countless threads. Pull on the top of this by evaporating water out of the leaves and you simply pull up more water by its own rope. This implies that throughout the tree, every single twig and bud and leaf is connected by unbroken threads of water with the roots. Not every tube may be full of water but enough are full to keep the lines unbroken. By the process of growth from the first shoot out of the seed, the inside of the tree is endowed with water. And it stays endowed, as it grows larger. When the leaves fall off in winter and the pull at the top on the rope stops, the fineness of the tubes tends to hold the water in the standpipe by capillary attraction. It doesn't fall back into the ground. Indeed, the loss of water by evaporation is halted when the leaves fall off and so the total volume of water inside a tree gradually *increases* in winter as it creeps up the tubes.

What is the tensile strength of sap—that is, how hard can you pull on it lengthwise without having it break? Will it hold together as a continuous stream, say 300 feet, against the pull of gravity? Sap has been found to have the amazing tensile strength of 2,250 pounds to the square inch, equal to 150 atmospheres. This is 150 times greater than suction, 75 times greater than root pressure. This strength could lift sap to the top of a tree 4,950 feet tall, almost a mile high.

To what end do trees lift so much water? It is certainly not for our delight since these mighty fountains are invisible. Water lifting by plants is not an indispensable link in the restless transfer of water from earth to clouds, as evaporation from open water in seas, lakes and streams is far more important. It is not to deliver water to the top of a tree for its own use, although a small percentage serves as a carrier for tree food. Water simply comes in at the bottom and goes out at the top. Botanists have not found any final explanation as to why so much water is lifted. Philosophically, the world's greatest waterworks are all the greater because they are not subordinate to anything else. Only a utilitarian mind asks why they lift so much water. They do because that is their nature. Like Keats' Grecian urn, a tree is the "foster child of silence and slow time." A hundred years of patience and sunlight lifts an inestimable amount of water and builds a great waterworks system.

*   *   *   *

Stand off and look at the crown of a tree. Although the leaves are beautifully massed, they may at first appear to be placed haphazardly. Look again. Stand under the arching limb of a beech or elm, or the flat angular branch of a dogwood. What do you see? A mosaic—one of the wonders of the plant kingdom. Note how this mosaic is pieced together, detail by detail, throughout the entire pattern of the tree.

Think of branches as projecting from a circle made by the cross-section of the trunk. If the distance between two successive branches is one third of the way around this circle their angle is 120°. As the branches mount the tree they go round and round with equal spacing. One kind of tree may put forth its branches at an angle of 90°, or 144°, or 180°—whatever the angle of the species *it is constant throughout that tree.* These angles made by the branches always divide the circle equally. In mature trees, of course, all limbs will not be in place but that is only because as twigs they were damaged or failed to develop. Their traces would be there; not one is missed at its true angle.

This same angular succession is true of twigs that grow out of a limb. Look still closer and you'll see that a leaf emerges from its twig at the same angle from its neighbor as the limbs make with the trunk. In place of twigs and leaves you may see unopened buds, and these too project from the bark in the same succession of angles. Limbs, twigs, leaves, all originate in buds, and these four structures are homologous. Throughout the tree, from trunk to the tip of every twig, both the leaves themselves and the skeleton on which they are hung are dispersed at equal angles in every direction. At least that is their basic plan although their equal angles may become distorted by later conditions of wind or light. The leaf mosaic is further perfected by the variation of the lengths of branches and the lengths of the stems of individual leaves, so that each leaf may be held away from its neighbor. Often the twigs and the stems of leaves are bent around or twisted to achieve a position more in the clear.

The net result is that thousands of leaves can grow together, above and below and around their tree, without overlapping or getting in each other's light. This is functional beauty in one of its purest forms.

Nature has two ways of dividing the circle around the trunk in order to give leaves the maximum dispersion. One of these is an *opposite* arrangement of leaves (or branches, twigs and buds). That is, two leaves grow out from the same height on the twig and they are located exactly opposite each other. You can see this arrangement in the dogwoods, maples, ashes and horse-chestnuts. Now look along the twig to the next pair of leaves. They are exactly at right angles to the first pair. The third pair will be exactly over the first. If you look at the twig end-on you will see the leaves project from the bark in four ranks of 90° angles. If, instead of a pair of leaves, the tree produces three or more at the same height of the stem (the catalpa, for example, produces leaves in whorls of three) then the next whorl is turned exactly the right amount to bring its leaves directly above the intervals. Each leaf has emerged with perfect accuracy at the best angle to give it the greatest clearance.

The second method by which nature divides the circle is based on *spiral* arrangement. This is far commoner. The chances are you will find it on almost every tree commonly seen with the four exceptions just mentioned of dogwood, maple, ash and horse-chestnut—and, of course, the catalpa with its whorls. The spiral arrangement is indicated when a single leaf or bud emerges from a given height on the twig and with no bud or leaf opposite.

Follow with your eye the points where leaves or buds emerge along the twig of an elm. As you travel along the twig the point of attachment of each leaf is discovered to be exactly 180° around the stem from the preceding leaf. Every second leaf, therefore, is in a straight line. If you look at the twig end-on, you will see two ranks of leaves, alternating first on one side, then on the other. The linden has the same arrangement.

If I take a piece of string and attach it to the bases of the leaf stems or buds along an elm or linden twig, it makes a steep spiral as it goes round and round the twig. To reach the next leaf directly above the starting leaf the string makes one complete turn of 360° and touches two leaves, not counting the first leaf. You can write this as a fraction by calling one complete turn the numerator "1" and the two leaves needed to complete that turn the denominator "2." This makes ½. In other words, each leaf is exactly one half of the way round the circumference of the stem. This is another way of saying that elm and linden branches and leaves are spaced at 180°.

The distance between leaves along the twig may vary considerably, according to the caprice of growing conditions. In wet spring weather the twig may grow vigorously and elongate far, or in dry weather it may push out slowly. *But the angle between two adjacent leaves never varies.*

Next I attach my string to the leaves of a beech. This time, instead of traveling half way round the stem to touch the next leaf, I go only 120° or one third of the way. To reach a leaf directly above the starting point my string makes one complete circle, but this time it touches *three* leaves. This gives me the fraction ⅓. In other words, if I look at the twig end-on I will see three ranks of leaves, diverging at 120° regardless of how much the distance between them along the twig may vary.

Now see what happens to a string diagram of the spirals along the twig of an oak, cherry, apple or poplar. This time to reach a leaf placed directly above my starting point, the string makes two complete circuits and it touches five leaves, not counting the first. This gives me a ⅖ spiral. The angle of each successive leaf is 144°. This is the commonest spiral of all.

In doing all this we are on the trail of one of nature's most fascinating mysteries. To discover it and build up a series of fractions, attach our string to one more tree. This time try a holly tree. Here it takes three complete circuits around the twig to reach a leaf in a straight line with the starting point. In so doing the string touches eight leaves, not counting the first. Here we have a ⅜ spiral. Three eighths of a circle is 135° and that is the angle of divergence in a holly tree and some others.

Have you detected a remarkable sequence in these spirals? Put them down in order: ½, ⅓, ⅖, ⅜. When you add the numerators and denominators of any two consecutive fractions you get the next one! This series can be continued thus—5/13, 8/21, 13/34 and so on ad infinitum. And that is exactly what nature does! Lurking in these numbers is the abstract quality of perfect dispersion. Here are beauty and function expressed as a mathematical formula.

Typical leaves on trees use spirals described in the small numbers of the first four fractions. The higher fractions are found, however, in hundreds of places where leaves grow more compactly than on trees, such as in mosses or in plants that make rosettes like cabbages and artichokes. Also, higher fractions of this series are found in plant parts that are leaf-like, such as bracts on daisies or the scales of pine cones. Our fifth fraction, namely 5/13, belongs to the white pine cone. In this cone the 14th scale (or leaf) is located exactly above the first and to reach it the spiral goes round the axis of the cone five times!

The centers of flowers (like that of a daisy or sunflower) are arranged in spirals whose proportions are identical with those of pine cones, although the fractions are different. Consider the beautiful spirals of the florets in the center of a daisy. At first glance these do not appear to resemble the spirals of branches and leaves on a tree. The latter are on an elongated axis like a corkscrew, while the center of a daisy is a more or less flat surface. But imagine looking at the spirals of the tree end-on and then imagine them collapsed into a plane instead of elongated and you have the same basic scheme. The spiral fractions of a daisy center are 13/34, 21/55 and in an extra large daisy 34/89. Oxford University has a record of a sunflower head (the same family as the daisy) 22 inches in diameter of which the spiral fraction, officially counted, came out 144/377. You will arrive at that if you add three more fractions to those just assigned to the daisy center.

With this spiral curve nature divides the circle equally, so that the leaves on a tree stand as far apart as their number permits. One of the properties of this curve is space. The other is time. Wherever this curve is found in nature its parts differ in age; they are produced serially.

This curve is identical throughout nature. Just as the circumference of a circle always has the same ratio to its diameter (3.1416 as we learned in school), the spirals in nature all have a uniform ratio.

Refer to the series of fractions—if you multiply any numerator by 2.618 you get its denominator, whether it's the leaves of an artichoke, or the scales of a spruce cone, or the intersecting curves in the center of a daisy. Thus, in the leafy crown of a tree we have discovered a fundamental principle of art, *dynamic symmetry*.

Behold then the world's greatest waterworks complete with its three departments:

The root system with its hundreds, perhaps thousands, of miles of minute channels and apparatus for collecting the tiniest molecules of moisture and merging these into a river of sap. This astonishing system is so endowed with power and pliancy that it can permeate solid ground which man needs dynamite to burst open.

The bole, or trunk, with its millions of tubes to carry sap upward, compactly organized between the core and the bark, its film of food channels running down the outer part of the cylinder where the tissue is young, all so deftly put together that every single twig, bud or leaf is connected with its own lines of communication.

The leaves placed by nature's universal spiral so precisely that each is given its chance for a maximum amount of light; each leaf with a dynamo powered by light, making, out of water and air, food by which alone all plants and animals are sustained.

This tree is fluid and beautiful. Non-essentials are eliminated. It is an honest expression of a purely utilitarian mechanism, well planned, with its parts grouped and all in proportion.

So considered, the tree is a marvelous invention and all the more so because it operates silently, efficiently, and continuously.

Loveliest of trees, the cherry now
Is hung with bloom along the bough,
And stands about the woodland ride
Wearing white for Eastertide.

Now, of my threescore years and ten,
Twenty will not come again,
And take from seventy years a score,
It only leaves me fifty more.

And since to look at things in bloom
Fifty springs are little room,
About the woodlands I will go
To see the cherry hung with snow.

A. E. HOUSMAN

A CENTURY OF PLATYPUS

by Willy Ley

Yes, this is the same Willy Ley who is the expert on jet and rocket propulsion and projected travel in outer space. He is a specialist in physics as well as natural history, and talks and writes well in both fields. He has done books and articles on matters animate and inanimate. His books on matters animate include Days of Creation *and* The Lungfish and the Unicorn, *from which this bit about the platypus was taken. He was born in Berlin, Germany, October 2, 1896, arrived in the United States in 1935, became a citizen, married here, has two daughters, and at last report lived in the Jackson Heights area of New York City. But the way he has been talking about the possibility of space travel, he may be halfway to Mars by the time you read this.*

AS has just been told, *Limulus polyphemus*, the horseshoe crab, is probably the oldest living animal of our planet, not counting a few small marine or aquatic forms of life and a few dull clams.

And *Latimeria* was no doubt the greatest surprise among the living fossils.

But the living fossil *par excellence* is a mammal from Australia, the platypus. Reasonably abundant in its native habitat some fifteen decades ago, it escaped earlier extinction solely due to the fact of Australia's geographical isolation. And for the same reason it escaped earlier discovery.

While the name of its first discoverer is not on record we do know when and where it took place. The place was the countryside near Hawkesbury in New South Wales, Australia. And the time was the month of November (summer down there) of the year 1797. The man who caught the small animal must have been struck by its curious appearance, as everybody else since his day, and for want of a better name called it a "water-mole."

One may infer from this choice of name that the original discoverer was an Englishman. For while the platypus does make burrows and possesses a fur which may be likened to that of the common black European mole, the resemblance is slight. A Canadian or American who was acquainted with beavers would probably have picked "Australian beaver" as a name, because a swimming platypus resembles a swimming beaver in its general motions, the habit of burrowing at the water's edge with an entrance hole under water is a beaver habit, and the platypus even has a somewhat flattened tail. Of course there is no real resemblance between the two, and beavers are much larger than platypi. Still, it would have been a more reasonable name.

It is no exaggeration to say that platypus caused a scientific headache (not bothering the common man at all) which lasted a full century. Aforementioned headache began in 1798, grew in intensity some twenty years later, stayed strong for a little longer than that, and slowly began to recede afterward. It petered out during the last decade of the nineteenth century. Whether it began with the skin of that animal that was caught near Hawkesbury is uncertain. Possibly the so-called "original skin" which arrived in London was the same. If not, another specimen must have been caught within a week or two, something which is entirely probable.

The reasons why platypus caused such a long-lasting scientific headache were many and complex; we'll come to them point by point. But the reason for the first twenty or so years can be stated with a few words: it began because platypus would not fit into the textbook!

Around the year 1800 zoologists had nice, clean, and orderly textbooks. They began with the *Mammalia*, or mammals, and every student had to learn their distinguishing features. It was easy. All mammals were warm-blooded and had a skin characterized by sweat glands and hairs. The latter might be absent in special cases, such as elephants, hippopotami, and the tops of the skulls of elderly males of *Homo sapiens*, but even in these cases still a few hairs could be found. All mammals produced live young and suckled them, for which purpose the females had mammary glands (which provided the name for the whole order); they all had four limbs, while a tail might be present or absent. They had a typical jaw construction and teeth or rudiments of teeth in those jaws. They usually had external ears . . . and so on, down the list.

The next large group were the *Aves* or birds.

All birds were warm-blooded and their skins produced feathers instead of hairs. Even though in some few cases the feathers might look very much like hairs, their true nature could always be established by careful examination. All birds were tailless (except for pseudo-tails formed by long feathers), they had no external ears, no teeth in their jaws ever, they laid eggs, and did not suckle their young.

Next came the *Reptilia* (for a while thrown together with the *Amphibia*) which were no longer warm-blooded, and so on, and then came the *Pisces* or fish, which lived in water, were also not warm-blooded, and so on, and that ended the vertebrate animals.

This was Linnaeus's system and it was a good system. The trouble was merely that people took it too seriously and had to be taught to realize that it was not a natural law but merely a means for keeping order in the files. Platypus did the job of teaching that lesson.

When the first platypus skin reached England, the zoologists of the Royal Society were almost ready to declare that there was no such animal. At first glance it appeared to be merely a little mammal with four webbed feet, a flattened tail, and fur that was deep umber brown on the back and sides and paler on the under parts, as is quite common in small mammals. It was the head that was unbelievable. It looked like the head of a four-footed mammal, but instead of a mouth it had a bill like that of a bird. A bill like a duck's on a four-footed, fur-covered animal naturally attracted immediate attention.

The task of writing the first scientific description fell to Dr. George Shaw of the British Museum, where the original skin, which is said to be still preserved, was received in 1798. Shaw's description was published in the tenth volume of *Naturalists' Miscellany* (1799), at that time one of the important scientific journals. Since Dr. Shaw had only the skin, the description was naturally far from complete. But it settled the first question that had arisen: whether the animal existed at all. Certain scientists who had seen the skin had declared it to be a fake, an imposture, a product of art—in short, a Jenny Haniver. Shaw had to assert solemnly that it was real.

"Of all the Mammalia yet known, it seems the most extraordinary in its conformation, exhibiting the perfect resemblance of the beak of a duck engrafted on the head of a quadruped. So accurate is this similitude, that, at first view, it naturally excited the idea of some deceptive preparation by artificial means; the very epidermis, proportion, serratures, manner of opening, and other particulars is the beak of a shoveler, or other broad-billed species of duck, presenting themselves to the view; nor is it without the most minute and rigid examination that we can persuade ourselves of its being the real beak or snout of a quadruped."

In spite of Shaw's description and another description by the German anatomist Blumenbach, which followed in 1801, doubts must have lingered, for in 1823 Robert Knox still felt obliged to defend the real existence of the platypus.

"It is well known that the specimens of this very extraordinary animal first brought to Europe were considered by many as impositions. They reached England by vessels which had navigated the Indian seas, a circumstance in itself sufficient to rouse the suspicions of the scientific naturalist, aware of the monstrous impostures which the artful Chinese had so frequently practiced on European adventurers; in short, the scientific felt inclined to class this rare production of nature with eastern mermaids and other works of art."

The "eastern mermaids" he mentions were examples of Chinese "art," frequently brought to Europe in those times. They consisted of the forepart of a monkey carefully sewn to the hindpart of a fish and dried so skillfully that it was hard to find the seam.

Following the rules of the game, Shaw had to give a scientific name to the creature he had been the first to describe. He termed it *Platypus anatinus* ("the flat-footed animal with the duckbill"). Thus began the second controversy. Professor Blumenbach of Göttingen, in writing the second scientific description, christened the animal *Ornithorhynchus* (the bird-beaked animal), and added *paradoxus* as the second name because of the creature's paradoxical characteristics. Shaw's name was given earlier, but *Platypus* as a generic was no longer permissible, for it had been used still earlier (in 1793) by the German scientist Herbst for a genus of small beetles. Therefore, Blumenbach's *Ornithorhynchus* was established; but his second name *paradoxus* was not permissible either, since Shaw's *anatinus* was older. So the two names merged into *Ornithorhynchus anatinus*; but "platypus," "duckbill," and "water-mole" have survived in the vernacular.

With its existence and its scientific name established, the next question to arise was how to classify it, and it was this question that gave the platypus the reputation of being Zoological Nuisance No. 1. Some of this stigma still attaches to it.

Meanwhile, another specimen of platypus had arrived, this time not only a skin, but the complete female animal preserved in alcohol. It was carefully examined, and another astonishing discovery was made. Platypus, which in spite of its beak looked so obviously mammalian, had no mammary glands to provide nourishment for its young; and it had no normal mammalian genitalia, but instead exhibited a common excretory cavity or cloaca, a characteristic of birds and reptiles.

To make matters worse, about this time a relative of platypus was discovered. This was the echidna, also called "native porcupine" and "spiny anteater." While in outer appearance this animal (*Tachyglossus* aculeatus) differed very much from the platypus and resembled more a small porcupine with perhaps a mixture of pangolin (scaly anteater), it nevertheless exhibited many of the platypus's characteristics. Its snout, for instance, was also like the bill of a bird, though to a lesser extent.

Dr. Shaw, in his first scientific descriptions, had suggested placing platypus with the lowest order of the class of mammals. Linnaeus had called his lowest mammalian order *Bruta*; and he had put into it whatever did not fit anywhere else. Later the name *Bruta* was changed to Edentata ("the toothless"), since all the heterogeneous animals assembled in this order were found to be distinguished by a complete or at least comparative lack of teeth even in the adult stage. Obviously, said Shaw, the duckbill platypus belongs to this order: not a trace of teeth is to be found in its mouth. This was not absolutely true, but the discoveries came slowly.

Shaw's colleague, Home, who had also pondered the second specimen in its alcohol bottle, was not so fully convinced. "Make a new order of animals out of these two," he suggested, influenced in his decision mainly by echidna. This was in 1803. One year later, temperamental Etienne Geoffroy Saint-Hilaire in France created the new order and called it *Monotremata* ("the single-holed animals"), but whether it should be an order of the class reptiles or of the class mammals he did not at first say. The German Tiedemann (1808) cautiously avoided the difficulties by placing platypus in an appendix. That was clever, no doubt, but it obviously was no solution.

The great Lamarck in France was apparently the first to suggest a new *class* for platypus and echidna, equal in rank with the great classes of birds, mammals, reptiles, and fish.† The designation he sug-

---

* Meaning "swift-tongue."
† The amphibians, intermediate between the reptiles and fishes, and including

gested for this class was *Prototheria*, a name that might be translated as "pre-mammals." Mr. Illiger, another respectable and distinguished zoologist, agreed in general with Lamarck, but not with his name for the new class. He wanted to call it *Reptantia*, meaning something like "almost-reptiles."

In the course of this interesting debate, one still unanswered question of fact gradually became the main issue of the controversy: How did these two Australian nuisances reproduce? There were persistent reports from Australia that platypus laid eggs. Sir John Jamison wrote as early as March 1817 that "the female is oviparous [egg-bearing], and lives in burrows in the ground." We know now that this is true, but Sir John did not furnish evidence, and so it happened that the matter remained open to doubt for another half-century or more. The French author R. P. Lesson summed up the general feeling when, as a firm believer that platypus laid eggs, he wrote that these animals were "creatures set across the path of the scientific method to show its worthlessness."

Matters became still more complicated in 1824 when Professor Meckel in Germany discovered the mammary glands. They had been overlooked, and we know now that they are very much reduced except in the breeding period. One might think that such a discovery would settle the argument of classification once and for all by making it necessary to class the disputed animal as a mammal, for, as the name indicates, the possession of mammary glands is a primary distinction of mammals. But it did not, because these mammary glands were very primitive, being, as Meckel expressed it, "merely composed of a considerable number of ampullae [membranous sacs] with long necks." The necks of the ampullae did not end in teats, but in a great number of large pores on a small area of the skin.

On the contrary, these glands posed another enigma and led to a further controversy that lasted for many years. On one side there were the Saint-Hilaires, father and son, in France, supported by the Frenchman Latreille and the Dutchman van der Hoeven; while the German Meckel and the Frenchmen Blainville and Cuvier were the antagonists. The Saint-Hilaires did not welcome the discovery of the milk glands, knowing that their existence would be unfavorable to their contention that the monotremes were not mammals. Their reasoning

---

the frogs, toads, newts, salamanders, etc., were not regarded as an independent class till later. The carving of this class out of Linnaeus's class of reptiles was regarded as a refinement, not a contradiction, of his system.

was that "in spite of fur, limbs, lungs, and a heart with two ventricles," the monotremes were not mammals, because they laid eggs, had no true mammary glands, and had a cloaca. But they argued that they were not birds, either, having neither feathers nor wings. Neither were they reptiles, for they showed mammalian features and warm blood and lungs enclosed in pleurae. In short, they were monotremes. "We may today regard it as certain," wrote Geoffroy Saint-Hilaire *fils*, "that the . . . vertebrate animals should henceforth be divided into the five following types: mammals, monotremes, birds, reptiles, and fishes." Meckel's mammary glands had to be explained away somehow, and the Saint-Hilaires therefore declared these organs to be scent glands. If they were milk glands, they asked, how were the young ones expected to suck milk with their horny beaks from a gland that did not even have a teat?

The question whether platypus actually laid eggs resulted in no less than three scientific parties, each defending firmly—*very* firmly—a different opinion about the method of reproduction. Meckel, Cuvier, Oken, and Blainville, all great names in science, argued that platypus was a mammal and therefore held that it must be viviparous, that is to say that it brought forth living young. The Saint-Hilaires and Blumenbach were convinced that it was egg-laying, or oviparous; while Home and Richard Owen believed that it must produce eggs, which, however, hatched within the parent's body, thus making the animal ovoviviparous. "The sad story of the eggs," as the Australian scientist Dr. Harry Burrell, top-ranking expert on the platypus, expressed it, began in 1829. In that year Etienne Geoffroy Saint-Hilaire triumphantly published a letter from a Mr. Robert E. Grant who reported the discovery of four *Ornithorhynchus* eggs. But a great disappointment was in store. The eggs were a bit large and in the drawing that was published they were so well reproduced that experts could classify them as having been laid by *Chelodina longicollis*, the common long-necked Australian tortoise.

The next name to be mentioned in connection with the eggs of platypus is that of Lieutenant Maule. In the years 1831 and 1832 he established the fact that Meckel's glands actually produced milk. He also reported finding eggshells in the nesting burrows, but this was not considered sufficient evidence, for these might not be platypus eggs. The next report that reached Europe came from one Jno. Nicholson, M.D., in a letter sent from Wood's Point, Victoria, Australia, dated September 21, 1864, and addressed to Richard Owen:

"Sir,—I have great pleasure in being able to inform you of a very interesting discovery in the anatomy of the *Ornithorhynchus paradoxus*, and one which I have no doubt you will hail with delight. About ten months ago, a female Platypus was captured in the River Goulbourn by some workman who gave it to the Gold-Receiver of his district. He, to prevent its escape, tied a cord to its leg and put it into a gin-case, where it remained during the night. The next morning, when he came to look at it, he found that it had laid two eggs. They were about the size of a crow's egg, and were white, soft and compressible, being without shell or anything approaching to a calcareous covering."

Dr. Nicholson failed to examine the eggs closely, but though the size mentioned in his letter is exaggerated, they certainly were platypus eggs. Owen, belonging to the party that believed the platypus to be ovoviviparous, did not doubt the statement, but he declared that the egg-laying was not normal, and had to be regarded as an "abortion due to fear." It was this tenacity of these foremost scientists of their day in clinging to their preconceived opinions that made the controversy lively and lasting.

Owen's attitude, however, was not really unreasonable. The English zoologist Bennett had made a trip to Australia in 1832 and had tried to settle the great question once and for all. Dozens of nesting burrows had been uncovered and young platypi in all stages of development had been found. The milk production, established already one year before by Maule, had been confirmed, but no egg was found, not even a shell. Nevertheless, since it is a fact that platypus lays eggs, Bennett must have arrived just a few days too late.

The matter was finally settled by the independent discoveries of Dr. W. H. Caldwell of Australia and Professor Wilhelm Haacke of Germany. Curiously, these two men obtained the final proof for the oviparous habits of platypus and echidna almost simultaneously—Caldwell during the second week of August 1884, and Haacke on August 25 of the same year. Haacke examined the pouch of a female specimen of echidna, and to his surprise he found an egg in it; his surprise was so great that he crushed it between his fingers. Another coincidence is that the discoveries that were made within a week of each other were reported by Haacke and Caldwell on the same day. They did not know about each other and afterwards it was difficult to decide to whom the priority belonged.

It was the last salvo in the great battle. Platypus was well established. It laid eggs, but it put them into a pouch. It fed its young with milk, but it had no teats. It had—another little item that had not been easy to establish—warm blood, but of a much lower temperature than all other mammals. It was in general either a reptile with many mammalian features, or a mammal with many reptilian habits. It was something between reptile and mammal: Lamarck's name *Prototheria* (pre-mammals) had been strikingly good. Why platypus and echidna represented such an unbelievable mixture of reptilian and mammalian features could be explained only by Darwin and his followers. Here was a survivor from a former geological period, possibly from the time when mammals evolved from reptilian ancestors. As soon as the smoke of battle had cleared away, this simple (and only) explanation became perfectly obvious.

But I have not yet told the whole story of platypus. In 1891–92 a German professor, Richard Semon, made a trip to Australia in pursuit of the lungfish *Ceratodus* (which will be the subject of the next chapter), and while waiting about a few weeks for his fish to lay their eggs, he made some observations on the two monotremes, mainly the echidna. Thanks to Caldwell, Semon, and Dr. Burrell, we now have a fairly good knowledge of platypus and echidna. The facts are as follows:

The monotremes live on the Australian continent, in Tasmania, and in New Guinea (also in the better zoological gardens). All monotremes lay eggs, but platypus differs from echidna in that its pouch is too small to hold the eggs and they are hatched in a sort of nest. It lays two eggs at a time, each three-fourths of an inch long and one-half inch wide, enclosed in a strong, flexible, white shell. The young are nourished on the secretion of the rudimentary mammary glands, contrary to the contention of the Saint-Hilaires and in spite of the apparently impracticable beak possessed by the adult. Observation has shown that the young of echidna are carried around in the pouch until they are almost one-third grown. The natural diet of echidna consists of ants and other small insects, while platypus feeds on insects, worms, and small crustaceans. In captivity one platypus ate half a pound of earthworms, forty shrimps, and forty grubs in one day! Platypus has cheek-pouches, but apparently does not use them for storing food.

There are still a number of open questions. For example, the duration of life is still unknown; so is the exact utility of the beak of platypus and the reason why this strange organ has been evolved. It is not as hard and horny as dried museum specimens would indicate, but is soft, like rubber, and extremely sensitive. Burrell believes that it serves as an ultrasensitive organ for feeling the way under water where eyes and ears are shut.

But the greatest of the unsolved mysteries is the movable spur, like a cock's, on the hind legs of the males of platypus and echidna. It has a canal, so thin that a horse hair does not pass through it, though a human hair does, and is connected with the duct of a gland. The spur was always reported to inflict poisonous wounds. Sir John Jamison wrote in 1816 that a man, in spite of immediate medical treatment, "exhibited all the symptoms of a person bitten by a venomous snake." The victim "was obliged to keep his bed for several days, and did not recover the perfect use of his hand for nine weeks." Since then many scientists have experienced or seen wounds inflicted by the spurs; the wounds are described as extremely painful, but not fatal. Rabbits injured by the spur did, however, die.

Since the spur is attributed only to the males it can hardly be regarded as a weapon. The French scientists agreed that it served to hold the female during copulation, but others refused to find this explanation adequate. Another theory occasionally advanced is that the spur is to inject a "drug" into the blood of the female to minimize her resistance. Burrell believes that the spur serves as a paralyzing weapon in the fights of the males for the possession of the females. Obviously, it is not the aim of these fights to kill, though fatal effects have been observed.

And the result of the fiercest of all the battles around platypus: how should the monotremes be classed? They have become a subclass of the mammals, the lowest subclass. Here they stand closest to the reptiles, with which they share the cloaca, the habit of laying eggs, and the low blood temperature, which is between five and twelve degrees centigrade lower than that of man. Yet, truth to tell, this classification is still somewhat problematic. It was attacked again some thirty years ago.

I have said that platypus and its cousins are survivors from a former geological period. Where then are the fossil platypi? They were finally found, though not at once recognized. Near Echterdingen in Württemberg, Germany, almost at the place where one of Count Zeppelin's first dirigibles was later to meet a sudden and tragic end, a number of tiny fossil teeth were discovered in 1874. It was assumed that these teeth had belonged to some mammal, and the name given this unknown creature was *Microlestes*. How *Microlestes* looked could not be said; only its teeth were known. Its size must have averaged that of a rat. But there are many mammals the size of a rat that are very different in appearance.

Then one day it was found that platypus develops teeth for a short period during early life. They are soon lost, but they show a surprisingly close resemblance to the teeth of *Microlestes*. Probably *Microlestes* was an extinct monotreme. Then when several other extinct little monotremes were found, it was suggested that the animals of this type, extinct and living, be brought together into a new class called *Allotheria* (meaning simply "other mammals"). However, the suggestion was not cheered by the majority of scientists. Apparently they were pretty tired of questions of classification, as far as monotremes were concerned, and the monotremes have remained a subclass of the mammals.

A TORRENT OF AIR

by Guy Murchie, Jr.

Guy Murchie, Jr., Harvard graduate, is an author, airman, and educator. He was a war correspondent in Europe when the United States entered World War II and welcomed him into our air force as a navigator on flights across the North and South Atlantic. After the war he worked for a commercial airline, but during the Korean adventure he journeyed back and forth across the Pacific as a civilian under army contract to aid the airlift from San Francisco to Tokyo. When that episode ended, he set up a school at East Sullivan, New Hampshire, taught for some years, closed up shop, went to Mexico, then to Europe, and was last reported somewhere in Spain, probably working on a book. The following selection, taken from his Song of the Sky, *published in 1954, could not have been written fifty years ago. This is something that was learned by men who flew in the stratosphere. With jet propulsion now fairly common and rocket transportation at least tentatively proposed for future travel, what follows is not offered as the last word on the sky above us and the air around us, but it will help to clear the atmosphere for the time being.*

THE most recently discovered of the world's important winds is a gigantic, elusive torrent of thin air that howls perpetually around the base of the stratosphere somewhere eight miles above the middle latitudes. It is shaped like a tape worm, follows the course of a shaken rope, and moves invisibly at a speed varying from 100 to 500 m.p.h.

Respectfully known as the jet stream, it is really a double whirlwind nearly as much bigger than the hurricane, as the hurricane is bigger than the tornado. In fact, each of the earth's two jet streams averages about 22,000 miles in circumference, and the Arctic and Antarctic circles form but the irises of their oppositely staring eyes, one looking perpetually at the North Star, the other gazing forever upon the Southern Cross.

Almost too tremendous for human conception, this lofty wind was first suspected by the navigators of the B-29 bombers flying to southern Japan near the end of World War II. The flight crews were amazed to find that near the horse latitudes at 35,000 feet, they regularly met west winds of more than 250 m.p.h., three times as swift as the average hurricane. Sometimes they found themselves actually flying backwards at 40,000 feet in 400-m.p.h. headwinds! They could not account for it nor find even a mention of it in the meteorology books. When the weather engineers heard the reports and collected all the information at hand, it was evident that something big was up. An entirely new kind of wind had been discovered, a sort of by-product of the age of jet, a supercharged Gulf Stream of the upper sky.

Special projects of exploration were immediately launched to investigate it thoroughly. This was not easy, for an invisible river eight miles straight up is something even the Air Force was not organized to handle, especially when its unknown course is constantly shifting both horizontally and vertically, sometimes by as much as a thousand miles in a day.

Gradually, however, as data accumulated in quantity, the jet stream began to take shape as a predictable wind. Some meteorologists started referring to it as the circumpolar vortex. It turned out to be the actual nerve center of the prevailing westerlies, the core of maximum speed, the volatile backbone of that greatest of wind systems on earth, blowing completely around the world between the polar fronts and the tropics. Thus obviously there are two jet streams, one howling over Argentina and around the watery southern temperate zone, the other sizzling through the skies over China, the United States, and the Mediterranean area, weaving about in conformity with the changing pressure contours of the great waves of the northern polar front, easing further northward in spring with the sun (as do the polar fronts, horse latitudes, and doldrums alike), working south again in fall.

The jet stream is shaped just as a river is supposed to be, wide and relatively shallow. But besides being a hundred times faster, it is also a hundred times bigger than any river you ever saw on earth, far bigger even than the Gulf Stream which would exceed all the continental rivers put together. Thus the jet stream of air is by all odds the world's greatest river—a twin river flowing continuously sometimes for nearly twenty-five thousand miles around each hemisphere, only a few miles deep but its volume amounting to five thousand cubic miles of air per minute past every point on its banks (if it had any banks)—its total course in both hemispheres: more than forty-five thousand miles, or a fifth of the way to the moon.

Yet while it is undeniably the super-Amazon of the heavens and far aloof from all lower circulations of sky, the jet vortex, no less than the lumbering hurricane and the fleeting earthbound tornado, springs from deducible dynamic sources—from the cyclonic clash of conflicting bodies of wind, from the inherent shear of crisp polar cold against sultry tropical heat. It is thus whipped to its frenzy by an uneasy pressure gradient that, like the slopes of the Alps, steepens with height, that, like boiling liquid, is made turbulent by disparate temperature.

The jet stream has also a rhythmic wave motion which sometimes follows the phases of the moon with an almost feminine fatality. Its cyclic month or longer starts with a straight west wind that very gradually begins to undulate in the manner of a snake coming out of hibernation. After ten days of continuous increase in amplitude, the wave curves are describing moving S shapes two or three thousand miles apart that presently develop signs of instability, actually breaking apart by the end of the second or third week into loose wheels and kidney whorls that fly off as separate circulations and may roll on, for all now known, as far as the equator and the poles.

After a wild week of such wanton discontinuity, the discordant waves have usually canceled each other out enough to permit new frontal pressures to oil the turbulence. Thus the trend turns again toward order and in another week the jet stream has notably ironed out its curves so it can stiffen back into the simple western component of its beginning.

Naturally this great wind offers wonderful possibilities for saving time and fuel on long easterly flights—especially where it has been rechecked as most virile in winter off southern Japan, over the southeastern United States, and in the clear skies of Egypt and Arabia. Since 1953 some of the trans-Pacific airliners have been regularly hopping the jet for free rides between Tokyo and Honolulu, a stretch that used to be a dog-legged 4320 miles by way of Wake Island for refueling, but is now less than 3900 via direct jet stream—the trimming of time even more striking from the former 17 hours to 11 hours, or

10, sometimes 9, depending on the mood and favor of the river of
winds.

Of course the jet current is of no help going the other way. Indeed
it can be a serious hindrance, as the B–29 boys found out. But in
midwinter eastward bound, it is almost invariably worth "2200 gallons
of gas" ($20,000 in air freight), even at present cruising levels miles
below the stratum of full jet strength. At 40,000 feet it will be the
bonanza of the blue, a golden Rio de Janeiro ever waiting to be
claimed, and the airline meteorologists are already perfecting techniques of adjusting payload to tailwind for the optimum exploitation
of whatever a great wind can give that they can take. The fact that
the jet core was clocked at 490 m.p.h. a few days ago over Spokane is
more than a hint of the future, for any old B–47 that had troubled to
climb into it would have looked a cinch to make New York in two
hours and a half!

Such interesting problems in calculus as to how far it is worthwhile
to go out of one's way in pursuit of the jet stream, how late in the
spring it can be used despite the seasonal slump, exactly where the
efficient navigator should cut into it or veer out for his optimum course
—these will occupy our minds in the coming years and should well
fill the gap left by the tedious spherical trigonometry of old. And although we are learning more every day of this upper world, it still
holds ample mysteries like the sudden turbulence that besets airplanes threading the jet rivers, the abrupt sequence of "short, sharp,
hammering repercussions" that remind pilots of a speedboat battering
choppy seas. These vibrations often begin with startling suddenness in
clear air around 35,000 ft. without warning, nor obvious cause. They
may be an aerial form of tide rip or cross current of conflict between
opposing oscillations of air striking each other at discordant angles
to the lee of mountains. Or might they possibly be a pressure counterpart of the cirro-cumulus cloud streaks that linger below jet streams
so often that they are getting to be officially associated with them—
the bouncing breath of Argestes—mackerel spindrift upon the timeless
river of wind?

The murderous bomb wind, born of the atomic age, is one of the
strangest of all the world's winds. Even with the earliest "model T"
atomic bombs the outward blast at a thousand feet from "zero" (directly under the bomb) blows at 800 m.p.h., or faster than sound.
Two miles away the wind is still whooshing out at 70 m.p.h. But this

vast expanding puff is exhausted in a couple of seconds and is followed by an instant of stillness as in the eye of a hurricane. Then immediately it reverses itself, the wind literally bouncing back into the vacuum at about half its outward velocity but lasting longer. This double-action wind is what causes most structural damage in an atomic explosion, and many buildings which are only weakened by the initial outward blow are collapsed by the rebounding blast. H-bomb winds and bigger and worse blasts from successively more powerful explosions can be expected to behave in similar patterns but with velocities and distances proportionately increased.

And don't imagine that winds are only out there in the sky or blown by special instruments. Winds are everywhere. Winds are moving air. That draft down the hall—that's a wind. That sneeze. That's a wind. That rise of warmth over the stove. That's the kid brother of the same wind that starts thunderstorms to growling. Some have names. Some have not. But in God's eye every one is a wind, however small—and any one of them somehow may grow into a whirlwind, even as the handful of dust that Mohammed threw at Badr.

It must be understood of course that all the winds man discovered up to the day he cracked the ancient chain that held his wings were those felt close to earth. They had to be, for till then he knew no way to probe the upper sky except with the vicarious aid of his friend the bird or an occasional kite or balloon. His precarious eighteenth-century balloon, though it carried the dauntless adventurer high in the air, was a poor ambassador to the wind because it was swallowed so completely by the wind itself that it put him in a position similar to Jonah on his introduction to the whale—a position hardly conducive to intelligent discourse.

Old balloonist Monc Mason's famous *Aeronautica* tells of the "awful silence" of the sky as known from a free balloon. It is the silence of astronomic equilibrium, of absence of the wind sounds made by the friction of air against the alien earth, against the ear, against houses and trees. For the well-ballasted free balloon riding the wind comes to rest in the wind's body until it is in perfect frictionless balance. As Mason expressed it, "The greatest storm is, in respect to its influence upon this condition of the balloon, as utterly powerless as the most unruffled calm . . . [A man] might look down from his airborne car and behold houses levelled, trees uprooted, rocks hurled into the sea, and all the various signs of desolation by which the path of the storm is marked, and yet he might hold in his hand a lighted taper without extinguishing the flame, or even indicating by its inclination to one side or the other the direction of the mighty agent by which such awful ravages had been created."

Monc Mason, if you'll recall, first won fame as one of three intrepid Englishmen who boarded the west wind by balloon in 1836, riding from London to a place five hundred miles away in the little Duchy of Nassau, Germany, a record flight of eighteen hours that amazed the world.

But it was to take man another century to plumb the real dimensions of the wind—a century of experimenting with theodolites and wings in which he demonstrated that wind extends as high as air, gradually thinning for hundreds of miles. The swiftest wind level, he found, is above the cirrus layer of six miles up where mackerel bones and mare's tails ride unreined around the world. It is the haunt of the jet stream and of less-known stratospheric gales, yet meteor trails up to twenty times higher have been clocked to prove that winds blow about as swiftly at even two hundred miles up, frequently from the opposite direction—for the direction of prevailing winds is reversed several times at different high altitudes according to the major circulations of ionic heat.

The wind's strength does not keep up with its speed all the way to the top, it must be remembered. Wind is a spineless ghost above ten miles, for the upper air becomes too thin to feel. In fact if any bird could fly that high it would flap helplessly in the eerie nothingness like a fish out of water.

Another wind discovery of importance was the vast tropospheric scope of our traffic rule: keep to the right. When you are flying around a thunderstorm or a tornado it may be the difference between life and death to go right instead of left. To right you're with the wind, to left against it. This is because all storms and low pressure areas in the northern hemisphere are surrounded by counterclockwise winds. The cause is the motion of the earth itself: the veering geostrophic, gyroscopic force known as coriolis. It is the reason why an east wind spells trouble, being part of a storm from the west. It is why the right side of a north-moving hurricane is the dangerous side of forward spin. It is why an airplane flying east (turning faster than the earth) is lighter than the same airplane flying west, or why an airplane flying over the equator (where centrifugal force is greatest) is lighter than one flying elsewhere. It is why a pendulum clock, taken to a northern country, will run fast. It is the secret of the gyroscopic compass: the ever present centrifugal component of net gravity.

A Dutch physicist, oddly named Professor Buys Ballot, discovered this basic wind principle in 1860. His law says: "Stand with your back to the wind and pressure is lower on your left hand than on your right in the northern hemisphere. South of the Equator the reverse is true." And that is why Australian flyers go to the left of storms while Americans go to the right.

A mighty planetary force is obviously at work here, causing everything from spinning tops to draining bathtubs to turn one way more easily than the other in each hemisphere. This is because the earth beneath the sky is forever turning "out from under" whatever is upon it, whether air or water or solid moving object. It is why arctic rivers cut faster into their right banks than their left ones, why the Trans-Siberian Railroad has to replace more right than left rails on each stretch of one-way track. It is why the German's Big Bertha gun in World War I, firing on Paris from seventy miles away, had to aim a mile to the left of target so the three-minute trajectory of its shells would be corrected. It is why a rocket missile aimed at New York today from the North Pole would, unless artificially guided en route, land near Chicago after an hour's flight. It is because the earth is constantly moving Chicago to where New York was an hour ago.

Coriolis is not so simple as this may seem, however, for it is complicated by the earth's spherical shape and by eddy effects which, like adjoining gear wheels, must turn in opposite directions. A hurricane, for example, is an eddy in relation to larger higher-pressure masses revolving clockwise north of the equator, yet it has slow-turning thunderstorms and sometimes eddying tornadoes within it, which may spin in both directions. Even large tornadoes often are surrounded by smaller reverse-spinning pilot twisters which have a tendency to act like ball bearings around a shaft, the prevalence of such subvortexes being suggested by the fact that about five per cent of 550 tornadoes investigated in North America are known to have turned clockwise despite the general coriolis law of counterclockwise for all northern low-pressure systems.

Could it be possible that something like the same majority of northern nations order their traffic to the right for the same subconscious reason that the edges of northern high pressure air masses naturally swing to the right, forcing their eddying low pressure vortexes to turn away from them to the left, counterclockwise, in the manner of rotary traffic around the "eye" of a "Keep to the Right" intersection—or aircraft spiraling into an airfield?

Could this also be why our northern merry-go-rounds turn counterclockwise, and our horse races and auto races counterclockwise around the track? Is it the reason why timber wolves in the north usually range counterclockwise around the territory they claim as theirs? Does it affect also pirouetting ballerinas, whirling dervishes, the spin of boomerangs, cowboys' lassos, circling seagulls, roulette wheels, and lazy Susans? Does it subconsciously influence you when you take a turn around the block? Does it guide the sensitive brown creeper as he spirals upward about the trunk of the tree? And what of the screw bean and the turning worm?

Curious consequences come to mind. If the trudging of the ox about the wheel is affected by the spinning of the earth, no matter how slightly, is not the earth's turning influenced in return by the motion of the ox—though more slightly still? Action and reaction. Broadside and recoil. The horses racing around the bend hurl themselves forward, their flying hoofs heeding not that they also kick the great earth out behind them—subtly but surely.

Possibilities do not tire. If it could be arranged that all the cooks and bakers of the hemisphere should stir their pots and tubs the other way, and all the dogs chase their tails but clockwise, and traffic circles and phonographs, dynamos and windmills reverse themselves, would not the cumulative force noticeably retard the spinning of the earth?

The velocity of the wind has long been a spicy topic of argument, especially among sailors, and many have sought ways of measuring and classifying it. One Charles Tomlinson worked out a sailing-wind scale which gave the olden skipper a kind of standard. Force zero in the Tomlinson scale was "dead calm"; force one: "steerage way." Increasing from there a few knots at a time, force 5 was "with royals"; 6, "three reefs in topsails"; 9, "close-reefed main topsail and courses"; 10, "close-reefed topsails and reefed foresail"; 11, "storm staysails"; 12, "hurricane" (or, likely, "hove to with sea anchor").

For a time they printed "wind stars" on sailing charts as a means of giving wind information at a glance. Added to the compass rose these irregular wind stars gave the old charts a fine artistic flavor. Each star had eight points, representing by their lengths the average wind force from the eight principal directions of the compass, with other graphic weather data between.

The old Admiral Sir Francis Beaufort devised the wind scale that is still used today in modern form, sorting the breezes from the gales, and defining the hurricane anew as a wind force of 75 m.p.h. or over. Though seventy-five is rarely exceeded in normal experience in the densely settled parts of the earth, it is commonplace in some mountainous regions. The blue ribbon for highest precisely measured wind speed is now held by the observatory on Mount Washington in New Hampshire which recorded a full hour's average of 173 m.p.h. on April 12, 1934, with brief gusts up to 231 m.p.h. The chief danger in such hurricane wind force is in the fact that air moving squarely against any surface creates pressure "proportional to the square of its velocity"— so that even a wind of 120 m.p.h. hits your house 144 times as hard as a ten-mile breeze.

The whirling cups of the anemometer, by the way, reveal things about the wind that no other instrument can. They show that a high wind is actually not a steady flow of air like a river but irregular like a tidal surge from the ocean when uneven surf is rushing into a shallow estuary. It is broken into multiform gusts and eddies and its average velocity ebbs and flows with the passing hours. Specifically, its main but invisible eddies vary from two to ten miles in diameter and fill most of the sky as "local circulation" cells up to 20,000 feet. These are almost constantly if slowly bubbling and boiling past any given point on the earth. Their effect has been measured also as a fluctuation of about two knots of average wind velocity in a cycle of approximately ten minutes. This is the wind's basic rhythm.

It is what science is learning of the local shape of wind—wind that is the transport of air masses viewed from human perspective—wind whose differences at various sky levels are indicated by the leanings of clouds, whose smaller wave frequencies can be seen in the size of circles carved by the soaring hawks or perhaps in higher reaches by the bone patterns of herring cumulus or the scales of cirrus mackerel.

Have you ever noticed how sometimes on a calm day a sudden huff of wind will come out of nowhere? Just a momentary whoosh of breeze, a flaw in the blue ointment followed again by tranquility for a long time? Such a solitary gust always makes me feel as though a great stone had been tossed off some distant mountain into the ocean of air and that this brief breeze is the ripple expanding outward from the splash—traveling slower than sound, as surely as sight, and insolubly part of the little-sensed adagio of the sky.

At other times when the wind blows over rough wooded country interspersed with ravines and sharp ridges, I think it takes on the character of a babbling mountain brook with breeze bubbles of lighter air pouring and wimpling over the crested hills much as a brook's fingers purl over the rocks on the way to the valley.

Both moods are familiar degrees of what is known to science as the phenomenon of turbulence—in this case turbulence of free air, which means wind and cellular motion, backwash, large eddies that dissipate into smaller ones: ofttimes eddies within eddies within eddies.

Little is yet known about the seemingly interminable subject of turbulence, but it is now being actively studied from the gyrations of electrons to the motions of galaxies and it is considered vital to the future of flying. It is one key to the friction that lets propellers grab and grip the air in pulling the airplane forward. It is responsible in part for rain and weather—cells of motion in the sky. It promotes effective human breathing and digestion—local winds of torsion in the torso. It is what makes "big whirls have little whirls that feed on their velocity; and little whirls have lesser whirls—and so on to viscosity."

In the sky you can sometimes see the wind bouncing off the ground again and again after being stirred up by a high ridge. Dr. Charles F. Brooks of Blue Hill Observatory near Boston tells me he once counted twenty such bounces in the lee of Mount Washington, each bounce about five miles from the next and visible from the clouds that formed at each crest of the air waves.

It takes quite a while for such turbulence to get ironed out of the wind. When I owned a windmill I used to wish it could happen quicker, for an air flow that is steady as well as strong is important to a windmill's average output of power. In England they figure a wind averaging 20 m.p.h. or higher can produce cheaper power than coal. And I hear that some English windmills on hills enjoy average winds as high as 30 m.p.h. day and night, month after month. The best spots have turned out to be the tops of very smooth bare hills where the wind is speeded up "about five per cent" by its upward aerodynamic flow, where the slipstream is naturally tailored to a human purpose almost as by the precisely engineered surface of a man-made flying wing.

Tibet of all the inhabited lands is probably where the wind feels most at home. There it is free to scythe across "the roof of the world" three miles up bearing the full heft of an unobstructed sweep around the middle of the earth. A young American, Frank Bessac, who recently crossed Tibet in flight before the Reds, wrote: "The thing I will remember most about the Tibetan mountains was the wind . . . a howling, skin-blasting roar which never died for a moment throughout the day. So bad was it that if anyone had anything to say he got it said before midmorning. After that there was no conversation: it was impossible to do anything but hide our heads in our coat collars."

The Tsang Po winds are indeed so heady with altitude up there at 16,000 feet in the little city of the big winds that they say that on nights when the wind has been known to stop completely, the sky is so startled it feels dizzy with emptiness—"like an empty box."

Fortunate it is for the Tibetans that this drastic phenomenon is rare, for almost always it is accompanied with unaccountable illness and death. Perhaps life in that wind-lorn land is as mystically dependent on the wind as a candle flame is dependent on calmness. While the wind blows, the crust of life holds on, but when the wind dies a vital fuel valve seems to close and life quietly softens and ebbs away.

With its almost timeless devotion, the wind has shaped and colored much of the earth—and the task continues hourly. Wind deposits called loess, or eolation, blanket wide areas of the continents and the sea bottoms. Wind erosion carves lofty rocks and lowly knolls, small swales of grass and rolling dunes that creep like waves in largo.

One such wave of sand swallowed the whole village of Kunzen on the Baltic, then in a few years flowed on to uncover it again—leaving it little the worse for wear. Yet in the Sudan a sand haboob is known to have rasped down wooden telegraph poles in a night, and roughened windowpanes to intransparency in an hour.

Inexplicable indeed the moods and deeds of the wind, countless the mountain trees warped to its will, the whistling towers, the chimneys of stone sculped by its sightless chisel, the buttes and the graceful monoliths. Atolls in the Pacific are said to be designed entirely by the steadfast tradewinds. Even the scope of great windward rain jungles in the tropics are architectured by the wind, and vast leeward deserts across Africa, Australia, Asia, and the Americas.

In May 1937 during a southwest gale yellow sand fell in Canton Basle, Switzerland, so heavily that the countryside appeared swathed in a strange sulphuric fog. The sand was later proved to be from the Sahara Desert a thousand miles away and it must have been picked up by a simoom to be blown over the Alps at above 12,000 feet.

At the same time in the Engadine valley, also in Switzerland, a mysterious fall of red sand occurred, the origin of which has not yet been discovered. At other times and places pebbles, shells, and seaweed, even living frogs and fishes, have rained upon the earth, perhaps after being sucked aloft in a vortex, then carried inexplicably on the wind for great distances.

Can anyone ever say what shall not serve as grist for the wind?

And what of the wind's song—so familiar yet never quite repeated? The wind has a hundred voices, which have awed and lured and terrified mankind from his beginning. Have you heard the whine of the hound that grew from the wail of the wind, pleading at first, howling with rage as it freshened? Have you listened to the thresh of needled boughs in a gale when "that grand old harper smote his thunder-harp of pines?" Hark the warm sigh of the salt breeze sprawled in the bellying sail, the flutey trickle of air from the knothole in the fence, the limp flutter of shirts and aprons on the line.

Did you ever take pencil and book to scrib down the sounds the wind makes as it sifts and soughs through trees? Each kind of tree is a sort of musical instrument: the apple a cello, the old oak a bass viol, the cypress a harp, the willow a flute, the young pine a muted violin. Put your ear close to the whispering branch and you may catch what it is saying: the brittle twitter of dry oak leaves in winter, the faint breathing of the junipers, the whirring of hickory twigs, the thrumming of slender birch clumps, the sibilant souffle of the cedars, the mild murmuring of the sugar maple, and behind them all the trafficky thunder of whole bare trees torn in a headlong tide of air.

Inclining your accustomed ear downward you may even tune in on the soft purring of pussy willow buds, the burr of the wild cranberry, and the swish of swamp grass barely rising above the clicking of reeds and cattails, blending again into the over-all cataract of sound.

The humming telephone wires along the road seem to have a further significance in the language of the wind. Is it the harmonics of those aeolian strands or the mumbling gossip of the breezes as they eavesdrop on the long-distance calls? Sometimes martins and swallows sit by hundreds on those vibrant wires—listening in—perhaps divining more than we know of the business and hope and love that pulse mile on mile within the clasp of their tiny toes.

THE CONTEMPLATIVE TOAD

by Joseph Wood Krutch

What a man does when he is free to choose is the thing in which he is most interested. By that criterion it would appear that the author of this selection has been most interested—in recent years at least—in natural history and the philosophy behind the facts of natural history. Joseph Wood Krutch, born in Knoxville, Tennessee, November 25, 1893, was graduated from the University of Tennessee in 1915 with an A.B. degree, journeyed to New York to earn an M.A. degree from Columbia University in 1916, and turned to teaching literature as a profession. He added to his stature in that field by winning his Ph.D. at Columbia in 1923 and branched out the following year by taking the job of drama critic for the Nation *as a sideline. He was much interested in dramatic literature, wrote books on the subject, and indeed went on to become Brander Matthews Professor of Dramatic Literature at Columbia in 1943.*

This keen and competent drama critic, successful author, and revered college professor quietly walked off to another field—one that he found among the Connecticut hills at Redding, where he lived—and blossomed out as a naturalist when he published The Twelve Seasons, *a book about the march of the months across the New England countryside, in 1949. Then he went to the sun-drenched arid region of our Southwest, lured by the memory of a brief glimpse of that colorful country years ago, and out of his observations and reflections he wrote* The Desert Year (1952), *from which the following account of his batrachian friend and neighbor is taken.*

THOSE toads who surprised me by coming from nowhere after our first big rain and who sang their hallelujah chorus on every side have surprised me again. They have disappeared as mysteriously as they came. The desert floor and the desert air are as toadless as ever. Obviously, they are creatures as moderate as all amphibia should be, and one night of revelry was enough.

The next evening I did, to be sure, hear a few scattered voices, like those of stubborn guests who won't go home when a party is over. But all the rest had lapsed into silence and retired into invisibility. More than a month has passed, and despite one more rain as heavy as that which summoned them forth, not one has made himself heard. Nevertheless, I have a very good way of knowing that I did not dream the night they took over.

Forty-eight hours afterward, the largest of my puddles was swarming with tadpoles quite unaware of the fact that fate had assigned them an impossible situation. One more day of hot sun and the puddle was only a damp spot in the sand, covered at its very center with a mass of what had once been potential toads. Obviously the tadpoles had drawn closer and closer together as the puddle shrank, much as a human community might have concentrated itself as the waters of some rising flood drove all its members to the last remaining area of high ground. And they had been overwhelmed at last by the suffocating air, as human beings might have been by relentless water.

But how on earth do any ever survive to carry on the population which is obviously in quite a flourishing state? This puddle was an unusually large one. So far as I know, there was no other larger (and there is certainly no permanent water) within a mile or two of its position. I took it for granted that the tadpoles of this particular species must turn into toads in a remarkably brief period. But however brief it might be, it was obviously not brief enough to be covered by my puddle's duration. These toads, it would appear, ought to have become extinct in this region long ago. Obviously, they haven't.

Before long, I found that my ignorance was ceasing to be a pleasure. The first thing I discovered was that I need not have determined —as originally I did—to preserve it for a while; it has turned out to be not easy to dispel. My confidence that of course someone could answer all my questions was faith misplaced. No one, it now appears, knows very much more about my toads than I do.

Fortunately, I captured one of the two-inch adults and I kept him prisoner until I could consult Wright and Wright's authoritative check list of American toads and frogs. It was easy enough to identify him as the Sonoran spadefoot (*Scaphiopus couchii*) who inhabits Arizona, Utah, Mexico, and parts of Texas. He has an eastern relative, not especially uncommon but seldom recognized by the layman. Like all the spadefoots, he is a great digger with his hind legs and he is conveniently distinguished from all the Bufos (the genus to which the common garden toad belongs) by the fact that the contracted pupil of his eye is vertical like a cat's, not round or horizontal like that of the Bufos.

There is, then, no trouble about naming him, but the available information does not go much beyond that. He is believed to mate only once a year and always after a summer rain. At other periods he has been accidentally dug up out of the earth. But in what sort of pool does he successfully raise his family? How much of the time does he remain buried? Does he come out to eat occasionally during the almost year-long period when he is rarely if ever seen? Finally, how does he like the extraordinary existence which he seems to lead? On these questions, the books cover their silence with the air of not having the space to go in for that sort of thing. Queried face to face, the authorities shrug their shoulders: "Wish I knew."

Now, this situation offers a splendid opportunity for the favorite employment of the amateur in any field—namely, expert-baiting. Having been myself sometimes taken for an expert in fields far removed from the present, I know a great deal about the subject and how the occasions arise. To begin with, all laymen are stubbornly incurious about the thousand and one things you could tell them. All that is pedantry and they are bored. "Who cares?" is their chronic attitude. And then one morning the telephone rings and a voice introduces itself by saying "I have been told that you are an expert on. . . ."

This statement is made in a voice which plainly implies that the speaker believes himself to have been imposed upon by an unjustified reputation, and the form of the introductory remark is intended not to compliment you by acknowledging your expertness but to make sure of one thing. If you *can* answer the question, it is little to your credit since you pose as an expert and ought to know what is being asked even if you don't know anything else. If you cannot answer promptly, positively, and fully, then you ought to be ashamed of yourself since you are obviously a fraud. "Did they, in the eighteenth century, have an intermission between each of the conventional five acts of a play?" "What was the color of Dr. Johnson's eyes?"

To the first of these questions I think I have found the answer. Nobody—I think—knows the answer to the second, for Johnson squinted, and the best portraits are rather noncommittal. But I have been compelled often enough to disappoint the eager inquirer not to suppose that any biologist ought to feel disgraced because he does not know how a Sonoran spadefoot spends his time. There are so many things that might be known about the hundreds of thousands of creatures sharing this earth with us. And biologists are not exempt from the truth that life is short.

There is a tale, long current in academic circles, about an indolent student who took a course in "The Bible" because it was reported to be a cinch. He attended class infrequently and because he had been told that the only question ever asked on the final examination was "Give a list of the kings of Israel" he spent a night with a towel wrapped around his head learning the list. Next day he was outraged to be faced with only a single sentence on the blackboard. "Criticize the acts of Moses." Not one act could he remember, good, bad, or indifferent. And so, after due thought, he wrote: "Far be it from me, humble as I am, to criticize the acts of the great Moses. But if you would like a list of the kings of Israel *with their dates*, it follows." Not infrequently, I have met that sort of response from experts. Not less frequently, I myself have given it.

But if one *were* going to bait the biologists (which of course I am not), the line of attack would go something like this: Biologists spend too much time in laboratories—which is a highly reputable occupation —and too little observing creatures who are not specimens but free citizens of their own world. The odor which clings to these scientists is too seldom that of the open air, too often that biologist's odor of sanctity, formaldehyde. They learn an enormous number of the things which can be learned in a laboratory, especially the things which can be learned by dissecting preserved corpses, but comparatively few of the things which it would take a much longer time to find out in the field.

If, for example, you should want to know just what is the difference between a toad and a frog and if, perhaps, you have some vague sort of idea that one spends more time in the water than the other, or that toads are the kind that have (and give) warts, you will promptly be set right. "A toad is a tailless amphibian having a divided sternum, the cartilaginous element of one side overlapping the other; a frog is a tailless amphibian whose sternum is otherwise." Better yet, if all you want is a name, you will either get it or (most improbably unless you have been traveling in some very remote place) you will become famous in very limited circles as the discoverer of a new species, which may even be called Somethingorother smithii after you. But if you want to know more than a name, you may very easily run into difficulty. There are thousands of creatures, some of them quite common in well-frequented places, which are *Nomen et praeterea nihil.*

Names are important, of course, and it is worth while to make a good deal of fuss over them because otherwise two observers would not know whether or not they were talking about the same creature, and endless confusion would result. But it is a great pity that all information—and, too often, all curiosity—should stop with what is really only a preparation for learning something. Any biologist whose field of interest includes the amphibia would recognize my toad at a glance. Even a rank amateur like myself can, thanks to the care with which keys to the species have been worked out, find his name without difficulty. He is even rather readily distinguished from a very similar species common in the same region and called *Scaphiopus hammondii.* But very little is known about the lives of either one of them.

At least since the time of Thoreau, amateurs of natural history have been grumbling about this state of affairs. Thoreau himself, when he got hold of a large and costly monograph on the turtle, was outraged to find that in the whole volume not one word was said about how any turtle conducted his life. Since Thoreau's time, a great deal has been discovered and published concerning the sort of thing which he wanted to know about his fellow creatures. But a century after my time others will probably be complaining, as I am now complaining (mildly) a century after Thoreau's.

That is partly because the distinguishing of species is a relatively easy as well as a rather gratifyingly esoteric business. Any young beginner in academic circles who demonstrates to his colleagues that the members of an accepted species can be divided into two slightly different species gets a very conspicuous good mark against his name. In many cases he even helps along a colleague who, a decade later, will again reduce the two species to one, and get an equally good mark against his. Usually, when further study of a carefully named creature is taken up, the next thing to be investigated is the details of his anatomy—simply because that also can be done in a laboratory and from thoroughly dead specimens. Moreover, since most college teachers have been trained in this sort of thing, the introductory college course almost invariably begins not with the observation of some living creature—and it is certainly only because they were once alive that the dead ones are interesting—but with the dissection of a preserved but still smelly earthworm or frog. It is as though the subject of the course were not, as the catalogues maintain, *biology* but rather *thanatology* instead.

Since I am, by trade, a Professor myself, it hardly becomes me to indulge in contemptuous remarks about "the professors," but a certain amount of it is almost obligatory in a book of this sort. Having discharged the obligation, I shall conclude with one concession and one admission. The concession is that the most important reason why there are so many gaps in the available life histories of even the commoner animals is less the perversity of professors than the fact that there are an awful lot of these common creatures and that actually to follow their lives from day to day is a very difficult, time-consuming task. The admission is that, despite my special interest, the definitive monograph on the life history of *Scaphiopus couchii* will not be written by me.

Certain face-saving things I have, however, undertaken to do. Before disappearing among the bound volumes of *Copeia* and the other technical journals in the library of the University of Arizona, I rescued about a score of the tadpoles from the pool to which a careless Mother Nature had unkindly consigned them. Only later did I discover that in Wright and Wright these tadpoles are said to be, unlike other tadpoles of my acquaintance, carnivorous. Perhaps by preference they are. But mine got such green algae as I could lay hands on, plus wheat germ, now so favorably known as a health food. They ate both eagerly, and they not only thrived but beat by four days an official record—transforming themselves into toads in eleven instead of the official minimum of fifteen days.

The first signs of leg buds had appeared in seven days. Forty-eight hours later these legs were functioning, and two days after that the toads left the water. This all but incredible speed of transformation, so fast indeed that one could all but see the body completely reshaping itself while, in the little insides, the vital organs were at the same time changing over from a water- to an air-breathing mechanism, is obviously the explanation of a part of the mystery. These toads can

breed in the desert because instead of requiring water, as most frog
and toad tadpoles do, for a period running from three months to two
years, they require it for only the short time that at least some rain
pools must last.

Mine climbed out of the water into which I had put them, still
carrying behind them tails of scarcely reduced size. In the course of
twenty-four hours these tails shrank to stubs, like the tail remnant of
a fox-terrier, and only rarely, perhaps only by accident, did the toads
ever get back even briefly into the water I kept available. Yet, rapid
as the transformation was it was not rapid enough to permit the survival of those I had left where nature put them. *Scaphiopus couchii*
doesn't ask for much. But like exceptionally modest men, he sometimes doesn't get even the little he thinks he could do with.

The technical journals didn't yield much. Seven or eight years ago,
a biologist living in Tucson had noted the sudden appearance and
sudden disappearance of my friend the Sonoran spadefoot fifteen or
twenty miles from where I observed him—about two weeks earlier in
the season and under almost exactly the same conditions. But he did
not raise any tadpoles and I have no local check on the time I established for transformation. Most of the other references were from
somewhat less arid parts of *Scaphiopus*' range and they offered little
more than guesses that he breeds but once a year—in midsummer—
and that he spends most of the rest of his time buried in the sand.

The only biologist whom I could find sweating out the Summer
Session at the University was a specialist in fishes to whom frogs were
a matter of considerable indifference. He gave me the address of Dr.
Hock, the faculty member who would know most about the subject
but who had gone to Alaska—not, as I supposed, merely to get away
from frogs for a while but, as it turned out, to become director of a
health research center. In any event, I brashly wrote him by air mail,
got back a generous letter which had evidently cost him some time,
and also the advice to wait for Dr. Lowe, the new herpetologist who
was to take his place at the University.

Dr. Lowe greeted me more cordially than, I'm afraid, I always greet
those who come to my office in New York to ask whether or not it is
all right for them to say "It is me" when answering an intimate friend.
He told me some things, politely wished he knew the answers to some
other questions, and expressed some interest in my observations on
my spadefoot pets. There is even the dizzy possibility that with per-
sistence, luck, and Dr. Lowe's advice, I might some day get five or six

lines in *Copeia*. Anyone who has had the experience knows that there is nothing so gratifying as the tiniest recognition outside one's own field. Perhaps, even, I may be able to experience again something like one of the proudest moments of my life. It occurred fifteen years or more ago when a gentleman to whom I was being introduced asked me if I was, by any chance, the person of my name who had written, a year or two previously, an article in *Aquatic Life* with the title "A Successful Caesarian Operation on a Guppy."

Meanwhile the toadlets to whom I, not nature, played the tender mother have been leading artificial but perhaps not unpleasant lives. In the rough world they would, I presume, have been compelled before now to take refuge underground, at least from time to time. But since I did not know just how soon they would be prepared to endure such desiccation and since I was anxious not to lose them, they have been protected against all rigors. The sand on the bottom of the box to which they have been confined has been slightly sprinkled daily. Theirs is a world where it showers pleasantly every afternoon and where food appears at regular intervals rather than when some luckless bug happens to wander by. They have been given such small insects as I could find, plus bits of meat—waved in front of them on the end of a toothpick—which the more up-and-coming have learned to take, though the stubborner or the stupider will have none of it. They have grown prodigiously and it is worth noting just how high the percentage of viability is under favorable conditions. Of the seventeen original tadpoles, not one failed to become a toad. Of the four toads I kept, only one failed to survive for at least the two months I tended them all in their box. Obviously, were nature as kind as I, the earth would soon be knee-deep in toads.

Most of them I released to make their own way in the world, taking care only to place them in what looked to me like a good place for creatures of their kind. I have decided to keep indefinitely only one— partly to reduce the trouble of feeding, partly because he or she is to change his status from that of a specimen to that of a pet and it is a bad plan to spread affection too thin. I have bestowed a name—Ina, in honor of the road near which the original puddle collected—and thus I have determined that, whatever anatomy may say, my toad is, by human convention, a she.

All her brothers and sisters had the habit of digging little resting pits for themselves in the damp sand, and once or twice an individual buried himself completely. After their numbers had been reduced, a favorite refuge for those who remained was the narrow crevice between the sand and the edge of a water saucer in which they exhibited otherwise little interest. The daily shower usually brought them out, but most of the time they just sat.

At the present moment, Ina is, as usual, resting—though I don't know from what—in a little cup which her body exactly fits. Her body long ago assumed perfectly the shape of a toad, which is a shape not without dignity and charm if one is broad-minded enough to accept it. She measures well over an inch from the tip of her nose to the place where her tail would be had she cared to keep it. And since the tadpole from which she developed was only one-fifth of an inch, exclusive of tail, I calculate that she has increased her weight one hundred and twenty-five fold; which is as though a human baby were to reach eight hundred pounds in a similar period.

Last night she had raw spareribs for dinner and seemed to find it a tasty dish. But of course I don't know what effect an unusual and probably unusually plentiful diet, as well as other artificial conditions, have had upon her growth. Indeed, I know very little about what her history would have been had she been leading the normal life of her species. And that, of course, is the trouble with laboratory specimens, to say nothing of pets like Ina.

Had I so much as aspired clumsily to science, I should have divided my seventeen baby toads into groups, tried to find out how soon each could endure a given degree of desiccation, what they would do if food was denied them, etc., etc. Even then, to be sure, it would still have been no satisfactory substitute for an attempt to live with the toads in the field, at least as far as that is humanly possible. Going to an opposite extreme, I made a pet of Ina; I am probably oversolicitous of her comfort; and letting science go hang, I grumble mildly at "the professors" for not having found out for me what I am not taking the trouble to learn even as well as I might.

For all I know, Ina may not like the pampering she gets. I can hardly believe that she objects to confinement, for she seldom moves over the fairly generous space allotted her. But perhaps she objects to being kept so continuously warm, damp, and therefore awake. Perhaps she is sleepy; perhaps she is longing to cover her head and sink into some sort of passivity, by comparison with which the four or five hops a day which at present she takes are frenetic. Perhaps she is sick of the sight of food and wishes it were not dangled so frequently before her eyes in such a way as to make it impossible for her to inhibit the reflex which forces her to dart forth a tongue to take it. For all I know, I may be making a Strasbourg goose out of my toad.

In all fairness to myself I must say that she does not look unhappy, only—like all the toad kind—serious, introverted, plunged into Buddhistic meditation. And whether she is happy or not, the details, at least, of the mystery of the desert spadefoots are as mysterious as ever. What on earth do they do with themselves during that nearly year-long period when they seldom, if ever, leave their burrows? Dr. Lowe thinks they may leave them for short periods to feed. He is sure that they are not in that state of suspended animation which the layman thinks of when he hears the word "hibernation." Toads and frogs, he tells me, are always as much alive as the temperature which their bodies have taken on from their surroundings permits. But what a life the Sonoran spadefoot's must be! What does he *do*, buried in the sand for perhaps four-fifths of his time, even allowing for the supposition that he does venture forth to eat?

Gilbert White made famous the ancient tortoise in his garden who spent in naps most of the time he was not officially sleeping his winter sleep. It was, White thought, an odd whim on the part of God to bestow so long a life on a creature who seemed to care so little for it. But the case of the Sonoran spadefoot seems at least as remarkable. Many creatures hibernate and not a few estivate; but he is the only one of my acquaintance who does both, and his condition calls to mind that of the hillbilly of legend who suffered from insomnia. "I sleep fine nights; I sleep pretty well mornings; but in the afternoon I gets kinda restless." Yet on that rainy night when he did wake up, the spadefoot seemed very wide awake indeed.

I sincerely hope that in his underground cell he suffers no touch of claustrophobia. Perhaps this is Hamlet's nutshell and perhaps my toad feels himself, as Hamlet thought he would feel, "king of infinite space." I hope that it is not for him only one long morning-after, spent in recovering from his one big night; and if he meditates, I hope it is not exclusively and liquorishly of some July eleventh, or twelfth, or thirteenth.

Few creatures, surely, have ever been assigned by nature to a life more suited to contemplation. Spadefoots can have little experience of the outside world and hence little material on which to base any conclusions concerning nature or society. But there are subjects for which no experience is necessary. Some think that music, at least in its purely formal as opposed to its expressive aspects, is one. Less disputably, mathematics requires no experience of the world. Presumably a prisoner brought up in solitary confinement all his life might have developed the Pythagorean theorem or even invented Cartesian geometry. If the spadefoots are as thoughtful as they look, they must be engaged with some great abstract question to the pondering of which solitude and immobility are conducive. Perhaps it is something like the possible reconciliation of fate with free will. Or perhaps it is the real significance of the square root of minus one.

I rather hope it is the last, for I have never been satisfied that the practical use of the symbol for it as a direction indicator is the real, or at least the only logical, meaning. Someday, after Ina has had a little more time to think, I am going to whisper suddenly in her ear "Complex variable!" The experiment will be as sensible as some I have read about.

MACHARIA THE MAMBA-CATCHER

by Arthur Loveridge

Although Arthur Loveridge was a British soldier in Africa all through the four years of World War I, he never ceased being a naturalist during the same period, a situation that often disturbed his tentmates and superior officers. He was born in Penarth, South Wales, May 28, 1891, and educated at the University of South Wales. He loved the outdoors and was particularly interested in reptiles, wherefor he decided to make a career of it if he could. By the time he was twenty-three he had found his way to Africa and was the curator of the Natural History Museum in Nairobi in the Kenya colony. He was just settling himself in this position, which was much to his liking, when World War I broke out in August, 1914, and young Loveridge joined up for the duration. He returned to his museum work after the war and remained there for several years. In 1921 he took a job as game warden in Tanganyika Territory and worked over that region for two years. In 1924 he came to the United States to join the scientific staff at Harvard, where he continued as Curator of the Museum of Comparative Zoology until his retirement in 1957. His books on his African adventures include I Drank the Zambesi, Tomorrow's a Holiday, *and* Many Happy Days I've Squandered, *from which the following is an extract and a fair sample of its most amusing and informative content.*

WITH the removal of General Collier's headquarters from Morogoro, for a time I was attached to the 15th Stationary Hospital, in charge of their native personnel which numbered two hundred or more. I had my own quarters, tent, telephone, and personal servant. My attempts to locate the Nyamwezi, Macharia by name, who had caught the pickled snakes I had just salvaged, seemed likely to be successful for I had enlisted the sympathies of the local chief—Kingo Morogoro as he was called—in the search.

A week or so later, while walking along the river bank, I heard a cry of *"Bwana Nyoka"* and, turning, saw an elderly native being dragged along by half a dozen excited youngsters who were clinging to him. On coming up to me the man explained in the most diffident manner that he had heard that I wanted him; that Kingo Morogoro had told him to come and see me, for he was the man who had collected the snakes for the German who formerly lived near there. He lacked a finger; it had been bitten by a puff adder, he said, and his former employer, in an excess of zeal, had chopped the digit off. Macharia maintained that he would have been all right without the operation, claiming that he was immune to snake bite. He appeared quite consoled for the loss of the finger by the forty rupees which he was given in compensation.

He explained that he was in the employ of the railway, then under military administration, so I accompanied him to the station master and made arrangements for his discharge, so that I might engage him. Telling me that snakes were not to be caught every day, he said that he would like to live at home and work on his land and he would come in once a week with his catch, for which I should pay him on a commission basis.

His tribe, the Nyamwezi, inhabit the Tabora District, but, being great travelers, they are to be met with everywhere. Macharia undoubtedly belonged to that subsection of the tribe known as Yeye who are snake charmers, magicians, and tricksters who ply their trade throughout the Territory. Some district officers discourage them from settling in their districts because of their alleged duping of less sophisticated peoples. Not all are rogues, however, and Macharia served me faithfully.

He was one of the most picturesque natives I have ever seen. He wore a slouch hat adorned with an ostrich feather which he removed with a graceful sweep when addressing a *mzungu* (European). He had a kindly old face and was very popular with the children. After we had arranged matters with the station master, Macharia departed to his hut to fetch a snake. In the late afternoon he turned up at the camp with the reptile tied up in a dirty scrap of cloth. It was a large spitting cobra.

I put it in an improvised cage, but, unlike the other cobras which I had caught myself, it never fed. It seemed dispirited for a freshly caught snake so, after keeping it for a couple of weeks, I chloroformed it. Then I discovered that in three places its lips were neatly sewn together *inside*; looking at its closed mouth there was no indication of this. When the old rascal returned, I scolded him roundly for his cruelty; in self-defense he explained that when he brought the cobra he did not know whether I was to be trusted with a poisonous snake. Not having seen my snakes at that time, he feared that he would be held responsible if an accident occurred. Assuring me that his present catch had not been tampered with, he opened the bolster case which I had given him, peered in as he shuggled it, then thrust in a hand and drew out an eight-foot mamba. There were cobras, puff adders, and many smaller fry in that bag. Shortly afterwards he brought me a second mamba slightly over seven feet long. I kept the two of them in a glass-fronted tin-lined Huntley and Palmer biscuit box measuring approximately 1½ by 1¼ by 2 feet—one of eight that I had wangled from the Y.M.C.A. canteen. Despite such cramped quarters these mambas fed well and displayed great activity, striking at the glass whenever anyone approached. Possibly realizing the futility of this procedure, which only gave them sore snouts, they eventually abandoned it, but for a couple of months they continued to draw themselves up and menace the visitor with widely open jaws. I cannot recall having seen any other species adopt this attitude. After a time they ceased even to threaten, but till the last they continued to follow every movement of the onlooker with bright eyes and quick turns of the head.

These mambas were of the common savanna species (*Dendroaspis angusticeps*) which enjoys a wide distribution in the east from Ethiopia to Natal. Variously called "green mamba" and "black mamba," it is in reality a single species, being a lovely vivid green when hatched, but darkening to olive as it grows larger. I have never seen a green one over six feet long though I believe they have been recorded up to eight feet; so-called "black" mambas, on the other hand, are rarely found under eight feet and are said to attain a length of fourteen feet. Darkening of the pigmentation is accompanied by a change in environment, for with increase in size the mamba is inclined to leave its arboreal habitat for a terrestrial one where it stands a better chance of securing bigger prey. In build and speed the *kiboko*, as the Yeye call the mamba, resembles a North American whip snake. Strangely enough, *kiboko* is Swahili for a whip made of hippopotamus hide as well as for the hippopotamus itself; the Swahili themselves call the mamba *fune*.

Major Horne, then political officer at Morogoro, told me how he and another European had entered a *banda* and found it apparently empty. Horne left, and was being followed by his companion when a mamba which they had not seen in the gloomy interior struck this man in the back just above the kidneys. Though everything possible was done, the victim died twenty-four hours later.

One of my comrades in the East African Mounted Rifles related how he had called on a fellow planter and the two of them sat chatting at one end of the veranda while the planter's servant prepared tea. As the boy, carrying a tray, came up the veranda steps he gave a cry, took a few steps, dropped the tray, and pitched forward. The startled Rhodesians sprang to their feet and hurried to the lad but he expired within a minute. Occupied with the tray, he had failed to see a mamba stretched upon the steps enjoying the late afternoon sun. Apparently the snake's fangs had penetrated a vein since it is unusual for even the virulent poison of a mamba to act so quickly.

My two mambas met a purely accidental end. It was my custom to take them from their cage once a fortnight in order that it might be cleaned. Their removal was accomplished by opening the sliding glass pane an inch and pinning down the head of the nearer snake with a straight stick, usually an ordinary flat foot rule. As it was strong enough to throw this off, the snake had to be seized and withdrawn immediately; any attempt on the part of its companion to follow it through the open door was frustrated by simply menacing it through the glass with my free hand upraised; this was sufficient to cause it to draw back its head on the defensive in readiness to strike. Once, when I had taken the larger one out and was holding it firmly by the neck between a finger and thumb of my left hand, it threw such strong coils round my arm that I felt a numbness creeping into my fingers, and it was all that I could do to retain my grip while my boy unwound the coils. On the last occasion, while their cage was being cleaned, I had transferred them to another tin-lined box which happened to be exposed to the late afternoon sun. Just as this was accomplished, a friend unexpectedly called and we withdrew for tea; on returning an hour later I found the reptiles dead. Undoubtedly they had succumbed to the heat of the sun; had there been water in the box so as to create a moist atmosphere, in all probability they would have survived. Only that morning one of them had eaten two full-grown black rats and now measured six and a quarter inches round the stomach. When I opened this snake I found that the fur and some of the flesh of one rat (*Rattus rattus kijabius*) swallowed only eight hours previously had been digested already.

The python which so intrigued Dinkie [a tame monkey] had been brought to me by Macharia. To accommodate it I tore down an abandoned chicken run and rebuilt it between my tent and *banda*. On completion the cage measured 12 feet by 6 feet by 6 feet, and in its center I sunk a cracked iron caldron discarded by the Germans. Its being cracked was of no consequence for I diverted a little stream to it; thus the huge caldron was always full and overflowing, making it possible for the python to have a bath whenever it chose.

Despite such consideration the snake was not content, for with a thirty-pound push it forced a weak spot in the wire netting and absconded one night. A broad track in the dust led right past my tent door and down through the camp where three hundred natives were sleeping. One old man admitted having seen it about midnight but hurried back to bed, "for I thought," he said, "that it was a Swahili." The idea that the souls of outstanding chiefs or other distinguished people enter into the bodies of snakes is a belief common to a number of tribes.

Nearly a week later, at eight o'clock in the morning, there were cries of "*nyoka*" (snake), and presently a boy came running to say that a big snake had been found in the bush near the police askari's village about three hundred yards from my tent. As my snake stick had been broken the previous evening and had to be repaired, and as my boot lace broke, as boot laces invariably do in an emergency, ten minutes elapsed before we reached the spot, where I soon recognized my deserter lying beneath a heap of brushwood alongside a fallen tree in fairly dense bush. A native woman was hopping about like a restless sparrow on the trunk of the tree and shouting information to three others who had withdrawn to what they considered a reasonable distance. All were armed with *pangas* with which they had been lopping off the branches of the fallen giant when they had discovered the python. Despite the fact that the woman was shrieking information about it back to the village in answer to a hail of questions, the reptile remained motionless; it did not even stir when Salimu lifted off the brambles and thorn bush immediately above it. As I advanced my

hand to seize it, it lunged at me with open jaws, not necessarily with
the intention of biting, but rather to intimidate after the manner of
a dog showing its teeth and growling. Almost simultaneously it commenced sliding backwards, but this was circumvented by placing my
boot lightly on its neck, which I then grasped with both hands. For
a few minutes a tussle ensued and I had to exert considerable strength
before I could get it clear of the brushwood and push it into the sack
being held by the faithful Salimu. When we reached camp and tipped
it out into its cage, it flew open-mouthed at the wire netting, striking
it forcibly several times and causing considerable consternation among
the front row of natives who had come up from the camp and were
jostling each other to catch a glimpse of the big snake.

Eight days later I was roused shortly after midnight by the voice of
an orderly politely inquiring if I wanted "a fine big snake." Indeed I
did, so I hastily put on socks and slippers and accompanied him, re-
marking as we hurried up the road that it would be a fine thing for my
python to have a companion. Our destination was the mess marquee
in the officers' wards of the 15th Stationary Hospital. It was only a
couple of hundred yards from my quarters and on the way the orderly
invited my attention to a broad track in the dust. Then for the first
time it occurred to me that my quarry might be my own restless pet
strayed from home. As we entered the marquee our only illumination
was the rather feeble light shed by the hurricane lantern carried by my
companion, but it was sufficient to reveal a python lying beneath the
table. Naturally enough, being a nocturnal species, it was more lively
than by day and struck twice at me with gaping jaws, then began
to retire as I approached. Making a detour of the table I had just
grabbed it by the neck when the orderly, in answer to a call, started off
with the lantern; recollecting himself as I shouted, he left it in the
doorway. For fully two minutes I struggled with the creature, slipping
its coils off my arm before it could tighten them. Having my foot
on its tail gave me an advantage, and as soon as I got its head into a
sack there was no further trouble. As a general rule, when once shown
the way, a python will readily slide into the darkness and fancied
security of a sack.

For a month after this it spent the nights roaming round its cage,
running its snout up and down the netting in search of an exit. This
made its jaws sore and a fungoid growth appeared on the raw place. To
remedy this I bathed the sore spot with a concentrated boric solution,
then put three dead rats into its mouth; it swallowed them somewhat

reluctantly. These rats were the only food it took, so far as I knew, between September 12 and November 27, when it cast its "skin" and came forth resplendent in a new and iridescent garment. The sore was also healed. In such a condition the African rock python (*Python sebae*) is a handsome creature, with the arrowhead on the crown linked to the striped tail by a chain of rich brown blotches, each blotch set off from the paler ground color by its deep black edging. Naturally there is a good deal of variation according to habitat, and the snake-loving Yeye profess to divide these pythons into three "species." They employ the Swahili name *satu* for full-grown snakes which they regard as a bush-dwelling form. Pythons ranging from nine to eighteen feet which have a light spot on the head are called *sawaka*, and young or brightly colored pythons are referred to as *dilemma*; both the latter are believed to favor a waterside habitat.

Shortly after shedding, my python caught and ate a newly fledged goshawk and kingfisher which I had thought might safely share its cage. A few days later I tossed a dead fowl into the cage; this was followed by a dead rat and two headless, wingless, tailless blue rollers (*Coracias garrulus garrulus*) that were smelling badly. The snake swallowed all, quite an achievement in domestication for a creature used to catching live prey. Blue rollers are slightly similar to blue jays with which they are often confused. Almost two weeks later the python further distinguished itself by accepting not only a dead and wingless fruit pigeon but the skinned body of a cattle egret. Having got the body crosswise in its mouth, it was in great difficulties, but when I took hold of its neck the python gaped and dropped the food with ease. Then it took up the body again, this time lengthwise so that it was swallowed without further trouble. The reptile was certainly becoming civilized when it was willing to take not only dead but skinned food. During January it swallowed eleven fowls, two ducks, and a white-breasted raven which was approximately the size of the European raven. Previously it had consistently refused crows, I suppose on account of their large beaks. Fortified by such fine fare it broke out of its cage in March and I never saw it again, for I left shortly afterwards.

One evening Macharia turned up with three more pythons measuring approximately four, six, and eight feet in length. It was too late to find suitable quarters for them that night so I returned them to their sack and put it under my bed. That evening, as I was reading in bed beneath the security of my mosquito bar, a couple of officers dropped in to see my snakes. Finding that I had already retired, they volunteered to return next day. I agreed that this would be better as most of the occupants of my cages were diurnal species which could not be seen to advantage by lamplight. Then I invited them in and sat on the edge of my camp bed while we talked snakes for some time. When the conversation drifted to pythons, I pulled the sack between my legs and, untying the cord which closed it, drew forth a few feet of snake for their inspection. Omitting to fasten the sack, I pushed it back beneath the bed with my heel, intending to tie it afterwards; but when they left half an hour later I ducked under the mosquito curtain and was soon fast asleep. Next morning I was aroused at daybreak by the exclamations of my servant, who was standing, tea tray in hand, at the entrance to my tent, ejaculating at the numerous snake tracks in the dust about the tent door. Even then it did not dawn on me immediately what had happened till, springing from bed, I drew out the limp sack. The three pythons had departed; two of them I never saw again.

Some weeks later I was summoned to catch a snake in a most unusual situation. Two soldiers had been detailed to unpack a crate containing a stove newly arrived from England. They got something of a shock when, in response to their hammering, two feet of snake came sliding out from one of the circular holes on which pots and pans were destined to be placed. The hammering ceased abruptly; the snake retired within the stove to finish its siesta; and one of the men kept watch while his companion came in search of me. On arrival I fished the reptile out with little trouble. It was a handsome six-foot python which had probably entered the building in search of rats; quite probably too it was one of those which had escaped from beneath my bed a month or so before.

SMOKE FROM A VALLEY CABIN

by Brooks Atkinson

There is more than a gentle touch of Thoreau in the output of Brooks Atkinson on Nature. There should be. Born in Melrose, Massachusetts, November 28, 1894, and legally named Justin Brooks Atkinson, the future drama critic of the New York Times *grew up in New England with a fondness for Nature and an admiration for Thoreau that have increased with the years. He wrote a book titled* Henry Thoreau, the Cosmic Yankee. *He edited an anthology of selected writings from Thoreau's books and journals. He has a farm in Greene County, New York, to which he betakes himself whenever he has leave of absence from his duty as drama critic of Broadway productions. He looks on Nature with a reflective eye, as Thoreau did. And further like Thoreau, he often pens a pithy sentence laden with dry New England humor. His books on Nature include* Skyline Promenades, Once Around the Sun *and* East of the Hudson, *from which this selection has been taken. The compiler of this volume must confess an honest belief that nobody today writes better English than Brooks Atkinson, whether it's on Nature, the drama, or any other topic. There must be further admitted a deep affection for him as an old friend and field companion on many a wintry sortie to wild places.*

ALTHOUGH I had rented the cabin up-river as a place merely to visit occasionally in the winter I was astonished to find how soon it began to assert authority of its own. Within a month it reduced me from master to student. Each time I visited it I found myself busier than before in accounting for all the changes in the landscape.

Nature, no doubt, was pretty; but I revelled most in its relentless progress through the seasons,—its complete mastery over the landscape and its infectious vitality. Autumn foliage and morning frosts, winter snows and ice storms, the deep life of the early spring, put summer in its true perspective as a pleasant interlude in the rugged cycle of the year. In a sense I had to unlearn everything I had learned during the preceding week before I could hear the elemental vibrations of the earth, like the huge bass pipes—the "roarers"—of an organ. Nature commanded everything that I was. In fact, it was not sufficiently related to my civil life to be even an expedient contrast; and the most lucid phrases of civil writing could not begin to express it. My week-ends, designed for recreation, became quite as serious as that.

Four miles from the railroad and the main thoroughfare, the cabin appeared to be as remote from New York as the Catskills or the Adirondacks. As a matter of fact, it was about two hours journey from my apartment—fifty miles up the west bank of the Hudson River by railroad to Bear Mountain Station, in the Palisades Inter-State Park, and then four miles by auto to the backlands of the river hills. In the summer a vast horde of city vacationists swarmed through these woods, picnicked everywhere and bumped row-boats excitedly in Queensboro Lake. In the winter, visitors were less common than the birds. No one ever climbed those hills or patrolled the thick woods north of the water.

The cabin was set in a cleared field beside the brook, a one-room peak-roofed, shingled building with a tiny kitchen ell, plain and rather squalid. On all four sides rose modest hills, mountainous in contour and proportion. To the northeast a rambling lake in the rough shape of a cross lapped at the edge of rolling woods. A patch of hemlocks a few rods up the brook made grateful contrast with the prevailing hardwood trees and attracted a special group of the winter birds. What I enjoyed most was the variety of uninhabited country in all directions and my proximity to the out of doors even when I was inside. Rabbits, squirrels, chipmunks, woodchucks, muskrats, phlegmatic skunks and an occasional deer wandered through the valley, sometimes timidly up to the kitchen door in search of scraps. Two colonies of beaver, introduced several years before, lived in houses in the lake. And only a reluctance to believe the improbable kept me from publishing one series of broad, flat, heavy footprints in the snow as the tracks of Bruin. According to a newspaper item, dated several days later, three bears had recently escaped from a neighboring park. Had one of them lumbered through the woods near camp? I liked to think that he had. It was no time of year for a bear to be roaming the frozen countryside, but it seemed like a neighborly thing for him to do.

The Heating Problem

I shall not pretend that I did not have moments when I doubted the wisdom of my enterprise. As I came up to it from the station on Saturday afternoons, the cabin was far from inviting with its cold chimney and firmly bolted shutters, particularly in the dead of winter. When I unlocked the door and entered the dark, silent, stone-cold living room, dropping my pack in the corner, I felt more like an intruder than a guest. I felt lonely. The prospect of a week-end there became suddenly forbidding. But there was no time to squander on drooping spirits. After flinging back the shutters to let in the sunshine I kindled fires on the hearth and in the kitchen stove, chopped a hole in the brook-ice for drinking water, set out the provisions and busily divided the next hour between cooking luncheon and piling dry logs on the fire. Gradually I retrieved the cabin from a sort of bleak indifference. During luncheon the roaring fire steadily drove the cold across the room and fairly scorched me with hospitality; and I expanded slowly like the field-stone chimney. Demoralized by the heat, a mug of tea, a pipe and a comfortable chair, I became as pleasantly torpid as a woodchuck in his hole. My phlegmatic mind could no longer retain the frenzied image of Times Square where I had been two hours before. As much as it was lost to me, I was lost to it; and we both went about our immediate affairs independently.

In Honor of a Shingled Hut

As a city-dweller I had hoped to surprise Nature in her fleeting glories by living close to them on week-ends. Being a part of Nature, the cabin set all those beauties before me, and I soon became sentimentally attached to it. Like the elms in the valley, it humbly bore the rain and the snow, it reflected the daylight and it cast a creeping shadow as the sun moved across the sky. I knew every caprice of the out of doors the instant it happened, for my winter retreat caught the natural impulse at once. Sometimes I knew without stirring from the fireside; the patter of rain, the gentle brush of snow, the uncanny howl of the North wind, the cracking of shingles on a cold night, needed

no investigation. Sometimes I heard the muffled boom of the frozen
lake as it wrestled with the warmth or cold—a deep-toned gong in the
moonlight. When the fox sparrows began to sing in March I had only
to open the door cautiously and listen to the Pan-pipe of the spring.
I kept tabs on the season by regular expeditions to the lake across
certain fields, through variegated woods, along the brook, over Round
Hill, through an apple orchard. On each visit I relished what I saw,
not only for its own beauty, but for its comparison with my last visit.
These weekly changes in the fabric of Nature were the imponderable
mysteries. Thus by May I had stolen time to see the leaves drop and
the new ones expand, the ice form, thicken, and disappear; and nearly
all the birds I had seen migrating South in the autumn I greeted upon
their return in the spring. I saw a November frost before sunrise, a
magnificent spectacle; I was treated to a long snow storm in February,
white and untrammeled to the horizon; and I was outdoors in April
to hear the new birds salute the dawn. In December I saw icy ledges
on Bear Mountain gleaming like precious jewels in the moonlight. I
was always newly surprised by the brilliance of the universe at night.
I felt the warmth of the day and the chill of the night as quickly as
any part of the valley. For eight months I felt every turn of the season
in my bones or I sniffed it in the air. Indeed, it seemed to me that my
capacity for feeling increased tremendously with each visit, and that
nothing could happen outdoors without leaving, however faintly, its
impress on me.

Hearth and Stove

To write of my winter trips appreciatively, however, was to celebrate
the supernatural wonders of the hearth. The humble fires in my cabin
fairly dominated that corner of New York State with their beneficence
inside and their curls of smoke outside, beseeching the gods "to pardon my clear flame." Of the two fires the open hearth was the more
spectacular with its brave show of color and coals; but the ugly barrel
stove supplied the heat I needed and performed the major business of
civilization. Who loves the ugly duckling? I was fickle enough to condemn the stove to the base labors of cooking and to reserve my affection for the fireplace. What magic that open fire performed! When it
was new it crackled, smoked and blazed enthusiastically without softening the temperature of the cabin. But within an hour red embers
began to glow in sober, business-like fashion, and it settled the entire
day like the morning cup of coffee. It adorned everything. It trans-

muted this squalid cabin. It radiated cheer further than heat. I could scarcely keep my eyes from it long enough to read or to write at the table. I rushed to it as soon as I was up in the morning; I put off going to bed at night so that I might sit beside it longer, and I fed it once during the night, for it held vigil over me like a faithful dog. Part of the sensuous joy of night walking was the return to the fireside and the loosening of cold muscles warmed by the flames. But perhaps my most contented hours were in the early evening when I could sit in the firechair, writing notes of the day out of doors, and hear the kettles bubbling on the stove in the kitchen. All that was sufficient for companionship, for a general sense of well being. When a stray puff of wind came down the chimney and scattered the ashes I felt like one whom the gods had signally honored. All the world seemed designed for me.

The Rhythm of the Seasons

In stressing the importance of the seasons in this chronicle I mean to suggest what came to be the chief attraction of my cabin experiences. The seasons! If we could understand them, not scientifically but spiritually, if we knew why they come so silently and why they are so forceful, might we not analyze the essence of immortal life? Although we hastily regard them as a thing apart from ourselves, we are really united to them closely. Not merely because they bring the harvest upon which we depend, or because they fertilize the soil with falling leaves and store the mountains with the water we need in spring and summer; but because as natural beings we are drawn into their movement, emotionally and physically. Winter, spring, summer and autumn regulate our lives; willy-nilly, they govern our daily and yearly progress. We have not yet come so far from primeval nature that we can remain indifferent to them. After one or two preliminary visits to my cabin I became oriented in Nature and was chiefly absorbed in the rhythm of the seasons. And when I was happiest, I was feeling the touch of the season most keenly.

By good fortune I happened to be at the cabin on one perfect day in each season. Many days were indifferent to the season's splendor; they were too warm and sluggish in the autumn, or too crisp in the spring. But on the three ideal days of autumn, winter and spring I fancied that I reflected within myself the mood of the landscape and felt in my blood the throb of the universe.

Each season was bright with beauty. I felt no melancholy about the autumn. After the leaves had fallen, clean and crackling under foot, the woods were full of light, the views widened through bare branches, the evergreens bathed the eye more soothingly than ever and the structural design of the deciduous trees was revealed as perfect symmetry. Shorn of its summer verdure the shagbark cut against the sky like an etching; its sharp network of twigs and branches seemed acid-bitten. I felt that the season was not merely dying, but preparing its rebirth with submission and composure. The tree sparrows had come down from the north for their winter sojourn, apparently in the best of spirits. Fox sparrows and white-throated sparrows were scratching contentedly in the leaves. Pushing through the fields and woods and watching the birds everywhere, I found myself looking forward to the next seasons—anticipating the crystal beauties of the winter landscape and regarding the swamps in terms of the spring migration. As the old year faded the new year lay waiting the summons. Everywhere the beech-tips were rolled tightly, ready for the encouragement of warm sunshine. The same wind that whirled the dead leaves through the woods distributed the seeds in the fields. The roots of spring were deep in the autumn. November was courier of May. When I went out to the wood pile with a lantern after supper, the nipping air foretold, not so much the death of Nature, as the coming of a glorious season in which every field and hill would be newly transfigured. After this perfect autumn day I found myself instinctively facing forward, towards the new, not only confident but eager.

Winter at Zero

My emotions had not deceived me. The perfect week-end of the winter redeemed every promise. During the preceding night the thermometer had dropped below zero where it hung without much variation for two days. The morning was clear, crisp and invigorating. Although I kept the fire roaring in dangerous fury, the cabin was never actually warm. At the warmest time the surface of the bucket of water skimmed over. A patch of snow about seven feet from the fireplace never melted all the time I was there. But I was generally comfortable and I fancied myself extremely well sheltered.

The outdoors was glorious. Conscious of the tingling cold, I felt a kinship with everything—with the crusted snow, the sparkling ledges on Bear Mountain, the restless, hidden lake, the muffled brook flowing under huge covers of glittering ice. Every bird note sounded the universal theme. The hairy and downy woodpeckers, blue jays and chickadees seemed vividly alive. Chickadees scampered through the bare branches and followed me, *deeing* with curiosity and excitement, as I made the usual rounds. But the perfect expression of this dynamic season was the activity of a flock of rosy and gray birds in a hemlock tree beyond. I had heard their sweet call-note some distance away. All at once I saw them clinging to the cones, tearing out the seeds, swirling off for no accountable reason, round and round and back again—a whirligig of animation. Wanderers from the far north, they were white-winged crossbills whom I had seen once or twice in the mountains. Like true vagabonds they were enjoying themselves completely. I could never anticipate their next movement. One of them dropped to the brook and flew timidly over the black, turbulent water. Then others came down, one by one, splashes of warm color against the snow; and after a time the brookside became a carnival of chattering crossbills perching on the snow and ice and hovering over the water. Only two or three of them, it seemed to me, mustered up courage enough to dip. But they all took a fling at the sport. I stood in the snow, watching them, until my fingertips began to tingle. Then I raced back to the fireplace.

The moon was full that night. After supper I visited the lake and woods again, occasionally disturbing a rabbit in the thicket. The light was softer than by day and the woods were full of mysterious shadows lying gently on the snow. In general, the winter season was self-sufficient—a complete state, an entity. I could hardly remember when the lake was open. Winter dominated every sense; I could not add to it, take away from it or withhold myself. I could not play truant by dreaming of balmier days. Every sensation seemed complete and final, and beyond human equivocation.

When the Ice Broke Up

When spring came I was there to extend the official greeting of Queensboro Valley. For several days even the city had been softening unaccountably. When I reached the cabin at noontime the temperature was 50, the air warm, the haze gentle and pastel-colored; and the sun was gradually working out of the clouds and creating, single-handed, a fine spring afternoon. The brook, now almost free of ice, roared vigorously. Pussy willows enlivened the swampy woods. Everywhere there was the sweet content of natural release. While I was indoors, impatiently cooking lunch, I knew that the early birds would be back; and in my mind I checked off the most likely ones—song sparrows, red-winged blackbirds, robins, bluebirds and meadowlarks. After lunch I found chickadees, goldfinches and one song sparrow in the hemlock woods, but they were all wearing their winter manners. On the way to the lake I found song sparrows in every thicket. Finally I heard one singing—olit, olit, olit, chip, chip, chee, char, chewiss, wiss, wiss—the first spring serenade. Although at the same time I heard the red-winged blackbirds stuttering a few rods ahead, I was satisfied with the song sparrow completely as though the season had kept its vows to the letter and need offer no further proof of divine guidance. Suddenly the warm warble of a bluebird melted the air in the south. As I turned to look for him the air everywhere began to flow with the strains of bluebird melody, and presently fifteen or twenty birds fluttered into the north. They were gone before I could focus my glasses. If there had been anything tentative about the song sparrow, the bluebirds now clinched the season definitively. With their dancing, buoyant passage, spring flushed and expanded, as though they had sprinkled the air with a magic compound while they hurried along, liberating the country over which they flew. They were the appointed deliverers.

When I turned my back to the road I saw bluebirds everywhere. They had just arrived. Like returned vacationists they were examining every nook of the land—flying from twig to ground to telegraph wire to fence post in numbers hard to estimate. At last I saw a male spread his wings to reveal their loveliest color. At least for that moment he was the center of the universe. All along the road for a mile the soft air danced with their flecks of summer sky. They were not pagan birds; they were the distilled foam of heaven dripping from twig to grass, and as they sang the air quivered with sound. The miracle of spring was accomplished. Again I felt like one whom the gods had signally honored.

By Sunday morning, of course, the intensest excitement was over, and the bluebirds had enraptured the land. During breakfast I left the door open to hear their warble as they adorned the trees near the cabin. Other migrants had come in during the night. On the way to the lake I saw the robins and the meadowlarks. In an open bay, between margins of thin ice, six male American mergansers were courting two of their ladies. They dove bravely under cakes of ice, swam passionately here and there; and occasionally they half-rose from the water to reveal their enchanting salmon bellies. I enjoyed them. But the bluebirds had released the floods of spring with their "slant blue beams down the aisles of the woods" and I was thoroughly content in their company.

The Hounds of Spring

During the remaining week-ends of my tenancy, life streamed through my little valley in a mighty flood of rejoicing and expectation —of hopes born in the warm south and blown northward on the blossoms of the season. Although I had sworn to play no favorites, to study the texture of each season impartially and to transcribe its symbols without prejudice, I found myself dissolved by the spring. Now the green began to edge the woods with color, the violets, bloodroot, arbutus, and wild geranium sweetened the ground, and the birds went by in a mysterious wave of motion until every thicket, field and glade rang with song. Lounging on a hill behind the cabin one March evening I heard bluebirds, song sparrows, juncos, red-winged blackbirds, blue jays, crows, meadowlarks, and the fragile, luminous aria of the fox sparrow—all these songs simultaneously so that it was difficult to distinguish them as individual voices. Collectively they were the grand summons to spring like the ringing of many vesper bells in a mountain village. Long before our ancestors travelled this country, these birds made their way north each spring through this tiny valley in response to the mighty forces that governed them; and long after we are dead they will make the same journey each year and serenade the valley with the same purity. How do they know when to come or where to go? Why do they follow the same courses? None of us knows. But to quiet every worldly alarm it is sufficient to know that they do come. When the bluebird fails to leap out of the sky, when the bloodroot no longer pushes through the dead leaves, then it will be time to stitch up our ascension robes for immediate and serious action.

PHILOMELA

Hark! ah, the nightingale!
The tawny-throated!
Hark! from that moonlit cedar what a burst!
What triumph! hark,—what pain!
O wanderer from a Grecian shore,
Still—after many years, in distant lands—

Still nourishing in thy bewildered brain
That wild, unquenched, deep-sunken, Old-World pain,—
   Say, will it never heal?
And can this fragrant lawn,
With its cool trees, and night,
And the sweet, tranquil Thames,
And moonshine, and the dew,
To thy racked heart and brain
   Afford no balm?

   Dost thou to-night behold,
Here, through the moonlight on this English grass,
The unfriendly palace in the Thracian wild?
   Dost thou again peruse,
With hot cheeks and seared eyes,
The too clear web, and thy dumb sister's shame?
   Dost thou once more essay
Thy flight; and feel come over thee,
Poor fugitive! the feathery change;
Once more; and once more make resound,
With love and hate, triumph and agony,
Lone Daulis, and the high Cephisian vale?

Listen, Eugenia,—
How thick the bursts come crowding through the leaves!
Again—thou hearest!
Eternal passion!
Eternal pain!

                           MATTHEW ARNOLD

THE LONG SNOWFALL

by Rachel Carson

What amounted to a literary sensation in 1951 was the appearance in that suave, sophisticated and somewhat cynical magazine, The New Yorker, of chapter after chapter from a forthcoming book of deep scientific content. It was The Sea Around Us, offered in great chunks week after week to New Yorker subscribers and newsstand addicts. Probably it was the first time that many of those readers ever were exposed to such scientific fare, but events proved that the editors had well judged not only the worth of the book but also the taste of the literate public. The book became a "runaway best-seller," and Rachel Carson soared to fame almost overnight.

The author was born in Springdale, Pennsylvania, May 27, 1907, was graduated with a degree in zoology from Pennsylvania College for Women, put in a year of postgraduate study in the same field at Johns Hopkins, and then took a position as marine biologist with the United States Fish and Wildlife Service. After much field work along the Atlantic Coast and considerable laboratory work at Woods Hole, Massachusetts, she began to write of her work.

Her first literary effort was an article for the Atlantic Monthly. Then, in 1941, she published Under the Sea Wind, a good book that was largely ignored. Ten years later came The Sea Around Us and a flood of scientific and literary awards for the author, who, quiet and unassuming, was almost embarrassed by so much public notice. Eventually she managed to slip away and get back to work again, the result of which may be found in another delightful and informative book, The Edge of the Sea, published in 1955. Rachel Carson has a great interest in—and a wide knowledge of —landward natural history too, but her chosen province is between the high-tide mark and the depths of the ocean, and there

she holds sway with scientific accuracy and literary artistry. The
selection that follows is a chapter from The Sea Around Us.

EVERY part of earth or air or sea has an atmosphere peculiarly its own, a quality or characteristic that sets it apart from all others. When I think of the floor of the deep sea, the single, overwhelming fact that possesses my imagination is the accumulation of sediments. I see always the steady, unremitting, downward drift of materials from above, flake upon flake, layer upon layer— a drift that has continued for hundreds of millions of years, that will go on as long as there are seas and continents.

For the sediments are the materials of the most stupendous "snowfall" the earth has ever seen. It began when the first rains fell on the barren rocks and set in motion the forces of erosion. It was accelerated when living creatures developed in the surface waters and the discarded little shells of lime or silica that had encased them in life began to drift downward to the bottom. Silently, endlessly, with the deliberation of earth processes that can afford to be slow because they have so much time for completion, the accumulation of the sediments has proceeded. So little in a year, or in a human lifetime, but so enormous an amount in the life of earth and sea.

The rains, the eroding away of the earth, the rush of sediment-laden waters have continued, with varying pulse and tempo, throughout all of geologic time. In addition to the silt load of every river that finds its way to the sea, there are other materials that compose the sediments. Volcanic dust, blown perhaps half way around the earth in the upper atmosphere, comes eventually to rest on the ocean, drifts in the currents, becomes waterlogged, and sinks. Sands from coastal deserts are carried seaward on offshore winds, fall to the sea, and sink. Gravel, pebbles, small boulders, and shells are carried by icebergs and drift ice, to be released to the water when the ice melts. Fragments of iron, nickel, and other meteoric debris that enters the earth's atmosphere over the sea—these, too, become flakes of the great snowfall. But most widely distributed of all are the billions upon billions of tiny shells and skeletons, the limy or silicious remains of all the minute creatures that once lived in the upper waters.

The sediments are a sort of epic poem of the earth. When we are wise enough, perhaps we can read in them all of past history. For all is written here. In the nature of the materials that compose them and in the arrangement of their successive layers, the sediments reflect all that has happened in the waters above them and on the surrounding lands. The dramatic and the catastrophic in earth history have left their trace in the sediments—the outpourings of volcanoes, the advance and retreat of the ice, the searing aridity of desert lands, the sweeping destruction of floods.

The book of the sediments has been opened only within the lifetime of the present generation of scientists, with the most exciting progress in collecting and deciphering samples made since 1945. Early oceanographers could scrape up surface layers of sediment from the sea bottom with dredges. But what was needed was an instrument, operated on the principle of an apple corer, that could be driven vertically into the bottom to remove a long sample or "core" in which the order of the different layers was undisturbed. Such an instrument was invented by Dr. C. S. Piggot in 1935, and with the aid of this "gun" he obtained a series of cores across the deep Atlantic from Newfoundland to Ireland. These cores averaged about ten feet long. A piston core sampler, developed by the Swedish oceanographer Kullenberg about ten years later, now takes undisturbed cores seventy feet long. The rate of sedimentation in the different parts of the ocean is not definitely known, but it is very slow; certainly such a sample represents millions of years of geologic history.

Another ingenious method for studying the sediments has been used by Professor W. Maurice Ewing of Columbia University and the Woods Hole Oceanographic Institution. Professor Ewing found that he could measure the thickness of the carpeting layer of sediments that overlies the rock of the ocean floor by exploding depth charges and recording their echoes; one echo is received from the top of the sediment layer (the apparent bottom of the sea), another from the "bottom below the bottom" or the true rock floor. The carrying and use of explosives at sea is hazardous and cannot be attempted by all vessels, but this method was used by the Swedish *Albatross* as well as by the *Atlantis* in its exploration of the Atlantic Ridge. Ewing on the *Atlantis* also used a seismic refraction technique by which sound waves are made to travel horizontally through the rock layers of the ocean floor, providing information about the nature of the rock.

Before these techniques were developed, we could only guess at the thickness of the sediment blanket over the floor of the sea. We might have expected the amount to be vast, if we thought back through the

ages of gentle, unending fall—one sand grain at a time, one fragile
shell after another, here a shark's tooth, there a meteorite fragment—
but the whole continuing persistently, relentlessly, endlessly. It is, of
course, a process similar to that which has built up the layers of rock
that help to make our mountains; for they, too, were once soft sediment under the shallow seas that have overflowed the continents from
time to time. The sediments eventually became consolidated and
cemented and, as the seas retreated again, gave the continents their
thick, covering layers of sedimentary rocks—layers which we can see
uplifted, tilted, compressed, and broken by the vast earth movements.
And we know that in places the sedimentary rocks are many thousands of feet thick. Yet most people felt a shock of surprise and wonder when Hans Pettersson, leader of the Swedish Deep Sea Expedition,
announced that the *Albatross* measurements taken in the open Atlantic basin showed sediment layers as much as 12,000 feet thick.

If more than two miles of sediments have been deposited on the
floor of the Atlantic, an interesting question arises: has the rocky floor
sagged a corresponding distance under the terrific weight of the sediments? Geologists hold conflicting opinions. The recently discovered
Pacific sea mounts may offer one piece of evidence that it has. If they
are, as their discoverer called them, "drowned ancient islands," then
they may have reached their present stand a mile or so below sea
level through the sinking of the ocean floor. Hess believed the islands
had been formed so long ago that coral animals had not yet evolved;
otherwise the corals would presumably have settled on the flat, planed
surfaces of the sea mounts and built them up as fast as their bases
sank. In any event, it is hard to see how they could have been worn
down so far below "wave base" unless the crust of the earth sagged
under its load.

One thing seems probable—the sediments have been unevenly distributed both in place and time. In contrast to the 12,000–foot thickness found in parts of the Atlantic, the Swedish oceanographers never
found sediments thicker than 1000 feet in the Pacific or in the Indian Ocean. Perhaps a deep layer of Lava, from ancient submarine
eruptions on a stupendous scale, underlies the upper layers of the
sediments in these places and intercepts the sound waves.

Interesting variations in the thickness of the sediment layer on the
Atlantic Ridge and the approaches to the Ridge from the American
side are reported by Ewing. As the bottom contours become less even
and begin to slope up into the foothills of the Ridge, the sediments

thickened, as though piling up into mammoth drifts 1000 to 2000 feet deep against the slopes of the hills. Farther up in the mountains of the Ridge, where there are many level terraces from a few to a score of miles wide, the sediments were even deeper, measuring up to 3000 feet. But along the backbone of the Ridge, on the steep slopes and peaks and pinnacles, the bare rock emerged, swept clean of sediments.

Reflecting on these differences in thickness and distribution, our minds return inevitably to the simile of the long snowfall. We may think of the abyssal snowstorm in terms of a bleak and blizzard-ridden arctic tundra. Long days of storm visit this place, when driving snow fills the air; then a lull comes in the blizzard, and the snowfall is light. In the snowfall of the sediments, also, there is an alteration of light and heavy falls. The heavy falls correspond to the periods of mountain building on the continents, when the lands are lifted high and the rain rushes down their slopes, carrying mud and rock fragments to the sea; the light falls mark the lulls between the mountain-building periods, when the continents are flat and erosion is slowed. And again, on our imaginary tundra, the winds blow the snow into deep drifts, filling in all the valleys between the ridges, piling the snow up and up until the contours of the land are obliterated, but scouring the ridges clear. In the drifting sediments on the floor of the ocean we see the work of the "winds," which may be the deep ocean currents, distributing the sediments according to laws of their own, not yet grasped by human minds.

We have known the general pattern of the sediment carpet, however, for a good many years. Around the foundations of the continents, in the deep waters off the borders of the continental slopes, are the muds of terrestrial origin. There are muds of many colors—blue, green, red, black, and white—apparently varying with climatic changes as well as with the dominant soils and rocks of the lands of their origin. Farther at sea are the oozes of predominantly marine origin—the remains of the trillions of tiny sea creatures. Over great areas of the temperate oceans the sea floor is largely covered with the remains of unicellular creatures known as foraminifera, of which the most abundant genus is Globigerina. The shells of Globigerina may be recognized in very ancient sediments as well as in modern ones, but over the ages the species have varied. Knowing this, we can date approximately the deposits in which they occur. But always they have been simple animals, living in an intricately sculptured shell of carbonate of lime, the whole so small you would need a microscope to see its details.

After the fashion of unicellular beings, the individual Globigerina normally did not die, but by the division of its substance became two. At each division, the old shell was abandoned, and two new ones were formed. In warm, lime-rich seas these tiny creatures have always multiplied prodigiously, and so, although each is so minute, their innumerable shells blanket millions of square miles of ocean bottom, and to a depth of thousands of feet.

In the great depths of the ocean, however, the immense pressures and the high carbon-dioxide content of deep water dissolve much of the lime long before it reaches the bottom and return it to the great chemical reservoir of the sea. Silica is more resistant to solution. It is one of the curious paradoxes of the ocean that the bulk of the organic remains that reach the great depths intact belong to unicellular creatures seemingly of the most delicate construction. The radiolarians remind us irresistibly of snow flakes, as infinitely varied in pattern, as lacy, and as intricately made. Yet because their shells are fashioned of silica instead of carbonate of lime, they can descend unchanged into the abyssal depths. So there are broad bands of radiolarian ooze in the deep tropical waters of the North Pacific, underlying the surface zones where the living radiolarians occur most numerously.

Two other kinds of organic sediments are named for the creatures whose remains compose them. Diatoms, the microscopic plant life of the sea, flourish most abundantly in cold waters. There is a broad belt of diatom ooze on the floor of the Antarctic Ocean, outside the zone of glacial debris dropped by the ice pack. There is another across the North Pacific, along the chain of great deeps that run from Alaska to Japan. Both are zones where nutrient-laden water wells up from the depths, sustaining a rich growth of plants. The diatoms, like the radiolaria, are encased in silicious coverings—small, boxlike cases of varied shape and meticulously etched design.

Then, in relatively shallow parts of the open Atlantic, there are patches of ooze composed of the remains of delicate swimming snails, called pteropods. These winged mollusks, possessing transparent shells of great beauty, are here and there incredibly abundant. Pteropod ooze is the characteristic bottom deposit in the vicinity of Bermuda, and a large patch occurs in the South Atlantic.

Mysterious and eerie are the immense areas, especially in the North Pacific, carpeted with a soft, red sediment in which there are no organic remains except sharks' teeth and the ear bones of whales. This red clay occurs at great depths. Perhaps all the materials of the other sediments are dissolved before they can reach this zone of immense pressures and glacial cold.

The reading of the story contained in the sediments has only begun. When more cores are collected and examined we shall certainly decipher many exciting chapters. Geologists have pointed out that a series of cores from the Mediterranean might settle several controversial problems concerning the history of the ocean and of the lands around the Mediterranean basin. For example, somewhere in the layers of sediment under this sea there must be evidence, in a sharply defined layer of sand, of the time when the deserts of the Sahara were formed and the hot, dry winds began to skim off the shifting surface layers and carry them seaward. Long cores recently obtained in the western Mediterranean off Algeria have given a record of volcanic activity extending back through thousands of years, and including great prehistoric eruptions of which we know nothing.

The Atlantic cores taken more than a decade ago by Piggot from the cable ship *Lord Kelvin* have been thoroughly studied by geologists. From their analysis it is possible to look back into the past 10,000 years or so and to sense the pulse of the earth's climatic rhythms; for the cores were composed of layers of cold-water globigerina faunas (and hence glacial stage sediments), alternating with globigerina ooze characteristic of warmer waters. From the clues furnished by these cores we can visualize interglacial stages when they were periods of mild climates, with warm water overlying the sea bottom and warmth-loving creatures living in the ocean. Between these periods the sea grew chill. Clouds gathered, the snows fell, and on the North American continent the great ice sheets grew and the ice mountains moved out to the coast. The glaciers reached the sea along a wide front; there they produced icebergs by the thousand. The slow-moving, majestic processions of the bergs passed out to sea, and because of the coldness of much of the earth they penetrated farther south than any but stray bergs do today. When finally they melted, they relinquished their loads of silt and sand and gravel and rock fragments that had become frozen into their under surfaces as they made their grinding way over the land. And so a layer of glacial sediment came to overlie the normal globigerina ooze, and the record of an Ice Age was inscribed.

Then the sea grew warmer again, the glaciers melted and retreated, and once more the warmer-water species of Globigerina lived in the sea—lived and died and drifted down to build another layer of globigerina ooze, this time over the clays and gravels of the glaciers.

And the record of warmth and mildness was again written in the sediments. From the Piggot cores it has been possible to reconstruct four different periods of the advance of the ice, separated by periods of warm climate.

It is interesting to think that even now, in our own lifetime, the flakes of a new snow storm are falling, falling, one by one, out there on the ocean floor. The billions of Globigerina are drifting down, writing their unequivocal record that this, our present world, is on the whole a world of mild and temperate climate. Who will read their record, ten thousand years from now?

And what is so rare as a day in June?
   Then, if ever, come perfect days;
Then Heaven tries earth if it be in tune,
   And over it softly her warm ear lays:
Whether we look, or whether we listen,
We hear life murmur, or see it glisten;
Every clod feels a stir of might,
   An instinct within it that reaches and towers
And, groping blindly above it for light,
   Climbs to a soul in grass and flowers;
The flush of life may well be seen
   Thrilling back over hills and valleys;
The cowslip startles in meadows green,
   The buttercup catches the sun in its chalice,
And there's never a leaf or a blade too mean
   To be some happy creature's palace;
The little bird sits at his door in the sun,
   A-tilt like a blossom among the leaves,
And lets his illumined being o'errun
   With the deluge of summer it receives;
His mate feels the eggs beneath her wings,
And the heart in her dumb breast flutters and sings;
He sings to the wide world, and she to her nest,—
In the nice ear of Nature, which song is the best?

JAMES RUSSELL LOWELL

A SPARROW'S NEST

by George Miksch Sutton

In all fairness, Major George Miksch Sutton (U. S. Air Force, Ret.) should be presented as an artist. He is both an artist and a writer, but the painting of birds was his first love and still is. He had the privilege of studying under the great Louis Agassiz Fuertes. He had sent some drawings to Fuertes, who recognized youthful talent and invited the youngster to his camp on the shore of Lake Cayuga, New York. What started the career of young Sutton as an author was the necessity of supplying some text to go with his drawings and paintings, which he was offering for sale and publication. Now he is distinguished in both fields.

It's merely a coincidence that he was born in Bethany, Nebraska, May 16, 1898, and in 1919 was graduated from Bethany (no relation) College, West Virginia, with the degree of Bachelor of Science. He was invited to go on a Carnegie Museum trip to Labrador that same summer and was launched as a scientist. He has written and illustrated numerous books and has made repeated field trips to the Arctic and much warmer lands. Dr. Sutton—he received a Ph.D. from Cornell University in 1932—at different times has served on the scientific staff at Cornell, the University of Michigan, and the University of Oklahoma. He was the first man to find the nest and eggs of the blue goose, which he discovered on Southampton Island in Hudson Bay, and the first to come upon the eggs of the Harris's Sparrow, as chronicled in the selection that follows, taken from his Birds of the Wilderness *published in 1936. He took time out from ornithology to serve as an Air Force officer in World War II. It can be added here, from experience, that George Miksch Sutton is a most cheerful and helpful companion on a field trip.*

IF you are not an ornithologist you probably never have heard of a Harris's Sparrow. And if you have never heard of a Harris's Sparrow you cannot be expected to know that it took us learned scientists almost a hundred years to find its eggs; that the long search ended in two weeks of warfare between the Americans and the Canadians; and that the final, decisive battle of this conflict was won by the Americans.

The Harris's Sparrow is a handsome member of the finch tribe. It is considerably larger than an English Sparrow. It has a pink bill; black crown, face, and throat; streaked back and sides; and white underparts. It inhabits the middle part of North America, nesting in the stunted spruce woods at the edge of the Barren Grounds, migrating across south central Canada and our midwestern States, and wintering in Kansas, Oklahoma, and Texas. It was discovered, in 1837, by a young naturalist named Thomas Nuttall, who described it three years later, naming it *Fringilla querula*, the Mourning Finch. A few years later the famous ornithologist-artist, John James Audubon, rediscovered the bird, bestowing upon it, in honor of his "excellent and constant friend Edward Harris, Esq.," the common name it now bears. Ornithologists since the time of Nuttall, Audubon, and Maximilian, Prince of Wied, have been observing it, tracing its routes of migration northward, hoping to find its summer home. Its breeding grounds were discovered in 1900, or thereabouts; but even so recently as five short years ago its eggs were yet unfound and undescribed.

On June 16, in the year 1931, a few minutes before nine o'clock in the morning, the Harris's Sparrow's eggs were discovered. They were in no way extraordinary in appearance. In size, shape, and color they were much like the eggs of several closely related fringilline species. They were very light greenish-blue, heavily blotched with brown. A complete description of them appeared in our leading ornithological journals three years ago. But the story of the finding of these eggs—of the battle waged at the edge of the tundra between the Americans and the Canadians—this story has never been published. I purpose to tell this story here, albeit I have no desire to disturb the peace that has so long existed along our northern boundary line.

The story begins a good many years ago. As a boy of fifteen I dreamed fond dreams of discovering the Harris's Sparrow's eggs. As I read in my bird books such statements as 'the eggs of this sparrow are unknown,' I squirmed, felt strange stirrings inside me, and pondered. Where would the nest of such a sparrow be—on the ground, under a thick bush, in a tree? Would it be hidden away in some shadowy place, or would it be at the tip of some high, cone-bearing bough? And how many eggs would be in it?

In the early fall of 1930, while returning from my year with the Eskimos of Southampton Island, I had occasion to wait some days at Churchill, Manitoba, for the train that would carry me south. There at Churchill, on the west coast of Hudson Bay, I for the first time encountered the Harris's Sparrow on its breeding ground. I did not see much of it, to be sure, for I had little opportunity to walk through the country which it preferred to frequent. But I could see that it had nested thereabouts, and the idea of finding the unfound eggs took fresh hold upon me.

I talked the matter over with my good friend J.B. Characteristically enthusiastic over the prospect of such a quest he decided to organize an expedition to Churchill the following Spring. "We must be there early," I advised. "The nest has been found, remember, and the young birds have been described; so we must be there early enough to get the eggs!"

We got there early enough, all right. Alighting from our comfortable Pullman on that evening of May 24, 1931, we found ourselves standing in snow two feet deep. A strong wind from the Bay struck us full in the face. The drifts along the ridge just to the north of us were, we learned, over twenty feet deep. Springtime indeed! The Churchill River was frozen shut miles back from the mouth. The Bay was a vast field of ice chunks that rose and sank with the tides. Husky dogs were pulling sledges to an encampment on the opposite side of the River. Our thin, short topcoats and shining oxfords were ridiculous in this Arctic land. But we were there!

There were four of us: our good friend J.B., he of the eagle's eye and unquenchable enthusiasm; Sewall Pettingill, at that time my fellow graduate student at Cornell, and an expert photographer; Bert Lloyd, an ornithologist who had collected birds extensively and who knew the Churchill region from personal experience; and myself.

We were eager as fox terriers. Each of us dreamed of discovering those eggs. We didn't give voice to our inner feelings in the matter, but there was an ardent glitter in every eye. True, there was snow everywhere about us. True, the River was covered with ice four feet thick. True, the Harris's Sparrow had not yet returned from the south. But Spring would come. The tamaracks would turn green with the sinking away of the snow, the ptarmigan would doff their winter garb, and the tundra lakes would thaw. And somewhere out in those silent, all but colorless, half-buried spruce woods there would be a Harris's Sparrow's nest. And in that nest there would be eggs. And one of us, one of us four men, would find them!

We piled our luggage on a tractor-truck, picked our way across the winter-bound construction camp to some lighted windows, and interviewed the Department of Railways and Canals. We were, we explained, strangers in a strange land. We had come to study birds. We had the necessary permits from the government. We hoped to be able to establish camp somewhere near the mouth of the River. We would not be in anybody's way, we promised, nor cause any disturbance.

The Department of Railways and Canals contemplated us a full moment, cleared his throat with a bark, and informed us that he would find us beds for the night; that he would get a tent for us on the morrow, that we could take our meals with the sixteen hundred workmen if we wanted to, but that we'd have to be at the mess hall on time and clear out when we were through. Thanking the Department for his courtesies and creeping off like thieves caught in the act we went to bed. I am not sure that my three confreres felt as I did. As for me, I felt myself wholly unwanted at Churchill—decidedly a *persona non grata*. But what about those Harris's Sparrow's eggs? Could they be found without me?

And next morning we felt better. We were at breakfast at the appointed hour—six o'clock. The food was good and there was plenty of it. We were hungry. A long day was ahead of us. We tried a little conversation between the first mouthfuls, but gave that up. Our 'pleases' and 'thank yous' drew frowns. We were not there to talk. We were there to stoke our furnaces. And stoke we did. The flapjacks were grand, and easy to manage. We got them down almost without chewing or swallowing. Prunes took more time because the pits had to be discarded somehow. And bacon rinds slowed us up. But in the first three minutes we learned from our hosts how to spread butter on a slice of bread with one hand and pour canned milk with the other. In the next three minutes we learned to stuff cookies and oranges into our pockets while gulping coffee. And at the end of the next three minutes we were rising, wiping our mouths with our sleeves, and 'clearing out.' Breakfast that morning must surely have taken us all of nine minutes. Our hosts finished long before we did. Though I am breaking the

strict continuity of my story in telling you this, we learned in time to
eat more rapidly.

Churchill was an incredible place. It was not a town, for there were
only one or two dwellings and one or two women. It was an enterprise. Huge dredges were gouging away the river bottom. A vast
cement grain elevator was rising. Under the snow about us lay a network of narrow-gauge tracks over which 'dinkey engines' were soon to
pull cars filled with gravel, workmen, and water. On the higher ground
between the River and the Bay stood row upon row of barracks, a
little hospital, some mission buildings, one or two banks, a motion
picture palace of sorts, the headquarters of the Royal Canadian
Mounted Police, and a wireless station. Churchill, an ocean port in the
making!

We got our big tent and J.B.'s little silk tent up that day, built ourselves a worktable, unpacked our equipment, and unrolled our sleeping bags. And Bert Lloyd and I, eager to make certain that the sparrows were not ahead of us, walked six miles upriver to the spruce
woods, wallowed for hours through slushy drifts, dark-brown muskeg
streams, and waist-deep, ice-filmed pools. The sparrows had not come.
We saw some Snow Buntings and Lapland Longspurs, a few Pipits and
Horned Larks, and three Pintail Ducks. We got back just in time for
dinner—dead tired. At dinner we stoked again.

On May 27, the Harris's Sparrow arrived from the south. We had
beaten him by three days. We thought he looked a bit disconsolate,
but the notes of his whistled song reassured us that Spring was on its
way.

We continued to eat at the mess hall, but we usually missed the
noon meal. Walking six miles in order to begin our day's work took
time and energy. We were glad when the gravel trains began running.
We became acquainted with the engineers and firemen and sometimes
had a chance to bum a ride. By the time we got back from our day
afield we were half-starved. Our evening meal, large as it invariably
was, invariably made us sleepy. Existence was simple. We rose,
dressed, stoked, walked or rode six miles to the spruce woods, tramped
the tundra, woodlands and muskeg for hours, walked or rode six miles
back from the spruce woods, stoked, undressed, and went to bed. Here
and there during this busy program of nest-hunting we found time
to prepare birdskins, write notes, make drawings, and take photographs.

Whenever we four men conversed we usually conversed about the

Harris's Sparrow, though there were other interesting birds in the region. Bert Lloyd, we learned, had once found what he thought was a Harris's Sparrow's nest. This nest had been under a little bush. Yes, it had been of the right size for a Harris's Sparrow. No, it hadn't been completely hidden by leaves and moss. Yes, it had been made of grass. But Bert had had no chance to identify the parent birds. So, in the last analysis, we knew next to nothing about a Harris's Sparrow's nest. We were prepared for anything. The fact that the one or two nests on record had been described thus and so didn't help us much. At night I was wont to say to my companions: "We must look everywhere—on the ground, under bushes, in trees, in holes in the ground—everywhere. And we must watch the birds constantly. The easiest way to find some nests is to watch a bird that has a wisp of grass, or a feather, or a twig in its bill."

We came to an agreement concerning our procedure in the event a nest was found. If a full set of eggs were discovered, these were to be collected immediately, lest in our absence from the nest they be destroyed by some Whiskey Jack, weasel, or other predatory creature. We wanted photographs of the first nest if possible, to be sure, but the important thing was to collect and preserve those eggs so that an adequate description of them might be published. By the end of our first week we were somewhat fagged by our exertions, puzzled by our failure to find what we felt to be mated pairs, annoyed at our inability to distinguish male and female birds in the field (their coloration was almost precisely the same), and more fervently, desperately, even frantically eager than ever. Personal pride was at stake by this time. There were reputations to uphold. J.B., the oldest of our party, was also the sharpest eyed—an exceedingly keen observer with an enviable record as a rifle, shotgun and revolver shot. Sewall Pettingill was a youngster, a grand chap too, who felt that his name would flash in electric lights across the land if only he could find that nest. Bert Lloyd had been in the Churchill region before. He had become familiar with the summertime ways of the Harris's Sparrow, and what was more, thought he had already seen a nest. As for me, I was half mad, half downright crazy. I'd dream, quite literally dream at night, about sparrows as big as cows, with huge black eyes and long white lashes. That sort of thing. The less we say about it the better.

And then came the Canadians! One week after our arrival, almost to the minute, on the very train that had brought us, came four stalwart Canadians from the Province of Alberta—four men quite as capable and quite as eager as ourselves, each one of them just as determined as each one of us to be the first to find the Harris's Sparrow's eggs!

We were in bed when the Canadians came. In fact, we were asleep, dreaming about sparrows with long eyelashes. All at once we heard a booming voice outside our tent. The Canadians were making a call. We did our best at wakening, half sat up, rubbed our eyes, and tried to talk. No, we hadn't found a Harris's Sparrow's nest. Oh yes, there were lots of Harris's Sparrows about, dozens of them, but we weren't even sure these birds were mated yet. I fail to remember whether we rose to light a candle or not. I think we didn't. We weren't very hospitable, I fear. And J.B., our indomitable leader, was nettled. "These Canadians!" he was saying as soon as they left. "What do they mean by trying to spoil our game? We came up here to do this thing ourselves and they haven't a right to bust in this way!" There was quite a bit of muttering from the little tent in which J.B. slept. We all felt a good deal the same way, I guess, but Sewall, Bert and I didn't mutter. We lay in our sleeping bags with eyes wide open, wondering how we could beat these unexpected, unwelcome newcomers. If only they'd play fair and go to bed and not begin their search until the morrow!

Next morning there was a new light in our eyes. We four men were no longer pitted against each other. We were pitted against a new, a formidable, a mighty foe—the Canadians.

We three younger men, generous creatures that we were, had decided amongst ourselves that if we possibly *could* do so we'd let J.B. find that first nest. There is nothing written down in black and white to prove this, but I am telling the truth. J.B. had been a good scout. Finding the nest would be a sort of peak in his ornithological career. We younger men could do something else some time that would win us renown. In our inner hearts we hoped that Fate would somehow force us to find that first nest, but our tongues spoke phrases that were as unselfish and altruistic as any ever spoken.

The coming of the Canadians changed all this. The contest was a free-for-all now. And come what may, America must win. We had been the first on the ground. We had made the greater sacrifice in getting there. Feeling ran high.

The egg-hunting tactics of the Canadians were different from ours. Armed with what must have been dishpans, sections of stovepipe, tin trays and canes they marched through the spruces making the wildest sort of noise. Their purpose was to frighten the mother sparrows from the nests. We laughed as we listened, but scowled as we laughed. This was a silly, childish procedure—a ridiculous method of bird study —but what if it worked! After all, *we* had not found a nest. Our irreproachable methods had thus far failed. We went on with our quiet, determined, methodical searching, but the sound of the enemy's drums made us nervous. Perhaps at this very moment they are finding the nest, we would think. Perhaps a bird is flitting out from under their feet—and in her flitting is giving away the century-old secret! Each and every evening we talked about our experiences of the day, and wondered if the enemy had won. We did not go to see them. They did not come to see us. We had no friendly symposiums on the habits of Harris's Sparrows. We were on speaking terms, yes; but we were uncomfortable whenever we met each other. Occasionally, out on the tundra, we ran into them face to face. At such times we conversed about the weather (and there is weather to talk about at Churchill); about the interesting birds we had been seeing; and about methods of bird-skinning. Sooner or later, of course, the matter of *the nest* was sure to come up, and at this juncture we blushed and fidgeted and looked afar off and did our doomed-to-failure best to appear uninterested and casual. The enemy continued to tell us that they had not found the nest. We wondered if they were telling us the truth. They may have had similar doubts concerning us.

The enemy were encamped in a freight car that stood on a siding at the edge of the construction camp. Here they slept and ate and prepared their specimens. We passed the place at least twice a day, sometimes more frequently. But we never called. And we rarely saw them.

The precious days passed. By June 10, I began to be genuinely and deeply worried. Unless we found the nest before the summer waned there would be young birds, not eggs. We had been finding and observing pair after pair of birds. We had heard the male birds singing day after day. We felt that by this time they must surely have chosen their nesting-territories. But we had found no sign of a nest.

On the evening of June 15, Sewall (by this time we were calling the lad 'Sewall the Beautiful' and 'Sewall the Cruel') drew me aside to tell me that he had seen a Harris's Sparrow with grass in its bill; that he had watched the bird for hours; and that he had found a nest! Sewall was excited, to say the least. He was fairly shaking. And when I looked upon him and listened to his words a pang shot me through. What right had Sewall, unlettered, callow, inordinately smug youth that he was, to find that nest! "Do you think we'd better say anything about it to the others?" he was asking in a wobbly whisper. "The nest is down under the moss, at the end of a sort of burrow. I watched the bird for a long time, and followed it on hands and knees—but I saw it with grass in its bill only once."

That nest (poor, beautiful, downcast Sewall!) proved to be the nest of a mouse.

And then came the morning of June 16. That morning a strange, in fact a very strange, thing happened—something in the nature of an omen. I had walked to a favorite part of the section of woodland I had been studying most closely. I was watching a pair of Harris's Sparrows, wondering as usual which was the male and which the female, when all at once one of the birds flew across a clearing to an old box that had been tossed aside by the men who had built the railroad through the woods. As the bird sat on the box it began to sing. I watched it with my binocular and chanced to note that there were large black letters on the box. Looking at the letters one by one I found to my complete amazement that the word HARRIS was printed there. It was a box in which bacon or ham had been shipped from the Harris Abbatoir, a Canadian meat-packing firm.

I fairly gasped when I realized that a fine male Harris's Sparrow was perching there in front of me on a box that was labeled HARRIS. I rose with the determination of a Perseus or a Columbus and marched through the woods. I cannot very scientifically explain my feelings, but I knew that a sign had been given.

At a little before nine o'clock, while marching across an all but impassable bog, I frightened from a sphagnum island underfoot a slim, dark-backed bird. It made no outcry, but from the explosive flutter of its wings I knew it had left a nest. I searched a moment, parting with my hand the tough, slender twigs of flowering Labrador tea. And there was the nest—with four eggs that in the cool shadow had a dark appearance. The mother bird, by this time, was chirping in alarm. I looked at her briefly with my glass. A Harris's Sparrow! I raised the gun, took careful aim, and fired. Marking the nest, I ran to pick her up. Upon my return, the male appeared. I shot him also, for I knew the record would not be complete unless I shot both parent birds. To say that I was happy is to describe my feelings all too tamely. I was beside myself. Shooting those important specimens had taken control. I had been so excited I had hardly been able to hold the gun properly. As I knelt to examine the nest a thrill the like of which I had never felt before passed through me. And I talked aloud! "Here!" I said. "Here in this beautiful place!" At my fingertips lay treasures that were beyond price. Mine was Man's first glimpse of the eggs of the Harris's Sparrow, in the lovely bird's wilderness home.

Then I began to wonder how many other nests had been found that morning. The enemy! My comrades! Had they, too, been favored by Heaven with a sign? I had a wild desire to gather everybody about me—friend and foe alike—so that we might work together, compare notes, make plans, take photographs. I looked at my watch. Perhaps some Canadian had found a nest at eight o'clock! Perhaps several nests had been found before nine o'clock that morning! I fired my shotgun loudly as I could (have you ever tried this?) three times, and was a little surprised, as the echoes died, that no familiar form of friend nor unfamiliar form of foe materialized. I fired again. There was no answer.

So, happy in a way that was quite new to me, but dubious as to the priority of my achievement, I hippity-hopped across the bogs. I wasn't much of an ornithologist those next few hours. I was too gay for Ornithology. At a little before noon I chanced to see Bert Lloyd ahead of me. I started to call him—then decided not to. A wild fear seized me. Perhaps all this happiness of the last three hours was unwarranted. Perhaps all this had been some weird hallucination. I knelt on the moss, opened my collecting creel, got out those two specimens I had shot at the nest, and looked at them closely. Yes, they were Harris's Sparrows, there could not be the slightest doubt of that. They were not White-crowned Sparrows, nor Fox Sparrows, nor Tree Sparrows. No, there was nothing wrong with me this time.

"Bert!" I shouted, trying to keep my voice normal. And Bert turned and came. "What luck?" I asked. And Bert gave me the usual report— plenty of birds, mated pairs too, but no nest. Queer that he couldn't see how boiling over I was with excitement.

So I told him. And Bert's response was the response of a good friend, a good sport, a good ornithologist. His words were cordial and the exultant delight that shone from his face was genuine. I showed him the specimens. And from that time until the reunion of our party that evening, two of us wondered how many other nests had been found that day.

To be perfectly honest, I was hoping that nobody else had found a nest. In a vague sort of way I wanted my good friend J.B. to have the thrill of it all—but he had been successful in so many ways that I felt this purely ornithological triumph might quite justly be mine. And Sewall—well, if Sewall had found a nest before nine o'clock that morning he was just too lucky for tolerance. But the Canadians!

Bert and I got back about six o'clock. We were a little late at the mess hall. The workmen frowned as we came in, for they knew the cook would be angry, and we were wet and dirty. But we didn't care. Let them frown. Let them despise us. We were above being despised. J.B. and Sewall were busy stoking—almost too busy to notice us. We sat down. When there was a clatter of departing workmen I leaned toward J.B. and said, "Did you find the nest today?" J.B. said he hadn't. "I found one—with four eggs in it," I rejoined. And the stoking stopped.

I have never, neither before nor since, seen J.B. look as he looked at precisely that moment. He may have been wishing that he had found the nest. He may have been as jealous as a successful, vigorous, fair-minded, generous sportsman can at times be. He may quite possibly have hated me for my insolence. But I think he was happy. For I know he felt, as I did, that beating dishpans in the woods was no way to study birds; that our Harris's Sparrow was a bird of rare discernment; that in this hectic battle of the past sixteen days it was only right that the Americans should win. For they had.

TO A MOUNTAIN DAISY

On Turning One Down with the Plough, in April 1786

Wee, modest, crimson-tippèd flow'r,
Thou's met me in an evil hour;
For I maun crush amang the stour
    Thy slender stem;
To spare thee now is past my pow'r
    Thou bonie gem.

Alas! it's no thy neibor sweet,
The bonie lark, companion meet,
Bending thee 'mang the dewy weet,
    Wi' spreckl'd breast!
When upward-springing, blythe, to greet
    The purpling east.

Cauld blew the bitter-biting north
Upon thy early, humble birth;
Yet cheerfully thou glinted forth
    Amid the storm,
Scarce rear'd above the parent-earth
    Thy tender form.

The flaunting flow'rs our gardens yield,
High shelt'ring woods and wa's maun shield:
But thou, beneath the random bield
    O' clod or stane,
Adorns the histie stibble field,
    Unseen, alane.

There, in thy scanty mantle clad,
Thy snawie bosom sun-ward spread,
Thou lifts thy unassuming head
    In humble guise;
But now the share uptears thy bed,
    And low thou lies!

Such is the fate of artless maid,
Sweet flow'ret of the rural shade!
By love's simplicity betray'd,
    And guileless trust;
Till she, like thee, all soil'd, is laid
    Low i' the dust.

Such is the fate of simple bard,
On life's rough ocean luckless starr'd!
Unskilful he to note the card
    Of prudent lore,
Till billows rage, and gales blow hard,
    And whelm him o'er!

Such fate to suffering worth is giv'n,
Who long with wants and woes has striv'n,
By human pride or cunning driv'n
    To mis'ry's brink;
Till wrench'd of ev'ry stay but Heav'n,
    He, ruin'd, sink!

Ev'n thou who mourn'st the Daisy's fate,
That fate is thine—no distant date;
Stern Ruin's plough-share drives elate,
    Full on thy bloom,
Till crush'd beneath the furrow's weight,
    Shall be thy doom!   ROBERT BURNS

THE WELL-TRAVELED EEL

by Paul Bulla

There are few living creatures with a stranger life cycle than that of the eel, the fish that looks like a snake. The following account of the almost incredible journeys of these elongated fishes was originally published some years ago in Natural History, *the official magazine of the American Museum of Natural History. The biography of an eel that leads a natural life and meets a natural death needs no embellishing. The bare facts are astonishing. They are presented here with all the clarity of a straightforward news story, which is not surprising in view of the author's considerable experience as a staff reporter and feature writer for the Washington (D.C.)* Times-Herald.

OFF the North American continent, southeast of Bermuda and northeast of Puerto Rico, lies a vast tract of slowly swirling water known to mariners as the Sargasso Sea. Here, according to song and story, the Gulf Stream is born, and here far below the weed-choked surface is the breeding and spawning grounds of our fresh-water eel.

Here these strange fish have their rendezvous. In this sea-within-a-sea they are born, and here, after years spent in far places, they return to reproduce themselves and die, for no spent eels have ever been seen, and adult eels have never been known to run upstream.

Of all the fish known to mankind, few have a more remarkable life history, and none have puzzled scientists for so long as have these snake-like denizens of the rivers and lakes of Europe and America. Down through the ages they have been a food delicacy in the European and Mediterranean countries, but centuries passed before their migratory habits and method of propagation were explained. Each autumn uncounted numbers of these slimy creatures moved downstream to the sea, where many were caught in the nets of fishermen awaiting their migration. But great numbers avoided this fate and disappeared never to return.

In the spring and summer of each succeeding year, tiny eel-like creatures appeared from somewhere in the vast ocean spaces and swarmed along the coast of Europe and through the Straits of Gibraltar into the Mediterranean. Later they entered the fresh-water streams and rivers that ran down to the sea, penetrating to the interior, where they grew to maturity. Confusion further confounded the minds of scientists and simple fisherfolk alike by the fact that eggs of unborn eels were never found in the bodies of adults, and males of the species were never seen.

Many strange theories were advanced in explanation of how they were produced, ranging from spontaneous generation to the transformation of horsehairs into little eels. Aristotle, in the fourth century B.C., held that eels were born from earthworms, which were in turn produced from mud or damp soil. The early Greeks, failing to find spawn or male reproductive glands within the eels, named Jupiter as the father, as all children of doubtful parentage were ascribed to this god.

Pliny the Elder, great Roman naturalist and author, declared with conviction that eels had neither masculine nor feminine sex. In accounting for their multiplication, he concluded that they rubbed themselves against rocks, and the pieces scraped from their bodies came to life as little eels. He dismissed the subject as a matter for further controversy with the laconic statement that "they have no other mode of procreation." With the acceptance of such beliefs it is small wonder that centuries elapsed before such theories were dispelled and such superstitions overcome.

It was not until 1777 that the ovary of the eel was first recognized by Carlo Mundini, a professor of anatomy at the University of Bologna, thus definitely establishing a female sex. Ninety-five years later Reinhold Hornbaum-Hornschuch announced the discovery of a male individual. The enigma that had endured for over 2000 years was then on its way to being solved.

But while these discoveries partly answered the riddle of their existence, where the eels came from and how they were produced still remained a mystery. It was left to a German named Johann Jakob Kaup, in 1846, to find in the sea a small ribbon-like fish with a tiny head. Curious as to its species, he took it home and placed it in a bottle of alcohol. After labeling it *Leptocephalus brevirostris*, a name that exceeded the length of the specimen itself, he left it there to be forgotten.

Half a century passed before the subject emerged from the obscurity into which it had been relegated. On a day in 1896 two Italians, Gracci and Calandrucci, found one of Kaup's little fish in the Mediterranean, but one much larger and more fully developed. This they identified as the leptocephalus or larva of the edible eel that inhabited the streams of the European continent. With that beginning the stage was set for a Danish scientist named Johannes Schmidt.

As director of the Danish Commission for the Exploration of the Sea, Schmidt sailed in 1906, on the first of many subsequent expeditions, to locate the breeding and spawning grounds of this specter of the deep. For fifteen years he towed nets up and down the Atlantic, taking specimens of leptocephali from the English Channel to Chesapeake Bay, and from Greenland to Puerto Rico. Over this vast area he collected and correlated sizes of eel larvae, carefully noting the latitude and longitude in which they were obtained.

He reasoned that the larvae were growing as they moved from the place in which they were spawned toward the coast and their fresh-water homes. It followed, therefore, that the smaller the larva found in any part of the ocean, the nearer such specimen must be to the place where it was born. After years of tireless effort he was able, through this method, to fix the breeding and spawning grounds of the European eel (*Anguilla vulgaris*) and the American species (*Anguilla rostrata*) within the latitudes 20 to 30 degrees north, and longitudes 60 to 78 degrees west. He further established the fact that the European beds overlapped those of the American species.

But this discovery uncovered but one phase of the life cycle of the eel. During the period of growth in the waters of their home continent, both males and females are a uniform green to yellowish-brown above, shading to a pale dirty white underneath, and are called "yellow eels." When the migratory instinct asserts itself at the breeding stage, which is in the autumn when they are between the ages of seven and fifteen years, the sides of their bodies take on a metallic sheen and their backs become a deep black. This is their breeding dress, and they are then known as "silver eels."

Upon assuming this dress, certain other marked changes take place in the females. Their snouts become sharp, the eyes larger, and the pectoral fins, just back of the gill slits, more pointed than usual. Although they have been voracious eaters all their lives, they cease feeding at this time and, leaving the lakes and rivers in which they have lived, move downstream to the sea. But while these visible changes have been taking place, it is not until after they have reached salt water that the ovaries mature. In fact, no perfectly ripe female eel and only one ripe male has ever been seen. Upon arriving in the bays and estuaries of their home shores they are joined by the mature males that have been living there, and together they start the journey back to their birthplace, over 2500 miles distant.

It is not known how far below the surface they swim, but somewhere beyond the continental shelf they pass from the range of observation. Neither is it known how long it takes them to reach their destination, but it has been estimated that the eel requires about six months to make the crossing, swimming at the rate of one-half mile an hour. As the migration from the European continent begins in early autumn, and spawning starts in early spring at the breeding grounds, this estimate of the period of time for the trip seems to be justified.

Upon arrival at the breeding grounds, the European species find they must share it with their American cousins, whose beds overlap their own but extend westward from it. From Labrador southward to Panama and the West Indies, the "silver eels" from America have journeyed to the rendezvous in from one to two months after reaching salt water. Hundreds of fathoms below the seaweed-clogged surface of this tropical sea the eggs of both species are spawned; the females producing from five to 20 million tiny eggs, transparent and almost colorless.

Spawning begins in late winter or early spring, and a week or so after fertilization the eggs are hatched. Larvae of both species begin life with a length of about one-fourth inch. Ribbon-like in shape and so transparent that newsprint can be read through their bodies, they float for a time from 600 to 900 feet below the surface. Later they rise into the upper layers of water and slowly move northward. Reaching the latitude of Bermuda, a separation occurs. The larvae of the European species move eastward on the long journey back to their native shores, while their tiny American relatives turn toward the coast line of America.

During their first summer of life, the European larvae are found in the western Atlantic. By the second summer they have reached the central Atlantic, and by the third they have arrived off the coastal banks of Europe. During their two and one-half years in the ocean they have attained a length of two to three and one-half inches, but they still retain their flat, leaf-shaped larval form. They are now faced with a new way of life and must be prepared to meet it. In the course of the autumn and winter a metamorphosis takes place. They cease feeding, lose their larval teeth, shrink in depth and length, and become elvers, or little eels. While they are shaped like their parents in miniature, they are still transparent, and so are known as "glass eels."

Our American eel has a shorter larval history. Here again the timing is perfect, for it reaches its home shores and the elver stage of existence in about one year.

After the transformation from larva to elver, the females of both species ascend the fresh-water streams of their "native" land to live their lives in the interior, until the moment when the migratory instinct drives them back to the sea. In these journeys upstream they use pipe lines and sewers and clamber over falls and surmount dams to reach their destination. The males, however, remain in the brackish waters of lagoons and estuaries, where they grow to maturity and await the downstream migration of the females.

As eels have been found in ponds having no outlets or inlets, it is believed (though without conclusive evidence) that they will travel overland to reach these oases, choosing nights when the grass is damp for the journey. They are also at home in high as well as low altitudes, having been found in Swiss lakes 3000 feet above sea level.

All eels in the headwaters of large streams are found to be females. As a rule they lie buried by day in the muddy bottoms where there is still water, and venture abroad to feed at night. Being scavengers and omnivorous, they will eat almost any available food, either living or dead. They have even been known to eat their own kind.

Female eels average from two to three and one-half feet in length, but they have been known to reach four feet and weigh as much as sixteen and one-half pounds. Males average around fourteen to eighteen inches in length, but never grow larger than two feet. The vertebrae of this fish mark the only difference between the American and the European species: the former has an average of 107 segments, while the latter averages 114.

Differing from their salt-water cousins, the lower jaw of both species projects beyond the upper, while the large mouth gapes back to a point even with or somewhat behind the eyes. On the side of the neck are gill slits with upper corners on a line with the center of the base of the pectoral fins. A single fin, soft and without spines, extends along the back, around the tip of the tail, and forward on the underside of the body. There is no separation into dorsal, caudal, or anal parts.

After the third or fourth year of life, eels develop small scales that are embedded in the skin. These are covered with a coating of slimy mucus, which has given rise to the simile, "as slippery as an eel."

Perhaps the most intriguing phase of the life cycle of this unusual fish is that neither European nor American elvers have ever been known to appear off the shores of any country but their own. This fact immediately presents two puzzling questions that challenge the imagination.

1. What causes the immature larvae of the European species to move eastward from the spawning grounds, while its American cousin works toward the west side of the Atlantic?

2. How does it happen that the timing is perfect for both species to reach the elver stage within a few months after arriving off the coast of their home continent?

These questions may be answered in part by the difference in their individual larval histories.

While the European larva requires from two and one-half to three years to reach the elver stage of development after life begins, the larval stage of the American species is terminated in about one year. This time element not only acts to keep the two species distinct, but makes it practically impossible for either to survive in waters other than their own after metamorphosis takes place. Should the larvae of the European eels, for instance, move westward, they would reach the American coast line in an undeveloped larval stage.

A geographical cause for their distribution is advanced by Doctor Schmidt, who points out that the center of production for the American eel lies farther west and south than the center of the European beds. This, together with the movement of the ocean currents as an aid to the journey in the early stages of larval development, must be considered as a cause directing the two species each to its own side of the ocean.

While much has been learned of the habits of these sluggish, sedentary fish since the turn of the century, much remains unexplained.

With a singleness of purpose and an unerring instinct that has confused scientists, untold thousands have deserted their home waters each autumn to seek adventure in a tropic sea and to keep their rendezvous with death. Weak and immature, their progeny is cast adrift far from their native land. Unguided, these feeble swimmers travel a road over which they have never journeyed, to reach their home continent.

Truly, the eel is one of the greatest of marine mysteries.

JUNGLES UNDER MOONLIGHT

by Lorus J. and Margery J. Milne

Here we have another husband-and-wife team as authors and naturalists, producers to date of five books on natural history. They work together in the field and at the University of New Hampshire, where Lorus J. Milne, with a bachelor's degree from the University of Toronto and a Ph.D. from Harvard, is Professor of Zoology, and his wife, a Radcliffe graduate, is an Honorary Fellow on his staff. They have traveled this continent from the subtropic Canal Zone to the tundra of the Arctic, and everything they see, hear, or learn is grist for their classroom lectures, magazine articles, and books. What happens in the dark is always a fascinating subject and often a mystery. The Milnes wrote about it in The World of Night, *from which the following selection is taken.*

MIDNIGHT, deep in a tropical jungle, is darker than anywhere else on the surface of the earth. No light at all reaches the soil even under the brightest stars. The most sensitive photographic film could be exposed for hours without fogging. Eyes are of no use whatever. Yet in this blackness live more kinds of plants, and among them more types of animals, than anywhere else in the world.

The wealth of jungle life is so well known that when a naturalist arrives in the tropics and visits a rain forest, he expects to find the richness of a zoological park set in a botanical garden. He is seldom warned that of each kind of creature, the total number of individuals is far smaller than in any temperate woods. Nor does he realize how expertly the animals keep out of one another's way—and out of human sight. Most of them are strictly nocturnal, and wary even then.

As a result, the rain forest floor gives a sense of empty finality. Nothing seems to happen. The lack of leaves within reach is matched by a lack of breeze to make them flutter. Even by day few birds fly through the dim aisles, and few sounds reach the ear except the timeless drip of moisture from downhanging vines or the accidental crash of a rotted limb. Other than ants, few insects crawl about. Even the ants act as though they were in constant fear of getting lost. They move quietly in single file, or scour the jungle litter in raiding parties whose individuals keep within sight of one another.

So inconspicuous are the jungle animals that the vegetation seems overwhelming. After forty years of directing scientific studies in the tropics, William Beebe concluded that "it is the silent, terrible war-fare of the plant world which is most impressive. A great tree at the trailside, perhaps two centuries from saplinghood, is being strangled by the snakelike coils of a huge liana or climbing vine, and not only by constriction but by smothering."

The scattering of fallen leaves and fading petals gives scant clue to the trees above. "It is next to impossible to look up and determine with certainty which leaves belong to a particular tree. The confusion of interlacing branches is complete, and a tree which bears, say, three tons of leaves may . . . support five tons of epiphytes ranging in bulk from microscopic algae, tiny mosses, and half-inch orchids to enor-mous, thick-leaved, woody parasites, one individual of which may re-place a third or even half of the original tree crown."

These differences from the temperate zone are so striking that every-one interested in living things should find an opportunity to experi-ence a jungle. Some years ago the plant explorer David Fairchild chided us gently: "You live in New England. Don't you know that's the *fringe* of the world? Most of the really interesting and unusual plants, and the strangest of all animals, inhabit the torrid zone. Get to the tropics and see for yourselves. Don't say you can't afford the travel costs. Whenever a small boy tells me he can't save enough money to go to the circus, I know he doesn't want to go badly enough!"

So we went to the tropics, and chose for our initiation the relatively safe though dense jungles of Panamá. On a sanctuary island only three miles across, we each carried a whistle by day, a whistle and a flash-light by night. One of us stayed on the trail whenever the other devi-ated into "the bush."

The naturalist Bates expressed a "feeling of inhospitable wildness" in the rain forests of the Amazon basin, and Charles Darwin reached the same conclusion elsewhere in South America. Tomlinson found the jungle "securely aloof and indifferent" to the point of impartial hostility.

Even the man-hewn trails were unlike any we had met before. Indian-style, they ran from one high point to the next, rather than following any contour line. At the brink of a V-shaped valley, they descended directly and went straight up the other wall. With the temperature high and humidity so great that sweat rolled off without evaporating, even a mile of trail presented a challenge. Intermittent rains kept the mud below our feet wet and slippery.

Robert Louis Stevenson wrote of the jungle that "a man can see to the end of nothing; whichever way he looks the wood shuts up, one bough folding with another like the fingers of your hand." We found this true enough at the borders or overhead. But once through the barrier at the water's edge, really tangled jungle proved to be far more local than we had anticipated. For the most part, a mature tropical rain forest is as open at the bottom as is a dense stand of California redwoods. So little light reaches the ground by day that seedlings have no chance. High humidity and temperature encourage the decomposing action of molds and bacteria. In a few short weeks fallen leaves and branches vanish, adding nothing to the soil. "Soil" of the sort that an Iowa farmer would recognize is absent altogether. The regular rains leach out soluble minerals. No humus accumulates. Instead, the jungle floor is a naked mud on which a few bits of plant debris lie loosely in varying stages of rapid decay.

Moving slowly along the ground at any hour of the twenty-four, man is a Lilliputian captive of gravity. Around him crowd upright boles and a warp of sinewy lianas stretching from the ground to the leafy canopy above. It is as though the jungle foliage were a dense green cloud tethered to the earth by pendant vines, and pierced at many points by the smooth trunks of giant trees.

All the world seems inaccessible and hidden from view. For forty or fifty feet straight up, the trunks neither fork nor bear a leaf. Then the tree tops visible from the ground send out horizontal limbs from which extend almost vertical branches. On these the greenery is borne— spread out flatly like flowers of wild parsley or Queen Anne's lace. Yet this is merely the understory of foliage. Above it, tier on tier, are other levels to heights of a hundred or a hundred and fifty feet. Over this, again, tower the real giants such as *Bombacopsis*, thrusting their crowns skyward two hundred feet or more. All nature seems arboreal.

The daytime birds, the flowers, the butterflies, are on the top. A person walking on the jungle floor is as isolated from their world as a worm crawling over the sand below a beachside boardwalk.

Unlike a temperate forest, where the dominant trees may be beech or oak or pine, the jungle includes no solid stands. An almendro tree here, a roble there, a silk-cotton (*Cieba*) just beyond. The next almendro may be half a mile away. Only when the tree-buttercups (*Tabebuia*) flaunt their waxy gold blossoms toward the sun can a census taker in an airplane count the separate similar trees in a square mile of bush.

Time in the jungle follows a special rhythm. The tick of the clock is the call of birds, of frogs and toads, of katydids. It is the whine of cicadas, the swish of swaying branches, the patter of feet on leaves, the pelt of down-pouring rain. Its rhythm is syncopated, with pauses full of silence. From eight in the morning until five in the afternoon, most animals are asleep. But as the burning sun slides toward the horizon, the nocturnal world responds to the approach of night. Butterflies and bees which have been busy on the jungle roof descend into the shadows and find familiar sleeping sites. Birds which were silent through the sunny hours take a new and active interest in their twilight surroundings. Gaily colored toucans flit from the leafy depths to upper limbs, then take off for some bare branch which commands the scene. The rapid flight, with long undulating course, displays the slender, crow-sized body and big bright beak held straight ahead.

Two toucans per dead tree seems to be the jungle rule. They perch facing one another in the sunset, a few feet apart, lifting their yellow-mottled bills into the air to yelp out strangely unbirdlike calls: Hí-kyuck, kyuck. Hí-kyuck, kyuck.

Late one afternoon we watched a pair of black spots against the flaming sky become a twosome of Amazona parrots, stout green birds which flap short wings as vigorously as any duck. They approached in a wide arc and settled in the same dead stub as two toucans. Throughout their heavy flight the parrots screamed to one another in short rasping syllables. Now on the tree they faced the black-bodied toucans and screeched defiantly. The toucans yelped back. At the outset, the parrots sounded hoarse. But in this contest they had the advantage in volume, though the toucan calls rang through the jungle, clear and loud.

As the sunset colors faded, a dozen parakeets rose in a cloud and circled over the parrot-toucan contestants. The smaller green birds added to the uproar with a chatter of sound. The parrots leaped from their perches and flapped off across the clearing, only a few wing-beats ahead of the parakeets. Behind them on the dead stub, the toucans continued a few victorious yelps, then lapsed into silence. Soon, with a whirr of wings, they too departed. A big red-crested woodpecker swooped in, following a course with shorter undulations and comparative quiet. It alighted on the dead stub and set up a tattoo of drumming in short bursts. The pitch varied as the bird shifted around the trunk. Finally it settled in one place where the note had a particularly deep resonance. Suddenly the sound ceased, and the woodpecker flew away into the gathering darkness.

By six in a July evening, human eyes could distinguish few hues. But hummingbirds produced a fluffy whirr as they darted from one blossom to another, hurrying to fill each crop with sugar water before night ended their feeding. From the colonnade of tree trunks came an occasional whine from a cicada—a long steady buzz which might deepen as though to run down, then rise again. The note would coast almost to a stop, pick up sharply, coast once more, and finally die altogether.

Exactly at six-thirty, night after night, we heard from the jungle a firm, flutelike whistle, followed by another in tremolo half a tone higher. A big, grouselike tinamou had begun the nocturnal serenade. Between two outflung buttresses of a *Bombacopsis* tree she had laid four turquoise-blue eggs in a close cluster. Now her mate—a smaller, quieter bird—was incubating them, and would continue alone at this task until they hatched and he had raised the chicks to independence. Her calls in the jungle were a summons for another unattached male. The sweet, sad cadence came deliberately, with exquisite timing; we never could hear a male reply. Visual confirmation seemed impossible. So rarely can any jungle singer be seen that Beebe considered having a rubber stamp made to use daily in his diary: "The leaves moved but I could not see a bird."

Usually the tinamou was joined audibly by others in the distance, each vocally staking out ownership of a patch of darkening jungle. A large cicada set up a whine with a rapidly rising and falling note, repeated over and over. A big tree frog began a birdlike churring, while from all directions came short staccato peepings of smaller amphibians. In the water-filled cavity of a five-foot stump left by the fall of an almendro tree, several small toads began a chorus. They were passing air from mouth to oversized sacs behind their ears, fretting their

vocal cords into an uneven bellow-and-chirp that included a dry rat-
tling sound and that of a plucked reed.

By six-fifty the katydids were replacing the cicadas, filling in the
gaps between the full-throated whistling of the tinamous. The inch-
long toads in the stump pond had reached a peak of volume, and a
flashlight revealed them—whipping the water to a froth with their ex-
haled breath. Each toad was behind a little heap of brown suds.

After seven o'clock the night activities of jungle animals were in full
swing. Now the climbing creatures had fewer enemies, and they traveled aloft to gather nuts and fruits. Occasionally an owl sailed by, but
no eagles, falcons, or hawks disturbed the foraging of monkeys and
honeybears (kinkajous).

Like the tree porcupines, the silky anteaters ripping open termite
nests (and the opossums, monkeys, and honeybears) have a fifth hand
to help them hold their place—a long prehensile tail which can be
curled around a branch.

Slower-moving foliage-eaters clamber about in the treetops. Giant
lizards—the green iguanas—stretch their six-foot length over the firm
jungle covering of interlacing vines, to munch on buds and fresh leaves.
Each is ready at a moment's notice to leap from the tree and crash
to the ground. There the lizard scampers off, or, falling in any shallow
waterway, hides in the bottom, waiting for a pursuer to give up the
chase.

By contrast, the sloths feeding in the treetops cling to the branches
below, from which they are suspended by hooked claws. These slowest
of all mammals prefer the broad, many-fingered foliage of the *Cecropia*, a member of the mulberry family common throughout the American tropics but found nowhere else. Apparently their thick matted fur
protects them from the hordes of small brown ants which make homes
far from the ground in the hollow stems of this tree and attack any
intruder.

On the soil far below the sloths, larger ants forage ceaselessly all
day. Systematically they explore every log and leaf and cranny, seiz-
ing any form of living meat—whether mouse or bird, lizard or frog,
grasshopper or spider. They tear apart each victim and distribute its
remains as loads of flesh to be carried back along the column—nourishment to be shared with the brood of young carried by still other members of the colony. These are the dreaded army ants—the American
Eciton—which resemble in their habits the driver ants of tropical
Africa. But like old-time armies which fought by day and slept at night,

these terrors of the rain forest respond to a silent, military tattoo at sunset. The columns cease their advance. The marching order is reversed. From everywhere the ants converge on a central rendezvous. And as the light fails, some inaudible signal leads these insects to climb a low bush or some strong liana to a point several feet above the ground. There they mass themselves into a tremendous quivering ball. Until daybreak this bivouac will cling together as a unit, ready to unfold, when morning comes, into a dozen raiding parties and a wholesale transportation system.

Other ants parade up and down a variety of trees. In the night they are safe from ant shrikes, honeycreepers, and other insect-eating birds. Sauba ants, known also as parasol or umbrella ants, climb to reach fresh foliage, choosing chiefly trees which are exceptional in the tropics in having small, thin leaves. Each half-inch ant employs one of its sidewise-working slender jaws to saw off an arc of leaf blade, handling the knife edge with the precision of a surgeon. Dexterous movements of all six legs transfer the fragment to the paired jaws, and the insect marches off with its booty held above its back like a green sail. Often whole petals are carried along in this fashion.

As the stevedores plod down the tree, they blunder every few steps into eager ants returning for another load. The two-way column wanders along the ground, converging with other living streams upon an irregular mound many feet across—the granular earth excavated from deep subterranean burrows. Down the many doorways the insects descend to transfer their burdens to still smaller sisters who drag the booty to chambers as large as bushel baskets. There the small ants mince the leaf pieces into a pulp.

Sauba ants are the agriculturalists of the tropical jungle. "In addition, they are the greatest defoliators known, their ravages far exceeding those of other famous leaf destroyers such as the Japanese beetle and the gypsy moth." All of their activities lead to the building of vast compost heaps in which strands of a particular kind of fungus grow. So far as is known the sauba ants eat nothing but this fungus, and they alone have the secret of its culture. When a young queen ant starts out to found a fresh colony, she carries with her a pellet of the fungus and tends it carefully until her first brood of young emerge.

Fortunately the sauba ants do not bite, and an explorer of the jungle night who stands unwittingly across their trail suffers no ill effects. By day their paths are clearly visible—little avenues four to seven inches broad, kept remarkably clear of sticks and stones, patted firm by myriad marching feet.

Far more irregular and plastic are the tracks of wild pigs—peccaries —whose sharp toes dig into the wet earth, and whose noses root vigorously in search of hidden food.

During nights in January, February, and early March these and other animals are particularly active under the spreading branches of great almendro trees. At this season the flattened elliptical nuts are ripening —each about two inches long and one inch wide. The brown outer covering has a slightly sweetish taste and is attractive to raccoonlike coatis and howler monkeys by day, to honeybears by night. Inside the skin, however, is a layer hard as stone, protecting the almond-shaped inner kernel for which the tree is named—even though it is a member of the pea family. The honeybears and monkeys pick the fruit, eat off the outer coat, and drop the shell-bound kernels. Waiting for this bounty, on the ground below are herds of white-lipped peccaries. A man needs a sledge-hammer to break the covering. Rabbitlike agoutis and squirrels gnaw through the hard shell. "The peccary, on the other hand, cracks the nut along the lateral seam that divides it into halves, a tribute to the hardness of his teeth and the power of his jaws."

Of all the known terrors in a jungle night, none compares with a herd of white-lipped peccaries. High boots and loose trousers can be worn as protection against poisonous snakes, and antivenins are available if one is bitten in spite of precautions. But "in the presence of a large herd of peccaries all of which rush viciously to the attack, a man, no matter how carefully chosen his arsenal, would have just about as much chance of coming off unscathed as a lightning beetle attacked by a regiment of army ants." Their armament is a pair of razor-sharp tusks in each jaw—weapons with which they slash an enemy to pieces.

These white-lipped wild pigs are frequently nocturnal and travel several abreast in bands of fifty to a hundred. Each adult animal weighs about a hundred pounds, and can demonstrate remarkable speed in either escape or attack. They are far more formidable than the collared peccaries which often scavenge the same jungle. The collared pigs are a third smaller, less odoriferous, form bands of eight or ten, and trot through the rain forest in single file. Tapir and deer, which pay no attention to the collared peccary, usually desert a region as soon as a band of white-lips moves in. Man must travel carefully in their neighborhood for, although they usually run off to avoid a meeting, they sometimes choose to charge, and do so with a terrifying clattering of teeth like "hundreds of castanets." The only haven from attack is in a tree. And smooth, branchless jungle trees are notoriously hard to climb.

The nearness of white-lipped peccaries is usually obvious to one's nose, since their musk is powerful and clings to the ground in the hothouse air of a jungle night. Eyes, however, seem more reliable. If for no other reason, the most stout-hearted night explorer of a jungle trail may be reluctant to turn off his flashlight and depend alone on his nose and ears. Often the patch of brightened area seems all too small. A soft treading puma or a spotted jaguar could easily be preparing to pounce from the blind rear. A constrictor snake might be looped from the next low limb—a thirty-foot anaconda or a twelve-foot boa. How many six-inch tarantulas are waiting along the trail, crouching at the mouths of their down-slanted burrows?

These animals seldom attack a man, but in the pitch blackness of the rain forest, statistics offer a puny shield! Although we knew how acoustically dead the tropical woodland was, it seemed that our stumbling steps must alert every creature within a radius of a mile. Perhaps it would be better to sit quietly on an ant-free log, and wait for some animal to become curious enough to approach. Then right behind us a limb would crash, tearing leaves from branches and branches from trees. Fungus and termites had done their work, digesting dead wood and returning part of a tree to its mother earth.

On one night, our confidence high, we sat resolutely on a stump with flashlights off, listening to the squeaks and twitterings in the foliage high overhead. Suddenly, something snorted and brushed an outstretched foot. Startled, we pressed our lamp switches and found ourselves facing a pair of quarter-ton tapirs. They were as startled as we. Down the trail they bolted, snorting, their broad backs wet and glistening. This largest animal native to Central and South America is a relative of the rhinoceros, but its flexible nose extends three or four inches as a soft proboscis which can be moved in all directions. Normally it hangs down over the mouth "like a drooping eyelid," but when frightened, the myopic mammal twists it from side to side and up and down, snorting and sniffing, apparently deciding which way to dash next.

Night still affords advantages not offered by day. For we barely glimpsed the brown bird which quietly vacated a pendant nest hung on the tip of a low palm leaf. Was it the large hummingbird known as a "Nicaraguan hermit"? In the dim afternoon light filtering through the ocean of leaves above us, no markings seemed distinctive as she flew. Yet after dark, when we returned, the mother sat as for her portrait, with only a bright eye cocked in our direction. We made a photograph of her from a distance of no more than ten feet. The flash bulb blazed, the shutter clicked, but the Nicaraguan hermit moved not a single feather. Whether in jungle or temperate forest, birds are reluctant to leave their nests at night, and pictures of them incubating their eggs are particularly easy to get.

Any field trip in the jungle night involves calculated hazards. If we dozed while sitting without a light, a hungry vampire might take advantage. We would miss seeing the specialist at work—opening a painless wound with razor-sharp teeth, and lapping the blood without disturbing the sleeper. A light will fend them off and so will movement. So long as we moved along the trail or kept a lamp burning, we had no need to fear them. Nor, in the wilder jungles of Guiana, was Beebe "conscious of the bloody fang, the poison tooth, of the wilderness. The peace of this jungle at night was the same peace as that of the trees in our city parks."

Even with a reliable flashlamp and no rain, events in a jungle night can be unpredictable. We found a brook less precipitous than most—one with permanent pools which cascaded gently down a slope. Time and again we visited the place a few hours after sunset, to watch the fresh-water shrimp sculling around, their big stalked eyes aglow with a reddish fire. If we stood downstream and held the light low, they would approach us, burning brilliantly by reflected eyeshine. On one of these occasions, while we were concentrating on shrimp, a wild yell cut through the darkness—probably the death scream of a coati which had been pounced upon by a jungle cat. Instantly the birds above awoke and began to clamor. In the topmost boughs a troupe of howler monkeys took up the cry with a crescendo of coughing barks that merged into one appalling roar, an "endless earth-shaking moan, followed by a quick series of grunts like staccato thunder." How many of the monkey tribe contributed to the hullabaloo we could not tell. But Bates, who commented on how much the howlers "deepened the feeling of solitude which crept on as darkness closed around us," was indulging in British understatement when he wrote that it is "a most fearful and harrowing noise, under which it is difficult to keep up one's buoyancy of spirit."

The chorusing of howler monkeys can begin at any time of night. Usually they are heard by day. A thunderstorm will start them, and the claps of exploding air are dimmed by the primate cries. "If contests were held among the beasts of the world to determine the one with the most powerful voice, the howling monkey would certainly be acclaimed champion on every occasion—the roar of the lion, the howl of the wolf, even the wail of a banshee dwindling to a mere whisper beside the efforts of the great, bearded vocalist of the South [and Central] American forests." Yet this is the sound of a jungle dawn. There is no cheerful chirruping of robins, as on a temperate lawn, welcoming the new day. Night surrenders above a tropical forest to the reverberating jeers and hoots of this Stentor among mammals—to a skirl of defiance which ends human sleep more effectively than any alarm clock.

ENIGMA OF THE PACIFIC

by C. J. Guiguet

This "Enigma of the Pacific" proves that there is still much to learn of many things that lie around us, open to our gaze. The author, C. J. Guiguet, holds the position of Biologist at the Provincial Museum in Victoria, British Columbia. He is thus within his province in spinning this true story as intriguing as a murder mystery. The difference is that in all proper murder mysteries the case is cleared up in the last few pages or paragraphs, and the breathless reader can put down the book with a deep feeling of relief. Here the suspense persists, still as baffling and as alluring as it was when the story was printed originally in Audubon Magazine. If that unsatisfactory state of affairs is enough to make an irate reader put down the book and go out and solve the mystery of the marbled murrelet, please send word.

OUT of the misty night from the darkening surge of the Pacific, small, fast-flying bodies hurtle over the headlands and disappear into the hinterlands of western North America. Their destination forms one of the last mysteries of the bird world, for no man has ever traced the route from sea to nesting grounds of the marbled murrelet. Nor has anyone studied its nesting habits, and no one has ever seen the newly-hatched young of this bird.

Authorities in ornithology of the Pacific Northwest have little to contribute apart from theories. Major Allan Brooks, J. A. Munro, I. McTaggart Cowan, Harry S. Swarth, Kenneth Racey, S. G. Jewett, H. M. Laing, R. M. Stewart—all keen, determined workers and wise in the ways of birds—have yet to unravel the mystery of this common little alcid. So let us go over what has been learned about *Brachyramphus marmoratus* as it is known to science; the dipchick as it is commonly called, or the marbled murrelet as it is known to bird-watchers.

The first egg of the marbled murrelet known to science was taken from the oviduct of a bird shot by G. G. Cantwell on the Prince of Wales Archipelago on May 23, 1897; subsequently others were gotten in the same manner. There are also two records of eggs said to have been taken *in situ*, that is, where laid. Unfortunately, these two records are contradictory and are not accepted by ornithologists. The first report was of an egg found on rocky land above the Tien River about 70 miles north of Nome, Alaska. Mr. A. H. Durham, the collector, is said to have taken this egg and the two parent birds on June 10, 1904. Later, in 1931, Mr. S. J. Darcus published the discovery of several nests situated in burrows in the ground on the Queen Charlotte Islands. Unfortunately, no birds were collected with these eggs and some ornithologists claim the eggs collected by Darcus are those of the ancient murrelet, a common and well-known nester in the area. No one questions the integrity of these workers, but since neither has followed up and proved his finds, science cannot but regard the nesting habits of these birds as still a mystery.

Apart from the war years, I have spent each summer since 1935 on zoological exploration in coastal British Columbia. On these expeditions, some lasting up to five months, I gathered much first-hand information about murrelets. In addition, fishermen, natives, settlers, loggers, and amateur ornithologists have added bits of information. Many of these have offered leads—many were contradictory. The following is an up-to-date account of what we know about the marbled murrelet:

It is a small sea bird approximately 10 inches long and weighs about half a pound. It lives more on the inner coastal waters than do most other members of the family Alcidae to which it belongs. It eats small crustacea such as euphausid shrimps, and fishes such as the sand launce, which it catches by diving after them. Its numbers upon the coast are legion; during the summer it is in all the off-shore waters from the Aleutians to Washington, and in the winter, it moves as far south as California.

In summer the marbled murrelet is a dark mottled brown; in winter it appears dark on the back, with white underparts. The molts take place in spring, in late February and March; in the fall, in September and through October. During the molts, it has a peculiar mottled appearance, intermediate between the summer and winter plumages. The name dipchick stems from the diving habit of these birds. Generally riding low on the water, its tail-parts up, it dives with a sudden flip, momentarily exposing a white rear as it disappears below the surface.

Marbled murrelets move about at night, to and from their terrestrial nesting grounds, and their daylight hours are spent on the sea. During the breeding season they become agitated as daylight fails, anxious it seems, to be off to the nesting area in order to relieve the incubating mate, or to feed the young one as the case may be. It seems that they may have only one young, as specimens collected have but a single brood patch. In addition, when the young appear on the sea, only one is usually seen accompanied by the two parent birds. The young appear to be raised in the nest until capable of flight. At that time they are in a plumage resembling that of the winter adult and are, consequently, easily distinguished from their brown-colored parents. They often retain vestiges of a grayish natal down adhering to the ends of feathers about the head and back; the egg tooth may still be prominent on the upper mandible. In my studies of the breeding colonies of sea birds, I have noted a characteristic pungent odor on those that occupy burrows, an odor often persisting for days after my scientific specimens of the birds have been skinned and preserved. This odor is not present on the marbled murrelet young when they first arrive upon the sea, which might suggest that this species does not nest underground.

Many theories have evolved as to the nesting place of the marbled murrelet. First, and quite naturally, it is thought that it may use a burrow; many birds of this family do excavate burrows in the ground and raise the young therein. A great deal of study has been done on the known breeding colonies of sea birds in British Columbia. Rev. J. H. Keene, W. H. Osgood, W. A. Newcomb, Brooks, Swarth, Stewart, Walter Maguire, and myself have all thoroughly worked Cox and Langara Islands in the Queen Charlotte group. In addition I have covered Frederick, Hippa, and many of the smaller islets along the west coast of the Charlottes—and when I searched the burrows for nesting sea birds, the marbled murrelet was always in my thoughts. Any burrow that appeared unusual I immediately excavated, but to date (apart from the questionable Darcus record) no one has ever found a marbled murrelet in an underground burrow.

On the Queen Charlottes, the Haida Indians take many birds and their eggs from the breeding colonies for food. I have questioned these natives at every opportunity, showing them specimens of the marbled murrelet and asking "where does she lay her egg?" Invariably I get the same reaction—the slow captivating native grin, or a chuckle, accompanied by a shake of the head and a "nobody knows." These natives know their birds. They excavate far more burrows than do any museum collectors. They do it year after year. If there were any marbled murrelets nesting in burrows close to the coast these people would have uncovered them long ago.

The tree theory—that they nest in hollow trees, or high in the branches, or under the roots of trees well inland—sounds logical enough when one has spent a few evenings near the ancient murrelet colonies and seen these web-footed sea birds perched on the limbs of Sitka spruce. However, the great stretches of logged-over land, thousands of square miles from sea coast to mountain top, in many sections of the breeding range, should have produced records of the marbled murrelet when the operators were denuding the slopes. Each species known to nest in the coniferous forests has been reported many times —why not the marbled murrelet? It seems unlikely that this species nests in the coastal forest.

Some ornithologists—Laing of Comox, for example—believe that the murrelet is a cliff-nester, breeding on the face of inaccessible mountain chasms, much I suppose, as does the black swift. The black swift is a common bird, and yet the total number of nests found can be counted on one's fingers. There are many cliff faces in the coastal range that could conceivably offer suitable niches for nesting murrelets. I personally have examined many of these close to the sea with no success. The mountaineers of British Columbia are an active lot, and many of them are bird-lovers as well. People like the late Don Munday and his family, who have climbed such coastal mountains as Saugstad and Waddington, have nothing to report. Moreover, most ornithologists agree that structurally the murrelet is not adapted for clinging to cliff faces. For these reasons and the fact that most cliffs near the sea have been examined by various ornithologists interested in falcons and other cliff dwellers, with no marbled murrelets reported, it would seem that the marbled murrelet does not nest there.

Ronald Stewart, a top-notch field man and resident ornithologist on the Queen Charlottes, once put forth the theory that the answer might be found about large fresh-water lakes in the interior of Graham Island. It was reported to him by a native friend that marbled murrelets had been seen taking off at dawn from Eden Lake, near the head of Naden Harbor. These birds, the Indian said, circled to great heights and then headed for the sea. To strengthen his theory, Ronald Stewart recounted a record of an egg taken from the oviduct of a bird shot at Harrison Lake on the lower mainland of the Province many years ago. This record has never appeared in the literature, but as I recall it, Stewart actually saw the specimen. Fresh-water lakes are numerous in the coastal area, and they abound with trout. Consequently, fishermen prowl many of these lakes, yet have never reported seeing marbled murrelets there. Also, if the birds nested in burrows leading from the water, muskrat trappers should have taken marbled murrelets long ago. If they nest on the ground, in the marshes, or on the banks, such men as J. A. Munro of the Dominion Wildlife Service, would surely have discovered them in the course of his waterfowl investigations. While it is possible that lakes may play some part in the life history of these birds, it seems unlikely that they nest in close proximity to such bodies of water.

The mountain-top theory, put forth on the strength of the nesting habits of the Kittlitz murrelet, a very closely related form, seems logical, and biologically the idea is sound. The story of the Kittlitz murrelet is an interesting one. For many years the breeding habits of this alcid were unknown, too. In 1913 F. E. Kleinschmidt, who was collecting specimens of birds at Pavloff Bay, Alaska, asked his guide if he knew where the bird nested. The Aleut guide pointed to the towering skylines and said "way far, on top of mountains, in the snow." Kleinschmidt must have taken this information with a large grain of the proverbial salt, although a local trapper corroborated the guide's statement. Later, he chanced to be up on the skylines hunting brown bear for the Carnegie Museum. In order to approach one, he took a circuitous route up through some snowfields. As he stalked carefully towards the bear, a bird flushed from a small patch of gravel that the receding snows had left. There, at his feet, was the first egg of the Kittlitz murrelet ever found in the nest.

It may be that the mystery of the marbled murrelet will be solved in a like manner. Certainly the birds are often at great heights on their way to and from the sea—but here again we have contradictory evidence. I have personally seen marbled murrelets flying in low over the timber, and upon one occasion, directly into the timber. At Masset, where Stewart, Maguire, and I have watched them returning northward to the sea at dawn, the country to the south is flat, and on the ground in those flat woods Stewart once found a fully feathered young one. Jewett, in Oregon, also found a young marbled murrelet;

this, I believe, was also in a timbered area. McTaggart Cowan at the University of British Columbia, picked up a young one on the campus in front of the library. All of these birds may or may not have been many miles from the nest in which they were hatched. All of them were in full juvenal plumage and were theoretically capable of flying. Whether they had been injured in flight, and had dropped from exhaustion, or were near the nest site prior to take-off, is unknown. Had these three birds been on the sea, no questions would have arisen, but their presence on the land, apparently uninjured, raises another problem, a point to be considered, weighed, and evaluated in the piecing together of evidence that will ultimately lead to the discovery of the marbled murrelet's nest. Jewett and others record the interesting find of E. J. Booth, who discovered a partially incubated marbled murrelet egg on the south fork of the Nooksack River in the State of Washington. There was no evidence of a nest of any kind, but the fact that the egg was about two thirds incubated eliminates the possibility of it having been accidentally dropped where it was found. Here we have evidence that ties in nicely with the theory that the immature birds found by Stewart, Jewett, and Cowan may have been near the place of hatching. It suggests also that these alcids may, perhaps, nest in a variety of habitats.

In July, 1946, Ronald Stewart told me of a great concentration of marbled murrelets in Masset Inlet on the Queen Charlotte Islands. We watched these birds, some 200, for a day. All were in breeding plumage and all were feeding on sand launces, a small silver fish shaped like a lead pencil, and about the same size. As dusk approached the murrelets began to rise off the water and fly, circling to heights of perhaps 500 feet. Still circling they would drop back into the water, the whole flock giving their weird little calls. When darkness had almost descended, some rose to great heights and disappeared inland to the west, others took off low over the water, gradually rising until they were lost in the gloom to the south. All of them were "packing feed" in their bills, and the silvery sand launce showed up in the darkness seconds after the birds themselves were lost to sight. Subsequently I have seen such concentrations on three occasions, at Cumshewa Inlet on Moresby Island, at Frederick Island, and near the mainland on the Bardswell Islands. In each case the first concentrations of young birds were seen on the sea the following morning. A very exciting possibility exists in this behavior, for here in a breeding concentration of adults feeding young, may lie the key with which to unravel the mystery.

I could tell more of this intriguing search—of hours spent by night on shores and skylines, listening for the cry of the marbled murrelet; of a series of camps, from skyline to a shoreline where they had been seen flying in; of searches in the talus slopes and rock slides of the alplands; and of hand and knee crawling with digging irons through Pacific West Coast salal jungle.

The latest evidence received at the British Columbia Provincial Museum is of great interest to us. A stunned marbled murrelet was taken from the debris of a large hemlock felled on the Queen Charlotte Islands in 1953. The logger, Walter Feyer of Masset, a reliable amateur bird-watcher, examined the murrelet and found it had a brood patch. Further search in the debris uncovered the fragments of a marbled murrelet's egg, but no evidence of a nest of any kind was found. That no nest was found is not important, for many birds do not gather material and build nests. However, there *was* a bird and a broken egg in the debris of that tree. Whether the tree had fallen upon a nesting site, or whether the egg and the bird were in the tree before it was felled we don't know. But there seems little doubt that Walter Feyer was very close to a nesting marbled murrelet that day. Unfortunately, he was unable to uncover further evidence.

Thus, as far as we know, the nesting behavior and nesting habitat of the marbled murrelet remains unsolved, and still presents an intriguing problem to ornithologists.

GOOD OAK

by Aldo Leopold

Born in Iowa in 1887, Aldo Leopold grew up on a farm and developed a great love of the outdoors. When he had finished his schooling he went to work for the United States Forest Service in Arizona and New Mexico and remained with the department from 1909 to 1924. In that period he learned much about forest preservation and replacement and wildlife management. Then he went into business for himself as a consultant to government and private organizations in that field. Colleges and universities in increasing numbers were setting up courses in forestry, ecology, game management, and similar subjects, and in 1933 Aldo Leopold accepted the chair of Game Management at the University of Wisconsin. He was still occupying that position when he lost his life fighting a grass fire on a farm near his own in Wisconsin. He died April 21, 1948. He was a popular figure in his field for his kindly ways as well as his expert knowledge. He was largely self-taught, and a touch of homespun philosophy ran through his speech and his writings and lent them an extra tang. The following selection is taken from A Sand County Almanac, which he completed only a few months before his death.

February

THERE are two spiritual dangers in not owning a farm. One is the danger of supposing that breakfast comes from the grocery, and the other that heat comes from the furnace.

To avoid the first danger, one should plant a garden, preferably where there is no grocer to confuse the issue.

To avoid the second, he should lay a split of good oak on the andirons, preferably where there is no furnace, and let it warm his shins while a February blizzard tosses the trees outside. If one has cut, split, hauled, and piled his own good oak, and let his mind work the while, he will remember much about where the heat comes from, and with a wealth of detail denied to those who spend the weekend in town astride a radiator.

The particular oak now aglow on my andirons grew on the bank of the old emigrant road where it climbs the sandhill. The stump, which I measured upon felling the tree, has a diameter of 30 inches. It shows 80 growth rings, hence the seedling from which it originated must have laid its first ring of wood in 1865, at the end of the Civil War. But I know from the history of present seedlings that no oak grows above the reach of rabbits without a decade or more of getting girdled each winter, and re-sprouting during the following summer. Indeed, it is all too clear that every surviving oak is the product either of rabbit negligence or of rabbit scarcity. Some day some patient botanist will draw a frequency curve of oak birth-years, and show that the curve humps every ten years, each hump originating from a low in the ten-year rabbit cycle. (A fauna and flora, by this very process of perpetual battle within and among species, achieve collective immortality.)

It is likely, then, that a low in rabbits occurred in the middle 'sixties, when my oak began to lay on annual rings, but that the acorn that produced it fell during the preceding decade, when the covered wagons were still passing over my road into the Great Northwest. It may have been the wash and wear of the emigrant traffic that bared this roadbank, and thus enabled this particular acorn to spread its first leaves to the sun. Only one acorn in a thousand ever grew large enough to fight rabbits; the rest were drowned at birth in the prairie sea.

It is a warming thought that this one wasn't, and thus lived to garner eighty years of June sun. It is this sunlight that is now being released, through the intervention of my axe and saw, to warm my shack and my spirit through eighty gusts of blizzard. And with each gust a wisp of smoke from my chimney bears witness, to whomsoever it may concern, that the sun did not shine in vain.

My dog does not care where heat comes from, but he cares ardently that it come, and soon. Indeed he considers my ability to make it come as something magical, for when I rise in the cold black pre-dawn and kneel shivering by the hearth making a fire, he pushes himself blandly between me and the kindling splits I have laid on the ashes, and I must touch a match to them by poking it between his legs. Such faith, I suppose, is the kind that moves mountains.

It was a bolt of lightning that put an end to wood-making by this particular oak. We were all awakened, one night in July, by the thunderous crash; we realized that the bolt must have hit nearby, but, since it had not hit us, we all went back to sleep. Man brings all things to the test of himself, and this is notably true of lightning.

Next morning, as we strolled over the sandhill rejoicing with the cone-flowers and the prairie clovers over their fresh accession of rain, we came upon a great slab of bark freshly torn from the trunk of the roadside oak. The trunk showed a long spiral scar of barkless sapwood, a foot wide and not yet yellowed by the sun. By the next day the leaves had wilted, and we knew that the lightning had bequeathed to us three cords of prospective fuel wood.

We mourned the loss of the old tree, but knew that a dozen of its progeny standing straight and stalwart on the sands had already taken over its job of wood-making.

We let the dead veteran season for a year in the sun it could no longer use, and then on a crisp winter's day we laid a newly filed saw to its bastioned base. Fragrant little chips of history spewed from the saw cut, and accumulated on the snow before each kneeling sawyer. We sensed that these two piles of sawdust were something more than wood: that they were the integrated transect of a century; that our saw was biting its way, stroke by stroke, decade by decade, into the chronology of a lifetime, written in concentric annual rings of good oak.

It took only a dozen pulls of the saw to transect the few years of our ownership, during which we had learned to love and cherish this farm. Abruptly we began to cut the years of our predecessor the bootlegger, who hated this farm, skinned it of residual fertility, burned its farmhouse, threw it back into the lap of the County (with delinquent taxes to boot), and then disappeared among the landless anonymities of the Great Depression. Yet the oak had laid down good wood for him; his sawdust was as fragrant, as sound, and as pink as our own. An oak is no respecter of persons.

The reign of the bootlegger ended sometime during the dust-bowl drouths of 1936, 1934, 1933, and 1930. Oak smoke from his still and peat from burning marshlands must have clouded the sun in those

years, and alphabetical conservation was abroad in the land, but the
sawdust shows no change.

Rest! cries the chief sawyer, and we pause for breath.

Now our saw bites into the 1920's, the Babbittian decade when everything grew bigger and better in heedlessness and arrogance—until
1929, when stock markets crumpled. If the oak heard them fall, its
wood gives no sign. Nor did it heed the Legislature's several protesta-
tions of love for trees: a National Forest and a forest-crop law in 1927,
a great refuge on the Upper Mississippi bottomlands in 1924, and a
new forest policy in 1921. Neither did it notice the demise of the
state's last marten in 1925, nor the arrival of its first starling in 1923.

In March 1922, the 'Big Sleet' tore the neighboring elms limb from
limb, but there is no sign of damage to our tree. What is a ton of ice,
more or less, to a good oak?

Rest! cries the chief sawyer, and we pause for breath.

Now the saw bites into 1910–20, the decade of the drainage dream,
when steam shovels sucked dry the marshes of central Wisconsin to
make farms, and made ash-heaps instead. Our marsh escaped, not because of any caution or forbearance among engineers, but because the
river floods it each April, and did so with a vengeance—perhaps a defensive vengeance—in the years 1913–16. The oak laid on wood just
the same, even in 1915, when the Supreme Court abolished the state
forests and Governor Phillip pontificated that 'state forestry is not a
good business proposition.' (It did not occur to the Governor that
there might be more than one definition of what is good, and even
of what is business. It did not occur to him that while the courts were
writing one definition of goodness in the law books, fires were writing
quite another one on the face of the land. Perhaps, to be a governor,
one must be free from doubt on such matters.)

While forestry receded during this decade, game conservation advanced. In 1916 pheasants became successfully established in Wauke-
sha County; in 1915 a federal law prohibited spring shooting; in 1913
a state game farm was started; in 1912 a 'buck law' protected female
deer; in 1911 an epidemic of refuges spread over the state. 'Refuge'
became a holy word, but the oak took no heed.

Rest! cries the chief sawyer, and we pause for breath.

Now we cut 1910, when a great university president published a

book on conservation, a great sawfly epidemic killed millions of tamaracks, a great drouth burned the pineries, and a great dredge drained
Horicon Marsh.

We cut 1909, when smelt were first planted in the Great Lakes,
and when a wet summer induced the Legislature to cut the forest-fire
appropriations.

We cut 1908, a dry year when the forests burned fiercely, and Wisconsin parted with its last cougar.

We cut 1907, when a wandering lynx, looking in the wrong direction for the promised land, ended his career among the farms of Dane
County.

We cut 1906, when the first state forester took office, and fires
burned 17,000 acres in these sand counties; we cut 1905 when a great
flight of goshawks came out of the North and ate up the local grouse
(they no doubt perched in this tree to eat some of mine). We cut
1902–3, a winter of bitter cold; 1901, which brought the most intense
drouth of record (rainfall only 17 inches); 1900, a centennial year of
hope, of prayer, and the usual annual ring of oak.

Rest! cries the chief sawyer, and we pause for breath.

Now our saw bites into the 1890's, called gay by those whose eyes
turn cityward rather than landward. We cut 1899, when the last passenger pigeon collided with a charge of shot near Babcock, two counties to the north; we cut 1898 when a dry fall, followed by a snowless
winter, froze the soil seven feet deep and killed the apple trees; 1897,
another drouth year, when another forestry commission came into being; 1896, when 25,000 prairie chickens were shipped to market from
the village of Spooner alone; 1895, another year of fires; 1894, another
drouth year; and 1893, the year of 'The Bluebird Storm,' when a
March blizzard reduced the migrating bluebirds to near-zero. (The
first bluebirds always alighted in this oak, but in the middle 'nineties
it must have gone without.) We cut 1892, another year of fires; 1891,
a low in the grouse cycle; and 1890, the year of the Babcock Milk
Tester, which enabled Governor Heil to boast, half a century later,
that Wisconsin is America's Dairyland. The motor licenses which now
parade that boast were then not foreseen, even by Professor Babcock.

It was likewise in 1890 that the largest pine rafts in history slipped
down the Wisconsin River in full view of my oak, to build an empire of red barns for the cows of the prairie states. Thus it is that

good pine now stands between the cow and the blizzard, just as good oak stands between the blizzard and me.

Rest! cries the chief sawyer, and we pause for breath.

Now our saw bites into the 1880's; into 1889, a drouth year in which Arbor Day was first proclaimed; into 1887, when Wisconsin appointed its first game wardens; into 1886, when the College of Agriculture held its first short course for farmers; into 1885, preceded by a winter 'of unprecedented length and severity'; into 1883, when Dean W. H. Henry reported that the spring flowers at Madison bloomed 13 days later than average; into 1882, the year Lake Mendota opened a month late following the historic 'Big Snow' and bitter cold of 1881–2.

It was likewise in 1881 that the Wisconsin Agricultural Society debated the question, 'How do you account for the second growth of black oak timber that has sprung up all over the country in the last thirty years?' My oak was one of these. One debater claimed spontaneous generation, another claimed regurgitation of acorns by southbound pigeons.

Rest! cries the chief sawyer, and we pause for breath.

Now our saw bites the 1870's, the decade of Wisconsin's carousal in wheat. Monday morning came in 1879, when chinch bugs, grubs, rust, and soil exhaustion finally convinced Wisconsin farmers that they could not compete with the virgin prairies further west in the game of wheating land to death. I suspect that this farm played its share in the game, and that the sand blow just north of my oak had its origin in over-wheating.

This same year of 1879 saw the first planting of carp in Wisconsin, and also the first arrival of quack-grass as a stowaway from Europe. On 27 October 1879, six migrating prairie chickens perched on the rooftree of the German Methodist Church in Madison, and took a look at the growing city. On 8 November the markets at Madison were reported to be glutted with ducks at 10 cents each.

In 1878 a deer hunter from Sauk Rapids remarked prophetically, 'The hunters promise to outnumber the deer.'

On 10 September 1877, two brothers, shooting Muskego Lake, bagged 210 blue-winged teal in one day.

In 1876 came the wettest year of record; the rainfall piled up 50 inches. Prairie chickens declined, perhaps owing to hard rains.

In 1875 four hunters killed 153 prairie chickens at York Prairie, one county to the eastward. In the same year the U.S. Fish Commission planted Atlantic salmon in Devil's Lake, 10 miles south of my oak.

In 1874 the first factory-made barbed wire was stapled to oak trees; I hope no such artifacts are buried in the oak now under saw!

In 1873 one Chicago firm received and marketed 25,000 prairie chickens. The Chicago trade collectively bought 600,000 at $3.25 per dozen.

In 1872 the last wild Wisconsin turkey was killed, two counties to the southwest.

It is appropriate that the decade ending the pioneer carousal in wheat should likewise have ended the pioneer carousal in pigeon blood. In 1871, within a 50-mile triangle spreading northwestward from my oak, 136 million pigeons are estimated to have nested, and some may have nested in it, for it was then a thrifty sapling 20 feet tall. Pigeon hunters by scores plied their trade with net and gun, club and salt lick, and trainloads of prospective pigeon pie moved southward and eastward toward the cities. It was the last big nesting in Wisconsin, and nearly the last in any state.

This same year 1871 brought other evidence of the march of empire: the Peshtigo Fire, which cleared a couple of counties of trees and soil, and the Chicago Fire, said to have started from the protesting kick of a cow.

In 1870 the meadow mice had already staged their march of empire; they ate up the young orchards of the young state, and then died. They did not eat my oak, whose bark was already too tough and thick for mice.

It was likewise in 1870 that a market gunner boasted in the *American Sportsman* of killing 6000 ducks in one season near Chicago.

Rest! cries the chief sawyer, and we pause for breath.

Our saw now cuts the 1860's, when thousands died to settle the question: Is the man-man community lightly to be dismembered? They settled it, but they did not see, nor do we yet see, that the same question applies to the man-land community.

This decade was not without its gropings toward the larger issue. In 1867 Increase A. Lapham induced the State Horticultural Society to offer prizes for forest plantations. In 1866 the last native Wisconsin elk was killed. The saw now severs 1865, the pith-year of our oak. In that year John Muir offered to buy from his brother, who then owned the home farm thirty miles east of my oak, a sanctuary for the wildflowers that had gladdened his youth. His brother declined to part with the land, but he could not suppress the idea: 1865 still stands in Wisconsin history as the birth-year of mercy for things natural, wild, and free.

We have cut the core. Our saw now reverses its orientation in history; we cut backward across the years, and outward toward the far side of the stump. At last there is a tremor in the great trunk; the saw-kerf suddenly widens; the saw is quickly pulled as the sawyers spring backward to safety; all hands cry 'Timber!'; my oak leans, groans, and crashes with earth-shaking thunder, to lie prostrate across the emigrant road that gave it birth.

Now comes the job of making wood. The maul rings on steel wedges as the sections of trunk are up-ended one by one, only to fall apart in fragrant slabs to be corded by the roadside.

There is an allegory for historians in the diverse functions of saw, wedge, and axe.

The saw works only across the years, which it must deal with one by one, in sequence. From each year the raker teeth pull little chips of fact, which accumulate in little piles, called sawdust by woodsmen and archives by historians; both judge the character of what lies within by the character of the samples thus made visible without. It is not until the transect is completed that the tree falls, and the stump yields a collective view of a century. By its fall the tree attests the unity of the hodge-podge called history.

The wedge, on the other hand, works only in radial splits; such a split yields a collective view of all the years at once, or no view at all, depending on the skill with which the plane of the split is chosen. (If in doubt, let the section season for a year until a crack develops. Many a hastily driven wedge lies rusting in the woods, embedded in unsplittable cross-grain.)

The axe functions only at an angle diagonal to the years, and this only for the peripheral rings of the recent past. Its special function is to lop limbs, for which both saw and wedge are useless.

The three tools are requisite to good oak, and to good history.

These things I ponder as the kettle sings, and the good oak burns to red coals on white ashes. Those ashes, come spring, I will return to the orchard at the foot of the sandhill. They will come back to me again, perhaps as red apples, or perhaps as a spirit of enterprise in some fat October squirrel, who, for reasons unknown to himself, is bent on planting acorns.

THE LOVE SONG OF THE WOLF

by Theodora C. Stanwell-Fletcher

*The Stanwell-Fletchers, husband and wife, spent two years on
the wooded shore of a lonely lake in a wild section of British
Columbia. They were two hundred miles from the nearest paved
road and thirty miles from their nearest neighbors, inhabitants of
an Indian village. As Theodora Cope, born in Germantown,
Pennsylvania, the author was a trained scientist when she met and
married John F. Stanwell-Fletcher in 1937. She had been graduated from Mount Holyoke College in 1928, had done years of
postgraduate work at Cornell, and had been as far as New Zealand and Indonesia on scientific expeditions.*

*The young couple decided to start married life in a little cabin
in Driftwood Valley in British Columbia. The husband was a
Canadian who knew and loved the northern wilds. He was a former member of the Royal Canadian Mounted Police who got
down from his horse to turn trapper and then gave up trapping
to draw and paint wildlife. He became a citizen of the United
States and during World War II served in the United States Air
Force, where his knowledge of the northern country was put to
good use. With the wife doing the writing and the husband doing the illustrations, the Stanwell-Fletchers produced* Driftwood
Valley, *published in 1946, and* The Tundra World, *published in
1952. The second book had to do with their experiences in the
Arctic, but the song of the wolf, as chronicled here, was heard in
the Driftwood Valley that had been their home in earlier years.*

February 15

LAST night we heard the love song of the wolf! There had been fresh snow followed by clear sky and a full brilliant moon. Our thermometer stood at 24 below. I proposed a snowshoe hike to Wolf Hill on the chance that we might be able to observe wolves down on the lake. J. scouted the notion of actually seeing them, but the night was so beautiful that he couldn't resist the idea any more than I could.

We stepped out in a dazzling world. At least a foot of new powdery snow covered the firm six-foot snow level and made ideal snowshoeing. We traveled swiftly and silently through silver glens and black shadows. Our snowshoes kicked up feathery clouds that twinkled like quicksilver. Our breath froze over jackets and caps and hair so that we were dressed from head to toe in white crystals.

When we reached the top of Wolf Hill, all below us spread the Driftwood Valley, clear as noontime, lit by the moon for a hundred miles, still and primeval as in the days before the few men who know it now had ever seen it. Belts of dark forest were interspersed by willow swamps which, deeply buried, lay like open fields brushed with gold. To the south the mountains of Takla were faint blue in the distance. The jagged, tumbled Frypans jutted like silver spearheads into the deep amethyst, star-studded sky. The Driftwoods, our own mountains, lay serene and golden, so close that we could almost reach out and touch them. The glacial-covered range far behind to the west showed distinctly, and the Bear Lake Mountains stood sharp and shining all around the northern horizon. Finally we moved across to the east side where a rock precipice falls down to Wolf Lake, crisscrossed with fresh black tracks, and looked on the miles of forested hills that rise gradually to the rolling Ominecas.

Utter silence, a deathlike hush over the land, and then, from somewhere below, came a sound that made our hearts stand still. Like a breath of wind, rising slowly, softly, clearly to a high, lovely note of sadness and longing; dying down on two distinct notes so low that our human ears could scarcely catch them. It rose and died, again and again. A wolf singing the beauty of the night, singing it as no human voice had ever done, calling on a mate to share the beauty of it with him, to come to him, to love him. Over and over it sang, so tenderly and exquisitely that it seemed as if the voice were calling to me and I could hardly keep from crying. The whole wilderness was musical with it. After an interval—I have no idea whether it was short or long —from far away across the eastern hills came a soft, distinct, answering call. Three times more the wolf below us sang and was answered. Gradually the other voice grew nearer and nearer, until we thought that the two must have come together, for the sudden quiet was not broken again.

Then I knew that I was shivering like a leaf and my arm, which J. had been grasping, was almost paralyzed.

J. was cussing to himself and saying: "Gad, what luck! What marvelous luck! I've heard wolves howling in India and the Arctic, but I never heard the like of that! Let's go home—if we're not too cold to move."

On the west, Wolf Hill slopes steeply, almost perpendicularly, for several hundred feet, and is clear of trees. Spurred to recklessness by the height of our emotions, we did something that we've never dreamed of daring to do before. We sat on the crossed heels of our snowshoes and tobogganed down the icy slope at terrific speed. Powdered snow flew up in clouds and turned to rainbows where the moon shone through it. That we arrived, unscathed, in a drift below, instead of being smashed to bits against trees, was just a part of the magic of the night.

We reached the warm cabin after midnight, stoked up a roaring fire, and drank hot scalding cocoa. I hardly remember getting into bed and to sleep, but all night in my dreams I thought I could hear a wolf calling and singing and sobbing in a voice of exquisite tenderness.

February 28

The other night, when the cabin was surrounded by the deep dark and snow of the winter evening, we were just sitting down to supper when a sound outside made us leap from our seats and fly to the door. Wolves again! This time there were many of them—a whole chorus —less than half a mile away. One voice after another—some deep, some high—caught up the song in perfect harmony. It was not the tender, longing voice of a lone wolf calling to his love, but a whole company—a family perhaps—singing together for the joy of making music. The song, starting low, rose ever fuller and higher, but always beautifully modulated.

One voice, singing on its own just before each big chorus began, was sweet and clear, exactly like a boy soprano. It started on a high, high note and slipped down, sadly and exquisitely, to a lower one.

Our supper grew stone cold and the open door chilled out the cabin while we listened, entranced. The only thing comparable to it was a stringed symphony, but the wolf voices seemed more full of soul and expression.

And each night since, this valley has become a concert hall filled with wolf music. No one who has really heard wolves at the time of mating could possibly describe it by any other term. The more familiar wolf hunting call is a very different sound and one which we occasionally heard here last fall. This appears to be always a prolonged series of high notes, persistent and savage. The movement of packs can be followed by their voices as they move along our valley. Undoubtedly it is the hunting and fighting songs, the idle calls, which possess the fearsomeness, and weirdness, or bloodcurdling quality commonly associated with the voices of wolves. Sometimes the wolf song comes from many miles away; it echoes and re-echoes melodiously up and down the hills. At other times it is close by Tetana, so that even when we are shut up warmly and tightly inside our cabin, we tingle and thrill at the first sound.

The wolves' singing seems to be definitely affected by weather; they are most active on beautiful nights, still, radiant ones lit by moon, or stars, or the faint glow of an aurora, nights so lovely that we ourselves are drawn out of the cabin to look and listen even before the wolf choruses begin.

A high mound, half a mile from Tetana, is a wolf meeting ground. We judge from the tracks that about eight or ten wolves gather together to sing. They also use several small hills which we often climb, including Wolf Hill. The very spots where we linger to look upon the world stretched out below are favorite gathering places for the wolf tribe. Their tracks lead directly from one vantage point to another and there are many imprints of huge hind quarters, hard and encrusted, such as are left by a dog that has sat or lain in snow for hours.

Why, J. and I argue, should the wolves sit there unless it is because they too recognize and appreciate something that we call beauty? There is no food to be had on these hilltops. Deep, untouched snow covers mouse holes. Rabbit and squirrel tracks are scarce or absent, and dense forest hides any sign of moving game in the valleys below.

Oddly enough, however, when the aurora comes with especial brilliance, the wolves are as silent as the grave. The owls and coyotes, whom we also hear frequently at this season, are noticeably quiet too. Perhaps they all know, as we do, that no sound should be made to detract from a miracle of sight and feeling. For, as February slips into March, we are being treated to another phenomenon of miraculous beauty. The Northern Lights, which we saw sometimes last autumn when they were not particularly spectacular, have begun to appear now in full glory.

The aurora borealis seems to precede great seasonal change. The lights appear on clear evenings around nine-thirty or ten. A saffron glow behind the forest on the east of Tetana grows gradually so bright that black spires of pines and spruces stand out sharply against it. Then, rising in tall columns of pale, glowing green, higher and higher toward the zenith, becoming suffused with vivid lavender and rose. Other columns begin in the north and northwest until they all meet, umbrella-wise, in the sky above Tetana. Never-still, ever-changing curtains of waving, swaying color—colors so intense that sometimes the snow across Tetana and the Driftwood Mountains is tinted pink, or green, or blue. Often as the colors bloom and die and bloom again, the air is full of sound. Something—actual noise or electric current—vibrates in our ears. This is what northerners mean when they say, "The Lights crackle." Something great and majestic is alive here in these night skies of late winter.

On such nights how can I bear to sleep and waste time in unconsciousness! But J. claims that Northern Lights are as common in his experience as sunsets and goes serenely to sleep at bedtime just as usual.

A feeling in the air makes one know spring is coming. The world is buried as deeply as ever in snow. Snowstorms still come and go. Snowshoes are as essential a part of moving as ever. Collecting sufficient firewood is a never-ending labor. The cabin roof and windows have still to be dug out, but snow on the ground is settling and crusts are forming. The sun is rising higher in the sky. The nights are as cold as ever. Temperatures still drop 20 or 30 degrees below zero, but we know that the hardness of winter is ended. The singing wolves remind us again and again of returning life and love. The throbbing colors of the aurora give warning of changing atmospheric conditions.

THE RIDDLE OF THE RIDLEY

by Archie Carr

This tale of a turtle is taken from The Windward Road, *a book that won for the author the John Burroughs Medal of 1957 by the unanimous vote of the judges. The author, Archie Carr, probably knows more about the subject matter than anybody else in the world, and it still remains a mystery to him. Born in Mobile, Alabama, June 16, 1909, Archie Carr attended local schools and sampled several colleges before he was granted a degree in science at the University of Florida in 1934. He added a Ph.D. there in 1937, and joined the staff as a biology teacher. He took time out for lengthy expeditions to Honduras and other countries fronting on the Gulf of Mexico, investigating the shores and waters in pursuit of knowledge of the life cycles of seagoing turtles. He suffered his share of heat and hardship, but he gives such a lively account of his labors as to force the conclusion that he thoroughly enjoyed treading and writing* The Windward Road.

THE twelve-foot pole flew a high arc and struck true over the skidding shadow. It plunged quarter-down and stopped short against the hard shell of the turtle. Then it fell free and floated to the top.

"Missed him," I said. I should have known better. It was Jonah Thompson who threw the iron.

But how does anyone hit a target like that? The bow of the little launch was bucking and shying in a cross-channel chop. A gusty breeze kept throwing the surface of the bay into crowds of tight wrinkles that raced by and shot back the light in confused reflections. The water was milky white to start with, and the turtle was thirty feet out and a yard down and dodging like a rabbit. It was like trying to hit a

scared pig from the bed of a truck lurching across a plowed field. Only
the pig would be out in plain view, while the turtle was a dim blur
in the cloudy water.

"He's carrying the iron," Jonah said. Then I saw the line snaking
out of the bucket in the bow.

"How do you do it?" I said.

"I'm sixty-five and I started early. It's worse with green turtles; they
run like a seagull. This here's a ridley."

He clawed in the pole with a boat hook. He took up the smoothly
paying line and slowly closed both hands on it. The tension pulled
us around a few points, and then a flipper broke water fifty feet out
in front. Very carefully Jonah began to take in line, and the boat and
the surfaced turtle drew together. When the gap closed he handed
the tight line to his boy and deftly dropped a loop of rope over one
of the flailing flippers. Then he heaved, and the turtle slid over the
gunwale and fell back-down on deck, where it scraped and thrashed
for purchase on the smooth planks.

"Stay clear of him," Jonah said. "He's mad. Ridleys is always mad."

I poked a rope end at the turtle's face. It seized the knot and
crunched and then flew into a long frenzy of flopping and pounding
about the deck.

"You can't keep a ridley on its back. Only a few hours. They're
crazy. They break their hearts."

That was how I got to know the Atlantic ridley. That was how the
great ridley mystery began for me.

It is the sea that holds the great mysteries. There is still much to
be learned in the land, to be sure, but it is the third dimension of
the oceans that hides the answers to broad elemental problems of natural history. Somewhere out there young salmon lose themselves, and
the Pribilof seals go there when they leave the rocks where they were
born. Through chance concordance of cryptic forces, the Red Tide
brews up and sporadically drifts in to the rich littoral of Florida, killing thousands of fishes, sending the tourists scurrying to flee the stink,
and then sweeping away again, unchecked and uncomprehended. As
long as man has had the wit to wonder, he must have puzzled over
the new eels in his pasture pond; and being told they come from the
sea where their parents went to spawn them is as preposterous as some
theory of astrophysics. When J. L. B. Smith found a coelacanth fish
fifteen years ago, it was a living fossil, as stirring a discovery to a biologist, and quite as great a probing of the past, as finding a dinosaur

would be. Who can trace the way of the great blue marlin or of Rhineodon, the whale shark, or tell anything worth hearing about the oarfish or the giant squid, or even say for sure where the homely mullet spawns its millions or where the gleaming hordes of tarpon come from?

And who can tell what the ridley is?

It was eighteen years ago when Jonah Thompson pulled in that first ridley out at Sandy Key in Florida Bay. I was there because of a letter from my friend Stew Springer, who is a gifted naturalist, versed in all sorts of seacraft. He was running a shark fishery at Islamorada on the upper Florida Keys at the time. He wrote to me to complain about a kind of turtle his fishermen brought in for shark bait. It was an evil-natured turtle, he said, flat and gray, with a big head and short, broad shell. Unlike the docile greens, which lie for weeks back-down on a ship's deck, or the formidable but philosophic loggerheads, this species made an unrestful, even dangerous, boatfellow. It snapped and fought, Stew said, from the moment it fell over the gunwale, biting the air and slapping its feet till it burned itself out from rage and frustration. The people on the keys called it ridley, and Stew said he could not even find the name—much less any information on it—in any of the books.

Neither could I. From the description I decided that Stew must be talking about a species that was first described some sixty years ago as *Lepidochelys kempi*, the specific name being taken from that of Richard Kemp of Key West, who sent the type specimen to Samuel Garman at the Museum of Comparative Zoology at Harvard. Practically nothing was known about the natural history of Kemp's turtle. Most people were unable to distinguish it from the loggerhead, and many even doubted that there really was such a thing. A scattering of herpetologists had published records of its occurrence or comments on its osteology, but the great majority of reptile students had never even seen one and the general attitude was that Kemp's turtle was a somehow inferior, if not altogether spurious form, not worthy of scholarly sweat. But Stew had a different opinion, and I had great respect for his perspicacity; I decided to go down and see his hotheaded sea turtle in the flesh. I suppose that one reason for my steadfast affection for ridleys is the memory of that trip to the keys.

My wife went with me. We were young then, and the keys were not yet real estate. A few outsiders were beginning to nose around, but most of the people living there were Conchs—descendants of the original English-Bahamian stock, the wreckers and turtlers of a hundred and two hundred years ago. You could still catch all the fish you wanted without a charter boat. The reefs were next to virgin, and the grouper and muttonfish would rise to a strip of your shirt tail; and even the mangrove snappers were still naive. Around any pass or coral head you could cover the bottom of your dinghy with yellowtails or heap a particolored cargo of porkfish, queen triggers, rock hinds and Spanish hogfish; or if rough weather sent you home you could always take back at least a mess of grunts to go with your grits. The grunts ran two sizes bigger then, and their mouths were more flaming scarlet; and they tasted far, far better.

If it was not something to eat but adrenaline in the blood you were after, you only had to drag a lure for a barracuda in the channel, or commune with the Bahía Honda tarpon train, or creep about the marl flats till you saw the tilted shadows of bonefish, foraging in their primitive peace; and if you made a proper approach you might hook one of these. After that your life would not be quite the same.

Over and above any mysteries of natural history they held, the keys were wonderful in those days. The overseas highway had just been built, but there was yet hardly a trickle of the stream that would one day make the islands a suburb of Miami. You could hardly notice it, but you knew it would come.

You knew the lovely bay would one day buzz with kickers, and the beaches be littered with people and their leavings, and the sunsets be dulled by neon. Among the first things to go would be the old crocodile in her hole too near the highway; and everywhere the fish would grow scarce or cynical. Even the ancient silvered logs of mahogany and princewood would be snaked off to cabinet shops and the gemlike tree snails snatched from the Jamaica dogwood limbs in the dim hammocks.

The lay and figure of the islands would not change. The indigo of the Gulf Stream would always lap the eastern rim of the arc, and inside, it would confine the incredible spectrum of the bay and its hot marl waters, swirled and banded with every shade from turquoise to green and milky jade. The thousand little mangrove-bordered islets would be there, and the big black niggerhead sponges; and new vast jewfish would move in to take the places of the ones the fishermen horsed out from among the piling at the old ferry slip.

Some things would last. But the year Margie and I went down to see Stew's ridleys, the keys were so fair and unplagued that we resented the existence of the road that led us there. No one else is so innately opposed to the more overt signs of human progress as a naturalist—expecially a young one; and I remember well how bitterly we wished the keys might be left forever to the sun and wind, to the white-crowned pigeons and red coons and little key deer, and to a few quiet people with names like Lowe and Thompson and Sweeting. And to us, of course.

I remember Margie asked me if I would really be so callous as to deny to my fellow man the joy of conch soup; and I said I damn sure would—because there was only a certain amount of conch soup in the world, while the fellow man had no limits to his abundance. And now, these short two decades later, you can go lusting the length of the archipelago and never find a spoonful of conch soup anywhere. The conchs are gone—unless you live there and know the little secret caches—like the stone crabs, and the easy fishing.

But the ridleys are still there and we must get around to them.

We had hardly thrown our things on the bed in one of Stew's cabins when he herded us out again and into a launch with two Matacumbe men, a Mr. Jonah Thompson and his grown son, who looked just like him. Mr. Thompson had lost one side of his buttocks in the '35 hurricane—the one when the glass fell to 26.35 and a two-hundred-mile wind slammed a twelve-foot wall of water across the low islands, shattering and carrying away everything in its path. The official list numbered eight hundred dead, mostly from the camp of bonus-marching veterans of World War I who were living in tents on Lower Matacumbe, but everyone knows the counting stopped too soon. The survivors were mostly natives, who weathered the raving wind and seas in small, flush-deck boats heavily anchored among dense mangroves. The driving water wrecked a locomotive on the railroad and carried huge masses of reinforced concrete twenty miles to the tip of the mainland, but some of the people in the little boats got by.

Jonah Thompson got by, but he lost half of his buttocks when a flying timber nearly cut him in two. The injury would have made an invalid of an average man, but Jonah quickly dominated it and soon regained his place as the best boatman on the upper keys. He could handle an iron better than any man of any color I ever saw. He knew weather and water and fish and, what was most important of all, he knew turtles.

And so, when he contemplated the irate ridley he had just pulled up on deck and said: "Some say these ridleys is crossbreeds," I took notice and urged him on.

"We don't know where they lay," he said. "All the rest come up on the beaches one time or other, but you never see the ridleys there. We all say they are made when a loggerhead pairs with a green." He mumbled something else in an embarrassed sort of way. I thought I heard him right, but I didn't think my wife did.

"We think they're so damn mean owing to them not getting to coot none," was what I believe he said.

"What did he say?" asked Margie.

"Shut up," I said.

"Did he say they are mean because they don't make love?"

"That was the gist of it."

"Isn't that anthropomorphic?" Margie asked, in an unpleasant way.

"Could be," I said. I could see nothing wrong with the man's reasoning, provided he was right about the ridley's not breeding; but this assumption I did not like, and still don't.

It bothered me that the ridley should be such a distinctive and original-looking creature, with his traits his own and nothing about him that seemed intermediate between the other species. A mule is clearly a mixture of the ass that sired him and the mare that bore him, but a ridley is his own kind of animal. I nodded over Jonah Thompson's theory, but I resolved then to get the straight of it somehow.

As I said, that was a long time ago, and I have made very little progress. Indeed, the ridley mystery has grown rather than shrunk, and I am farther from a solution than I seemed then. The answer is so elusive that I have come to regard the ridley as the most mysterious air-breathing animal in North America.

First of all, there is the unimportant but vexing question of the creature's name. Ridley! What kind of name is it anyway, and where did it come from? I've traced it all along the coast from Fernandina to Key West and out to Pensacola and people only look vague or grieved when I ask about the name. To most people it's like asking why they call a mackerel a mackerel, or a dog a dog. Once in a while I run into somebody who knows the ridley as "mulatto" or "bastard" or "mule-turtle," in reference to its supposed hybrid origin; but most places the name is ridley, and not a soul knows why. Maybe one out of a couple of dozen fishermen pronounce it "ridler"; and it may be that this form represents an earlier stage in the etymology of the term, but it seems impossible to confirm this. Anyway, compared to other things we don't know about the ridley, the question of its name is a bagatelle; and our ignorance here is exasperating, but not necessarily demoralizing.

A more unsettling eccentricity is the animal's range—the territory in which it has been found to occur. All the other sea turtles—trunk-back, green, loggerhead, and hawksbill—occupy pretty much the same area, each being found in the Atlantic, the Caribbean, the Pacific, and the Indian Ocean. Moreover, while the representative of each of these species in the Indo-Pacific is isolated by land or by great expanses of cold water from its counterpart in the Atlantic-Caribbean, the populations are remarkably similar. In fact, if you go to Colón, on the Caribbean side of Panama, and catch a green turtle, haul him across the Isthmus to Panama City, and compare him point for point with a green from the Pacific, you have to look very close indeed to see any difference at all. It is the same with a great number of other marine animals, both vertebrate and invertebrate, on the two sides of the Isthmus: they are separated by thousands of miles of alien territory but they nevertheless show very little of the divergence that such isolation usually brings. This is especially striking when you consider that the emergence of the isthmus that cut off the Caribbean animals from their eastern Pacific kin took place at least thirty million years ago.

The ridley partly fits this pattern; that is, there is an Atlantic ridley and a very similar one in the eastern Pacific. They are numerous only in the warmer parts of their ranges, and are apparently not in contact around the tips of either Cape Horn or the Cape of Good Hope, except perhaps as occasional, current-borne flotsam. But here the orthodoxy of the ridley stops. For some utterly unaccountable reason it is not found in the Bahamas or Bermuda, where all the rest are, or have been, abundant; and most peculiar of all, it is absent from the Caribbean.

It is not a simple matter to get a clear picture of the range of the ridley. You don't just go out and catch sea turtles on an afternoon collecting trip, and there are no really good sea-turtle collections in any of the world's museums.

Before Mr. Kinsey became preoccupied with sex, he worked on insects. At one time he wanted to learn all he could about a certain group of tiny wasps that make galls on twigs. In his spare time he went out and drove along the roads and stopped at hundreds of places where he collected the animals he was after. He caught seventeen thousand of them, and when he wrote a monograph on this material, it was a classic. This is the way to do a problem in animal distribution; but you can't do it with sea turtles.

Counting specimens I have begged or bought from fishermen or seen being butchered in fish houses, and the collections of the Museum of Comparative Zoology, the American Museum of Natural History, and the British Museum, I have managed to look at about a hundred ridleys in eighteen years. Add to what these show the small amount of information that has been published and the carefully sifted oral reports of fishermen, and there is still not a great deal to work with. But it is enough to give the outlines of the ridley story, and to show that it is a strange one.

There are two centers of abundance of ridleys: the Gulf coast of Florida from the Suwannee Delta to Florida Bay and the east coast from about St. Augustine to Melbourne. On the east coast, ridleys are best known by trawlers who work some distance off shore, perhaps indicating that even this far south the animals are being swept northward by the Florida Current—the headwaters of the Gulf Stream. I know a fisherman at Canaveral who claims to have caught a thousand ridleys during twenty years of fishing there. On the Gulf coast they are taken along with the green turtles that support the small turtle fisheries there, and are frequently sold with the greens to buyers who never know the difference. There they are caught in nets set across small channels among the flats, and like the young greens, they appear to be at home there. A single setting of a net will sometimes yield two or three of each species, while loggerheads are almost never taken.

Outside of Florida, ridleys occur all along the Gulf coast to Texas. At the Mexican border our information peters out; nobody knows what happens to the range of the ridley from there on. The few published articles on Mexican sea turtles mention the other four kinds, but not the ridley. On the Atlantic coast it seems to me that the distribution of the ridley is no true "range" in the zoo-geographic sense —an expanse of territory that an animal occupies or voluntarily moves across—but is a one-way, passive dispersal by the Florida Current and the Gulf Stream; an exodus with no return. Expatriate ridleys drift with the current with little more control over their ultimate fate than the plankton there. The ones near the edges may be able to move out into the coastal waters, reach shore, and live there more or less conveniently; but those deep within the stream go on. Where the Florida Current picks up its supply of ridleys is not known, for reasons that I shall reveal presently; but there can be little doubt that it is the north-

ward sweep of this current just off the eastern shore that accounts for
the occurrence in North Carolina and New York Harbor and Martha's
Vineyard. Little as we know about ridleys, we can be sure they are
not born in those places. They are carried there.

And they do not stop in Massachusetts. The Gulf Stream goes on,
and they go with it. How they are amusing themselves all this time
is hard to say, but they ride the great global drift out into the cold
North Atlantic, where it travels its new easterly course at a reduced
speed but glides on over the tail of the Grand Banks, pushes aside the
arctic icebergs, and splits at last against western Europe, making it
barely possible for human beings to stand the English climate, and
stranding ridleys on such shores as Ireland, Cornwall, the Scilly Isles,
southern France, and the Azores.

The range of the ridley, thus, is not an expanse of ocean or a strip
of shore. Mostly it is the Gulf Stream. Ridleys are part of a vast planetary swirl that starts when the equatorial current and the easterly
trades push water through the Yucatan Channel and pile it up in the
Gulf of Mexico. The surface there rises six to eighteen inches higher
than the Atlantic level and breeds the head that drives warm water
clockwise around the eastern Gulf and nozzles it out through the
Straits of Florida as the Florida Current. This soon meets the Antilles
Current, and the two now form the "Gulf Stream" in the new strict
sense, and this moves northward with an initial speed of about three
knots. Somewhere along the line ridleys are fed into this system, to
drift downstream to England through three thousand slow miles.

It would be wrong to give the impression that ridleys are of common occurrence in Europe. I recently looked at six English ridleys in
the collection of the British Museum, which is the best sea-turtle collection in the world, and those six represent all the European specimens in that museum. These may represent half of all the English
ridleys that have fallen into the hands of naturalists. Ridleys, and sea
turtles of all kinds, are very rare in European waters. But even so, I
wonder how many ridleys had to begin the voyage in America for each
of the six that lodged at last in the British Museum!

Two features of the British waifs must be of some sort of significance in the cryptic life history of the animal: they are all small—
none over eight inches long and one only four—and they have all
washed up during the months from October to December. I suppose
the small size merely means that baby turtles are swept away more

easily than big ones; but the meaning of the seasonal occurrence of the strandings is unexplained.

If we suppose that the point of injection of ridleys into the Gulf Stream system is somewhere about the tip of the Florida peninsula—and the slim evidence that seems to support this assumption will come out shortly—then the trip to Europe might take as much as a year or even more. It seems unlikely that even a turtle could survive this period with no food at all. So, even though the ridley is characteristically a bottom feeder—a crusher of crabs and mollusks—we must conclude that it finds some sort of fare in the Gulf Stream.

It must have occurred to you some time back that the sensible way to go about finding out where ridleys get into the Gulf Stream would be to locate the beaches where the young hatch out. That makes sense, certainly. The only trouble is, the beaches can't be found.

In fact, I can't find any evidence that ridleys breed at all; at least, by any of the accepted methods. I am still just about where Jonah Thompson's folk theory left me. As far as I can determine, nobody ever saw a pair of ridleys courting or copulating. People are constantly catching and butchering sea turtles and looking about inside them for eggs, but no female ridley has ever turned up pregnant—not even with the beadlike, yellow eggs that other female turtles carry for most of every year. No ridley has ever been seen on a nesting beach, and no hatchling has been found. The smallest ridley known is a four-inch specimen that washed up in England. This one was at least several months old. A newly hatched one should be little more than an inch long, because the loggerhead, a turtle two or three times the size of the ridley at maturity, is only slightly more than an inch long at birth. Not only that, all hatchling turtles have a soft umbilical scar, marking the place where they were attached to the yolk in the egg; and at the tip of the snout there is a sharp spine called an egg tooth that the little turtle uses in freeing itself from the shell. Turtles retain these signs of infancy for several weeks after hatching. No little ridley has ever been seen with them.

When Kemp sent the ridley to Harvard in 1880 he said: "We know that they come out on the beach to lay in the months of December, January and February, but cannot tell how often or how many eggs." I don't think he knew any such thing. When I made my first visit to Springer's shark camp on the keys, I went armed with this observation; and since it seemed a bizarre reversal of the usual nesting schedule, I went to some effort to authenticate it. I had no success at all. I talked with people who knew ridleys all the way from Homestead to Key West and none had ever heard of a turtle nesting in the wintertime or had seen a ridley nest or egg or baby at any time. Since then I have heard the same story from something over 160 of the most knowledgeable fishermen I could find between Cape Hatteras and the mouth of the Mississippi. I have dissected every mature ridley I could get and have cross-questioned the men who slaughter turtles for the market, and I have begun to feel the real weight of the enigma.

When the turtlers and fishermen are pressed to account for the facts of the case, they tell three different stories. Most of them agree with Jonah Thompson that the creature does no breeding on its own but is produced when two other species hybridize. The comment of an old pod at St. Lucie Inlet was the sort of thing you hear:

"This yer ridley don't raise. He's a bastard, a crossbreed you get when a loggerhead mounts a green—and a loggerhead will mount anything down to a stick of wood when he's in season. This yer ridley don't have no young 'uns. He's at the end of the line, like a mule."

A minority among the people I talk to say that ridleys breed all right—bound to; everything does; but they do it somewhere 'way off, outside our field of responsibility. On some remote shore of the Caribbean, maybe, where they have yet to be observed by sapient man. Sapient gringo, anyway.

This kind of talk used to reassure me. It was something to fall back on when the thought of a parentless, childless animal weighed me down. It was no disgrace not knowing where the brute bred if it happened in some far corner of the Caribbean. The Caribbean is a big place, and I knew its shore only in a couple of spots. Ridleys were unknown in those spots, but this proved nothing at all.

Imagine my state of mind, then, when I had completed a carefully spaced series of visits all the way around the Caribbean and had found no sign either of ridleys or of people who knew them, anywhere in a dozen countries and islands. I went out with turtle-hunters and looked at turtles in crawls, and at shells on trash heaps, and at stuffed turtles on museum shelves. I walked some of the finest turtle beaches in the hemisphere. I saw a lot of things, but no ridleys. Everywhere I went the people knew four kinds of sea turtles, and none of them was the ridley.

This was a body blow. It threw the whole problem back into the Gulf of Mexico—into my lap. My ignorance became embarrassing again.

The third explanation I commonly hear is the opinion of a still smaller group that the ridley is out there each June laying, along with the other species, in the same places and at the same time. I have heard this seriously proposed by responsible parties five times. That is, five times people have named definite stretches of beach on which they believed ridleys laid. Four of these stories fizzled out under cross-questioning, proving to have been based either on pure hearsay or on erroneous identification of the turtle involved. In one case only, the battering system of interrogation I have developed through the years was unable to find the weakness in a man's claim that he had seen a ridley lay on a certain beach; and we parted at deadlock—he clinging to his memory of one lone ridley in moonlight twenty-five years old, and I sure without any proof at all that he was off his rocker.

I will admit that there is a slight possibility that each June ridleys lumber up at first full moon and dig their nests on the shoulders of State Road A1A, like the loggerheads; but I rest no easier for it.

That, then, is the riddle of the ridley: a big, edible, shore-water beast, abundant and well known to everybody along the east-Gulf littoral and around the tip of Florida, is swept up the Atlantic coast by the Florida Current and the Gulf Stream, through some whimsey never crossing to the eastern side of the current and being unknown in the Bahamas and in Bermuda. The drifting migrants trickle out of the stream into coastal waters as far north as Massachusetts, straggle across to Europe, and very rarely stick with the deflected drift as far as the Azores and probably farther. Nowhere in this vast territory has any hint of reproductive activity been seen.

What do you make of it? I used to think the solution would one day fall into my lap, but I believe this no longer. It will have to be worked for, and the campaign will require drive and imagination and patience. It will probably resolve itself into a systematic ransacking of ideas and places on a purely trial-and-error basis. It will not be settled on week-end field trips, and there is nothing to take into the laboratory. The solution will very likely turn out to be absurdly simple and obvious, once we get hold of it; but meantime it is a tough and nagging mystery.

While waiting for something else to happen, it is interesting, if not really profitable, to take stock of the information at hand and see what can be done with it. Most of the laws of science, as we call them, have started out as theories; and theories are just figments of a disciplined imagination—until they can be proved. The scientific way to formulate a theory is to examine every possible explanation for your facts that presents itself, however outrageous it may seem at the time. Some of the craziest notions turn out to be the best.

In the case of the ridley mystery, then, we have to weigh without bias all the trial solutions at hand, whether conceived by unlettered menhaden hands or by sadistic colleagues, or by my own troubled mind. We must list these and evaluate each in its turn and then make an objective choice; and this will then be the current, tentative answer to the riddle of the ridley. It will probably be wrong, but it will be the best we can do.

Of all the explanations that suggest themselves, the simplest is that the ridley just doesn't reproduce, but arises by spontaneous generation. This is the most direct answer, in view of what we know, and in olden times it would have been accepted as the only reasonable solution. But nowadays biologists are pretty insistent that everything alive must have at least one parent, and this sets limits to our imagination.

As a variant of that idea, we might toy with this one, which has been suggested to me independently by several acquaintances, some of whom at least are perfectly sane. May not the ridley once have been able to reproduce its kind, but have suddenly lost the ability—have become sterile through some sudden racial mishap? In such a case, the ridleys we see today would be the last members of a line on its way toward extinction. It is hard to put your finger on the defect in this effort, but it seems a bit fey and irresponsible. Quite frankly, I get no real comfort out of the notion and mention it at all only to be scientific.

We just about have to start from the assumption that the animal breeds—somehow, somewhere. It must be, then, that it is the place or the manner of the breeding that bewilders. There must be something about where or how little ridleys come about that is just a bit beyond the scope of our imagining.

Maybe, for instance, this turtle lays no eggs, but bears its young alive, on the high seas, as a sea snake does. It is certainly conceivable, and it excuses our failure to find nests and eggs ashore. But don't forget the lack of pregnant females. You have to get just as pregnant to bear live young as to lay eggs. And not only that, an eggless turtle is too far out of character. Turtles are unwaveringly conservative. A live-bearing turtle would be almost as exciting as an egg-laying dog. No matter where they live—on dry land, in fresh water, or in the sea—

all known turtles inflexibly dig holes and lay white-shelled eggs in them; and they have been doing this since the Cretaceous.

Suppose, then, that the ridley abides by the conventions of its kind and lays eggs, but lays them in the water—lays buoyant eggs so far from land that the young stop being young before we ever get to see them. If the laying place is very far away, maybe it takes the females a long time to get there, and we see them only when they are not carrying eggs. This is a variation of the preceding theory and a slight improvement on it, but is unacceptable on the same grounds. It just seems like too much of an innovation for a turtle suddenly to make, after fifty million years of making hardly any innovations at all. Besides, prolonged wetting with salt water kills the embryos in the eggs of other reptiles and other sea turtles, and we would have to propose a brand-new and very ingenious kind of egg for our theoretical pelagic ridley.

Perhaps, instead of a strange *way* of breeding, it is a strange *time* of breeding that has thrown us off. Maybe the laying season is very short or very oddly scheduled and restricted in time. Maybe they lay only on New Year's Eve or Twelfth Night, or on the shortest night or coldest night of the year. All the other Atlantic sea turtles have a laying season of several weeks in late spring and early summer; but the ridley may lay in midwinter when turtle-hunters are doing something else. Why not? Well, mainly because it again brings us up against the failure of the females to turn up pregnant. And not only that, even in the dead of winter there is traffic on most Florida beaches—people driving, hotrodding, surf fishing, courting, catching coquinas, even swimming. It is impossible to believe that winter turtle tracks, or tracks laid at any time however unlikely, could simply have escaped notice. This was Kemp's theory, you remember, but I think he was just repeating idle talk.

Next we might try the possibility that the ridleys in the United States originate somewhere else and either migrate into the Gulf of Mexico or are carried there by currents. This looks good at first, because there are the currents to do the job—currents that could, and almost surely do, bring ridleys clear across the Atlantic from Africa to the Antilles and very probably into the Gulf of Mexico. But if you look closely at the foreign ridley colonies that could lose turtles into these currents, you see that the ridley population in the Gulf could not possibly be derived this way. In the first place the Gulf form is too abundant to qualify as an accumulation of accidental waifs; and even more conclusive, there is a simple but constant difference between the ridleys in the Gulf and those in West Africa and on the Pacific coast of South America, which are the only stocks adjacent to the currents that bring foreign drift into Florida waters. All extra-Floridian ridleys everywhere in the world have two to six more scales in the upper shell than our Gulf ridley does. If we suppose that all those in the Gulf were brought in by the Equatorial Current, then we have to believe that each of them stopped over somewhere along the way and had its shell remodeled. It is possible that an occasional Gulf ridley does come into American waters on the Equatorial Current; but if so it is surely one that began its voyage three years before when it was swept away by the Florida Current and survived the world-wide circuit to return at last to its native waters. Any African ridley that turned up in the Gulf would be easily recognized as such. There is, thus, little point in looking to the ocean currents for a solution to the puzzle.

Why not just take it easy and accept the popular notion that the ridley is a hybrid after all, and, like many hybrids, sterile? This is what most of the fishermen and turtle-hunters believe, as I have said, and you can even read it in the *Riverside Natural History*. Mostly the responsibility for furnishing us with ridleys is laid to a loggerhead father and a green-turtle mother, but sometimes you hear the sexes switched. A few say the *mésalliance* involves a loggerhead and a hawksbill, and rarely you may be told that it is a hawksbill and a green.

This is where the pressure is, and where my skepticism has lost me friends and made me out, in the eyes of men I respected, a plain damn fool. Nearly everything we know, and everything we don't know, about this animal makes it easy to say it is a half-breed, with no more personal continuity than a medieval choirboy, or a mule.

As I have said before, there are also ridleys in the Pacific. And in the Pacific the males chase the females about, and catch them, and they mate, and the females go ashore and dig holes in the sand and lay round, white eggs in them. The eggs hatch and release baby ridleys with egg teeth and umbilical scars, like any other new turtle.

Now, what earthly sense would it make for the ridley to be a hybrid in one part of his range and a separate species in another—to do his own breeding at Acapulco but rely on other kinds of turtles to do it for him at Tampa? It is a distressing thought. In fact, it is untenable.

As I have pointed out, the Atlantic and Pacific ridleys are separated by a great deal of territory and are not exactly alike. But they are very nearly alike, and far more like each other than like any other kind of turtle. In fact, the only differences I have been able to make out are the extra scales in the shell of the Pacific form and sometimes a slightly greener color; and maybe a few trifling disparities in proportions. Certainly nothing that would lead a person with bat brains to believe that a ridley begot one of them and a loggerhead the other.

The problem would be simple if we didn't know about the Pacific ridley. My friends around the fish houses don't know about the Pacific ridley. They are at peace. I am not. It's what a Ph.D. in biology gets you. . . . The ridley breeds, like anybody else.

The same objections that make the hybrid idea unsatisfactory seem also to throw out the possibility that the ridley is some sort of sport—an occasional freak occurring among normal offspring of one of the other kinds of turtles, the loggerhead, for instance. Here again the almost identical Pacific ridley, with its orthodox breeding habits, stares us in the face and makes the sport theory seem just a shade too easy. It is possible, but only very feebly so.

Now, what can be said to the people who suggest that the nests have just been overlooked—that ridleys nest right along with the other turtles, at the same time and in the same places, and have simply escaped notice by a person competent to distinguish between them and the other species?

Well, as far as I'm concerned those are fighting words. Maybe my own hundreds of hours of unproductive beach-walking, and those of my zoological friends and correspondents, are not a valid test. But how about the lifetimes spent without seeing ridleys by professionals like Joe Saklin and Tony Lowe and Paco Ortega, and by the band of my consultants among the illegal east-coast turtle-hunters? These men spend three months of every year patrolling the beaches in turtle buggies—cut-down cars with oversized tires—dodging the far-spaced conservation officers and turning turtles by the yearly hundreds. They have always done this and they keep doing it at growing risk—slowly growing risk—because a few commercial bakers have learned what Savannah and Charleston housewives always knew about the keeping qualities turtle eggs give cakes, and will pay fantastic prices for them; and because the shoddier jooks and barbecue joints along the Dixie Highway like to cut their fifty-cent-a-pound hamburger meat with twenty-five-cent loggerhead. These men don't hunt turtles for fun. They are tough and practical. I know a game warden whom they threw into the sea just to show how tough they are. They know their business. They know ridleys and know the beaches and what goes on there during the long summer nights, and it is wonderful what goes on there, but it is not the nesting of ridleys. All these men have told me that ridleys never come ashore. By not moralizing on their ways, I have made friends among these poachers, and if a ridley ever comes up on one of the good mainland beaches in the turtle season, I bet I hear about it within hours.

But suppose she should not come ashore on one of the good turtle beaches. There is a lot of coast between Tampico and Beaufort, and there are still some unpatrolled, unbathed-on segments of shore not even shown as sand on maps. And as long as this is true, we can never be sure but that we have missed what we were after simply because we have not looked in the right place. Till every one of the unsearched beaches has been walked with ridleys in mind we can never be sure they do not nest on some rarely visited little island or cluster of keys or short, broken strand somewhere on the coast of the southeastern United States.

This, I believe, is the theory we must choose. It best fits the known facts and introduces the fewest wild assumptions. It is distasteful, because it proposes the laborious ransacking of every scrap of sand along hundreds of miles of coast. It seems unlikely, because no other turtle anywhere is so fanatically finicky in choosing a breeding ground as this explanation would imply. But the ridley has shown its disregard for tradition in other ways, remember. In spite of the drawbacks, this hypothesis seems the best of the lot.

So I guess we must go looking for a small, isolated stretch of shore as the answer to the ridley mystery. It must be some improbable place right under our noses. Cape Sable may occur to you, or Dry Tortugas, but it will not be so easy as that. People have been turning turtles on those shores for too many years. I believe it can't be any of the good turtle territory on the east coast—the strip from Palm Beach up to Melbourne: it is too well known, too continuously visited. It is not Sanibel or Bonita Beach or Naples, and it almost surely is none of the islands along the bend of the Panhandle. It barely might be outside Florida—one of the Sea Islands of Georgia or South Carolina, or some place the Mexicans have somehow missed between Vera Cruz and Brownsville. But I doubt this; and I doubt that it is anywhere in all the island chain from Grand Bahama to Turks and Caicos.

As long as we believed the zoologists who kept quoting one another about there being ridleys in the Caribbean, we could just say, well, hell, the ridley must breed down there somewhere. But now there's no comfort there, for me at least. In all the poking about that I'm going to tell you of in chapters to come, the ridley mystery was right there with me. Stirred up as I may seem over other matters—over the green turtles I was mainly after down there, over the endless odd detours and distractions I relate—the one most exciting thing I found in all my wandering was no ridleys in the Caribbean.

What remains to be done, then, is slow, piecemeal searching. And before I look anywhere else I am going back to Florida Bay—to the shallow, island-set sea between the cape and the upper keys. There are dozens of little islands there like Sandy Key, and they have been little visited by naturalists with eyes open for ridley sign. The shores there are mostly mangrove thickets, where no turtle could nest; but in some the mangrove fringe is broken by sand; and while the strips of beach are short and narrow, they may be all the ridley needs. The bay is handy to both the Florida Current, which must be the agent that feeds the waifs into the Gulf Stream, and to the coastal waters of the peninsula of Florida, where ridleys are more abundant than anywhere else. It is at least possible that the natural secretiveness of sea-turtle hatchlings keeps baby ridleys out of sight, and that some local, seasonal migration of the egg-heavy females hides them from view. All this seems unlikely, but it is the most possible solution at hand.

So I guess I should have stayed on there in the bay to look for the answer, where Jonah Thompson threw the iron so long ago. Perhaps all the Atlantic ridleys everywhere come from down there where the first one was, in the hot, white water with the sea cows and bonefish and the last crocodiles. Maybe the long questing will come full circle there on some first full moon of summer, and the riddle of the ridley will end where it began.

ANTARCTICA

by Walter Sullivan

---

*The last great land mass on earth to be explored by man,
Antarctica still remains a mysterious and forbidding continent
swept by icy winds of fearful strength. Possibly great things for
the future are locked under its massive snowcap, but, up to the
present moment, hardy men of various nations have gained little
more than a bare foothold on its frozen edges. Walter Sullivan,
who was born in New York City in 1918 and was graduated from
Yale with an A.B. degree in 1940, is a staff reporter for the New
York Times and a veteran of two trips to the Antarctic under the
auspices of the United States Government. He is also a keen
student of natural history. The following selection is taken from
his book,* Quest for a Continent, *published in 1957.*

AT the bottom of the world lies a mighty continent still
wrapped in the Ice Age and, until recent times, unknown
to man. It is a great land mass criss-crossed by mountain
ranges, whose extent and elevation are still uncertain.
Much of the continent is a complete blank on our maps. A 1,000–
mile stretch of the coastline has never been reached by any ship. Man
has explored, on foot, less than one per cent of its area.

Antarctica differs fundamentally from the arctic regions. The arctic
is an ocean, covered with drifting pack ice and hemmed in by the
land masses of Europe, Asia, and North America. The antarctic presents the reverse situation. It is a continent almost as large as Europe
and Australia combined, centered roughly on the South Pole and surrounded by the most unobstructed water areas of the world—the Atlantic, Pacific, and Indian Oceans.

The continental ice sheet is over two miles high in its center and refrigerates the air over the bottom of the earth far more than occurs over the arctic. This cold air cascades off the land with such force that it makes the nearby seas the stormiest in the world and renders unlivable those regions whose counterparts at the opposite end of the globe are inhabited. Thus more than a million persons live within 2,000 miles of the North Pole in an area that includes most of Alaska, Siberia, and Scandinavia, a region rich in forest and mining industries. Within the same distance of the South Pole there is not a single tree, industry, or settlement, apart from a handful of weather stations.

While it is certain that no place in the world is as cold as the mountain-ringed South Polar Plateau, no one knows how cold it really gets during the six-month winter night, for no one has been there then. Unlike the vicinity of the North Pole, where men have camped for many months, only two parties of explorers have ever set foot at the South Pole—both of them during the southern summer of 1911–1912. No one has been there since except to fly over in aircraft, although the United States is placing an outpost there for the International Geophysical Year of 1957–1958.

Nearer the coast, where men have wintered, temperatures have been registered as low as –80°. In summer, on the other hand, when the sun shines brightly on a protected place, a man may strip to his waist. The seasons in Antarctica follow the pattern of the southern hemisphere. Summer begins in November and winter starts in June. The summer days and the winter nights become longer as one approaches the continent until, once the Antarctic Circle has been crossed, there is a period of continuous daylight in midsummer and of unbroken darkness in midwinter. If one keeps on moving toward the South Pole these periods lengthen until at the Pole itself there is only one "day" a year, with six months of daylight and six months of twilight and darkness. Here all directions are north and all time zones converge.

Until the moon or other planets are attained, Antarctica will remain the most unearthly region within the reach of man. The landscape is so alien that a completely specialized vocabulary is needed to describe it. Nunataks, the tips of mountain peaks, poke their heads above the ice sheet. Winds, pressures, tensions of almost inexpressible violence mold the ice and the granular snow, or névé, into countless strange shapes—sastrugi, bergschrunds, barrancas, dongas, hummocks, seracs. Even volcanoes thrust their fiery heads through the antarctic ice—how many no one knows. Mount Erebus continuously trails a plume of steam. And an erupting volcano so heats Zavodovsky Island that much of it is snow-free in a region of eternal snows.

The great mass of the continent is buried under a moving ice sheet. Just as other continents shed water, Antarctica sheds ice. Snow falls on the ice sheet, adding constantly to its bulk, and then the ice flows, sometimes over 1,000 miles, to the sea. Rivers of fast-flowing ice, or glaciers, cut through the plains of more stagnant ice to the ocean. Some, like the Beardmore Glacier, a dozen miles wide and a hundred miles long, flow majestically down mountain valleys, their surfaces marked by symmetrical patterns of crevasses. These clefts in the ice may be narrow and bridged with snow or large enough to hold the Washington Monument. In the steep valleys there are ice "rapids," broken into a chaos of crevasses. While they display no visible movement, they thunder with a sound of continuous artillery fire.

The ice sheet does not pour into the sea at certain places only, as is the case with watersheds. It pushes out in virtually all directions. Icebergs break off, or "calve," from the ice front along almost the entire coastline.

Where the ice sheet has pushed out over the sea and is afloat, though still attached to the continent, it is known as ice shelf. The largest example of it covers a mighty gulf on the Pacific coast of Antarctica. Known as the Ross Ice Shelf, it is roughly the size of France, with a seaward front of 400 miles. At its maximum it extends out 500 miles from the mountainous coast to the south. This ice shelf produces the flat-topped "tabular" icebergs typical of Antarctica—great wafers of ice about 800 feet thick and sometimes 100 miles long.

Though several thousand miles of antarctic coastline have not been reached by ship, it is evident from what we have seen that much of the shore consists of ice cliffs roughly 80 feet above the water. This is the "front" of the continental ice sheet where it has pushed out from one to several hundred miles over the sea. Of all the sights that greet the newcomer to Antarctica, the uniformity of these ice cliffs is the most impressive.

Because the ice sheet completely buries much of the shoreline, we do not know the true shape of Antarctica or where its coast would be if there were no ice. The "coast" as we see it on our maps generally marks the façade of the ice cliffs, which changes from year to year as icebergs break off. In some sectors mountains drop sheer into the water or divert the flow of ice so that there is an "oasis" of bare land along the coast, but these are exceptional.

The material from which the great antarctic ice sheet has been built is the lowly snowflake. By wind action or compression, the flakes become sandlike grains, and as they settle deeper under the weight of new snows they merge into larger and larger grains which finally congeal into true ice. Imprisoned bubbles of air are compressed as the entire structure sinks deeper. If you make a tall drink with the deeper glacier ice, no soda is needed, for the air escaping as the ice melts is under pressure and effervesces.

What does Antarctica "look like" under its icy shroud? Echo soundings in Queen Maud Land have revealed that beneath the smooth white plateau is land as rugged as the Norwegian coast. Mountains rise 4,200 feet, just poking their tips above the snow, alongside fiords that are more than 2,500 feet below sea level. There are islands and channels of sea water below the floating part of the ice sheet along the coast. The explorers who were measuring the ice had to travel over 130 miles inland before they detected ground that was above sea level. In places the ice sheet was 7,800 feet thick.

The buried fiords had been carved out by glaciers at an earlier time when the ice sheet of Antarctica was forming and beginning to fight its way to the sea—just as it did in Norway. If the ice of Antarctica retreats, the fiords will reappear.

In addition to the ice of the continent, Antarctica produces "sea ice"—the material of which the "pack" is made. The pack is a belt of drifting ice which girdles Antarctica. It is what kept the continent inviolate until the twentieth century. The seas around the coast freeze during periods of the winter, and under buffeting of the first violent storm, this sea ice breaks up into floes which wander with the prevailing winds, usually from east to west. The pack is often 600 miles wide, but thins in some sectors and at some seasons to only 20 or 30 miles. Explorers in recent decades have found that in a few places it may disappear altogether in late summer, allowing ships to sail right up to the ice and rockbound coasts.

The pack is the focal point of life in Antarctica, for here is "earth's richest pasture," providing the plant food that is absent on the mainland. So cold are the waters in the pack that a man without waterproof clothing becomes unconscious within ten minutes and dies soon thereafter. Yet so dense is this water with tiny living creatures that it resembles a murky soup. The opaqueness is due to plankton—a drifting cloud of little one-celled plants and tiny animals that feed on them. There is said to be more living matter per acre in these waters than anywhere on the globe, either on sea or land. When the sea freezes, layers of this plant life are caught in the ice. Thus the slush created when an icebreaker batters its way through is often greenish-brown.

The plants in the sea are eaten by tiny creatures, who in turn are swallowed by larger fish and by birds and mammals. Even the largest of all animals, the blue whale, depends for its food on the little shrimp-like krill of antarctic waters.

The chief enemies of these giants are the killer whales, the "wolves of the sea," who hunt in packs and are the most vicious and sinister of the animals in Antarctica. They run to 30 feet in length and are easily recognized by a tremendous sharklike dorsal fin that rises about 5 feet out of the water as they break the surface. The killers are the nemesis of the blue whale. Once they have killed their prey and eaten his tongue, they may abandon the rest of the gigantic carcass. In the pack they swim under the ice in groups of from 2 to 40, and when they sight a shadow overhead, they know it means a potential dinner. They swim deep, developing tremendous momentum, and strike the ice with their backs, shattering it and spilling their prey into the water to be torn apart. They then stick their heads six or eight feet out of the water and hang there for a few moments while they look around on the ice for more seals or penguins.

Ponting, the photographer on Scott's last expedition, saw killer whales skirting the ice that covered part of McMurdo Sound and ran toward the edge with his camera, but the killers vanished.

"I had got to within six feet of the edge of the ice—which was about a yard thick [he wrote]—when, to my consternation, it suddenly heaved up under my feet and split into fragments around me; whilst the eight whales, lined up side by side and almost touching each other, burst from under the ice and 'spouted.'

"The head of one was within two yards of me. I saw its nostrils open, and at such close quarters the release of its pent-up breath was like a blast from an air compressor. I was enveloped in the warm vapour of the nearest 'spout,' which had a strong fishy smell. . . . It was all I could do to keep my feet as I leapt from piece to piece of the rocking ice, with the whales a few yards behind me, snorting and blowing among the ice-blocks. . . . I recollect distinctly thinking, if they did get me, how very unpleasant the first bite would feel, but that it would not matter much about the second."

He leaped across the last patch of open water to safety and then looked back to see a huge black and tawny head rise out and rest on the ice, looking at him with its evil little eyes and displaying a fearsome array of teeth.

The pack abounds in seals, but none of them are of great commercial value. The fur seal was the first economic attraction in Antarctica. These animals were so decimated that they became almost extinct, but now they are reappearing at their old breeding grounds.

The antarctic pack is dominated by the crabeater seal, yet little is known of its life. Less than half a dozen crabeater pups have been seen, in all cases on the drifting floes of the pack. In the summer these great beasts—they weigh about 500 pounds—migrate to the shores of the continent, but when it comes time for breeding they return to the pack and disappear.

The crabeater is so named because crustaceans form the bulk of his diet. He dives to the bottom and scoops up both sand and crabs. His teeth are so arranged that he can use them as a sieve. He ejects the water and sand but keeps the crustaceans and a few stones that help his stomach break up the shrimp and crab shells.

The Weddell seal is considerably bigger, even, than the crabeater, for he may weigh 900 pounds and is roughly ten feet long. His life centers on the ice that covers the bays and inlets along the coast, especially where pressure has wrinkled the sea ice into ridges, creating havens out of the wind and lines of weakness in the ice where the seals can gnaw air holes. These holes enable the seals to take refuge from the terribly low temperatures that descend on the coast during the winter night. The water under the ice never gets below 28° above zero, whereas the air above drops to 75° below zero. By keeping their breathing holes open, the seals can stay under the ice almost constantly. Their colonies may be five miles or more from open water but they move along routes marked by "air filling stations" in the form of blowholes about every 180 yards. Every third hole, in general, is large enough to furnish an exit onto the surface. Weddell seals eat great quantities of fish and squid, and their stomachs are usually cluttered with cuttlefish beaks.

Rivaling the killer whale as the villain of Antarctica is the sea leopard, another member of the seal family. Not only is he a nimble swimmer but he has been seen to leap out and snatch penguins who were standing too close to the edge of a floe. He shakes the bird furiously, then bites off head and feet before swallowing it. A sea leopard has been known to eat a fully grown Emperor penguin, which itself is 3 feet long. The animal has often been seen chasing small boats. This has given him the reputation of being a man-eater. Actually there is no authentic record of a sea leopard's attack on a man, and his pursuit of boats may only be inspired by curiosity—but no one has put the question to a test. It is not known how or where sea leopards give birth to their pups. Presumably it is somewhere in the vast reaches of the pack.

The birds of Antarctica have helped man in many ways during his perilous journeys into the pack. They have fed him, guided him, and the blubbery penguins have even provided emergency fuel for his steamships. The mariner who sees shags in a fog knows that danger is near, for these birds—a form of cormorant—rarely fly more than a few miles from the rocks where they live. When Shackleton made his memorable escape from the antarctic in an open boat, it was the shags who first told him that a haven was near. The sighting of snow petrels, on the other hand, is often the first warning that ice is close by.

The snow petrel is one of the most beautiful of all birds, resembling in flight a form of white swallow, but it is less than attractive when defending its nest. It resorts to what appears to be a form of projectile vomiting and can deliver a foul-smelling jet of oily, orange-colored liquid with deadly accuracy at a distance of four feet. When a French photographer sneaked up on a snow petrel nest in 1952 the mother bird hit his camera square in the lens.

The "vultures" of the antarctic are the skua gulls. They prey heavily on the Adélie penguin rookeries, swooping in to snatch the unprotected chicks. Most remarkable of all, the skua penetrates to the barren heart of Antarctica. Scott's party met them only 184 miles from the Pole itself, hundreds of miles from the nearest food.

The most characteristic creatures of Antarctica are the penguins. The Adélie penguin and Emperor penguin, like the antarctic skua, are found nowhere else. The Adélie stands about two feet high and most closely resembles the cartoonist's concept of the penguin. He is the clown of Antarctica. The Emperor penguin is as dignified in stature and demeanor as his name implies. He is perhaps the most remarkable animal relic of the Ice Age. Both the Emperor and the Adélie are excellent swimmers. Their wings have become flippers and they "fly" under water with sufficient speed to catch fish. The Adélies can dive into the water from a height of twelve feet and can leap onto ice floes five feet high. This they do by swimming deep and soaring out of the water at great speed, landing feet first on the ice. Like most antarctic creatures, they are so wild that they are tame. They have no natural enemies on the ice, and when they see a man will waddle eagerly over to have a better look.

The Adélie penguin becomes a kleptomaniac when, in the spring, he migrates from the pack and begins building his nest at one of the rock-strewn rookery sites. The nest of the Adélie is made of small stones and pebbles. Mario Marret, who spied on an Adélie rookery in 1952, described it thus:

"The whole Adélie population seems to be subject to a sort of collective madness. Individual birds hurry around with stones in their beaks and deposit them on their nest, but as soon as their backs are turned other birds steal the stones. The community is not divided into honest birds and bad birds: they're all thieves, and there is an incessant round of stolen stones from nest to nest."

The collecting of stones is done by the male and is actually part of the courtship. The male comes up to the nest where his spouse is standing, bows low before her and then drops the stone at her feet. This is repeated over and over for many days.

The Adélies lay two eggs a season but the mortality is heavy—over 68 per cent in some cases—the weaker chicks being carried off by the skuas. The adults appear to be rather stupid and have been seen walking alone 60 and 70 miles inland, apparently lost.

The Emperor penguin is one of the largest of birds, for it weighs close to 90 pounds and stands 3 feet tall. It commutes in the opposite directions from the Adélie and all "normal" birds, for in the fall it heads south toward the Pole and the coldest weather, laying and hatching its single egg on ice during the winter night before heading north again into the pack and a less frigid climate. The egg is brooded in a snug corner between the tops of the penguin's feet and the rolls of fat on the lower abdomen. Here also the young chick is held. Explorers have been impressed by the wild yearning of "childless" adults to nurse a chick in this manner. Actually, an unattended chick is in danger of being torn apart or smothered in the scramble of the big, clumsy birds to get hold of it. Dr. Edward A. Wilson of Scott's expedition tells how the chicks preferred to flee and starve rather than be nursed. He estimated that of the 77 per cent that die before they shed their down, quite half were killed by kindness.

When it came time for the birds of the rookery to return to their summer home in the pack, Wilson found that they had free transportation. Every day when there was a brisk south wind a contingent of birds would gather on the seaward edge of a nearby patch of frozen ocean. Before long this section of ice would break off and blow north toward the pack beyond the horizon. The big birds were like orderly passengers during the rush hour, with about 100 at a time marching out single file to wait for the next floe going north.

The only land animals in Antarctica are a few species of insects which eke out their existence among the rocks and mountains in the hinterland, in the penguin rookeries, or in the small rivulets of melt-water that run down rocky slopes here and there on the coast. The winds are so furious that the spiders spin no webs and the flies are wingless. These species spend almost their entire lives frozen solid. They thaw out for a few days each year and hurriedly carry out their life processes in order to keep the species going.

Antarctica was once green with pine forests and jungles of tree-ferns, but today there is not a tree on the entire continent, and plants of any kind are so rare that explorers rejoice at finding even the lowliest moss or grass. The most widespread of the plants are the lichens—scaly, paperlike plants that cling to the rocks even on mountains bordering the South Polar Plateau—the coldest place on earth. Some of the lichens found on antarctic peaks, surrounded by hundreds of miles of barren ice sheet, display brilliant shades of red, yellow and orange.

Over a hundred kinds of lichen have been identified, more than fifty types of moss, and one or two species of coarse grass, but that is a desert vegetation compared to the flower-studded tundra of the arctic. The drifting plant life of the neighboring seas is always found in the fresh-water lakes that dot some of the snow-free valleys. This algae sinks to the bottom, creating peat-like deposits that may be three feet thick, but as a rule there is no visible soil in Antarctica. It has been ploughed into the sea by the glaciers or blown away by the furious winds.

The first clue that Antarctica was not always buried under an ice sheet was the discovery in the summer of 1892–1893 of what seemed to be part of a fossil pine tree on Seymour Island, near the tip of Palmer Peninsula. Sixteen years later, Shackleton and two companions, picking their way up Beardmore Glacier toward the South Pole, likewise found a petrified pine log and extensive seams of low-grade coal. When Scott's party passed along this same route, Wilson found a multitude of fossil leaves and twigs.

Thus it became known that the heart of Antarctica, now covered by its dense ice sheet, was once carpeted with waving swamp forests of palm and fern-like trees.

Forests may have covered all of Antarctica 135 to 165 million years ago in Jurassic times, for petrified logs up to 18 inches in diameter have been found at Mount Weaver, close to the South Pole. During that period the world was dominated by the dinosaurs, but it seems probable that the forests, at least on Palmer Peninsula, continued up to the period when mammals and other modern animals began to emerge.

Who trod the dark jungles of Antarctica? So far no remains have been found of true land animals. Because of the continent's isolation, separated from its nearest neighbor, South America, by 600 miles of stormy seas, there may never have been four-footed creatures there. Nearby New Zealand, for example, has no native land mammals. Five genera of pre-historic penguins have been discovered in the Palmer Peninsula area, one of them a giant bird perhaps as tall as a small man. Some have suggested that these might have been the survivors of bird species that sacrificed their ability to fly in these untrod forests where there were no rivals or enemies. Then, with the coming of the ice, according to this hypothesis, the birds adapted themselves to aquatic life.

Antarctica presents many unsolved problems of the most fundamental sort. The Permian trees and plants that grew 205 to 230 million years ago on the plateau near the South Pole are almost identical with those in the Permian deposits of South Africa, Australia, India, and South America—so much so, in fact, that geologists lump these scattered regions together under the name Gondwanaland. There have been various ingenious explanations for such close resemblance between such widely separated areas. One is the theory of continental drift, which supposes that the Gondwanaland continents were once a single land mass but broke up and drifted apart like huge ships floating on the plastic core of the earth. Others suspect that much of Gondwanaland has now subsided, leaving oceans in its place. Probably the most popular belief of today is in land bridges and island chains that bridged the gaps, following submarine ridges such as those which still connect Antarctica with South America, Australia, and New Zealand.

One of the American objectives in the International Geophysical Year is to test the theory of continental drift by seeking to determine the rock formations of Antarctica. If, in composition, they "fit" the formations of other Gondwanaland continents like pieces of a jigsaw puzzle, then the theory will tend to be confirmed.

Another of the basic questions confronting the scientists in Antarctica is the reason for the Ice Ages themselves. Here again many ideas have been discussed, including the suggestion that the poles themselves wander great distances across the face of the earth, carrying their frigid climate with them. Perhaps the most favored explanation is a cycle of changes in the volume of heat reaching the earth from the sun.

What does the future hold? Is the antarctic ice retreating? Will the fringe of that region become more habitable in the foreseeable future? These are questions that cannot be answered until we know more of Antarctica's past. New techniques have now been developed which should greatly aid in these studies.

One of the tasks of the International Geophysical Year will be to reconcile seemingly conflicting evidence as to whether the antarctic ice is in advance or retreat. Our interest in the question grows in the light of what seems to have been the influence of ice fluctuations in the past. In earlier stages of the earth's history the great periods of glaciation brought about radical changes in the development of the animal kingdom. Lesser fluctuations in climate occurring within the great cycles of advance and retreat can be of more immediate concern. Our information is far too meager to know where we stand at the beginning of this great scientific assault on Antarctica. However, even a relatively slight modification in climate and ice conditions might tend to make the coasts of Antarctica more accessible and bring some of its hidden—and as yet unknown—mineral resources closer to the rest of the world.

TO THE PLIOCENE SKULL

(A Geological Address)

"A human skull has been found in California, in the pliocene formation. This skull is the remnant, not only of the earliest pioneer of this State, but the oldest known human being. . . . The skull was found in a shaft one hundred and fifty feet deep, two miles from Angel's, in Calaveras County, by a miner named James Matson, who gave it to Mr. Scribner, a merchant, and he gave it to Dr. Jones, who sent it to the State Geological Survey. . . . The published volume of the State Survey on the Geology of California states that man existed contemporaneously with the mastodon, but this fossil proves that he was here before the mastodon was known to exist."—Daily Paper.

"Speak, O man, less recent! Fragmentary fossil!
Primal pioneer of pliocene formation,
Hid in lowest drifts below the earliest stratum
    Of Volcanic Tufa!

"Older than the beasts, the oldest Palaeotherium;
Older than the trees, the oldest Cryptogamia;
Older than the hills, those infantile eruptions
    Of earth's epidermis!

"Eo—Mio—Plio—whatsoe'er the 'cene' was
That those vacant sockets filled with awe and wonder,—
Whether shores Devonian or Silurian beaches,—
    Tell us thy strange story!

"Or has the Professor slightly antedated
By some thousand years thy advent on this planet,
Giving thee an air that's somewhat better fitted
    For cold-blooded creatures?

"Wert thou true spectator of that mighty forest,
When above thy head the stately Sigillaria
Reared its columned trunks in that remote and distant
       Carboniferous epoch?

"Tell us of that scene,—the dim and watery woodland,
Songless, silent, hushed, with never bird or insect,
Veiled with spreading fronds and screened with tall club-mosses,
       Lycopodiacea—

"When beside thee walked the solemn Plesiosaurus,
And around thee crept the festive Ichthyosaurus,
While from time to time above thee flew and circled
       Cheerful Pterodactyls.

"Tell us of thy food,—those half-marine refections,
Crinoids on the shell, and Brachipods *au naturel,—*
Cuttle-fish to which the *pieuvre* of Victor Hugo
       Seems a periwinkle.

"Speak, thou awful vestige of the earth's creation,—
Solitary fragment of remains organic!
Tell the wondrous secrets of thy past existence,—
       Speak! thou oldest primate!"

Even as I gazed, a thrill of the maxilla
And a lateral movement of the condyloid process,
With post-pliocene sounds of healthy mastication,
       Ground the teeth together;

And from that imperfect dental exhibition,
Stained with expressed juices of the weed Nicotian,
Came these hollow accents, blent with softer murmurs
       Of expectoration:

"Which my name is Bowers, and my crust was busted
Falling down a shaft, in Calaveras County,
But I'd take it kindly if you'd send the pieces
       Home to old Missouri!"

                                                 BRET HARTE
                                                 (1836–1902)

IS THERE LIFE ON OTHER WORLDS?

by Gary Webster

Here is a topic that offers a hint, if no more, of some possibly wider outlook on life in the future. It is a forward-looking article, and, as we approach the end of this book, it reminds us that there is still much to learn about the universe around us. It is more or less pure speculation at the moment, but at least it brings us up to date on some matters of deep interest to scientists, theologians, and many others. "Gary Webster" is the pen name of Webb B. Garrison of Nashville, Tennessee, an ordained Methodist minister who has been active in teaching science and writing articles and books on the same subject. The following selection appeared originally in the December, 1956, issue of Natural History *magazine.*

ARE there men on other celestial bodies? Is *Homo sapiens* actually as remarkable a creature as he appears from the perspective of an insignificant planet revolving about a minor sun? What place does our puny world and its two-legged inhabitants occupy in the cosmic pattern?

Questions like these are not limited to readers of comic books and viewers of science-fiction TV programs. They are being asked—and sometimes answered—by sober scientists who command a world audience.

The subject is not only affecting intellectual but spiritual life, as evinced by a statement made by Father Francis J. Connell, Dean of the School of Sacred Theology, Catholic University: "It is well for Catholics to know that the principles of their faith are reconcilable with even the most astounding possibilities regarding life on other planets." Father Connell had no new information concerning "space men." He was simply ahead of most religious leaders in grappling with the theological implications of an idea that has burst into great prominence in our times.

Typical of the serious scientific studies is a recent volume by H. Spencer Jones, Astronomer Royal of Britain. Significantly, he calls his book *Life on Other Worlds*. Interest runs so high that the volume has been issued in a soft-cover edition for mass distribution, and it was recently discussed in *Reader's Digest*.

Speculation on the theme is far from new. A few early Greek thinkers were of the opinion that the stars are inhabited. Hardly any sensible person accepted such a notion in ancient times, however. Was it not obvious that this solid Earth is central in the scheme of things?

Centuries later, Copernicus, Galileo, and their followers thought of themselves as pioneers in the new astronomy. But they were much more than that. Their discoveries affected major areas of philosophy. Earth was relegated to an obscure role in a boundless star-filled universe. Man's once-secure central place was challenged. Old ideas concerning his status were shaken; they rocked violently, then fell and shattered.

Echoes of the crash are still rumbling. Four centuries of intensive investigation have produced no final answers to some of the questions raised by modern conceptions of the physical universe.

Eager guesses have been offered in abundance, however. In 1601, Nicholas Hill solemnly announced his conviction that the sun and stars swarm with living creatures. That sounds absurd in the light of present-day knowledge of solar temperatures. But until recent generations, even astronomers had only a fraction of the data now available to general readers. With no facts to disprove them, many vague theories flourished.

In an atmosphere of such eager optimism, it was comparatively easy for Richard Locke to perpetrate a monumental hoax. He wrote a series of vivid articles, complete with scientific terminology and descriptive details, purporting to describe "lunar men" seen through a huge new telescope. These stories were published in the *New York Sun* in 1835. Millions took them as sober fact. Religious enthusiasts even began collecting funds with which to send missionaries to the Moon.

Though the fraud was quickly exposed, it did not curb interest in the possibility of genuine discoveries. Improved apparatus showed the Moon to have little or no atmosphere, so attention shifted to Mars—

the planet thought most likely to have conditions approximately like Earth's.

Percival Lowell, among the most distinguished of American astronomers, became convinced that the red planet supports life. His views were largely influenced by narrow streaks that he dimly perceived on the surface of Mars. After years of study, he concluded these to be canals built by intelligent beings who were making a gallant attempt to preserve civilization on the arid sphere.

Lowell's theories are now generally discredited. But the quest continues with undiminished zeal. Just as growing information about the Moon led men of the last century to shift their hopes to more distant Mars, so an increase of knowledge about that planet has resulted in a shift of attention to sections of the universe that are beyond observation.

So long as our solar system was considered to be the product of a celestial collision, planets were thought extremely rare. New "explosion" concepts of planet formation assume that many stars have families of encircling satellites.

Evidence provided by giant telescopes suggests that there may be some 100 million billion stars in visible galaxies. In no case is it possible to see their planets. But if the typical life history of a star involves the loss of fragments, there may be myriads of unseen planets. Assuming them to exist, it seems reasonable that a small percentage have physical conditions similar to those that prevail on Earth. And where there are myriads, a small percentage may mean quite a lot. Therefore, life must exist on many spheres . . .

So runs the typical argument.

Present theories make it statistically likely that *Homo sapiens* is not alone in the cosmos. However, of direct evidence that "men" live anywhere other than upon Earth's crust, we possess not one shred.

Before accepting a probability estimate as "proof," it may be profitable to take additional factors into account. How did life itself originate? Through what influences did the manifold forms we know evolve? What are the minimum conditions under which such forms can continue to exist?

With all its tenacity, life is fragile. Because a high degree of organization is involved, environmental factors must be relatively constant. If any of a score of conditions were altered considerably, the human race would perish.

Temperature is among the most obvious of the factors bearing upon the life process. Heat tends to affect molecular structures in direct ratio to their complexity. Molecules that serve as building blocks in living cells are enormously more elaborate than those of most inorganic compounds. Hence, high temperatures destroy every form of life. Though low temperatures do not so certainly lead to death, metabolism and reproduction are geared to moderate ranges.

Earth's most extreme annual variations never exceed 250 degrees F.—and that figure is not reached at any one spot. True, temperatures as high as 133 and 136 degrees F. have been reported from desert regions in North Africa. And at the other end of the scale, the mercury has been known to plunge below minus 100 in Siberia. But most land surfaces are only about 100 degrees warmer in midsummer than in dead of winter. Oceans and tropical lands do not vary nearly so widely.

Cosmic temperatures range from the frozen death of absolute zero to hellish fury at the surface of stars—differences so great that no instrument can measure them accurately.

Our nearest celestial neighbor, the Moon, might be thought likely to enjoy a climate similar to that of Earth. But proximity is a false clue. Lacking the regulating effect of our planet's atmosphere and oceans, the surface of a satellite like the Moon alternately sears and freezes. During an eclipse, the Moon's temperature has been observed to fall from about 160 degrees above to 110 degrees below zero in a single hour.

No other body known to astronomy, except possibly Venus, even approaches Earth's efficiency in maintaining a global temperature that keeps water constantly liquid. Weirdly, however, that same narrow band is of maximum efficiency in organic chemistry. The temperature conditions on our planet give carbon compounds the instability that fosters change—without producing molecular chaos.

Water is the most important of solvents. Global temperatures constantly below freezing or above the boiling point would eliminate the possibility of life.

In order to enjoy the special range of climatic change that permits survival, a planet must be neither too close to its sun nor too far away. There must be an insulating blanket of air that is neither too thin nor too thick. The planet must rotate upon its axis at such a rate that days do not become too hot nor nights too cold.

Many other factors are involved. Their relationships are so complex that life-sustaining climates are rare almost beyond possibility of computation.

Even given a favorable heat band, there are fantastic odds against a planet's having all other essentials for life. Water is one of them, for it is the chief component of both plant and animal cells.

Oxygen is needed by animals; most plants require a constant supply of carbon dioxide. On Earth, these problems are neatly dove-tailed: photosynthesis uses carbon dioxide as a raw material, releases oxygen as a waste product. Meanwhile, animal metabolism burns oxygen and throws supplies of carbon dioxide back into the atmospheric bank. Strip vegetation from the planet, and the broken cycle would cause man to suffocate—assuming that he could ward off starvation.

Air is essential for life-sustaining gases, but it also serves as a shield against death-dealing radiation. Its ozone, water molecules, and layers of ions block or alter ultraviolet light and other emanations that rain upon our globe. No other heavenly body has yet been discovered to have anything even roughly comparable to our atmosphere.

At the Moon's surface, air is nonexistent or so thin that it cannot be detected. Failure has dogged every attempt to discover oxygen in the atmosphere of Mars, and astronomers agree that the red planet has only negligible traces of water vapor. Jupiter and Saturn are thought to be surrounded by clouds of ammonia and methane. Venus seems blanketed in gases unsatisfactory for the support of life. The planet Mercury is thought to be almost or entirely without air. Uranus and Neptune are known to be swathed in methane. Pluto, revolving in the celestial deep-freeze at the remote outer edge of our system, shows no signs of possessing anything resembling Earth's mantle of air.

Our planet's crust contains high concentrations of silicon, iron, and other comparatively heavy substances. Light gases are rare. Study of luminous bodies such as the sun and stars indicates that they are largely composed of hydrogen and helium—with only traces of elements that loom large in Earth's shell.

The chemistry of the human body is known to utilize at least fifteen elements: hydrogen, oxygen, carbon, iodine, sodium, nitrogen, sulphur, phosphorus, manganese, copper, calcium, iron, magnesium, potassium, chlorine. Lacking any one of these in usable form, life would be greatly modified if not quickly eliminated. Vegetable organisms—which produce all Earth's oxygen and food—rely upon oxygen, carbon, hydrogen, and nitrogen, with traces of other essential elements.

Given a planet with suitable temperature range, adequate water, precisely-balanced atmosphere, and a supply of essential elements, would not survival of its organisms be guaranteed?

Not quite.

Distribution of solids and liquids must be just right. If Earth were a perfect sphere, rather than a scarred and wrinkled spheroid, water would cover the entire surface of the planet evenly. Most geologists affirm that the continents actually float upon molten rock—somewhat as icebergs project slightly above the water—but with all the hot rock underneath. A downward shift of less than three per cent in the granite-based segments of the planet's crust would sink every acre of land beneath unbroken oceans.

Only the precise ingredients—each in just the right amount and the whole molded neither too smooth nor too rough—can produce a planet boasting both seas and dry land. A modification of the proportions could reduce Earth to an arid desert or a sodden hulk eternally washed by huge globe-circling tides.

Viewed thus, it may seem incredible that even one heavenly body should provide an environment in which life can be maintained. But difficulties in accounting for the preservation of Earth's organisms are trifling when compared with enigmas that shroud the origin of life itself.

No one has yet offered a satisfactory description of the phenomenon called life. We know that the same chemical elements and physical forces are involved in both living and nonliving aggregations of matter. But it helps very little to agree that the living state is marked by unique electro-chemical relationships—for we do not know what those relationships are. "When we speak of Life itself," said D'Arcy W. Thompson, "we know that we speak of a great mystery. We seem to have stepped unbidden upon holy ground."

Thompson was neither a mystic nor a visionary but a hard-minded scientist with an international reputation, who simply made articulate what many have recognized.

At breakfast, you and I can share a piece of toast or divide a waffle in half. It is a major enigma that food is so transformed in digestion and metabolism that part of it enters *your* life structure and part is incorporated within the organism that is *me*.

This much is clear: life must utilize not-life in order to extend the duration of its own intricately-balanced state. Yet all the evidence points to the conclusion that only a living organism can beget new life. We are left with a neat riddle upon our hands: how did life originate?

There are three classical solutions; none has won anything like universal acceptance.

Religious seers urge that life was launched through a special creative act on the part of a divine being. Ancient scientists—and many modern ones—have thought that living organisms arose spontaneously through the interaction of natural forces. A few noted analysts have urged that "life" is a special ingredient of the cosmos, no more created or originated than matter and energy.

Proponents of the third theory hold that sperms or spores have always been scattered throughout the universe. Whenever they fall into a suitable environment, they multiply. Thus, life did not originate—because there never was a time when it did not exist. Earth owes her vast panorama of organisms to the fact that particles of this eternal "life substance" happened to reach the planet at an appropriate stage in its development. No less a thinker than Lord Kelvin supported this view. According to him, life reached Earth as a passenger upon a chance meteorite.

Careful laboratory study of numerous fragments from space has failed to reveal the presence of cosmic hitchhikers. There is no experimental evidence to support this theory of "panspermia."

Precisely the same can be said of the view that is most popular with contemporary scientists. Many authorities are rather confident in saying that life must have arisen spontaneously from not-life. There is of course indignant repudiation of such notions as Van Helmont's, who as late as the sixteenth century thought he succeeded in bringing about spontaneous generation of mice from a paste of damp flour and soot!

Contemporary views are much more refined than Van Helmont's. Natural forces, say many thinkers, caused gradual establishment of more and more complex molecules. Carbon formed the skeleton of many. Eventually, chance combinations produced molecular field conditions of such nature that the giant carbon-founded cluster began to perpetuate itself. This took place in the warm shallows of a primeval sea whose waters contained all requisite materials in solution or suspension. Once launched in this fashion, life has been shaped and modified by environmental influences. From this primitive beginning, ages of natural processes have produced every living creature on Earth.

Some ask: "Why, if life once began spontaneously, is the process

not continually being repeated? We should see new forms arising all
the time in swamps, lagoons, and inlets." One fairly obvious answer
would be that man has only been in a position to watch for such
events for a "split second" as geologic time is measured. But the
specialist may point out that there was apparently no free oxygen in
Earth's early atmosphere and that when it came, the origin and per-
sistence of primitive organisms became an accomplished fact. That is
as much as biochemistry can yet tell us.

That is where the matter rests. It is impossible to prove the validity
of any view. Divine creation, cosmic sperms, spontaneous generation
—each rests upon belief rather than observation.

Lacking experimental evidence to support any view, the scientist is
forced to admit with D'Arcy Thompson that life's origin is at present
an insoluble riddle. The existence of living organisms upon our tiny
planet neither weakens nor supports the idea that other heavenly
bodies have civilizations of their own.

Somewhat more satisfactory evidence is available in relation to our
final question: Through what influences did life assume its manifold
forms?

Without understanding how life was launched upon Earth, it is
possible to indicate some conditions without which Homo sapiens,
for example, could not have developed. Details are hopelessly obscure.
There is an uncharted abyss between "first life" in the form of a one-
cell organism and the 26 million million integrated cells of a human
child at birth. Indeed, the radical break between not-life and life is
hardly more inscrutable than steps in the progression from primitive
amoeba to a creature possessing nerves and bones, specialized organs,
sensory systems, and a brain that permits development of language,
culture, religion, and science.

Many significant links in the chain of organic modification are obscure or completely unknown. A few of the factors—such as gravity—
are sufficiently clear for crude analysis.

Jupiter, looming 317 times as massive as our planet, exerts a pull so
strong that human locomotion would be impossible on its surface.
The effect of a strong gravitational field upon the shape of the brain,
circulation of the blood, and structure of the skeleton is a matter for
conjecture. Precise possibilities of organic evolution under such influences are unknown.

Nor is there any certainty as to what forms could develop in a
gravitational field weaker than that of Earth. At the surface of Mars,

the incessant tug is only 38 per cent as strong as upon our own planet. On other spheres, gravity varies from a negligible force to pressures great enough to liquefy hydrogen.

Given a planet identical with Earth in every respect but gravity, and varying significantly at this point, *Homo sapiens* could never develop.

Nearly everything about Earth appears exceptional. Even the Moon is a celestial oddity. No other body in the solar system is remotely comparable to it. There are satellites about other planets, of course. But most are comparatively tiny. Jupiter and Saturn, to be sure, have sizable satellites but not so large as the Moon in comparison to their own great size. Weight ratios between satellites and the planets they circle range from 1:4000 to 1:16,000,000. Weight ratio between Earth's bright daughter and the parent planet is 1:81.

The Moon may have been torn or ejected from the side of Earth. One theory is that this took place after our planet had cooled sufficiently to form a thin shell about its molten interior. It has been argued by some that the Pacific Ocean represents the remnant of the jagged hole that the Moon left. But this is only one of the hypotheses.

Down through the geologic ages, Earth has been subjected to long-term climatic cycles, which have influenced the course of evolution. So also has the "accident" that gave our planet its annual progression of seasons. This is the result of its being tilted on its axis at about 23½ degrees, as is shown by every schoolroom globe. If the axis were either parallel with or perpendicular to the plane of revolution about the sun, seasonal changes would vanish into the deathly monotony of unvarying years.

Still another temperature cycle is linked with rotation. Because the planet spins comparatively rapidly, there is quick and regular alternation of light and darkness, heat and cold. Mercury's rate of rotation is geared to its passage about the sun. Hence one side continually bakes, the other is perpetually frozen.

Benefiting as it does from at least three types of cyclical temperature change, Earth becomes a planet of struggle-within-endurable-limits, never plunging above or below levels for life. The biological significance of this phenomenon is beyond estimate. Lacking ordered change within an extremely narrow temperature range, the history of organic development would be quite different.

In order to harbor creatures broadly comparable to the ones we know, other planets must not only possess conditions to sustain life, they must have passed through a pattern of cosmic development reasonably similar to Earth's. It is not a set of isolated qualities that must be matched, but the whole of an infinitely complex pattern extending through vast periods of time. And without a basically similar biological heritage, no planet would have produced a man or anything approaching it.

Earth's possession of living forms even in the broad sense, therefore assumes new significance—not in spite of the new astronomy but because of it. That each detail of the incredible panorama should be exactly duplicated in sequence is statistically about as likely as the proverbial re-creation of Shakespeare's entire works by a chimpanzee striking typewriter keys at random.

Even on the strangely sheltered planet that nurtures the only life we know to exist, there are perhaps ten million species—but only one *Homo sapiens*. Perhaps it is not too much to suggest that even in this special environment, it required an almost incomprehensible number of trials to produce a single strain of men.

Men of Earth think, talk, laugh, hope, experiment, compute, and manipulate symbols. Hence, until we know there are comparable creatures on other planets, we may consider man the central mystery of the cosmos.

Is he the product of accident . . . or the fruit of design? Did he develop as a result of purposeless forces which fitted him to live on the wandering sphere that is Earth . . . or was Earth created with infinite pains in order that it might be the cradle of man?

No one ventures to claim that man has been duplicated elsewhere, but we may ask whether scientific thought is not tending toward possibilities no less startling.

Harold C. Urey, atomic physicist at the University of Chicago, recently estimated that life exists on at least 100,000 planets. Less conservative analysts place the number of inhabited bodies at ten times that figure.

There are billions of heavenly bodies more or less like Earth. Each has billions of years in which to be affected by natural forces. "It would be at least strange," urges physicist George Gamow, "if life—even in its highest forms—had failed to develop in these 'inhabitable' worlds."

Our minds are being stretched beyond customary limits. Perhaps it will take electronic computers—products of man's brain but more capable of handling astronomic figures—to evaluate probabilities of other thinking creatures in the almost limitless realms of space.